MW00396002

ASM Handbook of Engineering Mathematics

By faculty members of
The Department of Mechanical Engineering,
The University of Akron

Mamerto L. Chu, Ph. D.
Paul Lam, Ph. D.
Richard J. Gross, Ph. D.
Benjamin T. F. Chung, Ph. D.

and by

Samuel J. Brown, Ph. D.
President, Quest Engineering &
Development Corp.

Editorial Coordinator

William G. Belding

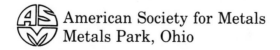 American Society for Metals
Metals Park, Ohio

Copyright © 1983
by the
AMERICAN SOCIETY FOR METALS
All rights reserved

No part of this book may be reproduced, stored in a retrieval system, or transmitted, in any form or by any means, electronic, mechanical, photocopying,
recording, or otherwise, without the prior written permission of the publisher.

Nothing contained in this book is to be construed as a grant of any right of
manufacture, sale, or use in connection with any method, process, apparatus,
product or composition, whether or not covered by letters patent or registered
trademark, nor as a defense against liability for the infringement of letters
patent or registered trademark.

Library of Congress Cataloging in Publication Data
Main entry under title:

ASM handbook of engineering mathematics.

    Includes index.
    1. Engineering mathematics—Handbooks, manuals, etc.
I. Drummond, Jerry. II. Brown, Samuel J. III. Belding,
William G. IV. University of Akron. Dept. of Mechanical
Engineering. V. American Society for Metals. VI. Title:
A.S.M. handbook of engineering mathematics.
TA332.A79   1983   510'.2462   82-22664
ISBN 0-87170-157-X

SAN 204-7586

PRINTED IN THE UNITED STATES OF AMERICA

Preface

This handbook has been compiled to serve as a practical reference for practicing engineers and engineering students who possess basic groundwork in college-level mathematics. In each area of basic mathematics, key equations are presented, without detailed derivations.

A major part of the handbook has been developed by a team of faculty members of the Department of Mechanical Engineering, The University of Akron. The faculty members participating in this program have significant industrial experience, which they bring to the classroom. Thus, this handbook becomes an extension of that enriching quality of experience.

The authors and editors do not claim completeness. The vastness of the field precludes it. But the equations presented here should prove useful to graduate engineers. To serve practical needs, the authors have emphasized practice and subordinated theory.

Because mathematics is an extremely broad field that includes a large and growing body of literature on computers, for example, choices had to be made. The choices represented here have been derived from course work in mechanical engineering, instead of the mathematics of physics or electrical and electronic engineering. Thus, the branches of mathematics emphasized are those useful in the design and manufacturing environment of the typical metalworking company.

Part I of this handbook contains basic equations and theorems of algebra, trigonometry, geometry, analytical geometry, calculus, etc., in ascending order of difficulty, as these subjects are frequently introduced to students.

In Part II, mathematical equations and illustrations present key elements of various disciplines of mechanical engineering. The focus is on those equations that help lead to solutions of practical problems in mechanical analysis and design.

To further aid students and practicing engineers, lists of selected references are presented at the end of each chapter in Part II. It is the sincere hope of the authors and editors that if the precise equation being sought by the reader isn't found in this handbook, our efforts will nevertheless help lead to the answer sought.

Contents

Contents

1
Algebra

FUNDAMENTAL CONCEPTS

An algebraic expression includes one or more algebraic quantities (numbers or letters) connected by such signs of operations as $+$, $-$, $:$, and $\sqrt{\ }$, with brackets indicating successive operations.

An equality of two algebraic expressions is an identity when the equality holds for all substitutions of arbitrary numerical values for the letters occurring in the expression. An equation is an equality that is valid only for certain definite values.

An identity transformation, the process of obtaining one algebraic expression from another equal expression, can be done in many ways, according to the aim of the transformation. An expression can be given a more compact form suitable for substitution of numerical values or a form suitable for such operations as solving equations, logarithmic calculation, differentiation, or integration.

DEFINITIONS

Monomial. A monomial is a single term: a, ab, or x^2y^3.

Binomial. A binomial defines two terms that are added or subtracted: $a + b$, $x^2 + y^3$, or $ab + x^4y^2$.

Polynomial. A polynomial includes two or more terms added or subtracted: $a + b + c$ or $x^2 + 3x - 5xy + y^2$.

Rational Term. A rational term is one not containing the root of a variable: x^2, $1/y$ or u.

Irrational Term. An irrational term contains a root of a variable: $a^{1/5}$ or $\sqrt{x}$.

Integral Term. An integral term is one in which the variable does not occur in the denominator. For example, x/y is integral with respect to x but not with respect to y.

Degree of a Term. The degree of a term means the number of literal factors in a term, and it also equals the sum of the exponents of the literal factors. The degree of $4a^2b^3$ is $2 + 3 = 5$, for example.

Variable. A variable is a symbol that represents any value of a given set of elements. For example, in $A = \pi r^2$, where A is the area of a circle with radius r, and $\pi = 3.14159$, A and r are variables. When A changes as r is varied, then r is the independent variable and A the dependent variable.

Constant. A constant is a variable with one element only. An absolute or numerical constant always has the same value. An arbitrary constant, or parameter, has one value under certain conditions and different values under other conditions. Symbols representing numbers 11 or $\sqrt{2}$ or 3.14159 are absolute constants. In the expression $e = kP$, where e is the elongation of a bar due to a load P, k is a constant that varies with different materials; hence, k is a parameter.

CLASSIFICATION OF NUMBERS

Real Numbers (positive and negative). Real numbers include rational and irrational numbers. A rational number is expressible as the quotient of two integers, that is, integers such as -1, 2, 53, or fractions, as $\frac{3}{4}$, $-\frac{5}{2}$. An irrational number is not expressible as the quotient of two integers, as $\sqrt{2}$, π. The absolute value of a real number is the number itself if the number is positive, and the number with its sign changed if it is negative, as, for example, $|3| = |-3| = 3$.

Imaginary Numbers. An imaginary number is a product of a real number and the imaginary unit $i(=\sqrt{-1})$. Electrical engineers use j to avoid confusion with i for current. Example: $\sqrt{-2} = \sqrt{2}i$.

Complex Numbers. A complex number is a sum of a real number and an imaginary number, as $a + bi$, with a and b real numbers, $-3 + 0.5i$. A real number may be regarded as a complex number in which $b = 0$, and an imaginary number as one in which $a = 0$. The absolute value of a complex number $a + bi$ is $\sqrt{a^2 + b^2}$, as, for example, $|-3 + 0.5i| = \sqrt{9 - \frac{1}{4}} = 3.04+$. Relationships of complex numbers can be expressed in the following forms:

$$i = \sqrt{-1},\ i^2 = -1,\ i^3 = -i,\ i^4 = 1,\ i^5 = i,\ \text{etc.}$$
$$a + bi = c + di \text{ if and only if } a = c,\ b = d$$
$$(a + bi) + (c + di) = (a + c) + (b + d)i$$
$$(a + bi)(c + di) = (ac - bd) + (ad + bc)i$$

$$\frac{a + bi}{c + di} = \frac{(a + bi)(c - di)}{(c + di)(c - di)} = \frac{ac + bd}{c^2 + d^2} + \frac{bc - ad}{c^2 + d^2} i$$

NOTATIONS

The main points of separation in a simple algebraic expression are the $+$ and $-$ signs. Thus, $a + b \times c - d \div x + y$ is interpreted as $a + (b \times c) - (d \div x) + y$. The range of operation of the symbols $\times$ and $\div$ extends only to the next $+$ or $-$ sign. Between the signs $\times$ and $\div$ themselves, $a \div b \times c$ means $a \div (b \times c)$. The $\div$ sign is the stronger separative. Because this rule is not strictly followed, parentheses should be used to avoid ambiguity.

Exponents and radical signs influence only the next adjacent quantity. Thus $2ax^3$ means $2a(x^3)$, and $\sqrt{2}ax$ means $(\sqrt{2})(ax)$. Instead of $\sqrt{2}ax$, it is safer, however, to write $\sqrt{2} \cdot ax$, or $ax\sqrt{2}$. Any expression within parentheses is to be treated as a single quantity. A horizontal bar serves the same purpose as parentheses.

The notation $a \cdot b$, or simply ab, means $a \times b$; and $a : b$, or a/b, means $a \div b$.

Factorials. The symbol $n!$ (when n is a whole number) means: "n factorial," and means the product of the natural numbers from 1 to n, inclusive. Thus $2! = 1 \times 2$; $3! = 1 \times 2 \times 3$ and $4! = 1 \times 2 \times 3 \times 4$. The Stirling formula gives approximate values of $n!$ for large n:

$$n! \approx n^n e^{-n} \sqrt{2\pi n}$$

BASIC LAWS

Existence Law for Addition. Adding any two numbers a and b always gives a single number c: $a + b = c$.

Commutative Law. Algebraic numbers can be added or multiplied regardless of order: $a + b = b + a$; $ab = ba$.

Associative Law. The sum or product of three or more algebraic terms is unaffected by the grouping of the terms:

$$a + b + c = a + (b + c) = (a + b) + c$$
$$abc = a(bc) = (ab)c = (ac)b$$

Distributive Law. $a(b + c) = ab + ac$.

Operations with Zero and Negative Numbers. A number or letter without a preceding sign is assumed to be positive.

$$a + 0 \equiv a \qquad\qquad 0 - a \equiv -a$$
$$a + (-a) \equiv 0 \qquad\qquad -(-a) \equiv a$$
$$a \cdot 0 \equiv 0 \qquad\qquad a(-b) \equiv -ab$$
$$0/a \equiv 0,\text{ if } a \neq 0 \qquad (-a)(-b) \equiv ab$$

If $ab = 0$, then either $a = 0$ or $b = 0$ or $a = b = 0$. $a/0$ is undefined.

Order Relationships. If a and b are real numbers, then either $a < b$ or $a = b$ or $a > b$. If c is a third real number, and if $a < b$ and $b < c$, then $a < c$.

Axioms. The following relationships apply in algebraic transformations:

- If equals are added to equals, the sums are equal
- If equals are subtracted from equals, the differences are equal
- If equals are multiplied by equals, the products are equal
- If equals are divided by equals (except zero), the quotients are equal
- Like powers or like roots of equals are equal
- Numbers or terms equal to the same number or equal numbers are equal
- The whole equals the sum of its parts

IDENTITIES

An identity is a statement in symbolic form that holds for all values of the variables involved. For example, $(a + b)(a - b) = a^2 - b^2$ is true regardless of the values substituted for a and b. Common identities are listed below.

POWERS

$$(-a)^n = a^n, \text{ if } n \text{ is even}$$
$$(-a)^n = -a^n, \text{ if } n \text{ is odd}$$
$$a^m \cdot a^n = a^{m+n}$$

$$\frac{a^m}{a^n} = a^{m-n}$$

$$(ab)^n = a^n b^n$$

$$\left(\frac{a}{b}\right)^n = \frac{a^n}{b^n} = \left(\frac{b}{a}\right)^{-n} = \frac{b^{-n}}{a^{-n}}$$

$$a^{-n} = \left(\frac{1}{a}\right)^n = \frac{1}{a^n}$$

$$(a^m)^n = a^{mn}$$

$$a^0 = 1; \; 0^n = 0; \; 0^0 \text{ is meaningless}$$

ROOTS

$$\sqrt[n]{a} = a^{1/n}$$

$$(\sqrt[n]{a})^n = \sqrt[n]{a^n} = a$$

$$\sqrt[n]{ab} = \sqrt[n]{a}\,\sqrt[n]{b}$$

$$\sqrt[n]{\frac{a}{b}} = \frac{\sqrt[n]{a}}{\sqrt[n]{b}}$$

$$\sqrt[m]{a}\,\sqrt[n]{a} = a^{(1/m)+(1/n)} = \sqrt[mn]{a^{m+n}}$$

$$\sqrt[m]{a^n} = (\sqrt[m]{a})^n = a^{n/m}$$

$$\sqrt[m]{\sqrt[n]{a}} = \sqrt[mn]{a} = \sqrt[n]{\sqrt[m]{a}} = (a^{1/m})^{1/n} = a^{1/mn}$$

$$\sqrt{a} + \sqrt{b} = \sqrt{a + b + 2\sqrt{ab}}$$

PRODUCTS

$$(a \pm b)^2 = a^2 \pm 2ab + b^2$$

$$(a + b)(a - b) = a^2 - b^2$$

$$(a + b + c)^2 = a^2 + b^2 + c^2 + 2ab + 2ac + 2bc$$

$$(a \pm b)^3 = a^3 \pm 3a^2b + 3ab^2 \pm b^2$$

$$a^3 \pm b^3 = (a \pm b)(a^2 \mp ab + b^2)$$

$$a(b + c + d) = ab + ac + ad$$

$$(a + b)(c + d) = ac + ad + bc + bd$$

$$(x + a)(x + b) = x^2 + (a + b)x + ab$$

$$(ax + by)(cx + dy) = acx^2 + (bc + ad)xy + bdy^2$$

QUOTIENTS

If $a \neq b$:

$$(a^n - b^n)/(a - b) = a^{n-1} + a^{n-2}b + a^{n-3}b^2 + \cdots + ab^{n-2} + b^{n-1}$$

If n is odd:

$$(a^n + b^n)/(a + b) = a^{n-1} - a^{n-2}b + a^{n-3}b^2 - \cdots - ab^{n-2} + b^{n-1}$$

If n is even:

$$(a^n - b^n)/(a + b) = a^{n-1} - a^{n-2}b + a^{n-3}b^2 - \cdots + ab^{n-2} - b^{n-1}$$

FRACTIONS

Signs. $\quad \dfrac{a}{b} = \dfrac{-a}{-b} = -\dfrac{-a}{b} = -\dfrac{a}{-b}$

Addition and Subtraction. $\quad \dfrac{a}{c} \pm \dfrac{b}{d} = \dfrac{ad \pm bc}{cd}$

$$\frac{a}{c} \pm \frac{b}{c} = \frac{a \pm b}{c}$$

$$\frac{a}{c} \pm \frac{a}{d} = \frac{a(d \pm c)}{cd}$$

$$\frac{a}{def} + \frac{b}{e^3g} - \frac{c}{df^2} = \frac{ae^2fg + bdf^2 - ce^3g}{de^3f^2g}$$

Multiplication. $\quad \dfrac{a}{b} \times \dfrac{c}{d} = \dfrac{ac}{bd} \qquad\qquad \dfrac{a}{b} = \dfrac{ac}{bc}$

Division. $\quad \dfrac{a}{b} \Big/ \dfrac{c}{d} = \dfrac{a}{b} \times \dfrac{d}{c} = \dfrac{ad}{bc} \qquad\qquad \dfrac{a}{b} = \dfrac{a}{c} \Big/ \dfrac{b}{c}$

SERIES

$$1 + 2 + 3 + 4 + \cdots + (n - 1) + n = \frac{n(n + 1)}{2}$$

$$p + (p + 1) + (p + 2) + \cdots + (q - 1) + q = \frac{(q + p)(q - p + 1)}{2}$$

$$2 + 4 + 6 + 8 + \cdots + (2n - 2) + 2n = n(n + 1)$$

$$1 + 3 + 5 + 7 + \cdots + (2n - 3) + (2n - 1) = n^2$$

$$1^2 + 2^2 + 3^2 + 4^2 + \cdots + (n - 1)^2 + n^2 = \frac{n(n + 1)(2n + 1)}{6}$$

$$1^3 + 2^3 + 3^3 + 4^3 + \cdots + (n - 1)^3 + n^3 = \frac{n^2(n + 1)^2}{4}$$

$$1^4 + 2^4 + 3^4 + 4^4 + \cdots + (n - 1)^4 + n^4 = \frac{n}{30}(n + 1)(2n + 1)(3n^2 + 3n - 1)$$

COMMON ALGEBRAIC OPERATIONS

Addition. If two numbers have the same sign, their absolute values are added. If they have opposite signs, absolute values are subtracted. For example:

$$5 + 6 = 11 \qquad 5 + (-6) = -1$$

Monomials that are alike, or similar, can be added or subtracted by adding or subtracting coefficients. For example:

$$3ab + 6ab - 2ab = 7ab$$

and

$$3ab + 6bc - ab = 2ab + 6bc$$

To add polynomials with similar terms, write them with like terms in the same column. Then add:

$$
\begin{array}{r}
3ab + 4ac - 3bc \\
2ab - 3ac + 2bc \\
-ab + 2ac + 6bc \\
\hline
4ab + 3ac + 5bc
\end{array}
$$

Subtraction. The sign of the subtrahend (number to be subtracted) is changed and the result added:

$$15 - (-6) = 15 + 6 = 21$$
$$15 - (+6) = 15 - 6 = 9$$
$$a - (b - c) = a - b + c$$

Multiplication. A product is the result obtained by multiplying two or more quantities. Each quantity is a factor of the product. Any factor is the coefficient of the product of the other factors. When two numbers with like signs are multiplied, the product is positive. The product of two numbers with different signs is negative:

$$(+6)(+5) = +30 \qquad (-6)(-5) = +30 \qquad (+6)(-5) = -30$$

The product of an odd number of negative factors is negative; the product of an even number of negative factors is positive.

Multiplication of a monomial and a polynomial involves multiplying each term of the polynomial by the monomial:

$$a(b + c - d) = ab + ac - ad$$

Two polynomials are multiplied by multiplying each term of one by each term of the other and adding. The technique is similar to multiplication in arithmetic:

$$
\begin{array}{r}
3x + 2y + 1 \\
x + y \\
\hline
3xy + 2y^2 + y \\
3x^2 + 2xy \phantom{{}+ 2y^2 + y} + x \\
\hline
3x^2 + 5xy + 2y^2 + y + x
\end{array}
$$

Factors. Factors are terms that are multiplied together to yield a given expression. Prime factors are integers that have no integer factors other than themselves and unity. For example, the prime factors of $12a^2b^3$ are 2, 3, a, and b. The number 12 also can be factored into ½ and 24, or ⅔ and 18, or $\sqrt{18}$ and $\sqrt{8}$.

Division. Division is equivalent to multiplication by the reciprocal of the divisor. When dividend and divisor have like signs, the quotient is positive; if they have unlike signs, the quotient is negative.

To divide two polynomials, use the following steps:

1 Arrange terms in descending powers of a common letter
2 Divide the first term of the dividend by the first term of the divisor. The result is the first term of the quotient
3 Multiply the divisor by this term and subtract the product from the dividend
4 Treat the difference as a new dividend and repeat the first three steps
5 Continue the process until the difference, or remainder, is zero, or until the highest power of the letter in the dividend is less than the power of the same letter in the divisor. For example, divide $36x^3 + 24x^2 + 10x + 4$ by $3x + 1$:

Divisor　　　　Dividend　　　　Quotient

$$3x + 1 \overline{\smash{) + 36x^3 + 24x^2 + 10x + 4}} \, 12x^2$$
$$\underline{+ 36x^3 + 12x^2}$$
$$+ 12x^2 + 10x + 4 \, \underline{| \; 4x}$$
$$\underline{+ 12x^2 + \; 4x}$$
$$+ \; 6x + 4 \, \underline{| \; 2}$$
$$\underline{+ \; 6x + 2}$$
$$+ \; 2$$

Answer: $12x^2 + 4x + 2 + \dfrac{2}{3x + 1}$

Synthetic Division. Division of a polynomial by a binomial of the form $x - r$ can be simplified by the following procedure:

- Write the coefficients of the variable x in a line, according to a descending order of powers of the variable. Represent coefficients of missing powers by 0
- Write the first coefficient as the first term of the quotient
- Multiply it by the nonvariable term $(-r)$ of the binomial with sign changed, and add the product to the second coefficient. This sum is the coefficient of the second term of the quotient
- Multiply this sum by the nonvariable term of the binomial with sign changed and add the product to the next coefficient. Continue until the last coefficient has been added

The last sum is the remainder, and the preceding sums in order are the coefficients of the quotient. For example, divide $2x^4 - 3x^3 - 5x^2 - 2x + 7$ by $x - 3$:

$$\text{Dividend} = 2 - 3 - 5 - \; 2 + \; 7 \, \underline{|3} = \text{divisor} \, (x - 3)$$
$$\underline{+ \; 6 + 9 + 12 \; + 30}$$
$$2 + 3 + 4 + 10; \, + 37$$

The quotient is $2x^3 + 3x^2 + 4x + 10$; the remainder is $+37$.

PARTIAL FRACTIONS

In a proper algebraic fraction, the numerator is of lower degree than the denominator. An improper fraction can be transformed to the sum of a polynomial and a proper fraction by dividing the numerator by the denominator. A proper fraction can be resolved into partial fractions, the denominators of which are factors, prime to each other, of the denominator of the given fraction.

Example 1. The denominator is factored into real linear factors, P, Q, $R, \cdots$, all different. Let:

$$\frac{\text{Num}}{PQR \cdots} = \frac{A}{P} + \frac{B}{Q} + \frac{C}{R} + \cdots$$

or

$$\frac{6x^2 - x + 1}{x^3 - x} = \frac{A}{x} + \frac{B}{x - 1} + \frac{C}{x + 1}$$

Clearing of fractions:

$$6x^2 - x + 1 = A(x - 1)(x + 1) + Bx(x + 1) + Cx(x - 1)$$

Using substitution, let $x = 0$, $A = -1$; $x = 1$, $B = 3$; $x = -1$, $C = 4$. Then:

$$\frac{6x^2 - x + 1}{x^3 - x} = -\frac{1}{x} + \frac{3}{x - 1} + \frac{4}{x + 1}$$

Using the method of undetermined coefficients, rewrite the expression in the following manner:

$$6x^2 - x + 1 = (A + B + C)x^2 + (B - C)x - A$$

Equating coefficients of like powers of x, $A + B + C = 6$, $B - C = -1$, $-A = 1$. Solving this system of equations, $A = -1$, $B = 3$, $C = 4$.

Example 2. The denominator can be factored into real linear factors, $P, Q, \cdots$, one or more repeated. Let:

$$\frac{\text{Num}}{P^2 Q^3} = \frac{A}{P} + \frac{B}{P^2} + \frac{C}{Q} + \frac{D}{Q^2} + \frac{E}{Q^3} + \cdots$$

or

$$\frac{x + 1}{x(x - 1)^3} = \frac{A}{x} + \frac{B}{x - 1} + \frac{C}{(x - 1)^2} + \frac{D}{(x - 1)^3}$$

Clearing of fractions:

$$x + 1 = A(x - 1)^3 + Bx(x - 1)^2 + Cx(x - 1) + Dx$$

A and D can be found by substituting $x = 0$ and $x = 1$. After these numerical values are inserted for A and D, B and C can be found by the method of undetermined coefficients.

Example 3. The denominator can be factored into quadratic factors, $P, Q, \cdots$, all different, which cannot be factored into real linear factors. Let:

$$\frac{\text{Num}}{PQ \cdots} = \frac{Ax + B}{P} + \frac{Cx + D}{Q} + \cdots$$

or

$$\frac{3x^2 - 2}{(x^2 + x + 1)(x + 1)} = \frac{Ax + B}{x^2 + x + 1} + \frac{C}{x + 1}$$

Clearing of fractions:

$$\begin{aligned} 3x^2 - 2 &= (Ax + B)(x + 1) + C(x^2 + x + 1) \\ &= (A + C)x^2 + (A + B + C)x + (B + C) \end{aligned}$$

Use the method of undetermined coefficients to find A, B, C.

Example 4. The denominator can be factored into quadratic factors, $P, Q, \cdots$, one or more repeated, which cannot be factored into real linear factors. Let:

$$\frac{\text{Num}}{P^2Q^3\cdots} = \frac{Ax + B}{P} + \frac{Cx + D}{P^2} + \frac{Ex + F}{Q} + \frac{Gx + H}{Q^2} + \frac{Ix + J}{Q^3} + \cdots$$

or

$$\frac{5x^2 - 4x + 16}{(x - 3)(x^2 - x + 1)^2} = \frac{A}{x - 3} + \frac{Bx + C}{x^2 - x + 1} + \frac{Dx + E}{(x^2 - x + 1)^2}$$

Clearing of fractions:

$$5x^2 - 4x + 16 = A(x^2 - x + 1)^2 +$$
$$(Bx + C)(x - 3)(x^2 - x + 1) + (Dx + E)(x - 3)$$

Find A by substituting $x = 3$. Then use the method of undetermined coefficients to find B, C, D, E.

RATIO AND PROPORTION

The following are laws of ratio and proportion:

- If $\dfrac{a}{b} = \dfrac{c}{d}$, then: $\dfrac{a}{c} = \dfrac{b}{d}$; $ad = bc$; $\dfrac{ma + nb}{pa + qb} = \dfrac{mc + nd}{pc + qd}$; $\left(\dfrac{a}{b}\right)^n = \left(\dfrac{c}{d}\right)^n$

  Further, if $\dfrac{e}{f} = \dfrac{g}{h}$, then: $\dfrac{ae}{bf} = \dfrac{cg}{dh}$

- If $\dfrac{a}{b} = \dfrac{c}{d} = \dfrac{e}{f} = \cdots$, then: $\dfrac{a}{b} = \dfrac{c}{d} = \dfrac{e}{f} = \cdots = \dfrac{pa + qc + re + \cdots}{pb + qd + rf + \cdots}$

Direct Variation. A variable varies directly as another variable if their ratio is a constant. $x \propto y$ if $x/y = k$, where k is a constant factor of proportionality (or variation).

Inverse Variation. A variable varies inversely as another variable if it varies directly as the reciprocal of the other. x varies inversely as y if $x \propto 1/y$. Hence, $xy = k$, where k is a constant.

Joint Variation. If x varies directly as y when all other factors are constant, and x varies directly as z when all other factors are constant, then x varies directly as yz. Thus, $x \propto yz$ if $x = kyz$, where k is a constant.

THEOREMS

Binomial Theorem. $(a + b)^n \equiv a^n + na^{n-1}b + \dfrac{n(n - 1)}{2!}a^{n-2}b^2 + \cdots +$

$$\frac{n(n - 1) \cdots (n - r + 1)}{r!}a^{n-r}b^r + \cdots + b^n \equiv$$

$$a^n + C(n, 1)a^{n-1}b + C(n, 2)a^{n-2}b^2 + \cdots + C(n, r)a^{n-r}b^r + \cdots + b^n$$

where $C(n, r) = n(n - 1) \cdots (n - r + 1)/r!$ is the combination of n things taken r at a time. For example:

$$(a + b)^4 \equiv a^4 + 4a^3b + \frac{4 \cdot 3}{2!}a^2b^2 + \frac{4 \cdot 3 \cdot 2}{3!}ab^3 + b^4$$

$$\equiv a^4 + 4a^3b + 6a^2b^2 + 4ab^3 + b^4$$

$$(a - 3)^3 \equiv a^3 + 3(-3)a^2 + \frac{3 \cdot 2}{2!}(-3)^2a + (-3)^3$$

$$\equiv a^3 - 9a^2 + 27a - 27$$

For $-1 \leq x \leq +1$:

$$(1 + x)^{1/2} \equiv 1 + \tfrac{1}{2}x + \frac{\tfrac{1}{2}(-\tfrac{1}{2})}{2!}x^2 + \frac{\tfrac{1}{2}(-\tfrac{1}{2})(-\tfrac{3}{2})}{3!}x^3 + \cdots$$

$$\equiv 1 + \tfrac{1}{2}x - \tfrac{1}{8}x^2 + \tfrac{1}{16}x^3 - \cdots$$

To expand $(a + b + c)^n$, let $a + b = k$ and expand $(k + c)^n$ by the binomial theorem. Then substitute $a + b$ for k in the expansion and use the theorem to expand the various powers of $a + b$.

Pascal's triangle is an arrangement of the coefficients of the binomial theorem for integral exponents, beginning with zero.

$(a + b)^0$								1								
$(a + b)^1$							1		1							
$(a + b)^2$						1		2		1						
$(a + b)^3$					1		3		3		1					
				1		4		6		4		1				
			1		5		10		10		5		1			
		1		6		15		20		15		6		1		
	1		7		21		35		35		21		7		1	
1		8		28		56		70		56		28		8		1

In this triangle, any number except 1 can be obtained by adding the two numbers to the left and right on the line above it.

Remainder Theorem. If an integral rational polynomial in x is divided by $x - m$, the remainder can be found by substituting m for x in the polynomial. For example, $(a^3 - 9a^2 + 27a - 15)/(a - 3)$ has the remainder $3^3 - 9(3)^2 + 27(3) - 15 = 12$, and $(4x^2 - 9)/(x + 1)$ has the remainder $4(-1)^2 - 9 = -5$. Conversely, the value of a polynomial in x for $x = m$ can be obtained by dividing the polynomial by $x - m$.

Factor Theorem. If an integral rational polynomial in x becomes zero when m is substituted for x, then $x - m$ is a factor of the polynomial. For example, if $a = 3$, then $a^3 - 9a^2 + 27a - 27 = 0$. Hence, $a - 3$ is a factor of the polynomial. Note also that if $a - 3$ is a factor, then 27 must be divisible by 3.

To find binomial factors of a polynomial in any variable, find the factors of the terms not involving that variable and determine which of these factors make the polynomial zero when they are substituted for the variable. For example, factor $p^3 - 7p^2 + 7p + 15$. The factors of 15 are ± 1, ± 3, ± 5, and ± 15. If $p = +1$, the polynomial is not zero, but for $p = -1$, $(-1)^3 - 7(-1)^2 + 7(-1) + 15 = 0$. Therefore, $p + 1$ is a factor. Division of the polynomial by $p + 1$ yields $p^2 - 8p + 15$. This expression can be factored into $(p - 5)(p - 3)$. Hence:

$$p^3 - 7p^2 + 7p + 15 = (p + 1)(p - 5)(p - 3)$$

FUNCTIONS

A function is a relationship between two or more variables and constants. For example, $3x^3 + 6$ is a function of x, and $3z + 4y$ is a function of y and z. The notation $f(x)$ represents a function of x and not multiplication. $P(x)$ is P function of x. The function $f(a)$ is formed by substituting a for x in $f(x)$. If $f(x) = x^2 - 2x + 1$, $f(2) = 2^2 - 2(2) + 1 = 1$. If $f(x)$ is a rational integral function, the remainder when $f(x)$ is divided by $x - a$ is $f(a)$. For example, if $f(x) = x^3 - 9x^2 + 27x - 27$, then $f(5) = 8$.

$$
\begin{array}{r}
1 - 9 + 27 - 27 \underline{|5} \\
+ 5 - 20 + 35 \\
\hline
1 - 4 + 7\underline{|+ 8} = \text{remainder} = f(5)
\end{array}
$$

The following rules apply to functions:

- A function is symmetrical with respect to two variables if it is unchanged by interchanging the variables
- A single-valued function has a single value for any value of the independent variable. $y = 2x$ is a single-valued function
- A multivalued function has more than one value for any given value of the independent variable. For example, $y = \pm x^{1/2}$ is a multivalued function
- An implicit function must be solved to express one variable in terms only of the other. $x^2 + 3y - y^2 = 9$ defines y as an implicit function of x
- An explicit function gives a variable directly in terms of the other. For example, $y = 12 - x^2$ gives y as an explicit function of x

Continuous Function. A function $f(x)$ is continuous where, for any value of x, an infinitesimal change in x produces an infinitesimal change in $f(x)$. That is, if $h \to 0$, $f(x + h) - f(x) \to 0$. The function ax^m is continuous if m is an integer. The function $a_0 x^n + a_1 x^{n-1} + \cdots + a_n$ is continuous if n is an integer.

Graph of a Function. A curve of a function shows how the magnitude of a function of one variable varies with the value of the variable. To plot the graph of a function, indicate along a horizontal axis the values of the variable. At each value, plot vertically (parallel to the y axis) the corresponding value of the function (ordinate). Connect the points thus determined. The intersection of the x and y axes is called the origin. The values of the abscissas and ordinates are called the coordinates of the points plotted.

PROGRESSIONS

An arithmetic progression is a sequence in which the difference, d, of any two consecutive terms is a constant. If n = number of terms, a = first term, l = last term, s = sum of n terms, then $l = a + (n - 1)d$, and $s = \frac{n}{2}(a + 1)$. The arithmetic mean, A, of two quantities, m and n, is the quantity that placed between m and n forms an arithmetic progression, $A = (m + n)/2$. For example, using the series $3 + 5 + 7 + \cdots$ to 10 terms, $n = 10$, $a = 3$, and $d = 2$; hence, $l = 3 + (10 - 1) \times 2 = 21$ and $s = (\frac{10}{2})(3 + 21) = 120$.

Geometric Progression. In a geometric progression, the ratio r of any two consecutive terms is a constant. If n = number of terms, a = first term, l = last term, and s = sum of n terms, then $l = ar^{n-1}$, and $s = (rl - a)/(r - 1) = a(1 - r^n)/(1 - r)$. The geometric mean, G, of two quantities m and n is the quantity which placed between them makes with them a geometric progression; $G = \sqrt{mn}$. For example, using the series $3 + 6 + 12 + \cdots$ to 6 terms, $n = 6$, $a = 3$, and $r = 2$; hence, $l = 3 \times 2^{6-1} = 96$, and $s = (2 \times 96 - 3)/(2 - 1) = 3(1 - 2^6)/(1 - 2) = 189$. If $|r| < 1$, then, as $n \to \infty$, $s \to a/(1 - r)$.

Harmonic Progression. A harmonic progression is a sequence in which the reciprocals of the terms form an arithmetic progression. The harmonic mean, H, of two quantities, m and n, is the quantity which placed between them makes with them a harmonic progression, $H = 2mn/(m + n)$.

The relationship among the arithmetic, geometric, and harmonic means of two quantities is represented by $G^2 = AH$.

PERMUTATIONS AND COMBINATIONS

In a sequence of s events, if the first event can occur in n_1 ways, the second in $n_2 \ldots$, the sth in n_s, then the number of different ways in which the sequence can occur is $n_1 n_2 \cdots n_s$.

A permutation of n objects taken r at a time is an arrangement of any r objects selected from the n objects. The number of permutations of n objects taken r at a time is:

$$_nP_r = n(n - 1)(n - 2) \cdots (n - r + 1) = \frac{n!}{(n - r)!}$$

In particular, $_nP_1 = n$ and $_nP_n = n!$. For cyclic permutations:

$$_nP_r^c = \frac{n!}{r(n - r)!} \text{ and } _nP_n^c = (n - 1)!$$

For distinguishable permutations, if the n objects are divided into s sets each containing n_i objects that are alike, $n = n_1 + n_2 + \cdots + n_s$ and:

$$_nP_n = \frac{n!}{n_1! n_2! \cdots n_s!}.$$

A combination of n objects taken r at a time is an unarranged selection of any r of the n objects. The number of combinations of n objects taken r at a time is:

$$_nC_r = \frac{_nP_r}{r!} = \frac{n!}{r!(n-r)!} = \, _nC_{n-r}$$

In particular, $_nC_1 = n$, $_nC_n = 1$. Combinations taken any number at a time, $_nC_1 + \, _nC_2 + \cdots + \, _nC_n = 2^n - 1$.

PROBABILITY

If, in a set M of m events which are mutually exclusive and equally likely, one event will occur, and if in the set, M, there is a subset, N, of n events $(n \le m)$, then the probability p that the event which will occur is one of the subset N is n/m. The probability, q, that the event that will occur does not belong to N is $1 - n/m$. For example, to find the probability of drawing an ace from a deck of 52 cards, $m = 52$, $n = 4$, and $p = \frac{4}{52} = \frac{1}{13}$. The probability of drawing a card that is not an ace is $q = 1 - \frac{1}{13} = \frac{12}{13}$.

If, out of a large number r of observations in which a given event might or might not occur, the event has occurred s times, then a useful approximate value of the experimental, or a posteriori, probability of the occurrence of the event under the same condition is s/r. For example, from the American Experience Mortality Table, 749 out of 100,000 persons living at age 10 years died within a year. Here $r = 100,000$, $s = 749$, and the probability that a person of age 10 will die within a year is 749/100,000.

If p is the probability of receiving an amount A, then the expectation is pA.

Addition Rule. The probability that any one of several mutually exclusive events will occur is the sum of their separate probabilities. For example, the probability of drawing an ace from a deck of cards is $\frac{1}{13}$, and the probability of drawing a king is the same. Then the probability of drawing either an ace or a king is $\frac{1}{13} + \frac{1}{13} = \frac{2}{13}$.

Multiplication Rule. The probability that two or more independent events will occur is the product of their separate probabilities. If p_1 is the probability that an event will occur, and if, after it has occurred, p_2 is the probability that another event will occur, then the probability that both will occur in the given order is $p_1 p_2$. This rule can be extended to more than two events. For example, the probability of drawing an ace from a deck of cards is $\frac{1}{13}$, and the probability of drawing a king from another deck is $\frac{1}{13}$. Then the probability that an ace will be drawn from the first deck and a king from the second is $\frac{1}{13} \cdot \frac{1}{13} = \frac{1}{169}$. After an ace has been drawn from a deck of cards, the probability of drawing a king is $\frac{4}{51}$. If two cards are drawn in succession without the first being replaced, the probability that the first is an ace and the second a king is $\frac{1}{13} \cdot \frac{4}{51} = \frac{4}{663}$.

Repeated Trials. If p is the probability that an event will occur in a single trial, then the probability that it will occur exactly s times in r trials is the binomial or Bernoulli distribution function:

$$_rC_sP^s(1-p)^{r-s}$$

The probability that it will occur at least s times is:

$$p^r + {_rC_{r-1}}p^{r-1}(1-p) + {_rC_{r-2}}p^{r-2}(1-p)^2 + \cdots + {_rC_s}p^s(1-p)^{r-s}$$

For example, if five cards are drawn, one from each of five decks, the probability that exactly three will be aces is $_5C_3(\frac{1}{13})^3(\frac{12}{13})^2$. The probability that at least three will be aces is $(\frac{1}{13})^5 + {_5C_4}(\frac{1}{13})^4(\frac{12}{13}) + {_5C_3}(\frac{1}{13})^3(\frac{12}{13})^2$.

DETERMINANTS

Determinants are used chiefly in formulating theoretical results; they are seldom of use in numerical computation.

Evaluation of Determinants. Determinants of the second order are expressed as:

$$\begin{vmatrix} a_1 b_1 \\ a_2 b_2 \end{vmatrix} = a_1 b_2 - a_2 b_1$$

Third order determinants are expressed in the following manner:

$$\begin{vmatrix} a_1 b_1 c_1 \\ a_2 b_2 c_2 \\ a_3 b_3 c_3 \end{vmatrix} = a_1 \begin{vmatrix} b_2 c_2 \\ b_3 c_3 \end{vmatrix} - a_2 \begin{vmatrix} b_1 c_1 \\ b_3 c_3 \end{vmatrix} + a_3 \begin{vmatrix} b_1 c_1 \\ b_2 c_2 \end{vmatrix}$$

$$= a_1(b_2 c_3 - b_3 c_2) - a_2(b_1 c_3 - b_3 c_1) = a_3(b_1 c_2 - b_2 c_1)$$

Determinants of the fourth order are given in the form:

$$\begin{vmatrix} a_1 b_1 c_1 d_1 \\ a_2 b_2 c_2 d_2 \\ a_3 b_3 c_3 d_3 \\ a_4 b_4 c_4 d_4 \end{vmatrix} = a_1 \begin{vmatrix} b_2 c_2 d_2 \\ b_3 c_3 d_3 \\ b_4 c_4 d_4 \end{vmatrix} - a_2 \begin{vmatrix} b_1 c_1 d_1 \\ b_3 c_3 d_3 \\ b_4 c_4 d_4 \end{vmatrix} + a_3 \begin{vmatrix} b_1 c_1 d_1 \\ b_2 c_2 d_2 \\ b_4 c_4 d_4 \end{vmatrix} - a_4 \begin{vmatrix} b_1 c_1 d_1 \\ b_2 c_2 d_2 \\ b_3 c_3 d_3 \end{vmatrix}$$

In general, to evaluate a determinant of the nth order, the elements of the first column are taken with signs alternately plus and minus to form the sum of the products obtained by multiplying each of these elements by its corresponding minor. The minor corresponding to any element a_1 is the determinant of next lower order obtained by striking out from the given determinant the row and column containing a_1.

Properties of Determinants. The following are general properties of determinants:

- The columns may be changed to rows and the rows to columns:

$$\begin{vmatrix} a_1 b_1 c_1 \\ a_2 b_2 c_2 \\ a_3 b_3 c_3 \end{vmatrix} = \begin{vmatrix} a_1 a_2 a_3 \\ b_1 b_2 b_3 \\ c_1 c_2 c_3 \end{vmatrix}$$

- Interchanging two adjacent columns changes the sign of the result
- If two columns are equal, the determinant is zero
- If the elements of one column are m times the elements of another column, the determinant is zero
- To multiply a determinant by any number m, multiply all the elements of any one column by m

- $$\begin{vmatrix} a_1 + p_1 + q_1, b_1 c_1 \\ a_2 + p_2 + q_2, b_2 c_2 \\ a_3 + p_3 + q_3, b_3 c_3 \end{vmatrix} = \begin{vmatrix} a_1 b_1 c_1 \\ a_2 b_2 c_2 \\ a_3 b_3 c_3 \end{vmatrix} + \begin{vmatrix} p_1 b_1 c_1 \\ p_2 b_2 c_2 \\ p_3 b_3 c_3 \end{vmatrix} + \begin{vmatrix} q_1 b_1 c_1 \\ q_2 b_2 c_2 \\ q_3 b_3 c_3 \end{vmatrix}$$

- $$\begin{vmatrix} a_1 b_1 c_1 \\ a_2 b_2 c_2 \\ a_3 b_3 c_3 \end{vmatrix} = \begin{vmatrix} a_1 + mb_1, b_1 c_1 \\ a_2 + mb_2, b_2 c_2 \\ a_3 + mb_3, b_3 c_3 \end{vmatrix}$$

ALGEBRAIC EQUATIONS

An equation with one unknown is an equality of two functions of the same variable, that is, $F(x) = f(x)$, which is valid only for certain values of the variable x. The variable involved in the equation is called the unknown, and the values $x_1, x_2, \ldots, x_n$ for which the equation is valid are the roots or solutions of the equation. Two equations are equivalent if all their roots coincide.

An equation is algebraic if the involved functions $F(x)$ and $f(x)$ are algebraic, that is, rational or irrational. One of the functions $F(x)$ or $f(x)$ can be a constant value. Any algebraic equation can be reduced, by algebraic transformation, to the form:

$$P(x) = a_0 x^n + a_1 x^{n-1} + \cdots + a_n = 0$$

Example 5. The equation:

$$\frac{x - 1 + \sqrt{x^2 - 6}}{3(x - 2)} = 1 + \frac{x - 3}{x}$$

can be reduced by using the following successive transformations:

- $x(x - 1 + \sqrt{x^2 - 6}) = 3x(x - 2) + 3(x - 2)(x - 3)$
- $x^2 - x + x\sqrt{x^2 - 6} = 3x^2 - 6x + 3x^2 - 15x + 18$
- $x\sqrt{x^2 - 6} = 5x^2 - 20x + 18$
- $x^2(x^2 - 6) = 25x^4 - 200x^3 + 580x^2 - 720x + 324$
- $24x^4 - 200x^3 + 586x^2 - 720x + 324 = 0$

The resulting equation is of the fourth degree.

A linear equation is an equation containing only the first power of the unknowns; for example, $3x + 4y = 70$.

A quadratic equation is an equation in which the highest degree of any term is 2; for example, $x^2 + 2xy + y^2 = 7$.

A cubic equation is an equation in which the highest degree of any term is 3; for example, $x^3 + 3x^2y + 6xy^2 - 3y^3 = 1$.

Roots of an Equation. A commensurable or rational root, or solution, of an equation is a value of an unknown that satisfies the equation and that is either an integer or a fraction. Any other solution is an incommensurable root, and it is an irrational, imaginary, or complex number.

If a rational integral function $f(x)$ is divisible by $x - a$, then a is a root of the equation $f(x) = 0$. For example, if 3 is a solution of $x^3 - 9x^2 + 27x - 27 = 0$, then division of this function by $x - 3$ leaves no remainder:

$$\begin{array}{r} 1 - 9 + 27 - 27 \,\lfloor\underline{3} \\ \underline{+\ 3 - 18 + 27} \\ 1 - 6 + \ 9 + \lfloor\underline{0} \end{array}$$

Rational integral equations of the nth degree have n roots. Roots occurring more than once are called multiple roots, and some of the roots may be imaginary or complex numbers. If a is a root of $f(x) = 0$, division by $x - a$ yields a quotient that is a function of next lower degree containing the remainder of the roots:

$$f(x) = (x - r_1)(x - r_2) \cdots (x - r_n) = 0$$

where $r_1, r_2, \ldots, r_n$ are all the roots of $f(x) = 0$.

Relationships Between Roots and Coefficients of an Equation. For equations written in the form:

$$x^n + p_1x^{n-1} + p_2x^{n-2} + \cdots + p_{n-1}x + p_n = 0$$

the following statements hold:

- The sum of the roots equals the coefficient of the second term p_1 with sign changed
- The sum of the products of the roots taken two at a time equals the coefficient of the third term p_2
- The sum of the products of the roots taken m at a time multiplied by $(-1)^m$ equals the coefficient of the $(m + 1)$th term p_m
- The product of all the roots and $(-1)^n$ equals the last term p_n
- If the second term is missing, the sum of the roots is zero
- If there is no constant term, at least one root is zero
- If all the coefficients are integers, the roots cannot be fractions. In addition, the integral roots are factors of the constant term
- If the coefficients are all real and a complex number $a + bi$ is a root, its conjugate $a - bi$ also is a root

- If the coefficients are all rational and $a + \sqrt{b}$ is a root, then its conjugate $a - \sqrt{b}$ also is a root
- If the signs of all the coefficients are positive, the equation has no positive roots
- If the signs of a complete equation (no terms missing) are alternately positive and negative, the equation has no negative roots

Transformation of Equations. By substituting a new variable for the original variable, an equation can be transformed into another equation with roots having a certain relationship to the roots of the original equation. For example, to transform the general equation:

$$f(x) = x^n + p_1 x^{n-1} + p_n x^{n-2} + \cdots + p_{n-1} x + p_n = 0$$

into a form whose roots are those of $f(x)$ with their signs changed, let $x = -y$; that is, change the signs of the coefficients of all odd powers of x. The equation, $x^5 - 3x^4 + 4x^3 + 2x^2 - 6x - 1 = 0$, can be transformed thus into an equation whose roots have signs opposite those of the original roots. The required equation is $-y^5 - 3y^4 - 4y^3 + 2y^2 + 6y - 1 = 0$.

To transform $f(x)$ into an equation whose roots are m times those of $f(x)$, let $x = y/m$. The required equation is obtained by multiplying the second term p_1 by m, the third term p_2 by m^2, ..., the kth term p_{k-1} by m^{k-1}, and the constant term p_n by m^n. Thus, the equation whose roots are ten times those of $x^3 - 9x^2 + 27x - 27 = 0$ is $y^3 - 90y^2 + 2{,}700y - 27{,}000 = 0$.

QUADRATIC EQUATIONS

The equation $f(x) = ax^2 + bx + c = 0$ is quadratic. It has two roots, both real or both complex, given by the formulas:

$$x_1, x_2 = \frac{-b \pm \sqrt{b^2 - 4ac}}{2a} = \frac{2c}{-b \mp \sqrt{b^2 - 4ac}}$$

To avoid loss of precision if $\sqrt{b^2 - 4ac}$ and $|b|$ are nearly equal, the form that does not involve the difference should be used.

Given that a, b, c are real it follows: if $b^2 - 4ac > 0$, the roots are real and unequal; if $b^2 - 4ac = 0$, the roots are real and equal; if $b^2 - 4ac < 0$, the roots are imaginary.

Solving Quadratic Equations with One Unknown. If the first power is not present, collect the variable terms on the left side of the equation and add the terms. Collect the constant terms on the right, add them and divide both sides by the coefficient of the unknown. Take the square root of both sides. For example, solve $3x^2 + 12 = 5x^2 - 6$.

Transposing terms with x to the left side and constant terms to the right yields $5x^2 - 3x^2 = 12 + 6$ after division by -1. Hence, $2x^2 = 18$. Division by 2 gives $x^2 = 9$. The square root operation gives the solution: $x = \pm 3$. If the first power is present, reduce the equation to the form, $x^2 + px = q$. Make the left side of the equation a perfect square by adding to both sides $p^2/4$, the square of one-half the coefficient of x. Extract the square root of both sides and solve the resulting first-degree equations.

Another example, solve $x^2 + x - 6 = 0$. First transpose the constant term to put this equation in the form of $x^2 + x = 6$. To make the left side of the transposed equation a perfect square, add the square of one-half the coefficient of x to both sides:

$$x^2 + x + \tfrac{1}{4} = (x + \tfrac{1}{2})^2 = 6 + \tfrac{1}{4} = 6.25$$

Take the square roots of both sides to obtain $x + 0.5 = \pm 2.5$, from which $x = +2$ and -3.

CUBIC EQUATIONS

The equation $f(x) = a_0x^3 + a_1x^2 + a_2x + a^3 = 0$ is cubic. It has three roots, all real or one real and two complex.

Algebraic Solution. The equation is written in the form $ax^3 + 3bx^2 + 3cx + d = 0$. Let:

$$q = ac - b^2 \quad \text{and} \quad r = \tfrac{1}{2}(3abc - a^2d) - b^3$$

and let:

$$s_1 = (r + \sqrt{q^3 + r^2})^{1/3} \quad \text{and} \quad s_2 = (r - \sqrt{q^3 + r^2})^{1/3}$$

then the roots are:

$$x_1 = [(s_1 + s_2) - b] \div a$$

$$x_2 = \left[-\frac{1}{2}(s_1 + s_2) + \frac{\sqrt{-3}}{2}(s_1 - s_2) - b \right] \div a$$

$$x_3 = \left[-\frac{1}{2}(s_1 + s_2) - \frac{\sqrt{-3}}{2}(s_1 - s_2) - b \right] \div a$$

If $q^3 + r^2 > 0$, the equation has one real and two complex roots. If $q^3 + r^2 = 0$, it has three real roots of which at least two are equal. If $q^3 + r^2 < 0$, the equation has three real roots but the numerical solution leads to finding the cube roots of complex quantities. In such a case, the trigonometric solution should be used. For example, given the equation $x^3 + 12x^2 + 45x + 54 = 0$ where $a = 1$, $b = 4$, $c = 15$, $d = 54$; $q = 15 - 16 = -1$; $r = \tfrac{1}{2}(180 - 54) - 64 = -1$; $q^3 + r^2 = -1 + 1 = 0$; $s_1 = s_2 = (-1)^{1/3} = -1$; $s_1 + s_2 = -2$ and $s_1 - s_2 = 0$. Thus, the roots are $x_1 = (-2 - 4) = -6$; $x_2 = x_3 = [-\tfrac{1}{2}(-2) - 4] = -3$.

Trigonometric Solution. The equation is written in the form $ax^3 + 3bx^2 + 3cx + d = 0$. As in algebraic solution, let $q = ac - b^2$ and $r = \tfrac{1}{2}(3abc - a^2d) - b^3$. The roots are:

$$x_1 = (y_1 - b) \div a$$
$$x_2 = (y_2 - b) \div a$$
$$x_3 = (y_3 - b) \div a$$

where y_1, y_2, and y_3 have the following values, with the upper of alternative signs being used when r is $+$ and the lower when r is $-$:

If q is $-$ and $q^3 + r^2 \leqq 0$, then:

$$y_1 = \pm 2\sqrt{-q} \cos\left[\frac{1}{3}\cos^{-1}\frac{\pm r}{\sqrt{-q^3}}\right]$$

$$y_2 = \pm 2\sqrt{-q} \cos\left[\frac{1}{3}\cos^{-1}\frac{\pm r}{\sqrt{-q^3}} + \frac{2\pi}{3}\right]$$

$$y_3 = \pm 2\sqrt{-q} \cos\left[\frac{1}{3}\cos^{-1}\frac{\pm r}{\sqrt{-q^3}}\ \frac{4\pi}{3}\right]$$

Example 6. For the equation $x^3 + 6x^2 - 9x - 54 = 0$ where $a = 1$, $b = 2$, $c = -3$, $d = -54$; $q = -3 - 4 = -7$; $r = \frac{1}{2}(-18 + 54) - 8 = 10$; $q^3 + r^2 = -343 + 100 = -243$. Note that q is $-$; $q^3 + r^2 < 0$; r is $+$.

Therefore, using the upper signs:

$$y_1 = 2\sqrt{7} \cos\left[\frac{1}{3}\cos^{-1}\frac{10}{\sqrt{343}}\right] = 2\sqrt{7} \cos 19.1° = 5$$

Thus, one root is $x_1 = 5 - 2 = 3$. The other roots can be determined similarly.

In the trigonometric solution, if q is $-$ and $q^3 + r^2 \geqq 0$, then:

$$y_1 = \pm 2\sqrt{-q} \cosh\left[\frac{1}{3}\cosh^{-1}\frac{\pm r}{\sqrt{-q^3}}\right]$$

$$y_2 = \mp\sqrt{-q} \cosh\left[\frac{1}{3}\cosh^{-1}\frac{\pm r}{\sqrt{-q^3}}\right] + i\sqrt{-3q} \sinh\left[\frac{1}{3}\cosh^{-1}\frac{\pm r}{\sqrt{-q^3}}\right]$$

$$y_3 = \mp\sqrt{-q} \cosh\left[\frac{1}{3}\cosh^{-1}\frac{\pm r}{\sqrt{-q^3}}\right] - i\sqrt{-3q} \sinh\left[\frac{1}{3}\cosh^{-1}\frac{\pm r}{\sqrt{-q^3}}\right]$$

and if q is $+$, then:

$$y_1 = \pm 2\sqrt{q} \sinh\left[\frac{1}{3}\sinh^{-1}\frac{\pm r}{\sqrt{q^3}}\right]$$

$$y_2 = \mp\sqrt{q} \sinh\left[\frac{1}{3}\sinh^{-1}\frac{\pm r}{\sqrt{q^3}}\right] + i\sqrt{3q} \cosh\left[\frac{1}{3}\sinh^{-1}\frac{\pm r}{\sqrt{q^3}}\right]$$

$$y_3 = \mp\sqrt{q} \sinh\left[\frac{1}{3}\sinh^{-1}\frac{\pm r}{\sqrt{q^3}}\right] - i\sqrt{3q} \cosh\left[\frac{1}{3}\sinh^{-1}\frac{\pm r}{\sqrt{q^3}}\right]$$

Cardan's Solution of Cubic Equations. With this method, the equation is reduced to the form, $x^3 + px + q = 0$. When the general form $a_0 x^3 + a_1 x^2 + a_2 x + a_3 = 0$ is given, this transformation is done by diminishing the roots by $-a_1/3a_0$. One solution is:

$$x = \sqrt[3]{-\frac{q}{2} + \sqrt{\frac{q^2}{4} + \frac{p^3}{27}}} + \sqrt[3]{-\frac{q}{2} - \sqrt{\frac{q^2}{4} + \frac{p^3}{27}}} = r + r'$$

The other two roots are $r\omega + r'\omega^2$ and $r\omega^2 + r'\omega$, where:

$$\omega = -\tfrac{1}{2}(1 + \sqrt{-3})$$
$$\omega^2 = -\tfrac{1}{2}(1 - \sqrt{-3})$$

Example 7. Solve the equation $x^3 - 6x^2 - 12x + 112 = 0$.

The first step is to eliminate the coefficient -6 by diminishing the roots by $-(-6)/3 = 2$:

$$
\begin{array}{l}
1 - 6 - 12 + 112 \ \underline{|2} \\
\quad + 2 - \ 8 - \ \ 40 \\
\overline{1 - 4 - 20} + \ \ 72 \\
\quad + 2 - \ \ 4 \\
\overline{1 - 2} - 24 \\
\quad + 2 \\
\overline{1 + 0}
\end{array}
$$

The transformed equation is $y^3 - 24y + 72 = 0$. Here $p = -24$ and $q = 72$, and:

$$y = \sqrt[3]{-\frac{72}{2} + \sqrt{\frac{72^2}{4} + \frac{-24^3}{27}}} + \sqrt[3]{-\frac{72}{2} - \sqrt{\frac{72^2}{4} + \frac{-24^3}{27}}}$$

$$= \sqrt[3]{-36 + \sqrt{784}} + \sqrt[3]{-36 - \sqrt{784}} = \sqrt[3]{-8} + \sqrt[3]{-64}$$

$$= -2 - 4 = -6$$

The other two roots are $-2\omega - 4\omega^2 = 3 - \sqrt{-3}$ and $-2\omega^2 - 4\omega = 3 + \sqrt{-3}$. Since $x = y + 2$, the solutions are $x = -4, 5 \pm \sqrt{-3}$.

QUARTIC EQUATIONS

An equation in the form $f(x) = a_0x^4 + a_1x^3 + a_2x^2 + a_3x + a_4 = 0$ is quartic. It has four roots, all real, all complex, or two real and two complex. To solve, divide the equation by a_0 to put it in the form $x^4 + ax^3 + bx^2 + cx + d = 0$. Find any real root y_1 of the cubic equation:

$$8y^3 - 4by^2 + 2(ac - 4d)y - [c^2 + d(a^2 - 4b)] = 0$$

Then the four roots of the quartic equation are given by the roots of the two quadratic equations:

$$x^2 + \left[\frac{a}{2} + \sqrt{\frac{a^2}{4} + 2y_1 - b}\right]x + (y_1 + \sqrt{y_1^2 - d}) = 0$$

$$x^2 + \left[\frac{a}{2} - \sqrt{\frac{a^2}{4} + 2y_1 - b}\right]x + (y_1 - \sqrt{y_1^2 - d}) = 0$$

GENERAL EQUATIONS OF THE nth DEGREE

Equations of the nth degree are expressed as:

$$P = a_0x^n + a_1x^{n-1} + a_2x^{n-2} + \cdots + a_{n-1}x + a_n = 0$$

If $n > 4$, no formula gives the roots of this general equation. The following methods may be used to advantage.

Roots by Factors. By trial, find a number r for which $x = r$ satisfies the equation, that is:

$$a_0r^n + a_1r^{n-1} + a_2r^{n-2} + \cdots + a_{n-1}r + a_n = 0 \qquad a_0 \neq 0$$

Then $x - r$ is a factor of the left member P of the equation. Divide P by $x - r$, leaving an equation with one degree less than that of the original equation. Next, proceed in the same manner with the reduced equation. All integer roots of $P = 0$ are divisors of a_n/a_0.

Roots by Approximation. Assume the coefficients a_i in P are real. Let a and b be real numbers. If for $x = a$ and $x = b$ the left member P of the equation has opposite signs, then a root lies between a and b. By repeated application, real roots to any desired degree of accuracy may be obtained.

Roots by Graphing. If a graph of P is plotted as a function of x, the real roots are the values of x where the graph crosses the x axis. By increasing the scale of the portion of the graph near an estimated root, the root may be obtained to any desired degree of accuracy.

Descartes' Rule of Signs. The number of positive roots in an equation:

$$f(x) = x^n + p_1x^{n-1} + \cdots + p_n = 0$$

cannot exceed the number of variations, or changes in sign between successive terms. In addition, the number of negative roots cannot exceed the number of permanences, or successive terms with the same sign. Missing powers of x are represented by zero with the sign of the preceding term, but in testing for negative roots, the equation is transformed into one whose roots have signs opposite those of $f(x)$ before the rule is applied. For example, what is the least possible number of imaginary roots of:

$$P(x) = x^6 - 3x^3 + 2x - 9 = 0$$

With the missing terms supplied with zeros, $P(x)$ becomes $x^6 + 0x^5 + 0x^4 - 3x^3 - 0x^2 + 2x - 9$. With three variations, the equation can have no more than three positive roots.

To estimate the negative roots, the equation is transformed by letting $x = -y$. $P(-y) = y^6 + 0y^5 + 0y^4 + 3y^3 + 0y^2 - 2y - 9$. Because the equation has one variation, it has no more than one positive root, indicating that the original equation $P(x)$ has at most one negative root.

Hence, $P(x)$ can have no more than three positive and one negative real roots. Since $P(x)$ is a sixth-degree equation, it has six roots. Consequently, it must have at least two imaginary roots.

The equation $x^n = a$. The n roots of this equation are:

$$x = \begin{cases} \sqrt[n]{a}\left(\cos\dfrac{2k\pi}{n} + \sqrt{-1}\sin\dfrac{2k\pi}{n}\right) & \text{if } a > 0 \\[3mm] \sqrt[n]{-a}\left(\cos\dfrac{(2k+1)\pi}{n} + \sqrt{-1}\sin\dfrac{(2k+1)\pi}{n}\right) & \text{if } a < 0 \end{cases}$$

where k takes successively the values $0, 1, 2, 3, \ldots, n-1$.

TRANSCENDENTAL EQUATIONS

The equation $F(x) = f(x)$ is called transcendental if at least one of the functions $F(x)$ or $f(x)$ is not algebraic. For example:

- $3^x = 4^{x-2} \cdot 2^x$
- $2^{x-1} = 8^{x-2} - 4^{x-2}$
- $2\log_5(3x-1) - \log_5(12x+1) = 0$
- $\sin x = \cos^2 x - \frac{1}{4}$
- $3\cosh x = \sinh x + 9$
- $x\cos x = \sin x$

Transcendental equations can be reduced in some cases to algebraic equations, and tables can be applied. In general, transcendental equations can be solved only approximately.

Exponential Equations. An exponential equation involves the unknown x or a polynomial $P(x)$ in exponents of powers of given bases $a, b, c, \ldots$. Such equations reduce to the algebraic ones in the following cases:

- If the powers $a^{P_1(x)}$, $b^{P_2(x)}$ are not to be added or subtracted, logarithms to an arbitrary base of both sides of the equation should be taken, for example:

$$3^x = 4^{x-2}2^x$$
$$x\log 3 = (x-2)\log 4 + x\log 2$$
$$x = \frac{2\log 4}{\log 4 - \log 3 + \log 2}$$

- If $a, b, c, \ldots$ are powers of the same number k with integral or fractional exponents, for example, $a = k^\alpha$, $b = k^\beta$, $c = k^\gamma, \ldots$. Substituting $k^x = y$ produces, in some cases, an algebraic equation with respect to y; solving the equation results in:

$$x = \frac{\log y}{\log k}$$

For example:

$$2^{x-1} = 8^{x-2} - 4^{x-2}$$

$$\frac{2^x}{2} = \frac{2^{3x}}{64} \frac{2^{2x}}{16}$$

Putting $2^x = y$ yields $y^3 - 4y^2 - 32y = 0$ and $y_1 = 8$, $y_2 = -4$, $y_3 = 0$; $2^{x_1} = 8$, $2^{x_2} = -4$, and $2^{x_3} = 0$. Thus, $x_1 = 3$. Other real solutions do not exist.

Logarithmic Equations. A logarithmic equation involves the unknown x or a polynomial $P(x)$ only under the logarithm sign. Such equations reduce to algebraic equations in the following cases:

- If the equation involves logarithms of one expression to the same base, then this logarithm can be taken as a new unknown. An algebraic equation is obtained, solved, and a result found by raising the base to the obtained power. For example, $m(\log_a P(x))^2 + n = a\sqrt{(\log_a P(x))^2 + b}$. Substitution of $y = \log_a P(x)$ gives the equation $my^2 + n = a\sqrt{y^2 + b}$. From the equation $P(x) = a^y$, x is determined from y.
- If the equation has the form:

$$m_1 \log_a P_1(x) + m_2 \log_a P_2(x) + \cdots = 0$$

where $m_1, m_2, \ldots$ are integers and $P_1(x), P_2(x), \ldots$ are polynomials of the variable x, then the left side of the equation reduces to a logarithm of one expression. Raising the base a to powers with exponents equal to both sides of the equation results in an algebraic equation:

$$(P_1(x))^{m_1}(P_2(x))^{m_2} \cdots = 1$$

For example, $2\log_5(3x - 1) - \log_5(12x + 1) = 0$

$$\log_5 \frac{(3x-1)^2}{12x+1} = \log_5 1 \quad \frac{(3x-1)^2}{12x+1} = 1 \quad x_1 = 0 \quad x_2 = 2$$

Because the solution $x_1 = 0$ leads to a logarithm of a negative number, it is discarded.

Equations Involving Hyperbolic Functions. Such equations are solved by expressing the hyperbolic functions of x by e^x and e^{-x} and then by substitutions $e^x = y$ and $e^{-x} = 1/y$. Then, $x = \ln y$ is determined from tables.

For example, consider $3\cosh x = \sinh x + 9$. Let $\frac{3}{2}(e^x + e^{-x}) = \frac{1}{2}(e^x - e^{-x}) + 9$ and $e^x + 2e^{-x} - 9 = 0$. Putting $e^x = y$ and $e^{-x} = 1/y$ results in:

$$y^2 - 9y + 2 = 0$$

$$y_{1,2} = \frac{1}{2}(9 \pm \sqrt{73})$$

$$x_1 = \ln\frac{1}{2}(9 + \sqrt{73}) \approx 2.1716$$

$$x_2 = \ln\frac{1}{2}(9 - -\sqrt{73}) \approx -1.4784$$

HORNER'S METHOD OF SOLVING EQUATIONS

Locate the roots approximately, graphically, or by determining upper and lower limits. Narrow the range in which the function changes signs by diminishing the roots of the equation by each digit determined. To simplify, remove the decimals by multiplying the roots by powers of 10. For example, find a root between 2 and 3 of $x^3 - 12x^2 + 45x - 53 = 0$. Diminish the roots by 2:

$$
\begin{array}{r}
1 - 12 + 45 - 53\,\underline{|2} \\
+\ \ 2 - 20 + 50 \\
\hline
1 - 10 + 25\,|-\ \ 3 \\
+\ \ 2 - 16| \\
\hline
1 -\ \ 8| +\ \ 9 \\
+\ \ 2| \\
\hline
1 -\ \ 6
\end{array}
$$

The transformed equation is $y^3 - 6y^2 + 9y - 3 = 0$. Because the next digit to be obtained is a decimal, multiply by 10 to eliminate decimals. The new equation becomes $y^3 - 60y^2 + 900y - 3{,}000 = 0$. A first approximation to its root can be obtained by neglecting powers of y that are higher than the first, $900y - 3{,}000 = 0$; $y = 3.3$. Try $y = 4$. Division of the left side of the equation by $y - 4$ yields a remainder with a negative sign, the same as the constant term. Division by $y - 5$ leaves a positive remainder. Therefore the first decimal of the original equation is 4. Diminish the new roots by 4:

$$
\begin{array}{r}
1 - 60 + 900 - 3{,}000\,\underline{|4} \\
+\ \ 4 - 224 + 2{,}704 \\
\hline
1 - 56 + 676| -\ \ \ 296 \\
+\ \ 4 - 208| \\
\hline
1 - 52| + 468 \\
+\ \ 4| \\
\hline
1 - 48
\end{array}
$$

Multiply the new roots by 10 to eliminate decimals, $z^3 - 480z^2 + 46{,}800z - 296{,}000 = 0$. The first approximation to z is $296{,}000/46{,}800 = 6+$. Because the function changes sign between 6 and 7, the second decimal is 6. Diminish the roots by 6:

$$
\begin{array}{r}
1 - 480 + 46{,}800 - 296{,}000\,\underline{|6} \\
+\ \ \ 6 -\ \ 2{,}844 + 263{,}736 \\
\hline
1 - 474 + 43{,}956| -\ \ 32{,}264 \\
+\ \ \ 6 -\ \ 2{,}808| \\
\hline
1 - 468| + 41{,}148 \\
+\ \ \ 6| \\
\hline
1 - 462
\end{array}
$$

The next decimal is then $10 \times 32{,}264/41{,}148 = 7+$. The required root is 2.467.

NEWTON'S METHOD OF SOLVING EQUATIONS

This method applies to high-degree algebraic equations and to other types, including trigonometric, exponential, and other transcendental equations. The given equation is written in the form $f(x) = 0$. Roots are located approximately, either graphically or by determining upper and lower limits. Assume a value of an unknown root and substitute in:

$$x_1 = x_0 - \frac{f(x_0)}{f'(x_0)}$$

where

$$x_0 = \text{assumed value}$$
$$f(x_0) = \text{value of given function for } x = x_0$$
$$f'(x_0) = \text{value of first derivative of function}$$
$$\text{for } x = x_0$$
$$x_1 = \text{second approximation to the root}$$

The value x_1 may be substituted for x_0 in this formula to obtain a third approximation x_2. For example, to find a root between 2 and 3 of $x^3 - 12x^2 + 45x - 53 = 0$, let $x = 2$. Find $f(2)$ by dividing by $x - 2$:

$$
\begin{array}{r}
1 - 12 + 45 - 53 \,\underline{|\,2} \\
+\ \ 2 - 20 + 50 \\
\hline
1 - 10 + 25 \,\boxed{-\ \ 3} = f(2)
\end{array}
$$

Then, $f'(x) = 3x^2 - 24x + 45$. Find $f'(2)$ by dividing by $x - 2$:

$$
\begin{array}{r}
3 - 24 + 45 \,\underline{|\,2} \\
+\ \ 6 - 36 \\
\hline
3 - 18 \,\boxed{+\ \ 9} = f'(2)
\end{array}
$$

$$x_1 = 2 - \left(\frac{-3}{9}\right) = 2 + \tfrac{1}{3} = 2.3$$

As a second trial, let $x_0 = 2.3$. Divide $f(x)$ and $f'(x)$ by $x - 2.3$ to find $f(2.3) = -0.813$ and $f'(2.3) = 5.67$:

$$x_2 = 2.3 - (-0.813/5.67) = 2.3 + 0.14 = 2.44$$

As a third trial, let $x_0 = 2.44$, $f(2.44) = -0.116416$, $f'(2.44) = 4.3008$:

$$x_3 = 2.44 - (-0.116416/4.3008) = 2.44 + 0.027 = 2.467$$

Modified Newton Method. Faster convergence than with Newton's method can sometimes be obtained with the approximation:

$$x_1 = x_0 - \frac{f'(x_0)}{f''(x_0)} \pm \sqrt{\left[\frac{f'(x_0)}{f''(x_0)}\right]^2 - \frac{2f(x_0)}{f''(x_0)}}$$

where

$$x_0 = \text{trial value of unknown root}$$
$$f(x_0) = \text{value of function for } x = x_0$$
$$f'(x_0) = \text{value of first derivative of function for } x = x_0$$

$f''(x_0)$ = value of second derivative of function for $x = x_0$
    x_1 = second approximation to root

The proper sign before the radical is the one opposite that of the term $-f'(x_0)/f''(x_0)$. If $f''(x_0)$ is small relative to $f(x_0)$ and has the same sign, Newton's method should be used. For example, to find a root between 2 and 3 of $x^3 - 12x^2 + 45x - 53 = 0$, let $x = 2$. Find $f(2)$ by dividing by $x - 2$:

$$
\begin{array}{r}
1 - 12 + 45 - 53\ \underline{|2} \\
+\ \ 2 - 20 + 50 \\
\hline
1 - 10 + 25\ \underline{|-\ \ 3} = f(2)
\end{array}
$$

The results are:

$$f'(x) = 3x^2 - 24x + 45 \qquad f'(2) = 9$$
$$f''(x) = 6x - 24 \qquad f''(2) = -12$$
$$f'(2)/f''(2) = 9/(-12) = -0.75 \qquad 2f(2)/f''(2) = 2(-3)/(-12) = 0.5$$
$$x_1 = 2 + 0.75 - \sqrt{0.75^2 - 0.5} = 2.75 - 0.25 = 2.50$$

As a second trial, let $x_0 = 2.5$. Then, $f(2.5) = 0.125$; $f'(2.5) = 3.75$; $f''(2.5) = -9$; $f'(2.5)/f''(2\ 5) = 3.75/(-9) = -0.417$; and $2f(2.5)/f''(2.5) = 2 \times 0.125/(-9) = -0.027778$.

Thus, $x_2 = 2.5 + 0.417 - \sqrt{0.417^2 + 0.027778} = 2.917 - 0.449 = 2.468$.

STEINMAN'S METHOD OF SOLVING EQUATIONS

This method has the advantage over Newton's method because calculus is not required for the solution of algebraic equations. First, the roots are located approximately, either graphically or by determining upper and lower limits. Then, the equation is written in the form:

$$a_0x^n = a_1x^{n-1} + a_2x^{n-2} + \cdots + a_n$$

A value of an unknown root is substituted in:

$$x_1 = \frac{a_1 + (2a_2/x_0) + (3a_3/x_0^2) + (4a_4/x_0^3) + \cdots}{a_0 + (a_2/x_0^2) + (2a_3/x_0^3) + (3a_4/x_0^4) + \cdots}$$

where

$$x_0 = \text{assumed value and}$$
$$x_1 = \text{second approximation}$$

For example, to find a root between 2 and 3 of $x^3 - 12x^2 + 45x - 53 = 0$, transpose the equation:

$$x^3 = 12x^2 - 45x + 53$$
$$a_0 = 1 \quad a_1 = 12 \quad a_2 = -45 \quad a_3 = 53$$

Let $x_0 = 2$. Then:

$$x_1 = \frac{12 + 2(-45)/2 + 3 \times 53/2^2}{1 - 45/2^2 + 2 \times 53/2^3} = \frac{12 - 45 + 39.75}{1 - 11.25 + 13.25} = \frac{6.75}{3.00} = 2.25$$

As a second trial, let $x_0 = 2.25$. Substitution in the formula gives $x_2 = 2.45$. A third trial with this value yields $x_3 = 2.467$.

SIMULTANEOUS EQUATIONS

Simultaneous equations are a group of equations with several unknowns that can be satisfied by the same values of the unknowns. Independent equations represent different relations between the unknowns. If they are linear and also consistent, they have only one solution. If they have no solution, the equations are inconsistent.

If the equations are satisfied by an unlimited number of values of the unknowns, the equations are dependent. This condition holds when there are more equations than unknowns or when a determinant formed by the coefficients of the unknowns equals zero. For example, in the system of equations:

$$2x - 3y + 4z = 8$$
$$x + 2y - 3z = -4$$
$$4x + y - 2z = 1$$

the determinant of the coefficients is:

$$\begin{vmatrix} 2 & -3 & 4 \\ 1 & 2 & -3 \\ 4 & 1 & -2 \end{vmatrix} = -8 + 4 + 36 - 32 + 6 - 6 = 0$$

Hence, the equations are dependent.

A system of equations is consistent if both the matrix of the coefficients and the matrix of the coefficients and constant terms (augmented matrix) have the same rank, that is, the largest determinants, not zero, formed from these matrices have equal numbers of terms. For example, in the system of equations:

$$2x + 3y = 1$$
$$x - 2y = 4$$
$$4x - y = 6$$

the matrix of the coefficients is:

$$\begin{vmatrix} 2 & 3 \\ 1 & -2 \\ 4 & -1 \end{vmatrix}$$

Its rank is 2, because it has at least one second-order determinant that is not zero. The augmented matrix is:

$$\begin{vmatrix} 2 & 3 & 1 \\ 1 & -2 & 4 \\ 4 & -1 & 6 \end{vmatrix}$$

Its rank is 3, because it forms a third-order determinant that is not zero. Further, because the ranks of the two matrices are not the same, the equations are inconsistent.

Solving Simultaneous Linear Equations. A common method for solving simultaneous linear equations is to eliminate one unknown at a time, until only one remains. When the value of this unknown is determined, the others can be found successively.

One unknown at a time can be eliminated by forming the equations in pairs, by addition or subtraction, substitution or comparison. In dealing with equations of the form $a/x + b/y + \cdots = c$, let $1/x = x'$, $1/y = y'$, etc., and first solve for x' and y'. For example, to solve the following system of equations:

$$3x + 2y - 2z = 4 \tag{Eq 1}$$
$$2x - 3y + 3z = 7 \tag{Eq 2}$$
$$4x + 5y - 4z = 7 \tag{Eq 3}$$

eliminate x by addition or subtraction:

$$2 \times (\text{Eq 1}) - 3 \times (\text{Eq 2}) \text{ produces } 13y - 13z = -13 \tag{Eq 4}$$

and

$$(\text{Eq 3}) - 2 \times (\text{Eq 2}) \text{ produces } 11y - 10z = -7 \tag{Eq 5}$$

Eliminate y by substitution. From Eq 4:

$$y = \frac{13z - 13}{13} = z - 1 \tag{Eq 6}$$

Substitute y from Eq 6 in Eq 5 to produce:

$$11(z - 1) - 10z = 11z - 11 - 10z = -7 \quad z = 4 \tag{Eq 7}$$

Eliminate z by comparison. From Eq 4:

$$z = \frac{13y + 13}{13} = y + 1 \tag{Eq 8}$$

From Eq 5:

$$z = \frac{11y + 7}{10} \tag{Eq 9}$$

Equate Eq 8 and 9:

$$y + 1 = \frac{11y + 7}{10} \quad 10y + 10 = 11y + 7 \quad y = 3 \tag{Eq 10}$$

Substitute $y = 3$ and $z = 4$ in Eq 1:

$$3x + 2 \times 3 - 2 \times 4 = 4 \quad x = 2$$

Solving Simultaneous Equations by Determinants. Solution of n linear equations with n unknowns can be reached by evaluating the ratio of two determinants for each unknown. The denominator for each unknown is the determinant of the coefficients of the unknowns in the system of equations. For a specific unknown, the numerator differs from the denominator only in that the constant terms of the system replace the coefficients of that unknown.

For example, to solve the following system of equations:

$$\begin{aligned} x - 2y + 3z &= 2 \\ 2x \qquad - 3z &= 3 \\ x + y + z &= 6 \end{aligned}$$

find the denominator of the solution by:

$$D = \begin{vmatrix} 1 & -2 & 3 \\ 2 & 0 & -3 \\ 1 & 1 & 1 \end{vmatrix} = 19$$

For the numerator of the solution of each unknown, replace its column of coefficients in D by the constant terms 2, 3, 6. Thus:

$$x = \frac{\begin{vmatrix} 2 & -2 & 3 \\ 3 & 0 & -3 \\ 6 & 1 & 1 \end{vmatrix}}{19} = \frac{57}{19} = 3$$

$$y = \frac{\begin{vmatrix} 1 & 2 & 3 \\ 2 & 3 & -3 \\ 1 & 6 & 1 \end{vmatrix}}{19} = \frac{38}{19} = 2$$

$$z = \frac{\begin{vmatrix} 1 & -2 & 2 \\ 2 & 0 & 3 \\ 1 & 1 & 6 \end{vmatrix}}{19} = \frac{19}{19} = 1$$

Solving Simultaneous Quadratic Equations. If x and y are two unknowns and if two of the quantities $x + y$, $x - y$, and xy are given, the third unknown can be obtained from $(x + y)^2 - 4xy = (x - y)^2$, and the equations may be solved. To solve the following system of equations:

$$x + y = 9. \tag{Eq 11}$$

$$xy = 20 \tag{Eq 12}$$

Square Eq 11 to produce:

$$x^2 + 2xy + y^2 = 81 \tag{Eq 13}$$

Multiply Eq 12 by 4 to produce:

$$4xy = 80 \tag{Eq 14}$$

Subtracting Eq 14 from Eq 13 gives:

$$x^2 - 2xy + y^2 = 1 \tag{Eq 15}$$

The square root of Eq 15 is:

$$x - y = \pm 1 \qquad \text{(Eq 16)}$$

Add and subtract Eq 11 and Eq 16, which results in:

$$x = 5 \quad x = 4$$

or

$$y = 4 \quad y = 5$$

If in both equations all the terms are of the same degree, or if quadratic terms can be eliminated by transformation, the system can be converted to solution of one linear and one quadratic equation. To solve the following system of equations:

$$4x^2 - 9xy + 3y^2 - 2y = 0 \qquad \text{(Eq 17)}$$

$$2x^2 - 2xy - y^2 - 6y = 0 \qquad \text{(Eq 18)}$$

multiply Eq 17 by 3 to produce:

$$12x^2 - 27xy + 9y^2 - 6y = 0 \qquad \text{(Eq 19)}$$

Subtracting Eq 18 from Eq 19 yields:

$$10x^2 - 25xy + 10y^2 = 0 \qquad \text{(Eq 20)}$$

Factor Eq 20 to the form:

$$(10x - 5y)(x - 2y) = 0 \qquad \text{(Eq 21)}$$

and equate the factors to zero:

$$x = \frac{y}{2} \text{ or } 2y \qquad \text{(Eq 22)}$$

Substitute Eq 22 in Eq 18 and solve for y:

$$y = 0, 2 \qquad x = 0, 4$$

Graphical Solutions. To solve a system of two equations with two unknowns, plot both equations. The coordinates of the intersections of the curves are the solutions. For example, to solve graphically $y = x^2$ and $6x - 2y = 4$, compute x and y for both equations and plot the values:

$y = x^2$		$6x - 2y = 4$	
x	y	x	y
0	0	1	1
± 1	1	2	4
± 2	4	3	7
± 3	9	4	10
± 4	16		

The equations are plotted in Fig. 1. The graphs intersect at (2, 4) and (1, 1). Hence, the solutions are $x = 2$, $y = 4$ and $x = 1$, $y = 1$.

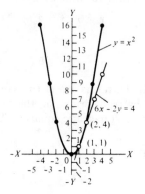

Figure 1

INEQUALITIES

The following are laws of inequalities for positive quantities:

- If $a > b$, then: $a + c > b + c$
  $a - c > b - c$
  $ac > bc$
  $\dfrac{a}{c} > \dfrac{b}{c}$

  $b < a$
  $c - a < c - b$
  $-ca < -cb$
  $\dfrac{c}{a} < \dfrac{c}{b}$

  Further, if $a - c > b$, then $a > b + c$

- If $a > b$ and $c > d$, then: $a + c > b + d$; $ac > bd$; but $a - c$ may be $>$ or $=$ or $< b - d$; a/c may be $>$ or $=$ or $< b/d$

LOGARITHMS

If $N = b^x$, then x is the logarithm of the number N to the base b. Common or Briggs, logarithms to the base 10 (abbreviated $\log_{10}$ or log) are used in computation. For theoretical work involving calculus, natural, or Naperian, logarithms to the irrational base $e = 2.71828 \cdots$ (abbreviated ln, $\log_e$, or log) are used. The relationship between logarithms of the two systems is:

$$\log_e n = \log_{10} n / \log_{10} e = \log_{10} n / 0.4343 = 2.303 \log_{10} n$$

The integral part of a common logarithm, called the characteristic, may be positive, negative, or zero. The decimal part is called the mantissa and can be found in published tables. It is always positive.

To find the common logarithm of a number, first find the mantissa from a table of logarithms, disregarding the decimal point of the number. Using the location of the decimal point, find the characteristic as follows. If the number is greater than 1, the characteristic is positive or zero. It is one less than the number of figures preceding the decimal point. For a number expressed in standard notation, the characteristic is the exponent of 10. For example, $\log 6.54 = 0.8156$ and $\log 6540 = \log(6.54 \times 10^3) = 3.8156$.

If the number is less than 1, the characteristic is negative and is numerically one greater than the number of zeros immediately following the decimal point. To avoid having a negative integral part and a positive decimal part, the characteristic is written as a difference. For example, $\log 0.654 = \log (6.54 \times 10^{-1}) = \bar{1}.8156 = 9.8156 - 10$ and $\log 0.000654 = \log (6.54 \times 10^{-4}) = \bar{4}.8156 = 6.8156 - 10$. To find a number whose logarithm is given, each of the above steps is reversed. The cologarithm of a number is the logarithm of its reciprocal. Hence, $\operatorname{colog} N = \log 1/N = \log 1 - \log N = -\log N$.

Use of Logarithms. In computation, use the following forms:

- To multiply a and b, use $\log ab = \log a + \log b$
- To divide a by b, use $\log a/b = \log a - \log b$
- To raise a to the nth power, use $\log a^n = n \log a$
- To find the nth root of a, use $\log a^{1/n} = (1/n) \log a$

Example 8. $68.31 \times 0.2754 = 18.81$

$$
\begin{array}{rl}
\log 68.31 & = \quad 1.8345 \\
\log \ 0.2754 & = \quad \underline{9.4400 - 10} \\
& \quad 11.2745 - 10 = 1.2745 = \log 18.81
\end{array}
$$

Example 9. $0.6831^{1.53} = 0.5582$

$$
\begin{array}{l}
\log 0.6831 = 9.8345 - 10 \\
1.53 \times (9.8345 - 10) = 15.0468 - 15.3
\end{array}
$$

To subtract 15.3 from 15.0468, add 10 to 15.0468 and subtract 10 from it:

$$
\begin{array}{l}
25.0468 - 10 \\
\underline{15.3} \\
\ 9.7468 - 10 = \log 0.5582
\end{array}
$$

Example 10. $\sqrt[5]{0.6831} = 0.9266$

$$\log 0.6831 = 9.8345 - 10$$

$$\frac{49.8345 - 50}{5} = 9.9669 - 10 = \log 0.9266$$

To solve a simple exponential equation of the form $a^x = b$, equate the logarithms of the two sides of the equation:

$$x \log a = \log b, \text{ from which } x = \frac{\log b}{\log a}$$

and

$$\log x = \log(\log b) - \log(\log a)$$

Example 11. $0.6831^x = 27.54$

$$x = \frac{\log 27.54}{\log 0.6831} = \frac{1.4400}{9.8345 - 10} = \frac{1.4400}{-0.1655} = -8.701$$

Slide Rule Theory. A slide rule is used for mechanical computation based on the use of logarithms. Multiplication, division, and the finding of powers and roots can be performed rapidly and with an accuracy sufficient for most engineering work.

The simple Mannheim rule consists of a fixed and a sliding part both of which are ruled with logarithmic scales, with divisions at distances equal to the logarithms of the numbers marking the division points. Since the logarithm of the product of two numbers is the sum of the logarithms of the numbers, and the logarithm of the quotient of two numbers is the difference of their logarithms, numbers can be multiplied or divided by moving the slide to the right or left to add or subtract the logarithms. The scales on the fixed part of the rule are called the A and D scales, and those on the slide the B and C scales. The A and B scales are each divided into two parts, each part being a half-size reproduction of the C and D scale. A runner, which consists of a glass plate with a fine vertical line on it, is used to facilitate some of the operations.

INTEREST, ANNUITIES AND SINKING FUNDS

If I is the simple interest on a principal P, r is the interest rate, and t is the time, then, $I = Prt$. The amount after a given number of interest periods is, $A = P(1 + rt)$.

Compound Interest. The amount A_n of a principal of P dollars invested at interest rate r compounded annually for n years is, $A_n = P(1 + r)^n$. If interest is compounded m times a year:

$$A_n = P\left(1 + \frac{r}{m}\right)^{mn}$$

At the end of mn periods the compound interest totals:

$$I = P \left(1 + \frac{r}{m}\right)^{mn} - P = A_n - P$$

Present Value of Sum Due in n Years. The sum P that, if invested now at a compound interest rate r, will amount to a given sum S after n years, is:

$$P = \frac{S}{(1 + r)^n} = S(1 + r)^{-n}$$

Annuity. An annuity is a fixed sum of money payable at equal intervals of time. The amount, or final value A_n, of an annuity of S dollars accumulated for n years at a compound interest rate r is:

$$A_n = \frac{S}{r}[(1 + r)^n - 1]$$

Present Value of an Annuity. The present value P of an annuity of S dollars for n years is the sum that, if invested now at a compound interest rate r, will equal the amount of the annuity in n years.

$$P = \frac{S}{r}\left[1 - \frac{1}{(1 + r)^n}\right]$$

Amount of a Sinking Fund. If a fixed investment N is made at the end of each successive year beginning at the end of the first year, and interest is paid at rate r, compounded annually, on the accumulated amount of the investment at the end of each year, the total amount S accumulated at the end of n years is:

$$S = N\frac{(1 + r)^n - 1}{r}$$

S is the amount of the sinking fund.

Fixed Investment. A fixed investment, or annual installment, is the amount N that must be placed at the end of each year, beginning one year hence, with compound interest paid at rate r on the accumulated deposit. The amount required to accumulate a sinking fund S in n years is:

$$N = S\frac{r}{(1 + r)^n - 1}$$

N is called a fixed investment or annual installment.

2
Geometry

CONCEPTS

MEASUREMENT OF PLANE ANGLES

A degree is 1/360 of a revolution (or perigon) and is divided into 60 units called minutes ('). Minutes are divided into 60 units called seconds (").

A radian is a central angle that intercepts a circular arc equal to its radius. One radian, therefore, equals $360/2\pi$ degrees or $57.295779513°$, and $1° = 0.017453293$ radian. An inscribed angle is measured by one half its intercepted arc. In Fig. 1, central angle AOB is measured by arc AB. Inscribed angle CDE is measured by one half arc CE.

An angle of 90° is a right angle, and the lines that form it are perpendicular. An angle less than a right angle is acute. An angle greater than 90° but less than 180° is obtuse. Two angles are complementary when their sum equals 90° and supplementary when their sum is 180°.

An angle APD formed by two chords intersecting inside a circle (Fig. 2) is measured by ½(arc AD + arc BC). Angle DPB is measured by ½(arc BD + AC).

An angle APB formed by a tangent and a chord drawn from the point of tangency (Fig. 3) is measured by one half arc PB.

An angle formed by two secants, two tangents, or a secant and a tangent drawn from an external point to a circle is measured by one half the difference of the intercepted arcs. In Fig. 4, angle CAE is measured by ½(arc CE − arc BD). Angle PTP' is measured by ½(arc $PBDP'$ − arc $PCEP'$), and angle PTD is measured by ½(arc PBD − arc PCE).

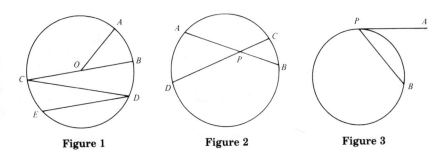

| Figure 1 | Figure 2 | Figure 3 |

POLYGONS

A polygon, or plane rectilinear figure, is a closed broken line.

A triangle is a polygon of three sides. It is isosceles if two sides and their opposite angles are equal; it is equilateral if all three sides and all three angles are equal.

Quadrilaterals are polygons of four sides. These include: (a) the trapezium, which has no two sides parallel; (b) the trapezoid, with two opposite sides parallel (isosceles trapezoid if the nonparallel sides are equal); and (c) the parallelogram, with both pairs of opposite sides parallel and equal. Parallelograms include: (a) the rhomboid, which has no right angles and, in general, adjacent sides not equal; (b) the rhombus, with no right angles but all sides equal; (c) the rectangle, which has only right angles and, in general, adjacent sides not equal; and (d) the square, having only right angles with all sides equal.

Similar polygons have their respective angles equal and their corresponding sides proportional.

A regular polygon has all sides equal and all angles equal, equilateral triangles and squares, for example. Two regular polygons of the same number of sides are similar. Other polygons are:

Polygon	Number of sides
Pentagon............................	5
Hexagon	6
Heptagon............................	7
Octagon.............................	8
Enneagon or nonagon	9
Decagon..............................	10
Dodecagon...........................	12

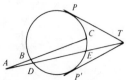

Figure 4

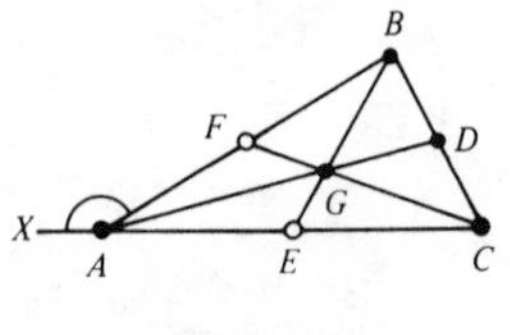

Figure 5

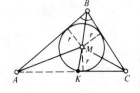

Figure 6

PROPERTIES OF TRIANGLES

General Triangle. The sum of the angles in a triangle equals 180°. In Fig. 5, $\angle XAB$ is an exterior angle of triangle ABC and equals the sum of the opposite interior angles, $\angle XAB = \angle B + \angle C$. The median joins a vertex to the midpoint of the opposite side. The three medians meet at the center of gravity, G, and G trisects each median; for example, $AG = 2/3\ AD$. Bisectors of angles of a triangle (Fig. 6) meet in a point M equidistant from all sides, and M is the center of an inscribed circle that is tangent to all sides. An angle bisector divides the opposite side into segments proportional to the adjacent sides of the angle; for example, $AK/KC = AB/BC$. An altitude of a triangle is a perpendicular line from a vertex to the opposite side. The three altitudes meet in a point called the orthocenter. The perpendicular bisectors of the sides of a triangle (Fig. 7) meet in a point O equidistant from all vertices. Point O is the center of the circumscribed circle that passes through all vertices. The line joining the midpoints of two sides of a triangle is parallel to the third side and half its length. If two triangles are mutually equiangular, they are similar, and their corresponding sides are proportional.

Orthogonal Projection. In Fig. 8 and 9, AE is the orthogonal projection of AB on AC, with BE perpendicular to AC. In any triangle, the square of the side opposite an acute angle equals the sum of the squares of the other two sides minus twice the product of one of those sides and the projection of the other side on it. In Fig. 8, $a^2 = b^2 + c^2 - 2b \cdot AE$. In any obtuse triangle, the square of the side opposite the obtuse angle equals the sum of the squares of the other two sides plus twice the product of one of those sides and the projection of the other side on it. In Fig. 9, $a^2 = b^2 + c^2 + 2b \cdot AE$.

Right Triangle. In Fig. 10, with h as the altitude drawn from the vertex of right angle C to the hypotenuse c, $\angle A + \angle B = 90°$; $c^2 = a^2 + b^2$; $h^2 = mn$; $b^2 = cm$; $a^2 = cn$; and (median from C) = $c/2$.

Isosceles Triangle. An isosceles triangle has two sides equal and their opposite angles equal. When a straight line from the vertex at which the equal sides meet bisects the base, it also bisects the angle at the vertex and is perpendicular to the base.

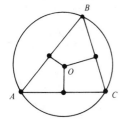

Figure 7

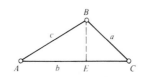

Figure 8

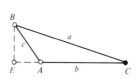

Figure 9

CIRCLES

A circle is a plane closed curve with all points equidistant from a fixed point, its center, in the plane. The length of the circle is its circumference.

A semicircle is one half of a circle. A minor arc is an arc less than one half of a circle, and a major arc is greater than one half of a circle.

A chord is any straight line with end points on the circle.

A central angle is an angle formed by two radii. An inscribed angle has its vertex on the circle and two chords as sides. In Fig. 1, angle *AOB* formed by radii *OA* and *OB* is a central angle. Angle *CDE* formed by chords *DC* and *DE* is an inscribed angle, as is angle *BCD*.

A segment of a circle is an area bounded by an arc and its chord, represented by the shaded area in Fig. 11.

A sector of a circle is the area enclosed by two radii and the arc intercepted by them, represented by the shaded area in Fig. 12.

A secant is a straight line that intersects a circle in two points (a chord extended).

A tangent is a straight line that meets a circle at only one point. The length of a tangent is the distance from a given point on it to the point of tangency.

The line of centers is a straight line joining the centers of two circles.

Two circles tangent to the same line at the same point are tangent to each other. The line is called the common tangent. The line of centers passes through the point of contact or tangency.

If two circles intersect, the line joining the points of intersection is the common chord, and the line of centers is the perpendicular bisector of the common chord.

If a diameter is perpendicular to a chord, it bisects the chord, and the two are subtended by the chord.

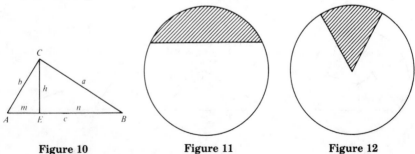

| Figure 10 | Figure 11 | Figure 12 |

Tangents drawn to a circle from a point outside the circle are equal and form equal angles with the line joining the point with the center of the circle.

A circle may be circumscribed about or inscribed within any regular polygon.

The circumference of a circle equals πd or $2\pi r$, where d is a diameter, r is a radius, and $\pi = 3.14159\ldots$.

The area of a circle equals one half the product of its radius and circumference (πr^2 or $\frac{1}{4}\pi d^2$).

The area of a sector of a circle (Fig. 12) equals one half the product of the radius and its arc.

Angle Measurement. With the arc of a circle expressed in terms of the central angle, which it subtends, the arc contains a certain number of degrees and hence can be used to express the measurement of other angles related to the circle. On this basis, an entire circle equals 360°. The inscribed angle formed by two chords intersecting on a circle equals half the arc intercepted by it; for example, in Fig. 13, $\angle BAC = \frac{1}{2}$ arc BC. An angle inscribed in a semicircle is a right angle. The angle formed by a tangent to a circle and a chord having one extremity at the point of contact equals half the arc intercepted by the chord. In Fig. 13, $\angle BAT = \frac{1}{2}$ arc BCA. As shown in Fig. 14, the angle formed by two chords intersecting within a circle equals half the sum of the intercepted arcs; that is, $\angle BAC$ (or $\angle EAF$) $= \frac{1}{2}$(arc BC + arc EF). The angle formed by two secants, or two tangents, or a secant and a tangent, intersecting outside a circle, equals half the difference of the intercepted arcs. For example, in Fig. 15, $\angle BAC = \frac{1}{2}$(arc BC − arc EF). In Fig. 16, $\angle BAE = \frac{1}{2}$(arc BDE − arc BCE), and $\angle BAD = \frac{1}{2}$(arc BD − arc BC).

Coaxal Systems. Coaxal systems are of several types as outlined below:

- A set of nonintersecting circles that have collinear centers and that are orthogonal to a given circle with center also collinear. The end points of the diameter of the given circle on the line of centers are the limiting

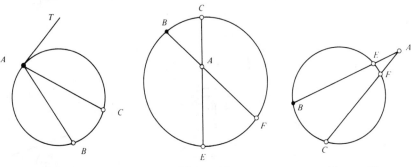

Figure 13   Figure 14   Figure 15

points of the system. Figure 17 shows such a system with centers on the horizontal line
- A set of circles through two given points with centers on the vertical axis. (See Fig. 17)
- A set of circles with a common point of tangency
- A set of concentric circles
- A set of concurrent lines
- A set of parallel lines

Two coaxal systems whose members are mutually orthogonal are conjugate. A conjugate pair may consist of combinations of the above, for example: (*a*) a system of type 1 and one of type 2, with the limiting points of one and the common points of the other (Fig. 17); (*b*) two systems of type 3; (*c*) a system combining type 4 and type 5; (*d*) two systems of type 6.

NONPLANAR ANGLES

Dihedral Angles. A pair of intersecting planes form a dihedral angle, as shown in Fig. 18. The intersection is called the edge, and the planes are called faces. Dihedral angles with a common edge and face are adjacent. If two planes meet, forming equal adjacent dihedral angles, each of the angles is a right dihedral angle. The plane angle of a dihedral angle is the angle formed by two straight lines, one in each face of the dihedral angle, perpendicular to the edge at the same point. In Fig. 18, angle *AOB*, with sides *OA* and *OB* perpendicular to edge *CD*, is the plane angle of the dihedral angle.

The plane angle of a dihedral angle has the same magnitude regardless of its location at the edge of the dihedral angle. Because two dihedral angles are equal if their plane angles are equal and also have the same ratio, the plane angle may be taken as the measure of the dihedral angle. The locus of points equidistant from the faces of a dihedral angle is the plane bisecting the angle.

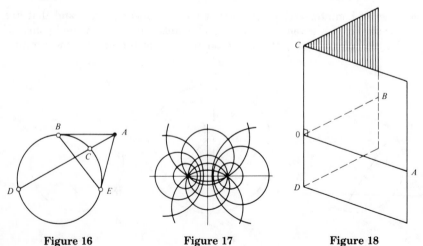

| Figure 16 | Figure 17 | Figure 18 |

Polyhedral Angles. A polyhedral angle is formed when three or more planes emanate from a point. In Fig. 19, for example, the common point O is the vertex. The intersections of the planes OA, OB, and OC are the edges. The planes are called the faces of the angle. Angles AOB, AOF, and BOC, formed by adjacent edges, are the face angles of the polyhedral angle. A polyhedral angle is convex if a section cut by a plane is a convex polygon. A trihedral angle is a polyhedral angle with three faces, and a tetrahedral angle has four faces. The following are characteristics of polyhedral angles:

- Two polyhedral angles are equal if they have equal parts correspondingly placed
- Polyhedral angles with equal parts arranged in reverse order are symmetric
- The sum of any two face angles of a trihedral angle is greater than the third face angle
- If three face angles of one trihedral angle are equal, respectively, to three face angles of another, the trihedral angles are equal or symmetric
- The dihedral angles of one are equal to the corresponding dihedral angles of the other
- The sum of the face angles of any convex polyhedral angle is less than four right angles

Solid Angle. A solid angle measures the opening between surfaces, either planar or nonplanar that meet in a common point. The polyhedral angle is a special case. In Fig. 20, the solid angle at any point P is subtended by any surface S. The solid angle is equal numerically to the portion A of the surface of a sphere of unit radius that is cut out by a conical surface with vertex at P and having the boundary of S for base. The unit solid

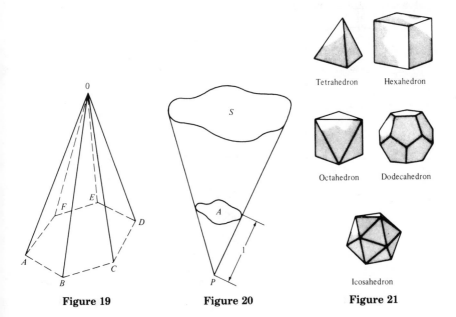

Tetrahedron   Hexahedron

Octahedron   Dodecahedron

Icosahedron

Figure 19   **Figure 20**   **Figure 21**

angle, the steradian, equals the central solid angle that intercepts a spherical area of any shape equal to the square of the radius. The total solid angle about a point equals 4π steradians.

Spherical Angle. A spherical angle is the opening between two arcs of great circles drawn on a sphere from the same point, the vertex, and is measured by the plane angle formed by tangents to its sides at its vertex. If the planes of the great circles are perpendicular, the angle is a right spherical angle.

POLYHEDRONS

Polyhedrons are solids bounded by planes, as shown in Fig. 21. The planes are the faces, the intersections of the planes are the edges, and the intersections of the edges are the vertices. A polyhedron is convex if every section cut by a plane is a convex polygon.

A regular polyhedron is a polyhedron with congruent regular polygons as faces and with equal polyhedral angles. Only five regular convex polyhedrons are possible: (*a*) a tetrahedron, with four faces; (*b*) a hexahedron, with six faces; (*c*) an octahedron, with eight faces; (*d*) a dodecahedron, with twelve faces; and (*e*) an icosahedron, with twenty faces (Fig. 21). The diagonal of a polyhedron is a line joining any two vertices not in the same face.

Two solids with equal volumes are equivalent. Two solids with equal parts similarly arranged are congruent. If the parts are equal, but arranged in reverse order, the solids are symmetric. Polyhedrons that have the same number of faces, respectively similar and similarly placed, and equal corresponding polyhedral angles, are similar.

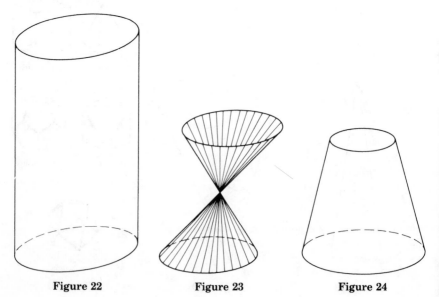

Figure 22   **Figure 23**   **Figure 24**

In any polyhedron, the number of edges plus two equals the sum of the number of vertices and faces, $n + 2 = v + f$. The sum of the face angles of any polyhedron with v vertices equals $(v - 2)$ times $360°$.

Prism. A prism is a polyhedron of which two faces (the bases) are congruent polygons in parallel planes, and the other (lateral) faces are parallelograms whose planes intersect in the lateral edges. Prisms are triangular, rectangular, quadrangular, etc., according to the form of their bases which are triangles, rectangles, or quadrilaterals. A right prism has lateral edges perpendicular to its bases. A prism with parallelograms as bases is a parallelepiped. It is a right parallelepiped if the edges are perpendicular to the bases. A rectangular parallelepiped is a right parallelepiped whose bases are rectangles. A cube is a parallelepiped whose six faces are squares. A truncated prism is that part of a prism included between a base and a section made by a plane oblique to the base. A right section of a prism is formed by a plane that cuts all the lateral edges perpendicularly.

Prismatoid. A prismatoid has two faces (the bases) that are polygons in parallel planes and the other (lateral) faces that are triangles or trapezoids with one side common with one base and the opposite vertex or side common with the other base.

Pyramid. A pyramid has one face (the base) formed by a polygon and the other (lateral) faces formed by triangles meeting in a common point called the vertex of the pyramid and intersecting one another in its lateral edges. Pyramids are triangular, quadrangular, etc., according to the form of their bases (triangles or quadrilaterals, for example). A regular pyramid, or right pyramid, has for its base a regular polygon whose center coincides with the foot of the perpendicular dropped from the vertex to the base. A frustum of a pyramid is the portion of a pyramid included between its base and a section parallel to the base. If the section is not parallel to the base, a truncated pyramid results.

SOLIDS WITH CURVED SURFACES

Cylinders. A cylindric surface is generated by a straight line, the generatrix, moving in a path that intersects a given curve, the directrix, and that is parallel to a given line not in the plane of the curve. The generatrix in any position is called an element of the surface. A cylinder is a solid bounded by a cylindric surface and two parallel planes (Fig. 22). All of its elements are equal. A right cylinder has all elements perpendicular to the bases. A circular cylinder has a circular base. A cylinder of revolution is a right circular cylinder generated by one side of a rectangle when it is rotated about its other side. The axis of a circular cylinder is a line joining the centers of the bases. It passes through the center of all sections parallel to the bases. The altitude of a cylinder is the perpendicular distance between bases. Bases of a cylinder are congruent. Every section of a cylinder made by a plane passing through an element is a parallelogram. In a right cylinder, the section is a rectangle. Any two parallel sections cutting all elements of a cylinder are congruent.

Cones. A conical surface is generated by a moving straight line, the generatrix, that intersects a given curve, the directrix, and passes through a given point, the vertex. The two parts of the conical surface on each side of the vertex are nappes (see Fig. 23). The generatrix in any position is called an element. A cone is a solid bounded by one nappe of a conical surface and a plane cutting all elements. Its altitude is the perpendicular from the vertex to the base. The lateral area is the area of the conical surface between base and vertex.

A circular cone has a circular base, and its axis joins the vertex with the center of the base. If the axis is perpendicular to the circular base, the cone is a right circular cone or cone of revolution. The cone is generated by the hypotenuse of a right triangle rotated about one leg. Any element of a right circular cone is the slant height.

The frustum of a cone is the portion between the base and a plane parallel to the base, as shown in Fig. 24. The section is also called a base. The altitude is the perpendicular distance between bases, and the slant height is the portion of an element included between the two bases. Every conical section made by a plane passing through its vertex forms a triangle.

Sphere. A sphere is a solid bounded by a surface, all points of which are equidistant from the center. Every plane section of a sphere is a circle. If its plane passes through the center of the sphere, it is a great circle. Otherwise, it is a small circle. Poles of such a circle are the extremities of the diameter of the sphere, which is perpendicular to the plane of the circle. Through two points on a spherical surface, not extremities of a diameter, one great circle can be passed. The shortest line that can be drawn on the surface of a sphere between two such points is an arc of a great circle less than a semicircumference joining those points. If two spherical surfaces intersect, their line of intersection is a circle with a plane that is perpendicular to the line of centers and whose center lies on this line.

A spherical sector is generated by the revolution of a circular sector about a diameter of the circle of which the sector is a part. A hemisphere is half of a sphere. A spherical segment is contained between two parallel plane sections, the bases, one of which may be tangent to the sphere. In this case, there is only one base. The term segment also is applied to various solids of revolution, and the planes in such cases are perpendicular to an axis. A zone is the portion of a spherical surface included between two parallel planes.

A spherical polygon is bounded by three or more arcs of great circles. The sum of the angles of a spherical triangle is greater than two right angles and less than six right angles.

CONSTRUCTIONS

LINES

Parallel Lines. To draw a line parallel to a given line at a given distance from the given line (Fig. 25), describe arcs xy and zw, with the given distance as radius and with any centers m and n on the given line AB. Draw CD touching these arcs. CD is the required parallel line.

To draw a line parallel to a given line through a given point (Fig. 26), let C be the given point and D be any point on the given line AB. Draw CD. Draw arcs bf and ce with equal radii and with D and C as centers. With radius equal to chord bf and with c as center, draw an arc cutting arc ce at E. CE is the required parallel line.

Bisecting Lines. To bisect a given line, for example, AB in Fig. 27, describe two arcs with A and B as centers and with any radius greater than $0.5\ AB$. The line CD, through points of intersection of the arcs, is the perpendicular bisector of the given line.

Dividing Lines. To divide a given line into a given number of equal parts, let AB in Fig. 28 be the given line, and let the number of equal parts be five. Draw line AC at any convenient angle with AB, and mark five equal lengths from A to b. Connect b with B, and draw parallels to Bb through the other points in AC. The intersections of these parallels with AB determine the required equal parts on the given line.

Perpendiculars. To erect a perpendicular at point C at or near the middle of the line AB (Fig. 29), describe arcs of equal radii intersecting AB at a and b, with C as center. With a and b as centers, and any radius greater than Ca, describe arcs intersecting at D. The required perpendicular is CD.

When point C is at or near the extremity of the line AB, as in Fig. 30, describe an arc intersecting AB at a, with any point O as center and with radius OC. Extend aO to intersect the arc at D. The required perpendicular is CD.

To erect a perpendicular to a given line through a given point outside the line, as shown in Fig. 31, describe an arc intersecting AB at a and b, with C as center. Then, with a and b as centers, describe arcs of equal radii intersecting at D. The required perpendicular is CD.

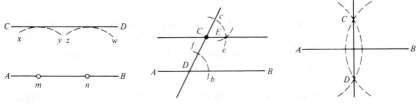

| Figure 25 | Figure 26 | Figure 27 |

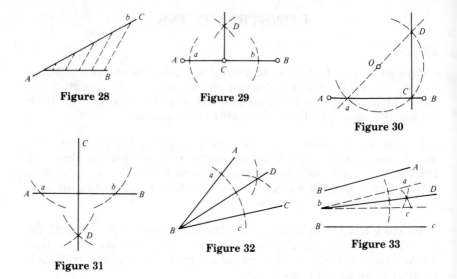

Figure 28

Figure 29

Figure 30

Figure 31

Figure 32

Figure 33

ANGLES

Bisecting Angles. To bisect a given angle, for which vertex *B* is accessible (Fig. 32), let *ABC* be the given angle. With *B* as center and with a large radius, describe an arc intersecting *AB* and *BC* at *a* and *c*, respectively. With *a* and *c* as centers, describe arcs of equal radii intersecting at *D*. *DB* is the bisector. When the vertex is inaccessible (Fig. 33), as when the angle is between lines *AB* and *BC*, draw lines *ab* and *bc* parallel to the given lines and at equal distances from them, intersecting at *b*. Construct *Db* bisecting angle *abc*, as in Fig. 32. *Db* is the bisector of the angle formed by lines *AB* and *BC*.

Constructing Angles. To construct angles of 60° and 30° (Fig. 34), describe with a convenient radius the arc *bc*, about any point *A* on a line *AB*. From *b*, using an equal radius, describe an arc cutting the former one at *C*. Draw *AC*, and drop a perpendicular *CD* from *C* to line *AB*. The angle *CAD* is 60° and *ACD* is 30°. To construct an angle of 45° (Fig. 35), mark any distance *AB*; draw *BC* perpendicular and equal to *AB*; and join *CA*. Angles *CAB* and *ACB* are each 45°.

CIRCLES

To describe an arc of a circle through two given points using a given radius (Fig. 36), let *A* and *B* be the given points. With the radius and these points as centers, describe arcs that meet at *C*. Using the same radius, describe the required arc *AB* from point *C*.

To bisect an arc of a circle, draw the perpendicular bisector of the chord of the arc. This bisector meets the arc at the midpoint.

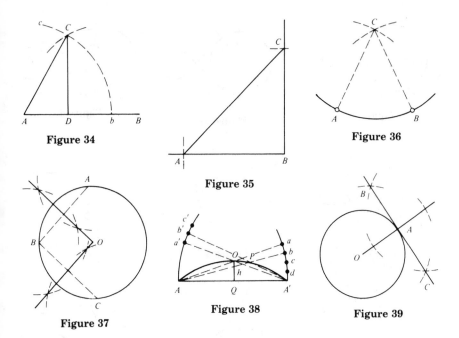

Figure 34

Figure 35

Figure 36

Figure 37

Figure 38

Figure 39

To locate the center of a given circle or circular arc (Fig. 37), select three points, A, B, C, located well apart on the circle (or arc). Draw chords AB and BC and their perpendicular bisectors. The bisectors intersect at point O, the required center.

To draw a circle through three points not in a straight line where the radius is small and center accessible (Fig. 37), let A, B, C be the given points. Draw lines AB and BC and their perpendicular bisectors. The bisectors intersect at point O, the center of the required circle of radius OA.

When the radius is long or center inaccessible (Fig. 38), let A, O, A' be the given points, with O not necessarily midpoint of AOA'. Draw arcs Aa' and $A'a$ with centers at A' and A. Extend AO to determine a, and extend $A'O$ to determine a'. From a on aA', mark equal parts ab, bc, etc., and mark off $a'b'$, $b'c'$, etc., equal to ab. Join A with any point as b and A' with the corresponding point b'. The intersection P of these joining lines is a point on the required circle.

To construct a circular arc without locating the center of the circle when the chord and the rise are known (Fig. 38), let AA' be the chord and QO the rise. In this case, O is midpoint of AOA'. The arc is constructed through the points A, O, A', as described for Fig. 38.

To draw a tangent to a circle through a point, with point A on the circle (Fig. 39), for example, draw radius OA. Through A, perpendicular to OA, draw BAC, the required tangent. When point A is outside the circle (Fig. 40),

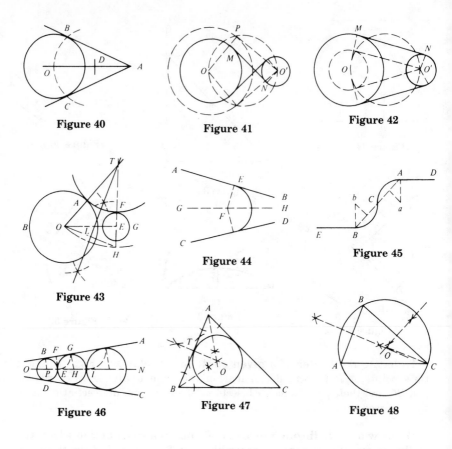

Figure 40

Figure 41

Figure 42

Figure 43

Figure 44

Figure 45

Figure 46

Figure 47

Figure 48

two tangents can be drawn. Join O and A, and bisect OA at D. With D as center and DO as radius, describe an arc intersecting the circle at B and C to form tangents BA and CA.

To draw a common tangent to two circles, let the circles have centers O and O' and corresponding radii r and r' $(r > r')$.

To construct common internal tangents when circles do not intersect (Fig. 41), construct a circle with the same center O as the larger circle and with a radius equal to the sum of the radii of the given circles $(r + r')$. Draw a tangent $O'P$ from center O' of the smaller circle to this circle. Construct $O'N$ perpendicular to this tangent; draw the line OP. A common tangent is formed by the line MN joining the radii OM and $O'N$.

To draw common external tangents (Fig. 42), draw a circle with the same center O as the larger circle and radius equal to the difference of the radii $(r - r')$. From the center of the smaller circle, construct a tangent to this circle. A common tangent is formed by the line joining the extremities, M and N, of the radii of the given circles perpendicular to this tangent.

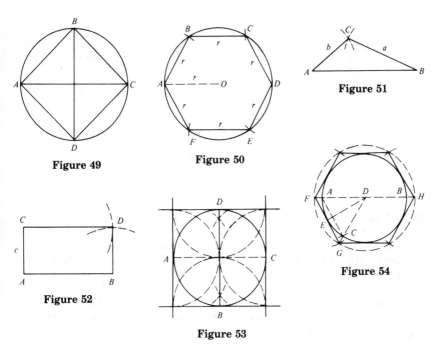

Figure 49

Figure 50

Figure 51

Figure 52

Figure 53

Figure 54

To describe a circular arc touching two circles, *AB* and *FG*, with one of them touching at a given point *F* (Fig. 43), draw radius *EF*, and extend it to produce *FH* equal to the radius *AC* of the other circle. Join *CH*, and bisect it by the perpendicular *LT*, intersecting *EF* at *T*. About center *T*, with radius *TF*, describe the required arc *FA*.

To draw a circular arc tangent to two given lines inclined to one another, with one tangential point given (Fig. 44), let *AB* and *CB* be the given lines and *E* the given point. Bisect the angle formed by *AB* and *CD* with line *GH*. From *E*, draw *EF* at right angles to *AB*. Its intersection with *GH*, the point *F*, is the center of the required circular arc.

To connect two parallel lines by a reversed curve, composed of two circular arcs of equal radius and with the curve tangent to the lines at given points (Fig. 45), let *AD* and *BE* be the given lines and *A* and *B* the given points. Bisect the line *AB* at *C*; then bisect *CA* and *CB* by perpendicular lines. At *A* and *B*, draw lines perpendicular to lines *AD* and *BE*. The intersections *a* and *b* are the centers of the arcs composing the required curve.

To construct a series of circles between two inclined lines, with the circles touching the lines and each other (Fig. 46), bisect the included angle of lines *AB* and *CD*. From a point *P* in this line, *NO*, draw the perpendicular *PB* to the line *AB*, and on *P* describe the circle *BD*, touching the

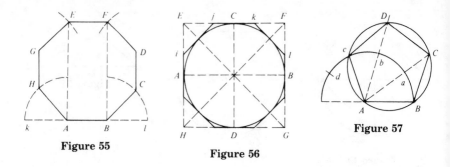

Figure 55

Figure 56

Figure 57

given lines and cutting the center line at E. Draw line EF perpendicular to the center line, intersecting AB at F. With F as a center, describe arc EG, cutting AB at G. Draw GH parallel to BP to produce point H, the center of the next circle, with radius HE. The process is then repeated for the next circle IN.

To inscribe a circle in a triangle, bisect any two angles A and B of the triangle. From the point of intersection O (Fig. 47), draw a perpendicular OT to any side. With OT as radius and O as center, draw the inscribed circle.

To circumscribe a circle about a triangle, draw the perpendicular bisectors of two sides AB and BC and extend them to meet at O (Fig. 48). With O as center and radius equal to the distance from O to any vertex, draw the circumscribing circle.

To inscribe a square in a circle, draw any two diameters AC and BD perpendicular to each other (Fig. 49). The lines joining their extremities form an inscribed square $ABCD$.

To inscribe a regular hexagon in a circle, start with a point A on the circle and mark off successive chords equal in length to the radius (Fig. 50). These chords form hexagon $ABCDEF$.

POLYGONS

To construct a triangle on a given base, the lengths of the sides being given (Fig. 51), let AB be the base and a, b, the sides. With A and B as centers, and b and a as radii, draw arcs intersecting at C. Draw AC and BC to complete the required triangle.

To construct a rectangle of given base and given height (Fig. 52), let AB be the base and c the height. Construct perpendicular AC equal to c. With C and B as centers, and AB and c as radii, draw arcs intersecting at D. Complete the rectangle with lines BD and CD.

To circumscribe a square about a given circle (Fig. 53), draw perpendic-

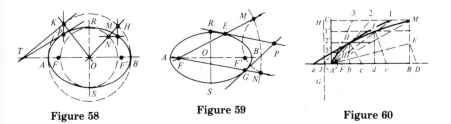

| Figure 58 | Figure 59 | Figure 60 |

ular diameters AC and BD. With A, B, C, and D as centers, and the radius of the circle as radius, describe four semicircular arcs. Their outer intersections form the vertices of the required square.

To circumscribe a regular hexagon about a given circle (Fig. 54), draw a diameter ADB, with center A and with radius AD, then construct an arc intersecting the circle at C. Bisect AC with the radius DE. Through E, draw FG parallel to AC, intersecting diameter AB extended at F. With center D and radius DF, describe the circumscribing circle FH. Within this circle, inscribe a regular hexagon, as shown in Fig. 50. This hexagon circumscribes the given circle.

To construct a regular octagon having a side of given length (Fig. 55), extend the length AB in both directions and draw perpendiculars AE and BF. Form lines AH and BC equal to AB as bisectors of the external angles at A and B. Draw CD and HG parallel to AE, and equal to AB; from the centers G and D, with the radius AB, draw arcs cutting the perpendiculars at E, F, and draw EF to complete the octagon.

To circumscribe a regular octagon about a given circle (Fig. 56), draw a square about the given circle. Draw perpendiculars ij, kl, etc., to the diagonals of the squares, touching the circle. Then ij, jk, kl, etc., form the octagon.

To construct a regular polygon of any given number of sides when one side is given (Fig. 57), draw the line AB. With A as center and AB as radius, draw a semicircle. Divide the semicircle into the same number of parts as sides of the polygon. Draw lines from A through the division points a, b, and c, omitting the last. With B and c as centers and AB as radius, cut Aa at C and Ab at D. Draw cD, DC, and CB, to complete the polygon.

ELLIPSE

The sum of the distances of any point on an ellipse from two fixed points (the foci) is constant.

To construct an ellipse when the axes are given (Fig. 58), let AB be the major and RS the minor axis. With O as center, and OB and OR as radii, draw two circles. From O draw a line intersecting the circles at M

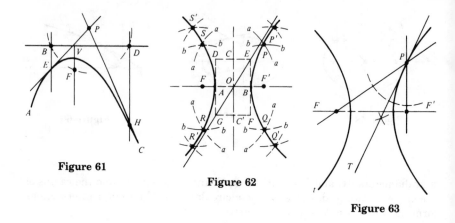

Figure 61

Figure 62

Figure 63

and N. Through M and N draw lines parallel to OR and OB. These lines intersect at H, one point on the ellipse. Other points are obtained in the same manner.

To locate the foci of an ellipse, when the axes are known (Fig. 58), use R as center with radius equal to AO and describe arcs intersecting AB at F and F', the required foci.

To draw a tangent to a given ellipse through a given point, point P on curve (Fig. 58), construct a circle with O as center and OB as radius. Draw a line through P parallel to OR, intersecting the circle at K. Draw a tangent through K to the circle, intersecting the major axis at T. PT is the required tangent.

To draw a tangent to an ellipse through point P that is not on the curve (Fig. 59), construct an arc with P as center and radius PF' as radius. With F as center and AB as radius, describe an arc intersecting the first arc at M and N. Draw FM and FN, intersecting the ellipse at E and G. PE and PG are the required tangents.

PARABOLA

The distance of any point on a parabola from a fixed line, the directrix, is equal to its distance from a fixed point, the focus.

To describe a parabola with known vertex, axis, and a point of the curve (Fig. 60), let A be the vertex, AB the axis, and M the point. Construct the rectangle $ABMC$. Divide both MC and CA into the same number of equal parts, four, for example, and number the divisions. Connect $A1$, $A2$, and $A3$. Through $1'$, $2'$, $3'$, draw parallels to the axis AB. The intersections of these lines are points on the required curve. A similar construction below the axis will give the other symmetric branch of the curve.

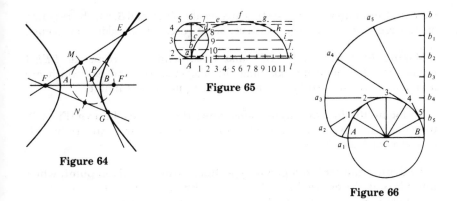

Figure 64

Figure 65

Figure 66

To locate the focus and directrix of a parabola, as shown in Fig. 60, construct perpendicular *MB* from *M* to *AB*. Bisect it at *E*, and draw *AE*. Draw *ED* perpendicular to *AE* at *E* and intersecting the axis at *D*. With *A* as center and *BD* as radius, describe arcs cutting the axis at *F* and *J*. Then *F* is the focus, and the line *GH*, perpendicular to the axis through *J*, is the directrix.

To draw a tangent to a parabola through a point, when the point is on the curve (Fig. 60), let *II* be the given point. Draw a perpendicular from *II* to the axis, cutting it at *b*. With *Aa* equal to *Ab*, a line through *a* and *II* is the required tangent. The line *IIc* perpendicular to the tangent at *II* is the normal at that point, and *bc* is the subnormal. All subnormals of a given parabola are equal to the distance from the directrix to the focus and thus are equal to each other.

To draw a tangent to a parabola through a point, when the point is off the curve on the convex side (Fig. 61), let *P* be the point and *F* the focus of the parabola. With *P* as center, and *PF* as radius, draw arcs intersecting the directrix at *B* and *D*. Draw lines through *B* and *D* parallel to the axis, intersecting the parabola at *E* and *H*. *PE* and *PH* are the required tangents.

HYPERBOLA

The difference between the distances of any point on a hyperbola from two fixed points, the foci, is constant. It has two distinct branches.

To construct a hyperbola with known foci and the difference of the focal radii (Fig. 62), let *F* and *F'* be the given foci and *AOB* the given difference of the focal radii. Draw the transverse axis *AOB* so that *AF* = *F'B* and *AO* = *OB*. *A* and *B* are points on the required curve. With centers *F* and *F'*, and any radius greater than *FB* or *F'A*, describe arcs *aa*. Again with centers *F* and *F'* and radius equal to the difference between the first radius and the transverse axis AOB, draw arcs bb, intersecting arcs aa at P, Q, R, and S, which are points on the required curve. The construction is repeated for additional points.

Making $BC = BC' = OF = OF'$ and constructing the rectangle $DEFG$ forms CC', the conjugate axis, and the diagonals DF and EG which are asymptotes. The hyperbola is tangent to its asymptotes at infinity.

To locate the foci of a hyperbola, when the axes are known (Fig. 62), use O as center with radius equal to BC and describe arcs intersecting AB extended, at F and F', the required foci.

To draw a tangent to a given hyperbola through a given point, when point P is on the curve (Fig. 63), draw lines connecting P with the foci. Bisect the angle $F'PF$. The bisecting line TP is the required tangent.

When point P is off the curve on the convex side (Fig. 64), draw an arc with P as center and radius PF'. With F as center, and radius AB, construct an arc intersecting the first arc at M and N. Produce lines FM and FN to intersect the curve at E and G. PE and PG are the required tangents.

CYCLOID

A cycloid is formed by a point on a circle rolling on a straight line. To construct a cycloid for which the generating circle is known (Fig. 65), let A be the generating point. Divide the circumference of the generating circle into an even number of equal arcs and set off the rectified arcs on the base. Through the points 1, 2, 3, etc., on the circle, draw horizontal lines. Set off distances $1a = A1$, $2b = A2$, $3c = A3$, etc. The points A, a, b, c, etc., are points of the cycloid.

An epicycloid is a curve generated by a point on one circle rolling on the outside of another circle. A hypocycloid is a curve generated by the point if the generating circle rolls on the inside of the second circle.

INVOLUTE OF A CIRCLE

The involute of a circle is a curve formed by the free end point of a straight circumferential line as it is unwound from a circle. To describe an involute of a given circle (Fig. 66), draw Bb through B perpendicular to circle AB. Make Bb equal in length to half the circumference of the circle. Divide Bb and the semicircumference into the same number of equal parts. From each point of division of the circumference, draw lines to the center C of the circle. Then draw $1a_1$ perpendicular to $C1$, $2a_2$ perpendicular to $C2$, and so on. Make $1a_1$ equal to bb_1, $2a_2$ equal to bb_2, $3a_3$ equal to bb_3, and so on. Join the points A, a_1, a_2, a_3, by a curve; this curve is the required involute.

3
Mensuration

RATIO AND PROPORTION

Two or more lines are divided proportionately if the ratio of the segments of one line equals the ratio of the segments of the other lines. Corresponding sides of similar polygons are proportional. The medians of a triangle divide each other into segments in the ratio $1:2$.

A line drawn through two sides of a triangle parallel to the third side divides the two sides proportionally. One side is to either of its intercepted segments as the other side is to its corresponding segment. In Fig. 1, with DE parallel to side AC of triangle ABC, $BD:DA = BE:EC$; $BA:BD = BC:BE$; and $BA:DA = BC:EC$.

Corresponding altitudes, medians, and angle bisectors of similar triangles have the same ratio as any two corresponding sides.

Three or more parallel lines form proportional segments on any two transversals. If two lines are cut by parallel planes, the corresponding segments are proportional (Fig. 2). Three parallel planes cut line AD at B, J, and C and line EH at F, K, and G. Then, $BJ:JC = FK:KG$.

The bisector of an interior angle of a triangle divides the opposite side into segments proportional to the adjacent sides (Fig. 3) with BD bisecting angle B of triangle ABC, $AB:AD = BC:CD$.

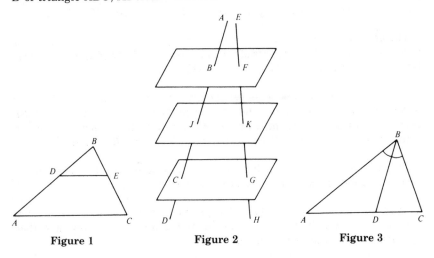

Figure 1   Figure 2   Figure 3

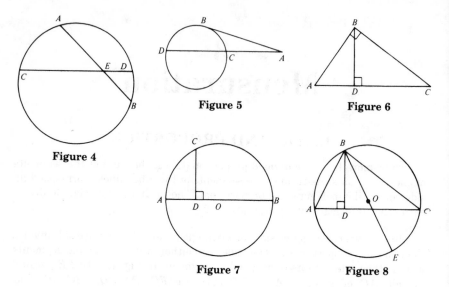

Figure 4

Figure 5

Figure 6

Figure 7

Figure 8

If two chords intersect inside a circle, the product of the segments of one equals the product of the segments of the other (Fig. 4). Chords AB and CD intersect at E. Hence, $AE:CE = ED:EB$ and $AE \times EB = CE \times ED$.

If a tangent and secant are drawn from a point outside a circle, the tangent is the mean proportional between the secant and its external segment (Fig. 5). With AB, a tangent, and AD, a secant, intersecting the circle at C and D, $AD:AB = AB:AC$.

The altitude on the hypotenuse of a right triangle is the mean proportional between the two segments of the hypotenuse; each leg of the triangle is the mean proportional between the hypotenuse and the segment adjacent to that leg (Fig. 6). With BD perpendicular to the hypotenuse AC of right triangle ABC, then $AD:BD = BD:DC$; $AC:AB = AB:AD$; and $AC:BC = BC:CD$.

The perpendicular from any point on a circle to a diameter is the mean proportional between the segments of the diameter (Fig. 7). With CD perpendicular to diameter AB, then $AD:CD = CD:DB$.

In any triangle, the product of two sides equals the product of the diameter of the circumscribed circle and the altitude on the third side (Fig. 8). With BD perpendicular to side AC of triangle ABC and BE the diameter of the circumscribing circle, then $BE:BC = AB:BD$; $BE \times BD = BC \times AB$.

The areas of two similar polygons are to each other as the squares of any two corresponding sides or the squares of their perimeters.

The perimeters of two regular polygons of the same number of sides are to each other as are their radii (distances from center to a vertex) and their apothems (radii of inscribed circles).

The areas of two regular polygons of the same number of sides are to each other as the squares of their radii or apothems.

The circumferences of two circles are to each other as their radii or diameters. The ratio of the circumference of any circle to its diameter is a constant (represented by π).

The areas of two circles are to each other as the squares of their radii or diameters.

MENSURATION FORMULAS

APPROXIMATE DECIMAL EQUIVALENTS

Value	Approximate decimal equivalents
π	3.1416
$\dfrac{\pi}{2}$	1.5708
$\dfrac{\pi}{4}$	0.7854
$\dfrac{\pi}{180}$	0.01745
$\dfrac{\pi}{360}$	0.00873
$\dfrac{1}{\pi}$	0.318
$\dfrac{1}{2\pi}$	0.159
$\dfrac{1}{4\pi}$	0.080
$\dfrac{180}{\pi}$	57.296
$\dfrac{360}{\pi}$	114.592
$\sqrt{2}$	1.414
$\sqrt{3}$	1.732
$\dfrac{1}{\sqrt{2}}$	0.707
$\dfrac{1}{\sqrt{3}}$	0.577

PLANE RECTILINEAR FIGURES

Lines are represented by a, b, c; angles by α, β, γ; the altitude, by h; sides, by l; diagonals, by d, $d_1 \cdots$; perimeter, by p; radius of inscribed circle, by r; radius of circumscribed circle, by R; and area, by A.

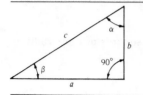

RIGHT TRIANGLE

$$p = a + b + c \qquad c^2 = a^2 + b^2$$

$$A = \frac{ab}{2} = \frac{a^2}{2} \tan \beta = \frac{e^2}{4} \sin 2\beta = \frac{c^2}{4} \sin 2\alpha$$

GENERAL OR EQUILATERAL TRIANGLE

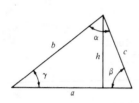

General triangle:

$$p = a + b + c \qquad \text{Let } s = \tfrac{1}{2}(a + b + c)$$

$$r = \frac{\sqrt{s(s - a)(s - b)(s - c)}}{s} \qquad R = \frac{a}{2 \sin \alpha} = \frac{abc}{4rs}$$

$$A = \frac{ah}{2} = \frac{ab}{2} \sin \gamma = \frac{b^2 \sin \gamma \sin \alpha}{2 \sin \beta} = rs = \frac{abc}{4R}$$

Length of median to side $c = \tfrac{1}{2} \sqrt{2(a^2 + b^2) - c^2}$

Length of bisector of angle $\gamma = \dfrac{\sqrt{ab[(a + b)^2 - c^2]}}{a + b}$

Equilateral triangle:

$a = b = c = l$ and $\alpha = \beta = \gamma = 60°$
Equal sides and equal angles

$$p = 3l \qquad r = \frac{l}{2\sqrt{3}} \qquad R = \frac{l}{\sqrt{3}} = 2r$$

$$h = \frac{l\sqrt{3}}{2} \qquad l = \frac{2h}{\sqrt{3}} \qquad A = \frac{l^2\sqrt{3}}{4}$$

RECTANGLE

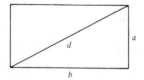

$$p = 2(a + b) \quad d = \sqrt{a^2 + b^2}; \quad A = ab$$

Square ($a = b = l$):

$$p = 4l \qquad d = l\sqrt{2} \qquad l = \frac{d}{\sqrt{2}} \qquad A = l^2 = \frac{d^2}{2}$$

PARALLELOGRAM

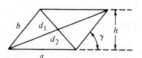

General parallelogram, rhomboid:

Opposite sides parallel

$$p = 2(a + b) \qquad d_1 = \sqrt{a^2 + b^2 - 2ab \cos \gamma}$$

$$d_2 = \sqrt{a^2 + b^2 + 2ab \cos \gamma} \qquad d_1{}^2 + d_2{}^2 = 2(a^2 + b^2)$$

$$A = ah = ab \sin \gamma$$

Rhombus ($a = b = l$):
Opposite sides parallel and all sides equal

$$p = 4l \qquad d_1 = 2l \sin \frac{\gamma}{2} \qquad d_2 = 2l \cos \frac{\gamma}{2} \qquad d_1^2 + d_2^2 = 4l^2$$

$$d_1 d_2 = 2l^2 \sin \gamma \qquad A = lh = l^2 \sin \gamma = \frac{d_1 d_2}{2}$$

TRAPEZOID

Let midline bisecting nonparallel sides $= m$.

Then, $m = \dfrac{a + b}{2}$

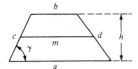

General trapezoid:
One pair of opposite sides parallel

$$p = a + b + c + d \qquad A = \frac{(a + b)h}{2} = mh$$

Isosceles trapezoid:
($d = c$)
Nonparallel sides equal

$$A = \frac{(a + b)h}{2} = mh = \frac{(a + b)c \sin \gamma}{2}$$

$$= (a - c \cos \gamma)c \sin \gamma = (b + c \cos \gamma)c \sin \gamma$$

GENERAL QUADRILATERAL (TRAPEZIUM)

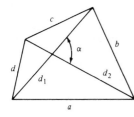

No sides parallel

$p = a + b + c + d$

$A = \frac{1}{2}d_1 d_2 \sin \alpha$ = sum of areas of the two triangles formed by either diagonal and the four sides

QUADRILATERAL INSCRIBED IN CIRCLE

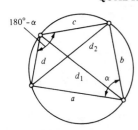

Sum of opposite angles $= 180°$

$ac + bc + d_1 d_2$

Let $s = \frac{1}{2}(a + b + c + d) = \dfrac{p}{2}$ and $\alpha =$ angle between sides a and b

$A = \sqrt{(s - a)(s - b)(s - c)(s - d)} = \frac{1}{2}(ab + cd) \sin \alpha$

POLYGON

Regular polygon:
Equal sides and equal angles
Let n = number of sides

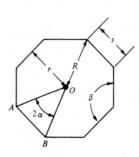

Central angle = $2\alpha = \dfrac{2\pi}{n}$ radians

Vertex angle = $\beta = \dfrac{(n-2)}{n}\pi$ radians

$p = ns$ $s = 2r\tan\alpha = 2R\sin\alpha$

$r = \dfrac{s}{2}\cot\alpha$ $R = \dfrac{s}{2}\csc\alpha$

$A = \dfrac{nsr}{2} = nr^2\tan\alpha = \dfrac{nR^2}{2}\sin 2\alpha = \dfrac{ns^2}{4}\cot\alpha$

= sum of areas of the n equal triangles such as OAB

General polygon:
A = sum of areas of constituent triangles into which it can be divided

PLANE CURVILINEAR FIGURES

Lines are represented by a, b, $\cdots$; radius, by r; diameter, by d; perimeter, by p; circumference, by c; central angle n radians, by θ; arc, by s; chord of arc s, by l; chord of half arc $s/2$, by l'; rise, by h; and area, by A.

ANNULUS

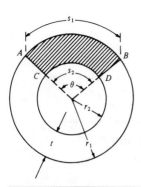

Region between two concentric circles:

$A = \pi(r_1^2 - r_2^2) = \pi(r_1 + r_2)(r_1 - r_2)$

A of sector $ABCD = \dfrac{\theta}{2}(r_1^2 - r_2^2) =$

$\dfrac{\theta}{2}(r_1 + r_2)(r_1 - r_2) =$

$\dfrac{t}{2}(s_1 + s_2)$

CYCLOID

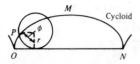

Arc $OP = s = 4r\left(1 - \cos\dfrac{\phi}{2}\right)$ Arc $OMN = 8r$

A under curve $OMN = 3\pi r^2$

CIRCLE

Circle:

$$d = 2r \qquad c = 2\pi r = \pi d \qquad A = \pi r^2 = \frac{\pi d^2}{4} = \frac{c^2}{4\pi}$$

Circular arc:

Let arc $PAQ = s$ and chord $PA = l'$. Then:

$$s = r\theta = \frac{d\theta}{2} \qquad s = \frac{8l' - l}{3}$$

The latter equation is Huygens' approximate formula. For θ small, error is very small; for $\theta = 120°$, error is about 0.25%; for $\theta = 180°$, error is less than 1.25%.

$$l = 2r \sin \frac{\theta}{2} \qquad l = 2\sqrt{2hr - h^2} \text{ (approximate formula)}$$

$$r = \frac{s}{\theta} = \frac{l}{2 \sin \dfrac{\theta}{2}} \qquad r = \frac{4h^2 + l^2}{8h} \text{ (approximate formula)}$$

$$h = r \mp \sqrt{r^2 - \frac{l^2}{4}} \ (- \text{ if } \theta \le 180°; + \text{ if } \theta \ge 180°)$$

$$= r \left(1 - \cos \frac{\theta}{2} \right) = r \text{ versin } \frac{\theta}{2} = 2r \sin^2 \frac{\theta}{4} = \frac{l}{2} \tan$$

$$\frac{\theta}{4} = r + y - \sqrt{r^2 - x^2}$$

Side ordinate $y = h - r + \sqrt{r^2 - x^2}$

CIRCULAR SECTOR

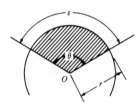

Circular sector:

$$A = \frac{\theta r^2}{2} = \frac{sr}{2}$$

Semicircle:

$$A = \frac{\pi r^2}{2}$$

CIRCULAR SEGMENT

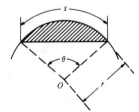

$$A = \frac{r^2}{2} (\theta - \sin \theta)$$

$$= \frac{1}{2}[sr \mp l(r - h)](- \text{ if } h \le r; + \text{ if } h \ge r)$$

$$A = \frac{2lh}{3} \text{ or } \frac{h}{15} (8l' + 6l)$$

Approximate formulas. For h small compared with r, error is very small; for $h = r/4$, the error in the first formula is about 3.5% and in the second less than 1.0%.

ELLIPSE

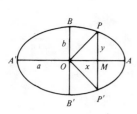

$$p = \pi(a + b)\left(1 + \frac{R^2}{4} + \frac{R^4}{64} + \frac{R^4}{256} + \cdots\right)$$

where $R = \dfrac{a - b}{a + b}$

$$p = \pi(a + b)\,\frac{64 - 3R^4}{64 - 16R^2} \quad \text{(approximate formula)}$$

$A = \pi ab \qquad A$ of quadrant $AOB = \dfrac{\pi ab}{4}$

A of sector $AOP = \dfrac{ab}{2}\cos^{-1}\dfrac{x}{a}$

A of sector $POB = \dfrac{ab}{2}\sin^{-1}\dfrac{x}{a}$

A of section $BPP'B' = xy + ab\sin^{-1}\dfrac{x}{a}$

A of segment $PAP'P = -xy + ab\cos^{-1}\dfrac{x}{a}$

PARABOLA

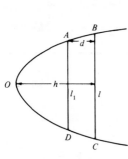

$$\text{Arc } BOC = s = \tfrac{1}{2}\sqrt{l^2 + 16h^2} + \frac{l^2}{8h}\log_e\frac{4h + \sqrt{l^2 + 16h^2}}{l}$$

Let $R = \dfrac{h}{l}$, Then: $s = l\left(1 + \dfrac{8R^2}{3} - \dfrac{32R^4}{5} + \cdots\right)$

(approximate formula)

$d = \dfrac{h}{l^2}(l^2 - l_1{}^2) \qquad l_1 = l\sqrt{\dfrac{h - d}{h}} \qquad h = \dfrac{dl^2}{l^2 - l_1{}^2}$

A of segment $BOC = \dfrac{2hl}{3}$

A of section $ABCD = \dfrac{2}{3}\,d\left(\dfrac{l^3 - l_1{}^3}{l^2 - l_1{}^2}\right)$

HYPERBOLA

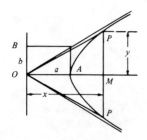

A of figure $OPAP'O = ab\log_e\left(\dfrac{x}{a} + \dfrac{y}{b}\right) =$

$ab\cosh^{-1}\dfrac{x}{a}$

A of segment $PAP' = xy = ab\log_e\left(\dfrac{x}{a} + \dfrac{y}{b}\right) =$

$xy - ab\cosh^{-1}\dfrac{x}{a}$

EPICYCLOID

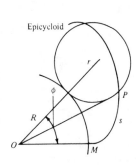

Epicycloid

$$\text{Arc } MP = s = \frac{4r}{R}(R + r)\left(1 - \cos\frac{R\phi}{2r}\right)$$

$$\text{Area } MOP = A = \frac{r}{2R}(R + r)(R + 2r)\left(\frac{R\phi}{r} - \sin\frac{R\phi}{r}\right)$$

HYPOCYCLOID

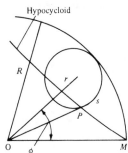

Hypocycloid

$$\text{Arc } MP = s = \frac{4r}{R}(R - r)\left(1 - \cos\frac{R\phi}{2r}\right)$$

$$\text{Area } MOP = A =$$

$$\frac{r}{2R}(R - r)(R - 2r)\left(\frac{R\phi}{r} - \sin\frac{R\phi}{r}\right)$$

CATENARY

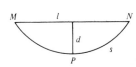

If d is small compared with l:

$$\text{Arc } MPN = s = l\left[1 + \frac{2}{3}\left(\frac{2d}{l}\right)^2\right] \text{ (approximately)}$$

HELIX (SKEW CURVE)

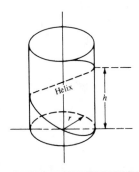

With length of helix = s; radius of coil (= radius of cylinder in figure) = r; distance advanced in one revolution = pitch = h; and number of revolutions = n, then:

$$s = n\sqrt{(2\pi r)^2 + h^2}$$

SPIRAL OF ARCHIMEDES

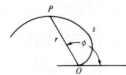

Let $a = \dfrac{r}{\phi}$. Then:

$$\text{Arc } OP = s = \frac{a}{2}[\phi\sqrt{1 + \phi^2} + \log_e(\phi + \sqrt{1 + \phi^2})]$$

IRREGULAR FIGURE

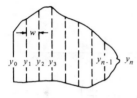

Divide the figure into an even number, n, of strips by means of $(n + 1)$ ordinates, y_i, spaced equal distances, w. The area can then be determined approximately by any of the following formulas, which are presented in the order of increasing accuracy. As the number of strips is increased in the first three rules, accuracy increases (approximate formulas):

Trapezoidal rule:

$$A = w\left[\frac{y_0 + y_n}{2} + y_1 + y_2 + \cdots + y_{n-1}\right]$$

Durand's rule:

$$A = w[0.4(y_0 + y_n) + 1.1(y_1 + y_{n-1}) + y_2 + y_3 + \cdots + y_{n-2}]$$

Simpson's rule:
n must be even

$$A = \frac{w}{3}[(y_0 + y_n) + 4(y_1 + y_3 + \cdots + y_{n-1}) + 2(y_2 + y_4 + \cdots + y_{n-2})]$$

Weddle's rule:
For 6 strips only

$$A = \frac{3w}{10}[5(y_1 + y_5) + 6y_3 + y_0 + y_2 + y_4 + y_6]$$

SOLIDS WITH PLANE SURFACES

Lines are represented by a, b, c, $\cdots$; altitude (perpendicular height), by h; slant height, by s; perimeter of base, by p_b or p_B; perimeter of a right section, by p_r; area of base, by A_b or A_B; area of a right section, by A_r; total area of lateral surfaces, by A_l; total area of all surfaces, by A_t; and volume, by V.

WEDGE AND RIGHT TRIANGULAR PRISM

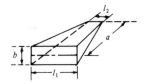

Wedge:

Narrow-side rectangular, $V = \dfrac{ab}{6}(2l_1 + l_2)$

Right triangular prism, or wedge having parallel triangular bases perpendicular to sides $l_2 = l_1 = l$

$$V = \frac{abl}{2}$$

RECTANGULAR PRISM OR RECTANGULAR PARALLELEPIPED AND CUBE

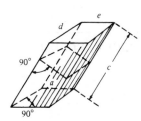

Rectangular prism or rectangular parallelepiped:

$A_l = 2c(a + b)$ $A_t = 2(de + ac + bc)$

$V = A_r c = abc$

Cube:
Letting $b = c = a$:

$A_t = 6a^2$ $V = a^3$ Diagonal $= a\sqrt{3}$

GENERAL PRISM

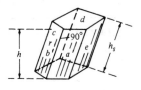

$A_l = hp_b =$
  $sp_r = s(a + b + \cdots + n)$

$V = hA_b = sA_r$

TRUNCATED PRISM

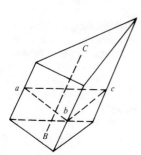

General truncated prism:

$V = A_r \cdot$ (length of line BC joining centers of gravity of bases)

Truncated triangular prism:

$$V = \frac{A_r}{3}(a + b + c)$$

PRISMATOID

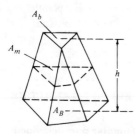

Let area of midsection = A_m

$$V = \frac{h}{6}(A_B + A_b + 4A_m)$$

RIGHT REGULAR PYRAMID AND FRUSTUM OF RIGHT REGULAR PYRAMID

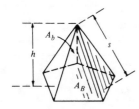

Right regular pyramid:

$$A_l = \frac{sp_B}{2} \qquad V = \frac{hA_B}{3}$$

Frustum of right regular pyramid:

$$A_l = \frac{s}{2}(p_B + p_b) \qquad V = \frac{h}{3}(A_B + A_b + \sqrt{A_B A_b})$$

GENERAL PYRAMID AND FRUSTUM OF PYRAMID

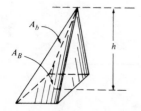

General pyramid:

$$V = \frac{hA_B}{3}$$

Frustum of general pyramid:

$$V = \frac{h}{3}(A_B + A_b + \sqrt{A_B A_b})$$

REGULAR POLYHEDRONS

With edge = a, and radius of inscribed sphere = r,

then $r = \dfrac{3V}{A_t}$, and total areas and volumes are:

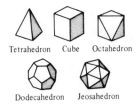

Tetrahedron   Cube   Octahedron

Dodecahedron   Jeosahedron

No. of faces	Form of faces	Total area, A_t	Volume, V
4	Equilateral triangle	$1.7321a^2$	$0.1179a^3$
6	Square	$6.0000a^2$	$1.0000a^3$
8	Equilateral triangle	$3.4641a^2$	$0.4714a^3$
12	Regular pentagon	$20.6457a^2$	$7.6631a^3$
20	Equilateral triangle	$8.6603a^2$	$2.1817a^3$

Factors shown only to four decimal places

SOLIDS WITH CURVED SURFACES

Lines are represented by a, b, c, $\cdots$; altitude (perpendicular height), by h, $h_1 \cdots$; slant height, by s; radius, by r; perimeter of base, by p_b; perimeter of right section, by p_r; angle in radians, by ϕ; arc, by s; chord of segment, by l; rise, by h; area of base, by A_b or A_B; area of a right section, by A_r; total area of convex surface, by A_l; total area of all surfaces, by A_t; and volume, by V.

RIGHT CIRCULAR CYLINDER AND TRUNCATED RIGHT CIRCULAR CYLINDER

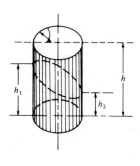

Right circular cylinder:

$$A_l = 2\pi rh \qquad A_t = 2\pi r(r + h)$$

$$V = \pi r^2 h$$

Truncated right circular cylinder:

$$A_l = \pi r(h_1 + h_2)$$

$$A_t = \pi r \left[h_1 + h_2 + r + \sqrt{r^2 + \left(\frac{h_1 - h_2}{2}\right)^2} \right]$$

$$V = \frac{\pi r^2}{2}(h_1 + h_2)$$

UNGULA (WEDGE) OF RIGHT CIRCULAR CYLINDER

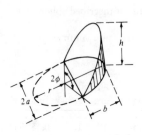

$$A_l = \frac{2rh}{b}[a + (b - r)\phi]$$

$$V = \frac{h}{3b}[a(3r^2 - a^2) + 3r^2(b - r)\phi]$$

$$= \frac{hr^3}{b}\left[\sin\phi - \frac{\sin^3\phi}{3} - \phi\cos\phi\right]$$

For semicircular base:
Letting $a = b = r$:

$$A_l = 2rh \qquad V = \frac{2r^2h}{3}$$

GENERAL CYLINDER

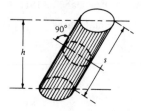

$$A_l = p_b h = p_r s$$
$$V = A_b h = A_r s$$

RIGHT CIRCULAR CONE AND FRUSTUM OF RIGHT CIRCULAR CONE

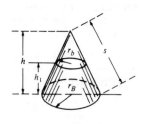

Right circular cone:

$$A_l = \pi r_B s = \pi r_B \sqrt{r_B{}^2 + h^2} \qquad A_t = \pi r_B(r_B + s)$$

$$V = \frac{\pi r_B{}^2 h}{3}$$

Frustum of right circular cone:

$$s = \sqrt{h_1{}^2 + (r_B - r_b)^2} \qquad A_l = \pi s(r_B + r_b)$$

$$V = \frac{\pi h_1}{3}(r_B{}^2 + r_b{}^2 + r_B r_b)$$

GENERAL CONE AND FRUSTUM OF GENERAL CONE

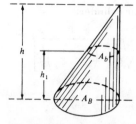

General cone:

$$V = \frac{A_B h}{3}$$

Frustum of general cone:

$$V = \frac{h_1}{3}(A_B + A_b + \sqrt{A_B A_b})$$

SPHERE

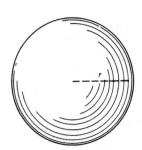

Let diameter $= d$

$$A_t = 4\pi r^2 = \pi d^2$$

$$V = \frac{4\pi r^3}{3} = \frac{\pi d^3}{6}$$

SPHERICAL SECTOR AND HEMISPHERE

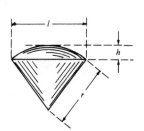

Spherical sector:

$$A_t = \frac{\pi r}{2}(4h + l) \qquad V = \frac{2\pi r^2 h}{3}$$

Hemisphere:

Letting $h = \dfrac{l}{2} = r$:

$$A_t = 3\pi r^2 \qquad V = \frac{2\pi r^3}{3}$$

SPHERICAL ZONE AND SPHERICAL SEGMENT

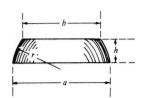

Spherical zone bounded by two planes:

$$A_l = 2\pi rh \qquad A_t = \frac{\pi}{4}(8rh + a^2 + b^2)$$

Spherical zone bounded by one plane:

$(b = 0)$:

$$A_l = 2\pi rh = \frac{\pi}{4}(4h^2 + a^2)$$

$$A_t = \frac{\pi}{4}(8rh + a^2) = \frac{\pi}{2}(2h^2 + a^2)$$

Spherical segment with two bases:

$$V = \frac{\pi h}{24}(3a^2 + 3b^2 + 4h^2)$$

Spherical segment with one base:

$(b = 0)$:

$$V = \frac{\pi h}{24}(3a^2 + 4h^2) = \pi h^2\left(r - \frac{h}{3}\right)$$

SPHERICAL POLYGON AND SPHERICAL TRIANGLE

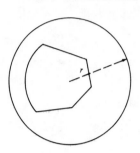

Spherical polygon:

Let sum of angles in radians = θ and number of sides = n:

$$A = [\theta - (n - 2)\pi]r^2$$

The quantity $[\theta - (n - 2)\pi]$ is called spherical excess.

Spherical triangle ($n = 3$):

$$A = (\theta - \pi)r^2$$

TORUS

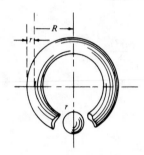

$$A_l = 4\pi^2 Rr$$
$$V = 2\pi^2 Rr^2$$

ELLIPSOID AND SPHEROIDS

Ellipsoid:

$$V = \frac{4}{3}\pi abc$$

Prolate spheroid:

Let $c = b$ and $\dfrac{\sqrt{a^2 - b^2}}{a} = e$

$$A_t = 2\pi b^2 + 2\pi ab\,\frac{\sin^{-1}e}{e} \qquad V = \frac{4}{3}\pi ab^2$$

Oblate spheroid:

Let $c = a$ and $\dfrac{\sqrt{a^2 - b^2}}{a} = e$

$$A_t = 2\pi a^2 + \frac{\pi b^2}{e}\ln\left(\frac{1 + e}{1 - e}\right) \qquad V = \frac{4}{3}\pi a^2 b$$

PARABOLOID OF REVOLUTION

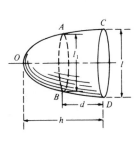

A_l of segment $DOC = \dfrac{2\pi l}{3h^2}\left[\left(\dfrac{l^2}{16}+h^2\right)^{3/2}-\left(\dfrac{l}{4}\right)^3\right]$

Paraboloidal segment with two bases:

V of $ABCD = \dfrac{\pi d}{8}(l^2 + l_1{}^2)$

Paraboloidal segment with one base ($l_1 = 0$ and $d = h$):

V of $DOC = \dfrac{\pi h l^2}{8}$

HYPERBOLOID OF REVOLUTION

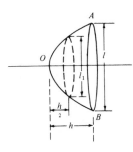

V of segment $AOB = \dfrac{\pi h}{24}(l^2 + 4l_1{}^2)$

SURFACE AND SOLID OF REVOLUTION

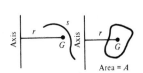

Let perpendicular distance from axis to center of gravity (G) of curve (or surface) = r. Curve (or surface) must not cross axis. **Area of surface** generated by curve revolving about axis:

$A_l = 2\pi rs$

Volume of solid generated by surface revolving about axis:

$V = 2\pi rA$

4
Trigonometry

PLANE TRIGONOMETRY

Trigonometric functions of an angle are defined in terms of a radius vector and its Cartesian coordinates (Fig. 1). Although the radius vector is always taken as positive, its components parallel to the axes are positive in the directions OX and OY and negative in the directions OX' and OY'. Trigonometric functions of the angle in Fig. 1 are:

$$\text{sine } \theta = \sin \theta = \frac{y}{r}$$

$$\text{cosine } \theta = \cos \theta = \frac{x}{r}$$

$$\text{tangent } \theta = \tan \theta = \frac{y}{x}$$

$$\text{cotangent } \theta = \cot \theta = \frac{x}{y}$$

$$\text{secant } \theta = \sec \theta = \frac{r}{x}$$

$$\text{cosecant } \theta = \csc \theta = \frac{r}{y}$$

$$\text{versine } \theta = \text{vers } \theta = \frac{r-x}{r}$$

$$\text{coversine } \theta = \text{covers } \theta = \frac{r-y}{r}$$

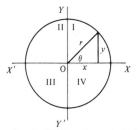

Figure 1

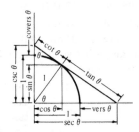

Figure 2

If the radius vector is taken as unity, the natural trigonometric functions may be represented geometrically as in Fig. 2.

Signs. The signs of trigonometric functions depend on the quadrant in which radius vector lies (Fig. 1), as follows:

Quadrant	Angle	sin	cos	tan	cot	sec	cosec
I..........	from 0° to 90°	+	+	+	+	+	+
II.........	from 90° to 180°	+	−	−	−	−	+
III........	from 180° to 270°	−	−	+	+	−	−
IV........	from 270° to 360°	−	+	−	−	+	−

Range of Values of Trigonometric Functions. The sine and cosine range from −1 to +1; the tangent and the cotangent, from −∞ to +∞; the secant and the cosecant, from −∞ to −1 and from +1 to +∞. Table 1 gives certain values of trigonometric functions.

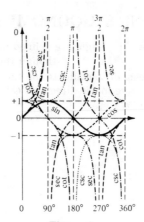

Figure 3

The variation of the trigonometric functions for angles increasing from 0° to 360° is illustrated by the graphs in Fig. 3. The values of trigonometric functions for an arbitrary angle can be found from the following rules:

• If the angle is greater than 360°, the function is reduced to a function of an angle between 0° and 360°, and the tangent and the cotangent are reduced to an angle between 0° and 180° according to the formulas (n denotes an integral number):

$$\sin (360°n + \alpha) = \sin \alpha$$
$$\cos (360°n + \alpha) = \cos \alpha$$
$$\tan (180°n + \alpha) = \tan \alpha$$
$$\cot (180°n + \alpha) = \cot \alpha$$

• If the angle is negative, the function is reduced to a function of a positive angle by the following formulas:

$$\sin (-\alpha) = -\sin \alpha$$
$$\cos (-\alpha) = \cos \alpha$$
$$\tan (-\alpha) = -\tan \alpha$$
$$\cot (-\alpha) = -\cot \alpha$$

Table 1 Values of trigonometric functions

θ, degrees	θ, radians	$\sin \theta$	$\cos \theta$	$\tan \theta$	$\cot \theta$	$\sec \theta$	$\csc \theta$
0	0	0	1	0	∞	1	∞
30	$\dfrac{\pi}{6}$	$\dfrac{1}{2}$	$\dfrac{\sqrt{3}}{2}$	$\dfrac{\sqrt{3}}{3}$	$\sqrt{3}$	$\dfrac{2}{3}\sqrt{3}$	2
45	$\dfrac{\pi}{4}$	$\dfrac{\sqrt{2}}{2}$	$\dfrac{\sqrt{2}}{2}$	1	1	$\sqrt{2}$	$\sqrt{2}$
60	$\dfrac{\pi}{3}$	$\dfrac{\sqrt{3}}{2}$	$\dfrac{1}{2}$	$\sqrt{3}$	$\dfrac{\sqrt{3}}{3}$	2	$\dfrac{2}{3}\sqrt{3}$
90	$\dfrac{\pi}{2}$	1	0	∞	0	∞	1
120	$\dfrac{2\pi}{3}$	$\dfrac{\sqrt{3}}{2}$	$-\dfrac{1}{2}$	$-\sqrt{3}$	$-\dfrac{\sqrt{3}}{3}$	-2	$\dfrac{2}{3}\sqrt{3}$
135	$\dfrac{3\pi}{4}$	$\dfrac{\sqrt{2}}{2}$	$-\dfrac{\sqrt{2}}{2}$	-1	-1	$-\sqrt{2}$	$\sqrt{2}$
150	$\dfrac{5\pi}{6}$	$\dfrac{1}{2}$	$-\dfrac{\sqrt{3}}{2}$	$-\dfrac{\sqrt{3}}{3}$	$-\sqrt{3}$	$-\dfrac{2}{3}\sqrt{3}$	2
180	π	0	-1	0	∞	-1	∞
210	$\dfrac{7\pi}{6}$	$-\dfrac{1}{2}$	$-\dfrac{\sqrt{3}}{2}$	$\dfrac{\sqrt{3}}{3}$	$\sqrt{3}$	$-\dfrac{2}{3}\sqrt{3}$	-2
225	$\dfrac{5\pi}{4}$	$-\dfrac{\sqrt{2}}{2}$	$-\dfrac{\sqrt{2}}{2}$	1	1	$-\sqrt{2}$	$-\sqrt{2}$
240	$\dfrac{4\pi}{3}$	$-\dfrac{\sqrt{3}}{2}$	$-\dfrac{1}{2}$	$\sqrt{3}$	$\dfrac{\sqrt{3}}{3}$	-2	$-\dfrac{2}{3}\sqrt{3}$
270	$\dfrac{3\pi}{2}$	-1	0	∞	0	∞	-1
300	$\dfrac{5\pi}{3}$	$-\dfrac{\sqrt{3}}{2}$	$\dfrac{1}{2}$	$-\sqrt{3}$	$-\dfrac{\sqrt{3}}{3}$	2	$-\dfrac{2}{3}\sqrt{3}$
315	$\dfrac{7\pi}{4}$	$-\dfrac{\sqrt{2}}{2}$	$\dfrac{\sqrt{2}}{2}$	-1	-1	$\sqrt{2}$	$-\sqrt{2}$
330	$\dfrac{11\pi}{6}$	$-\dfrac{1}{2}$	$\dfrac{\sqrt{3}}{2}$	$-\dfrac{\sqrt{3}}{3}$	$-\sqrt{3}$	$\dfrac{2}{3}\sqrt{3}$	-2
360	2π	0	1	0	∞	1	∞

- If the angle is acute, $0° < \alpha < 90°$, the value of the function can be found from tables, for example:

$$\sin(-1000°) = -\sin 1000° = -\sin(2 \cdot 360° + 280°)$$
$$= -\sin 280° = +\cos 10° = +0.9848$$

- If $90° < \alpha < 360°$, the function is reduced to a function of an acute angle by the following reducing formulas:

Function	$\beta = 90° \pm \alpha$	$\beta = 180° \pm \alpha$	$\beta = 270° \pm \alpha$	$\beta = 360° - \alpha$
$\sin \beta$	$+\cos \alpha$	$\mp \sin \alpha$	$-\cos \alpha$	$-\sin \alpha$
$\cos \beta$	$\mp \sin \alpha$	$-\cos \alpha$	$\pm \sin \alpha$	$+\cos \alpha$
$\tan \beta$	$\mp \cot \alpha$	$\pm \tan \alpha$	$\mp \cot \alpha$	$-\tan \alpha$
$\cot \beta$	$\mp \tan \alpha$	$\pm \cot \alpha$	$\mp \tan \alpha$	$-\cot \alpha$

FUNDAMENTAL FORMULAS OF TRIGONOMETRY

Functions of one angle are given below:

$$\sin^2\alpha + \cos^2\alpha = 1 \qquad \frac{\sin \alpha}{\cos \alpha} = \tan \alpha \qquad \sin \alpha \cdot \operatorname{cosec} \alpha = 1$$

$$\sec^2\alpha - \tan^2\alpha = 1 \qquad\qquad\qquad \cos \alpha \cdot \sec \alpha = 1$$

$$\operatorname{cosec}^2\alpha - \cot^2\alpha = 1 \qquad \frac{\cos \alpha}{\sin \alpha} = \cot \alpha \qquad \tan \alpha \cdot \cot \alpha = 1$$

Functions expressed in terms of other functions of the same angle, with the sign before the radicals chosen according to the quadrant in which the angle lies, are given below:

$$\sin \alpha = \sqrt{1 - \cos^2 \alpha} = \frac{\tan \alpha}{\sqrt{1 + \tan^2 \alpha}} = \frac{1}{\sqrt{1 + \cot^2 \alpha}}$$

$$= \frac{\sqrt{\sec^2 \alpha - 1}}{\sec \alpha} = \frac{1}{\operatorname{cosec} \alpha}$$

$$\cos \alpha = \sqrt{1 - \sin^2 \alpha} = \frac{1}{\sqrt{1 + \tan^2 \alpha}} = \frac{\cot \alpha}{\sqrt{1 + \cot^2 \alpha}}$$

$$= \frac{1}{\sec \alpha} = \frac{\sqrt{\operatorname{cosec}^2 \alpha - 1}}{\operatorname{cosec} \alpha}$$

$$\tan \alpha = \frac{\sin \alpha}{\sqrt{1 - \sin^2 \alpha}} = \frac{\sqrt{1 - \cos^2 \alpha}}{\cos \alpha} = \frac{1}{\cot \alpha}$$

$$= \sqrt{\sec^2 \alpha - 1} = \frac{1}{\sqrt{\operatorname{cosec}^2 \alpha - 1}}$$

$$\cot \alpha = \frac{\sqrt{1 - \sin^2 \alpha}}{\sin \alpha} = \frac{\cos \alpha}{\sqrt{1 - \cos^2 \alpha}} = \frac{1}{\tan \alpha}$$

$$= \frac{1}{\sqrt{\sec^2 \alpha - 1}} = \sqrt{\operatorname{cosec}^2 \alpha - 1}$$

Sums and Differences of Functions. The following formulas expressing sums and differences of trigonometric functions as products, are suitable
for logarithmic computations:

$$\sin \alpha + \sin \beta = 2 \sin \tfrac{1}{2}(\alpha + \beta) \cos \tfrac{1}{2}(\alpha - \beta)$$
$$\sin \alpha - \sin \beta = 2 \cos \tfrac{1}{2}(\alpha + \beta) \sin \tfrac{1}{2}(\alpha - \beta)$$
$$\cos \alpha + \cos \beta = 2 \cos \tfrac{1}{2}(\alpha + \beta) \cos \tfrac{1}{2}(\alpha - \beta)$$
$$\cos \alpha - \cos \beta = 2 \sin \tfrac{1}{2}(\alpha + \beta) \sin \tfrac{1}{2}(\beta - \alpha)$$
$$\sin^2 \alpha - \sin^2 \beta = \sin(\alpha + \beta) \sin(\alpha - \beta)$$
$$\cos^2 \alpha - \sin^2 \beta = \cos^2 \beta - \sin^2 \alpha = \cos(\alpha + \beta) \cos(\alpha - \beta)$$

$$\sin \theta + \cos \theta = \sqrt{2} \sin\left(\theta + \frac{\pi}{4}\right) = \sqrt{2} \cos\left(\theta = \frac{\pi}{4}\right)$$

$$\sec^2 \theta + \csc^2 \theta = \sec^2 \theta \csc^2 \theta = \frac{1}{\sin^2 \theta \cos^2 \theta}$$

$$a \sin \theta + b \cos \theta = \sqrt{a^2 + b^2} \sin(\theta + \varphi) = \sqrt{a^2 + b^2} \cos(\theta - \psi)$$

where
$$\varphi = \cos^{-1} \frac{a}{\sqrt{a^2 + b^2}} = \sin^{-1} \frac{b}{\sqrt{a^2 + b^2}}$$

$$\psi = \sin^{-1} \frac{a}{\sqrt{a^2 + b^2}} = \cos^{-1} \frac{b}{\sqrt{a^2 + b^2}}$$

$$\tan \alpha + \tan \beta = \frac{\sin(\alpha + \beta)}{\cos \alpha \cos \beta}$$

$$\tan \alpha - \tan \beta = \frac{\sin(\alpha - \beta)}{\cos \alpha \cos \beta}$$

$$\cot \alpha + \cot \beta = \frac{\sin(\alpha + \beta)}{\sin \alpha \sin \beta}$$

$$\cot \alpha - \cot \beta = \frac{\sin(\beta - \alpha)}{\sin \alpha \sin \beta}$$

$$\tan \alpha + \cot \beta = \frac{\cos(\alpha - \beta)}{\cos \alpha \sin \beta}$$

$$\cot \alpha - \tan \beta = \frac{\cos(\alpha + \beta)}{\sin \alpha \cos \beta}$$

Functions of Multiples of an Angle:

$$\sin 2\theta = 2 \sin \theta \cos \theta = \frac{2 \tan \theta}{1 + \tan^2 \theta}$$

$$\sin 3\theta = 3 \sin \theta - 4 \sin^3 \theta$$

$$\sin 4\theta = 4 \cos \theta (\sin \theta - 2 \sin^3 \theta)$$

$$\sin 5\theta = 5 \sin \theta - 20 \sin^3 \theta + 16 \sin^5 \theta$$

$$\sin 6\theta = \cos \theta (\sin \theta - 32 \sin^3 \theta + 32 \sin^5 \theta)$$

$$\sin n\theta = n \sin \theta - \frac{n(n^2 - 1^2)}{3!} \sin^3 \theta + \frac{n(n^2 - 1)(n^2 - 3^2)}{5!} \sin^5 \theta -$$

$$\frac{n(n^2 - 1^2)(n^2 - 3^2)(n^2 - 5^2)}{7!} \sin^7 \theta + \cdots \quad n \text{ odd}$$

$$\sin n\theta = n \cos \theta \left[\sin \theta - \frac{(n^2 - 2^2)}{3!} \sin^3 \theta + \frac{(n^2 - 2^2)(n^2 - 4^2)}{5!} \sin^5 \theta - \right.$$

$$\left. \frac{(n^2 - 2^2)(n^2 - 4^2)(n^2 - 6^2)}{7!} \sin^7 \theta + \cdots \right] \quad n \text{ even}$$

$$\cos 2\theta = \cos^2 \theta - \sin^2 \theta = 1 - 2 \sin^2 \theta - 2 \cos^2 \theta - 1$$

$$\cos 3\theta = 4 \cos^3 \theta - 3 \cos \theta$$

$$\cos 4\theta = 8 \cos^4 \theta - 8 \cos^2 \theta + 1$$

$$\cos 5\theta = 16 \cos^5 \theta - 20 \cos^3 \theta + 5 \cos \theta$$

$$\cos 6\theta = 32 \cos^6 \theta - 48 \cos^4 \theta + 18 \cos^2 \theta - 1$$

$$\cos n\theta = 2^{n-1} \cos^n \theta - 2^{n-3} n \cos^{n-2} \theta + 2^{n-5} \frac{n(n-3)}{2!} \cos^{n-4} \theta -$$

$$2^{n-7} \frac{n(n-4)(n-5)}{3!} \cos^{n-6} \theta +$$

$$2^{n-9} \frac{n(n-5)(n-6)(n-7)}{4!} \cos^{n-8} \theta - \cdots$$

$$\tan 2\theta = \frac{2 \tan \theta}{1 - \tan^2 \theta}$$

$$\tan 3\theta = \frac{3 \tan \theta - \tan^3 \theta}{1 - 3 \tan^2 \theta}$$

$$\tan 4\theta = \frac{4 \tan \theta - 4 \tan^3 \theta}{1 - 6 \tan^2 \theta + \tan^4 \theta}$$

$$\cot 2\theta = \frac{\cot^2 \theta - 1}{2 \cot \theta}$$

$$\cot 3\theta = \frac{\cot^3 \theta - 3 \cot \theta}{3 \cot^2 \theta - 1}$$

$$\cot 4\theta = \frac{\cot^4 \theta - 6 \cot^2 \theta + 1}{4 \cot^3 \theta - 4 \cot \theta}$$

Functions of Half Angles:

$$\sin \frac{\alpha}{2} = \sqrt{\frac{1 - \cos \alpha}{2}} \qquad \tan \frac{\alpha}{2} = \sqrt{\frac{1 - \cos \alpha}{1 + \cos \alpha}} = \frac{1 - \cos \alpha}{\sin \alpha} = \frac{\sin \alpha}{1 + \cos \alpha}$$

$$\cos \frac{\alpha}{2} = \sqrt{\frac{1 + \cos \alpha}{2}} \qquad \cot \frac{\alpha}{2} = \sqrt{\frac{1 + \cos \alpha}{1 - \cos \alpha}} = \frac{1 + \cos \alpha}{\sin \alpha} = \frac{\sin \alpha}{1 - \cos \alpha}$$

Products and Powers of Functions:

$\sin \alpha \sin \beta = \frac{1}{2} \cos (\alpha - \beta) - \frac{1}{2} \cos (\alpha + \beta)$
$\cos \alpha \cos \beta = \frac{1}{2} \cos (\alpha - \beta) + \frac{1}{2} \cos (\alpha + \beta)$
$\sin \alpha \cos \beta = \frac{1}{2} \sin (\alpha - \beta) + \frac{1}{2} \sin (\alpha + \beta)$
$\tan \alpha \cot \alpha = \sin \alpha \csc \alpha = \cos \alpha \sec \alpha = 1$

$\quad \sin^2 \alpha = \frac{1}{2}(1 - \cos 2\alpha); \cos^2 \alpha = \frac{1}{2}(1 + \cos 2\alpha)$
$\quad \sin^3 \alpha = \frac{1}{4}(3 \sin \alpha - \sin 3\alpha); \cos^3 \alpha = \frac{1}{4}(3 \cos \alpha + \cos 3\alpha)$
$\quad \sin^4 \alpha = \frac{1}{8}(3 - 4 \cos 2\alpha + \cos 4\alpha); \cos^4 \alpha = \frac{1}{8}(3 + 4 \cos 2\alpha + \cos 4\alpha)$
$\quad \sin^5 \alpha = \frac{1}{16}(10 \sin \alpha - 5 \sin 3\alpha + \sin 5\alpha)$
$\quad \sin^6 \alpha = \frac{1}{32}(10 - 15 \cos 2\alpha + 6 \cos 4\alpha - \cos 6\alpha)$
$\quad \cos^5 \alpha = \frac{1}{16}(10 \cos \alpha + 5 \cos 3\alpha + \cos 5\alpha)$
$\quad \cos^6 \alpha = \frac{1}{32}(10 + 15 \cos 2\alpha + 6 \cos 4\alpha + \cos 6\alpha)$

HARMONIC QUANTITIES

In many problems of mechanics and physics, quantities depend on the time t according to the formula, $u = A \sin (\omega t + \varphi)$.

Such quantities are called harmonic and their variation according to time is called a harmonic vibration. The graph of the function is a general sine curve (Fig. 4), which differs from the classical sine curve, $y = \sin x$, as follows:

- Amplitude, the maximal deviation from the t axis is equal to A
- Period T, the length of wave, is equal to $2\pi/\omega$, with ω called the frequency of vibration
- Initial phase is the angle φ

The formula can be written in the form, $u = a \sin \omega t + b \cos \omega t$, where $A = \sqrt{a^2 + b^2}$ and $\tan \varphi = b/a$. Relationships among a, b, A and φ can be expressed as relationships among elements of a right triangle (Fig. 5).

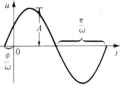

Figure 4

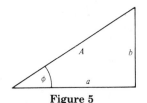

Figure 5

Operations with Harmonic Quantities. Two harmonic quantities of the same frequency ω equal a harmonic quantity of the same frequency:

$$A_1 \sin (\omega t + \varphi_1) + A_2 \sin (\omega t + \varphi_2) = A \sin (\omega t + \varphi)$$

where

$$A = \sqrt{A_1{}^2 + A_2{}^2 + 2A_1A_2 \cos(\varphi_2 - \varphi_1)}$$

and

$$\tan \varphi = \frac{A_1 \sin \varphi_1 + A_2 \sin \varphi_2}{A_1 \cos \varphi_1 + A_2 \cos \varphi_2}$$

Linear combination of several harmonic quantities with a common frequency is also a harmonic quantity of the same frequency:

$$\sum c_i A_i \sin(\omega t + \varphi_i) = A \sin(\omega t + \varphi)$$

Vector Diagram of Harmonic Quantities. Harmonic quantities can be represented on the plane as a radius vector u with polar coordinates $\rho = A$ and φ or with Cartesian coordinates $x = a$ and $y = b$. A sum of two harmonic quantities is the sum of vectors representing the sumands (Fig. 6). A linear combination of harmonic quantities is the linear combination of the corresponding vectors.

The quantity u corresponding to a given time t can be found in the vector diagram as seen in Fig. 7. The time axis OP (Fig. 7) passes through the origin O and revolves about O with a constant angular velocity ω in the clockwise direction. At time $t = 0$, the time axis coincides with the y axis. Then the projection ON of the vector u on the time axis gives, for a given time t, the value of the harmonic quantity $u = A \sin(\omega t + \varphi)$. At $t = 0$, $u_0 = A \sin \varphi$ is the projection of u on the y axis (Fig. 6).

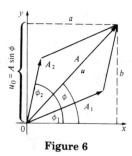

Figure 6

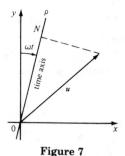

Figure 7

SOLUTION OF TRIANGLES

The fundamental relations for a right triangle with sides a, b and c, with c the hypotenuse, and with angles A and B, opposite sides a and b are:

$$a = c \sin A = c \cos B \qquad a = b \tan A = b \cot B$$

For the remaining elements, the formulas follow:

Given	Formulas	
c, A .... $B = 90° - A$	$a = c \sin A$	$b = c \cos A$
a, A .... $B = 90° - A$	$b = a \cot A$	$c = \dfrac{a}{\sin A}$
a, c .... $\sin A = \dfrac{a}{c}$	$b = c \cos A$	$B = 90° - A$
a, b .... $\tan A = \dfrac{a}{b}$	$c = \dfrac{a}{\sin A}$	$B = 90° - A$

Law of Sines. In any triangle, the sides are proportional to the sines of the opposite angles. In triangle ABC (Fig. 8), for example, $\dfrac{a}{\sin A} = \dfrac{b}{\sin B} = \dfrac{c}{\sin C} = d$. The constant d equals the diameter of the circumscribed circle.

Law of Cosines. In any triangle, the square of a side equals the sum of the squares of the other sides less twice the product of these sides and the cosine of their included angle. In triangle ABC of Fig. 8, $a^2 = b^2 + c^2 - 2bc \cos A$.

Law of Tangents. In any triangle, the sum of any two sides is to their difference as the tangent of half the sum of the opposite angles is to the tangent of half the difference of these angles. In triangle ABC (Fig. 8):

$$\frac{a + c}{a - c} = \frac{\tan \tfrac{1}{2}(A + C)}{\tan \tfrac{1}{2}(A - C)}$$

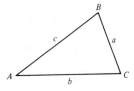

Figure 8

Mollweide's Equations. These equations are useful for checking solutions of triangles and for logarithmic computations. The equations involve the three sides and angles of a triangle:

$$\frac{a - b}{c} = \frac{\sin \tfrac{1}{2}(A - B)}{\cos \tfrac{1}{2} C}$$

$$\frac{a + b}{c} = \frac{\cos \tfrac{1}{2}(A - B)}{\sin \tfrac{1}{2} C}$$

INVERSE TRIGONOMETRIC FUNCTIONS

Inverse trigonometric functions of x are defined by the following equalities:

y = Arc sin x (the inverse sine), if $x = \sin y$
y = Arc cos x (the inverse cosine), if $x = \cos y$ $\Bigg\}$ y is measured
y = Arc tan x (the inverse tangent), if $x = \tan y$ in radians
y = Arc cot x (the inverse cotangent), if $x = \cot y$

Examples are:

$$\text{Arc sin } 0 = 0 \text{ or } \pi \text{ or } 2\pi; \text{ in general, Arc sin } 0 = k\pi$$

$$\text{Arc cos } \frac{1}{2} = \frac{1}{3}\pi \text{ or } -\frac{1}{3}\pi \text{ or } \frac{1}{3}\pi + 2\pi; \text{ Arc cos } \frac{1}{2} = \pm\frac{1}{3}\pi + 2k\pi$$

$$\text{Arc tan } 1 = \frac{1}{4}\pi \text{ or } \frac{5}{4}\pi; \text{ Arc tan } 1 = \frac{1}{4}\pi + k\pi$$

Principal Values. Inverse trigonometric functions are multiple valued. The principal values of these functions which are denoted as arc sin x, arc cos x, arc tan x, and arc cot x are found in the intervals:

$$-\frac{1}{2}\pi \leq \text{arc sin } x \leq \frac{1}{2}\pi \qquad 0 \leq \text{arc cos } x \leq \pi$$

$$-\frac{1}{2}\pi < \text{arc tan } x < +\frac{1}{2}\pi \qquad 0 < \text{arc cot } x < \pi$$

The graphs of the principal values of inverse trigonometric functions are given in Fig. 9.

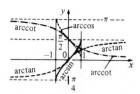

Figure 9

Expressions of one inverse trigonometric function by the others are given in the following formulas, which are valid only for the principal values of the inverse trigonometric functions. The formulas in rectangular brackets are valid only for positive values of x because the principal values lie in various intervals:

$$\text{arc sin } x = -\text{arc sin } (-x) = \frac{1}{2}\pi - \text{arc cos } x = \left[\text{arc cos } \sqrt{1 - x^2}\right]$$

$$= \text{arc tan } \frac{x}{\sqrt{1 - x^2}} = \left[\text{arc cot } \frac{\sqrt{1 - x^2}}{x}\right]$$

$$\text{arc cos } x = \pi - \text{arc cos } (-x) = \frac{1}{2}\pi - \text{arc sin } x = \left[\text{arc sin } \sqrt{1 - x^2}\right]$$

$$= \left[\text{arc tan} \frac{\sqrt{1-x^2}}{x} \right] = \text{arc cot} \frac{x}{\sqrt{1-x^2}}$$

$$\text{arc tan } x = -\text{arc tan } (-x) = \tfrac{1}{2}\pi - \text{arc cot } x = \text{arc sin} \frac{x}{\sqrt{1+x^2}}$$

$$= \left[\text{arc cos} \frac{1}{\sqrt{1+x^2}} \right] = \left[\text{arc cot} \frac{1}{x} \right]$$

$$\text{arc cot } x = \pi - \text{arc cot } (-x) = \tfrac{1}{2}\pi - \text{arc tan } x$$

$$= \left[\text{arc sin} \frac{1}{\sqrt{1+x^2}} \right] = \text{arc cos} \frac{x}{\sqrt{1+x^2}} = \left[\text{arc tan} \frac{1}{x} \right]$$

Fundamental relationships among the inverse trigonometric functions are given below:

$$\text{arc sin } x + \text{arc sin } y = \text{arc sin } (x\sqrt{1-y^2} + y\sqrt{1-x^2})$$
$$(xy \le 0 \text{ or } x^2 + y^2 \le 1)$$

$$= \pi - \text{arc sin } (x\sqrt{1-y^2} + y\sqrt{1-x^2})$$
$$(x > 0, y > 0 \text{ and } x^2 + y^2 > 1)$$

$$= -\pi - \text{arc sin } (x\sqrt{1-y^2} + y\sqrt{1-x^2})$$
$$(x < 0, y < 0 \text{ and } x^2 + y^2 > 1)$$

$$\text{arc sin } x - \text{arc sin } y = \text{arc sin } (x\sqrt{1-y^2} - y\sqrt{1-x^2})$$
$$(xy \ge 0 \text{ or } x^2 + y^2 \le 1)$$

$$= \pi - \text{arc sin } (x\sqrt{1-y^2} - y\sqrt{1-x^2})$$
$$(x > 0, y < 0 \text{ and } x^2 + y^2 > 1)$$

$$= -\pi - \text{arc sin } (x\sqrt{1-y^2} - y\sqrt{1-x^2})$$
$$(x < 0, y > 0 \text{ and } x^2 + y^2 > 1)$$

$$\text{arc cos } x + \text{arc cos } y = \text{arc cos } (xy - \sqrt{1-x^2}\sqrt{1-y^2}) \qquad (x + y \ge 0)$$

$$= 2\pi - \text{arc cos } (xy - \sqrt{1-x^2}\sqrt{1-y^2}) \qquad (x + y < 0)$$

$$\text{arc cos } x - \text{arc cos } y = -\text{arc cos } (xy + \sqrt{1-x^2}\sqrt{1-y^2}) \qquad (x \ge y)$$

$$= \text{arc cos } (xy + \sqrt{1-x^2}\sqrt{1-y^2}) \qquad (x < y)$$

$$\text{arc tan } x + \text{arc tan } y = \text{arc tan} \frac{x+y}{1-xy} \qquad (xy < 1)$$

$$= \pi + \text{arc tan} \frac{x+y}{1-xy} \qquad (x > 0, xy > 1)$$

$$= -\pi + \text{arc tan} \frac{x+y}{1-xy} \qquad (x < 0, xy > 1)$$

$$\text{arc tan } x - \text{arc tan } y = \text{arc tan} \frac{x-y}{1+xy} \qquad (xy > -1)$$

$$= \pi + \text{arc tan} \frac{x-y}{1+xy} \qquad (x > 0, xy < -1)$$

$$= -\pi + \text{arc tan} \frac{x - y}{1 + xy} \qquad (x < 0,\ xy < -1)$$

$$2 \text{ arc sin } x = \text{arc sin } (2x\sqrt{1 - x^2}) \qquad \left(|x| \leq \frac{1}{\sqrt{2}}\right)$$

$$= \pi - \text{arc sin } (2x\sqrt{1 - x^2}) \qquad \left(\frac{1}{\sqrt{2}} < x \leq 1\right)$$

$$= -\pi - \text{arc sin } (2x\sqrt{1 - x^2}) \qquad \left(-1 \leq x < -\frac{1}{\sqrt{2}}\right)$$

$$2 \text{ arc cos } x = \text{arc cos } (2x^2 - 1) \qquad (0 \leq x \leq 1)$$

$$= 2\pi - \text{arc cos } (2x^2 - 1) \qquad (-1 \leq x < 0)$$

$$2 \text{ arc tan } x = \text{arc tan } \frac{2x}{1 - x^2} \qquad (|x| < 1)$$

$$= \pi + \text{arc tan } \frac{2x}{1 - x^2} \qquad (x > 1)$$

$$= -\pi + \text{arc tan } \frac{2x}{1 - x^2} \qquad (x < -1)$$

$$\cos (n \text{ arc cos } x) = 2^{n-1} T_n(x) \qquad (n \geq 1)$$

where

$$T_n(x) = \frac{(x + \sqrt{x^2 - 1})^n + (x - \sqrt{x^2 - 1})^n}{2^n}$$

When n is an integer, then $T_n(x)$ is a polynomial of x (Tschebyscheff polynomial). The formula, $\cos (n \text{ arc cos } x) = 2^{n-1} T_n(x)$, holds also for non-integral values of n.

SPHERICAL TRIGONOMETRY

A section of a sphere formed by a plane passing through its center is a great circle with radius equal to the radius of the sphere. Every two points A and B of the sphere determine a unique great circle passing through A and B. Arc AaB, a geodesic line, of this great circle (Fig. 10) is the shortest of all lines on the sphere joining the points A and B.

Spherical Triangles. Three great circles form several spherical triangles on the sphere. In Fig. 11, the sides a, b, c of the triangle are measured by plane angles of the trihedral angle $OABC$, where O is the center of the sphere, and the angles A, B, C of the triangle are measured by dihedral angles of the trihedral angle. For a spherical triangle, the sum of its angles $A + B + C$ is always greater than 180°. The difference $(A + B + C) - \pi = \delta$ expressed in radians is called the spherical excess. The area of a spherical triangle is $S = R^2\delta$, where R is the radius of the sphere.

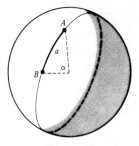

Figure 10

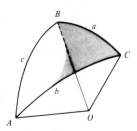

Figure 11

Law of Cosines for Spherical Triangles. Similar to the law of cosines for plane triangles, the law of cosines for spherical triangles is used to find the third side of a spherical triangle ABC when two sides and the included angle are known (Fig. 12). It is used to find the third angle when two angles and the included side are known. Law of cosines for sides:

$$\cos a = \cos b \cos c + \sin b \sin c \cos A$$
$$\cos b = \cos a \cos c + \sin a \sin c \cos B$$
$$\cos c = \cos a \cos b + \sin a \sin b \cos C$$

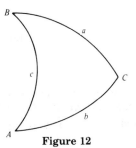

Figure 12

Law of cosines for angles:

$$\cos A = -\cos B \cos C + \sin B \sin C \cos a$$
$$\cos B = -\cos A \cos C + \sin A \sin C \cos b$$
$$\cos C = -\cos A \cos B + \sin A \sin B \cos C$$

Law of Sines for Spherical Triangles. For spherical triangle ABC in Fig. 12:

$$\frac{\sin A}{\sin a} = \frac{\sin B}{\sin b} = \frac{\sin C}{\sin c}$$

Functions of Spherical Triangle Angles and Sides. The functions of an angle in terms of three sides in spherical triangle ABC of Fig. 12 are given below, with $s = \frac{1}{2}(a + b + c)$ and $r = \sqrt{\sin(s - a)\sin(s - b)\sin(s - c)/\sin s}$:

$$\sin \tfrac{1}{2}A = \sqrt{\frac{\sin(s - b)\sin(s - c)}{\sin b \sin c}}$$

$$\sin \tfrac{1}{2}B = \sqrt{\frac{\sin(s-a)\sin(s-c)}{\sin a \sin c}}$$

$$\sin \tfrac{1}{2}C = \sqrt{\frac{\sin(s-a)\sin(s-b)}{\sin a \sin b}}$$

$$\cos \tfrac{1}{2}A = \sqrt{\frac{\sin s \sin(s-a)}{\sin b \sin c}}$$

$$\cos \tfrac{1}{2}B = \sqrt{\frac{\sin s \sin(s-b)}{\sin a \sin c}}$$

$$\cos \tfrac{1}{2}C = \sqrt{\frac{\sin s \sin(s-c)}{\sin a \sin b}}$$

$$\tan \tfrac{1}{2}A = \frac{r}{\sin(s-a)}$$

$$\tan \tfrac{1}{2}B = \frac{r}{\sin(s-b)}$$

$$\tan \tfrac{1}{2}C = \frac{r}{\sin(s-c)}$$

The functions of a side of a spherical triangle in terms of three angles in spherical triangle ABC of Fig. 12 are given below, with $S = \tfrac{1}{2}(A + B + C)$ and $R = \sqrt{-\cos S / \cos(S-A)\cos(S-B)\cos(S-C)}$:

$$\cos \tfrac{1}{2}a = \sqrt{\frac{\cos(S-B)\cos(S-C)}{\sin B \sin C}}$$

$$\cos \tfrac{1}{2}b = \sqrt{\frac{\cos(S-A)\cos(S-C)}{\sin A \sin C}}$$

$$\cos \tfrac{1}{2}c = \sqrt{\frac{\cos(S-A)\cos(S-B)}{\sin A \sin B}}$$

$$\sin \tfrac{1}{2}a = \sqrt{\frac{\cos S \cos(S-A)}{\sin B \sin C}}$$

$$\sin \tfrac{1}{2}b = \sqrt{\frac{\cos S \cos(S-B)}{\sin A \sin C}}$$

$$\sin \tfrac{1}{2}c = \sqrt{\frac{\cos S \cos(S-C)}{\sin A \sin B}}$$

$$\tan \tfrac{1}{2}a = R \cos(S-A)$$
$$\tan \tfrac{1}{2}b = R \cos(S-B)$$
$$\tan \tfrac{1}{2}c = R \cos(S-C)$$

Napier's Analogies. In spherical triangle ABC of Fig. 12:

$$\frac{\tan \frac{1}{2}(a - b)}{\tan \frac{1}{2}c} = \frac{\sin \frac{1}{2}(A - B)}{\sin \frac{1}{2}(A + B)}$$

$$\frac{\tan \frac{1}{2}(A - B)}{\cot \frac{1}{2}C} = \frac{\sin \frac{1}{2}(a - b)}{\sin \frac{1}{2}(a + b)}$$

$$\frac{\tan \frac{1}{2}(a + b)}{\tan \frac{1}{2}c} = \frac{\cos \frac{1}{2}(A - B)}{\cos \frac{1}{2}(A + B)}$$

$$\frac{\tan \frac{1}{2}(A + B)}{\cot \frac{1}{2}C} = \frac{\cos \frac{1}{2}(a - b)}{\cos \frac{1}{2}(a + b)}$$

Gauss' Equations (Delambre's Analogies). In spherical triangle ABC of Fig. 12:

$$\cos \frac{1}{2}c \sin \frac{1}{2}(A + B) = \cos \frac{1}{2}C \cos \frac{1}{2}(a - b)$$
$$\cos \frac{1}{2}c \cos \frac{1}{2}(A + B) = \sin \frac{1}{2}C \cos \frac{1}{2}(a + b)$$
$$\sin \frac{1}{2}c \sin \frac{1}{2}(A - B) = \cos \frac{1}{2}C \sin \frac{1}{2}(a - b)$$
$$\sin \frac{1}{2}c \cos \frac{1}{2}(A - B) = \sin \frac{1}{2}C \sin \frac{1}{2}(a + b)$$

Solution of Right and Quadrantal Spherical Triangles. A quadrantal triangle has one side equal to 90°. Its polar triangle, therefore, has an angle equal to 90°. A quadrantal triangle can be solved by first solving its polar right triangle and then by finding the supplements of the sides and angles of the polar triangle. These supplements equal the opposite angles and sides, respectively, of the triangle.

When any two parts of a spherical triangle ABC in Fig. 13, with a 90° angle at C, are known, the other parts can be computed from:

$$\cos c = \cos a \cos b = \cot A \cot B$$
$$\sin a = \sin A \sin c = \tan b \cot B$$
$$\sin b = \sin B \sin c = \tan a \cot A$$
$$\cos A = \sin B \cos a = \tan b \cot c$$
$$\cos B = \sin A \cos b = \tan a \cot c$$

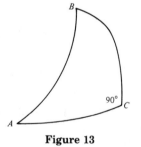

Figure 13

HYPERBOLIC TRIGONOMETRY

Hyperbolic angles are defined with reference to an equilateral hyperbola in a manner similar to circular angles. A circular angle is a central angle measured in radians by the ratio s/r or the ratio $2A/r^2$, where A is the area of the sector included by the angle α and the arc s (Fig. 14). For the hyperbola the radius ρ is not constant. Only the value of the differential hyperbolic angle $d\theta$ is defined by the ratio ds/ρ. Thus, $\theta = \int ds/\rho = 2A/a^2$, where A represents the shaded area in Fig. 15. If both s and ρ are measured in the same units, the angle is expressed in hyperbolic radians.

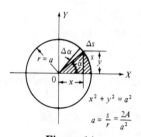

Figure 14

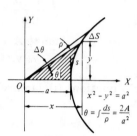

Figure 15

Hyperbolic functions are defined by ratios similar to those defining functions of circular angles:

Hyperbolic sine $\theta \qquad = \dfrac{y}{a} = \sinh \theta$

Hyperbolic cosine $\theta \qquad = \dfrac{x}{a} = \cosh \theta$

Hyperbolic tangent $\theta \qquad = \dfrac{y}{x} = \tanh \theta$

Hyperbolic cotangent $\theta = \dfrac{x}{y} = \coth \theta$

Hyperbolic secant $\theta \qquad = \dfrac{a}{x} = \operatorname{sech} \theta$

Hyperbolic cosecant $\theta \qquad = \dfrac{a}{y} = \operatorname{csch} \theta$

Values and Exponential Equivalents. The values of hyperbolic functions may be computed from their exponential equivalents:

$$\sinh \theta = \frac{e^\theta - e^{-\theta}}{2} \qquad \cosh \theta = \frac{e^\theta + e^{-\theta}}{2} \qquad \tanh \theta = \frac{e^\theta - e^{-\theta}}{e^\theta + e^{-\theta}}$$

The graphs are shown in Fig. 16. If θ is extremely small, $\sinh \theta \approx \theta$, $\cosh \theta \approx 1$, and $\tanh \theta \approx \theta$. For large values of θ, $\sinh \theta \approx \cosh \theta$, and $\tanh \theta \approx \coth \theta \approx 1$.

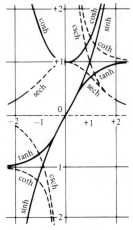

Figure 16

Fundamental Identities. Fundamental identities for hyperbolic functions are:

$$\cosh \theta = \frac{1}{\sinh \theta} \quad \text{sech } \theta = \frac{1}{\cosh \theta} \quad \coth \theta = \frac{1}{\tanh \theta}$$

$$\cosh^2 \theta - \sinh^2 \theta = 1 \quad \text{sech}^2 \theta = 1 - \tanh^2 \theta \quad \text{csch}^2 \theta = \coth^2 \theta - 1$$

$$\cosh \theta + \sinh \theta = e^{\theta} \quad \cosh \theta - \sinh \theta = e^{-\theta}$$

$$\sinh(-\theta) = -\sinh \theta \quad \cosh(-\theta) = \cosh \theta$$

$$\tanh(-\theta) = -\tanh \theta \quad \coth(-\theta) = -\coth \theta$$

$$\sinh(\theta_1 \pm \theta_2) = \sinh \theta_1 \cosh \theta_2 \pm \cosh \theta_1 \sinh \theta_2$$

$$\cosh(\theta_1 \pm \theta_2) = \cosh \theta_1 \cosh \theta_2 \pm \sinh \theta_1 \sinh \theta_2$$

$$\tanh(\theta_1 \pm \theta_2) = \frac{\tanh \theta_1 \pm \tanh \theta_2}{1 \pm \tanh \theta_1 \tanh \theta_2}$$

$$\coth(\theta_1 \pm \theta_2) = \frac{1 \pm \coth \theta_1 \coth \theta_2}{\coth \theta_1 \pm \coth \theta_2}$$

$$\sinh 2\theta = 2 \sinh \theta \cosh \theta = \frac{2 \tanh \theta}{1 - \tanh^2 \theta}$$

$$\cosh 2\theta = \sinh^2 \theta + \cosh^2 \theta = 1 + 2 \sinh^2 \theta = 2 \cosh^2 \theta - 1$$

$$= \frac{1 + \tanh^2 \theta}{1 - \tanh^2 \theta}$$

$$\tanh 2\theta = \frac{2 \tanh \theta}{1 + \tanh^2 \theta} \quad \coth 2\theta = \frac{1 + \coth^2 \theta}{2 \coth \theta}$$

$$\sinh \theta/2 = \sqrt{(\cosh \theta - 1)/2} \quad \cosh \theta/2 = \sqrt{(\cosh \theta + 1)/2}$$

$$\tanh \theta/2 = \sqrt{\frac{\cosh \theta - 1}{\cosh \theta + 1}} = \frac{\sinh \theta}{\cosh \theta + 1} = \frac{\cosh \theta - 1}{\sinh \theta}$$

$$\sinh \theta_1 \pm \sinh \theta_2 = 2 \sinh \frac{(\theta_1 \pm \theta_2)}{2} \cosh \frac{(\theta_1 \mp \theta_2)}{2}$$

$$\cosh \theta_1 + \cosh \theta_2 = 2 \cosh \frac{(\theta_1 + \theta_2)}{2} \cosh \frac{(\theta_1 - \theta_2)}{2}$$

$$\cosh \theta_1 - \cosh \theta_2 = 2 \sinh \frac{(\theta_1 + \theta_2)}{2} \sinh \frac{(\theta_1 - \theta_2)}{2}$$

$$\tanh \theta_1 \pm \tanh \theta_2 = \frac{\sinh (\theta_1 \pm \theta_2)}{\cosh \theta_1 \cosh \theta_2}$$

$$(\cosh \theta \pm \sinh \theta)^n = \cosh n\theta \pm \sinh n\theta$$

Antihyperbolic or Inverse Functions. The inverse hyperbolic sine of u is written as $\sinh^{-1} u$. Values of the inverse functions may be computed from their logarithmic equivalents:

$$\sinh^{-1} u = \log_e (u + \sqrt{u^2 + 1})$$
$$\cosh^{-1} u = \log_e (u + \sqrt{u^2 - 1})$$
$$\tanh^{-1} u = \tfrac{1}{2} \log_e \frac{1 + u}{1 - u}$$
$$\coth^{-1} u = \tfrac{1}{2} \log_e \frac{u + 1}{u - 1}$$

5
Plane Analytic Geometry

COORDINATES

The position of a point P_1 in a plane can be determined when its distance and direction from each of two perpendicular axes, OX and OY, are known. The distances x and y perpendicular to the axes are the cartesian or rectangular coordinates of the point (Fig. 1). The directions to the right of OY and above OX are positive; opposite directions are negative. The point O of intersection of OY and OX is the origin.

The position of a point P can be determined by its distance r from the origin and the angle θ between r and OX (Fig. 2). Coordinates r and θ are polar coordinates.

Transformation of Coordinates. To change the origin O to O', denote the coordinates of a point P by (x, y) with respect to the old axes, and by (x', y') with respect to the new axes (Fig. 3). If the coordinates of the new origin O' with respect to the old axes are $x = h, y = k$, the relationship between the old and new coordinates becomes:

$$\left. \begin{array}{l} x = x' + h \\ y = y' + k \end{array} \right\}$$

Rotation of Axes. To rotate the axes about the origin, assume θ (Fig. 4) to be the angle through which the axes are rotated. Then:

$$\left. \begin{array}{l} x = x' \cos \theta - y' \sin \theta \\ y = x' \sin \theta + y' \cos \theta \end{array} \right\}$$

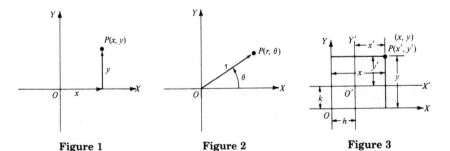

| Figure 1 | Figure 2 | Figure 3 |

If the axes are both translated and rotated, then:

$$\left.\begin{array}{l} x = x' \cos \theta - y' \sin \theta + h \\ y = x' \sin \theta + y' \cos \theta + k \end{array}\right\}$$

Coordinate Transformation. The relationship between the rectangular coordinates x and y and the polar coordinates r and θ are:

$$x = r \cos \theta \qquad y = r \sin \theta \qquad r = \sqrt{x^2 + y^2} \qquad \theta = \tan^{-1} \frac{y}{x}$$

STRAIGHT LINES

Equation of a Straight Line. Linear equations with respect to the coordinates represent straight lines. Conversely, the equation of an arbitrary straight line is a first-degree equation. The general equation of a straight line is $Ax + By + C = 0$. If $A = 0$, then the line is parallel to the x axis (Fig. 5). If $B = 0$, the line is parallel to the y axis, and if $C = 0$, the line passes through the origin. When a straight line is not parallel to the y axis (Fig. 6), its equation can be reduced to the form, $y = kx + b$, where k is the slope equal to $\tan \delta$, where δ is the angle between the line and the positive direction of the x axis and where b is the intercept on the y axis, with a corresponding sign.

Distance of Two Points. The distance between the points $P_1(x_1, y_1)$ and $P_2(x_2, y_2)$ in Fig. 7 is determined by, $d = \sqrt{(x_2 - x_1)^2 + (y_2 - y_1)^2}$. If polar coordinates are given as $P_1(\rho_1, \varphi_1)$, $P_2(\rho_2, \phi_2)$ as shown in Fig. 8, then, $d = \sqrt{\rho_1^2 + \rho_2^2 - 2\rho_1\rho_2 \cos(\phi_2 - \phi_1)}$.

Division of a Segment. To divide a segment in a given ratio (Fig. 9), coordinates of a point P defined as:

$$\frac{P_1 P}{P P_2} = \frac{m}{n} = \lambda$$

are given by:

$$x = \frac{nx_1 + mx_2}{n + m} = \frac{x_1 + \lambda x_2}{1 + \lambda} \qquad y = \frac{ny_1 + my_2}{n + m} = \frac{y_1 + \lambda y_2}{1 + \lambda}$$

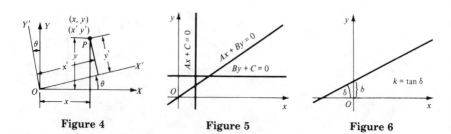

| Figure 4 | Figure 5 | Figure 6 |

Coordinates of the midpoint of the segment P_1P_2 are given by:

$$x = \frac{x_1 + x_2}{2} \qquad y = \frac{y_1 + y_2}{2}$$

The equation of a straight line through a known point $P_1(x_1, y_1)$ in a known direction (Fig. 10) is, $y - y_1 = k(x - x_1)$, where $k = \tan \delta$. The equation of a straight line through two known points $P_1(x_1, y_1)$ and $P_2(x_2, y_2)$ (Fig. 11) is:

$$\frac{y - y_1}{y_2 - y_1} = \frac{x - x_1}{x_2 - x_1}$$

Intercept of a Straight Line. If a straight line intersects the coordinate axes at points $A(a, 0)$ and $B(0, b)$, as shown in Fig. 12, its equation is:

$$\frac{x}{a} + \frac{y}{b} = 1$$

The normal equation of a straight line is given by $x \cos \alpha + y \sin \alpha - p = 0$, where p is the distance of the line from the origin, and α is the angle between a perpendicular line through the origin and the x axis ($p > 0$, $0 < \alpha < 2\pi$) (Fig. 13).

Intersecting Lines. Coordinates (x_0, y_0) of an intersecting point of two straight lines are obtained by simultaneous solution of their equations. Let $A_1x + B_1y + C_1 = 0$ and $A_2x + B_2y + C_2 = 0$ be the equations of two straight lines. Then:

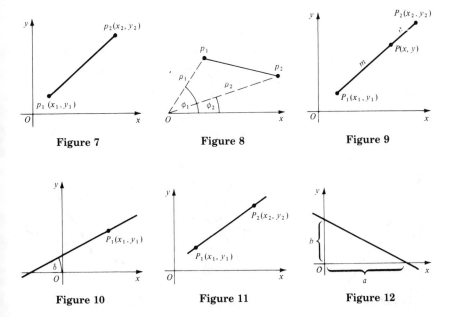

Figure 7   Figure 8   Figure 9

Figure 10   Figure 11   Figure 12

$$x_0 = \begin{vmatrix} B_1 & C_1 \\ B_2 & C_2 \end{vmatrix} : \begin{vmatrix} A_1 & B_1 \\ A_2 & B_2 \end{vmatrix} \qquad y_0 = \begin{vmatrix} C_1 & A_1 \\ C_2 & A_2 \end{vmatrix} : \begin{vmatrix} A_1 & B_1 \\ A_2 & B_2 \end{vmatrix}$$

Further, the lines are parallel, if:

$$\begin{vmatrix} A_1 & B_1 \\ A_2 & B_2 \end{vmatrix} = 0$$

The lines coincide if:

$$\frac{A_1}{A_2} = \frac{B_1}{B_2} = \frac{C_1}{C_2}$$

A third line, $A_3x + B_3y + C_3 = 0$, passes through the point of intersection of the first two lines, as shown in Fig. 14, if:

$$\begin{vmatrix} A_1 & B_1 & C_1 \\ A_2 & B_2 & C_2 \\ A_3 & B_3 & C_3 \end{vmatrix} = 0$$

The equation of any straight line passing through the point of intersection of two lines is $(A_1x + B_1y + C_1) + \lambda(A_2x + B_2y + C_2) = 0$, with λ an arbitrary real number. The equation represents a system of lines through the point of intersection.

Angle Between Two Lines. The angle ϕ between two straight lines, as shown in Fig. 15, can be determined as follows. If the equations of the lines are given in the general form:

$$A_1x + B_1y + C_1 = 0 \qquad A_2x + B_2y + C_2 = 0$$

then

$$\tan \phi = \frac{A_1B_2 - A_2B_1}{A_1A_2 + B_1B_2}$$

$$\cos \phi = \frac{A_1A_2 + B_1B_2}{\sqrt{A_1^2 + B_1^2}\sqrt{A_2^2 + B_2^2}}$$

$$\sin \phi = \frac{A_1B_2 - A_2B_1}{\sqrt{A_1^2 + B_1^2}\sqrt{A_2^2 + B_2^2}}$$

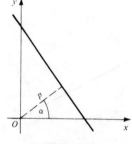

Figure 13

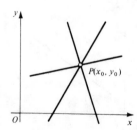

Figure 14

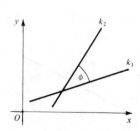

Figure 15

If the slopes k_1 and k_2 are known, then:

$$\tan \phi = \frac{k_2 - k_1}{1 + k_1 k_2}$$

$$\cos \phi = \frac{1 + k_1 k_2}{\sqrt{1 + k_1^2}\sqrt{1 + k_2^2}}$$

$$\sin \phi = \frac{k_2 - k_1}{\sqrt{1 + k_1^2}\sqrt{1 + k_2^2}}$$

with the angle ϕ measured counterclockwise between the first and second lines. The straight lines are parallel, as shown in Fig. 16(a), if:

$$\frac{A_1}{A_2} = \frac{B_1}{B_2}$$

or

$$k_1 = k_2$$

The straight lines are perpendicular, as shown in Fig. 16(b), if:

$$A_1 A_2 + B_1 B_2 = 0 \quad \text{or} \quad k_2 = -\frac{1}{k_1}$$

The equation of a straight line in polar coordinates, as described in Fig. 17, is given by:

$$\rho = \frac{p}{\cos(\phi - \alpha)}$$

where p is the perpendicular distance of the line from the pole, and α is the angle between the polar axis and perpendicular line.

Area of a Triangle. The area of a triangle (Fig. 18) having vertices $P_1(x_1, y_1)$, $P_2(x_2, y_2)$ and $P_3(x_3, y_3)$ can be determined by the following formula:

$$S = \tfrac{1}{2}\begin{vmatrix} x_1 & y_1 & 1 \\ x_2 & y_2 & 1 \\ x_3 & y_3 & 1 \end{vmatrix} = \tfrac{1}{2}(x_1(y_2 - y_3) + x_2(y_3 - y_1) + x_3(y_1 - y_2))$$

$$= \tfrac{1}{2}((x_1 - x_2)(y_1 + y_2) + (x_2 - x_3)(y_2 + y_3) + (x_3 - x_1)(y_3 + y_1))$$

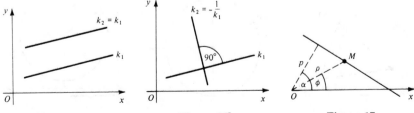

| Figure 16a | Figure 16b | Figure 17 |

The area of a polygon with vertices $P_1(x_1, y_1), P_2(x_2, y_2), \ldots, P_n(x_n, y_n)$ is given by:

$$S = \tfrac{1}{2}((x_1 - x_2)(y_1 + y_2) + (x_2 - x_3)(y_2 + y_3) + \cdots + (x_n - x_1)(y_n + y_1))$$

The area of a triangle or polygon thus obtained will be positive if the vertices are numbered counterclockwise and negative if numbered clockwise.

CONIC SECTIONS

A conic section is a curve traced by a moving point P in a plane. The distance PF of the moving point from a fixed point (focus) is in constant ratio to the distance PM of the point from a fixed line, called the directrix, in the plane of the curve. The ratio:

$$e = \frac{PF}{PM}$$

is known as the eccentricity; when $e < 1$, the curve is an ellipse, when $e = 1$, a parabola and when $e > 1$, a hyperbola. For a circle, which is a special case of an ellipse, $e = 0$.

Circle. In Cartesian coordinates, the equation of a circle of the radius R with the center at the origin (Fig. 19a) is $x^2 + y^2 = R^2$.

The equation of a circle of the radius R with the center $C(x_0, y_0)$ (Fig. 19b) is $(x - x_0)^2 + (y - y_0)^2 = R^2$. A general second-degree equation $ax^2 + 2bxy + cy^2 + 2dx + 2ey + f = 0$ represents a circle only if $b = 0$ and $a = c$. Under these conditions, the equation can be reduced to the form $x^2 + y^2 + 2mx + 2ny + q = 0$. The radius $R = \sqrt{m^2 + n^2 - q}$, and the coordinates of the center $x_0 = -m$ and $y_0 = -n$. If $q > m^2 + n^2$, the equation represents no real curve, and if $q = m^2 + n^2$, the equation is satisfied by a single point, $M(x_0, y_0)$.

The equation of a circle in parametric form is:

$$x = x_0 + R \cos t \qquad y = y_0 + R \sin t$$

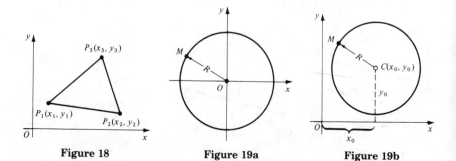

| Figure 18 | Figure 19a | Figure 19b |

where t is the angle between the moving radius and the positive direction of the x axis, as shown in Fig. 20.

A general equation of a circle (Fig. 21) in polar coordinates is, $\rho^2 - 2\rho\rho_0 \cos(\phi - \phi_0) + \rho_0^2 = R^2$. If the center lies on the polar axis and the circle passes through the origin, as shown in Fig. 22, the equation has the form, $\rho = 2R \cos \phi$.

Ellipse. The equation of an ellipse (Fig. 23) is:

$$\frac{(x - x_0)^2}{a^2} + \frac{(y - y_0)^2}{b^2} = 1$$

where (x_0, y_0) is the center, a = semimajor axis, and b = semiminor axis. In Fig. 23, $(x_0, y_0) = (0, 0)$. The coordinates of foci are $F_1 = (-ae, 0)$, $F_2 = (ae, 0)$, and:

$$e^2 = \frac{(F_1 P)^2}{(MP)^2} = 1 - \frac{b^2}{a^2} < 1$$

The directrices are the lines $x = -\dfrac{a}{e}$ and $x = \dfrac{a}{e}$. The chord LL' through F in Fig. 23 is the latus rectum with length:

$$\frac{2b^2}{a} = 2a(1 - e^2)$$

If P_1 is a point on the ellipse, $F_1P_1 = a - ex_1$, $F_2P_1 = a + ex_1$, and $F_1P_1 + F_2P_1 = 2a$ (a constant). The area of the ellipse with semi-axes a and b is $A = \pi ab$. The tangent to the ellipse, as shown in Fig. 23, at point (x_1, y_1) is represented by:

$$\frac{xx_1}{a^2} + \frac{yy_1}{b^2} = 1$$

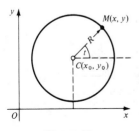

Figure 20

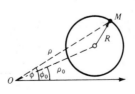

Figure 21

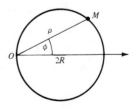

Figure 22

and the equation of the tangent with slope m is:

$$y = mx \pm \sqrt{a^2 m^2 + b^2}$$

The normal to the ellipse at the point (x_1, y_1) is represented by the equation:

$$a^2 y_1 (x - x_1) - b^2 x_1 (y - y_1) = 0$$

A line through the center of an ellipse is a diameter; if the slopes m and m' of the two diameters $y = mx$ and $y = m'x$ are characterized in a manner that:

$$mm' = -\frac{b^2}{a^2}$$

each diameter bisects all parallel chords and the diameters are conjugate. Other forms of the equation of the ellipse are given as:

$$\frac{x^2}{a^2} + \frac{y^2}{a^2(1 - e^2)} = 1$$

and

$$ax^2 + by^2 + 2gx + 2fy + c = 0$$

If a, b, and:

$$\left(\frac{g^2}{a} + \frac{f^2}{b} \right) - c$$

have the same sign, the equation $ax^2 + by^2 + 2gx + 2fy + c = 0$ is an ellipse with axes parallel to the coordinate axes. The parametric form is:

$$x = a \cos \phi \qquad y = b \sin \phi$$

Hyperbola. A hyperbola is the locus of a point with a constant ($= 2a$) difference in distances from two fixed points (the foci). The points as determined by $r_1 - r_2 = 2a$ belong to one branch of the hyperbola, the left branch in Fig. 24, and the points determined by $r_2 - r_1 = 2a$ belong to the other branch. Each distance, the focal radius vector of a point of hyperbola with the abscissa x, is expressed by the formula $r_1 = \pm (ex - a)$, $r_2 = \pm (ex + a)$, and $r_2 - r_1 = \pm 2a$.

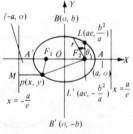

Figure 23

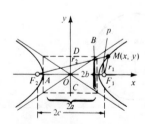

Figure 24

The elements of a hyperbola, as shown in Fig. 24, are:

- The transverse (real) axis $AB (= 2a)$
- The vertices A, B
- The center O
- The foci F_1 and F_2 which are the points on the transversal axis on both sides of the center at the distance c (greater than a) from the center
- The conjugate (imaginary) axis $CD (= 2b = 2\sqrt{c^2 - a^2})$
- The semi-latus rectum p, which is one half of the chord passing through a focus and perpendicular to the transverse axis:

$$p = \frac{b^2}{a}$$

- The eccentricity $e = \frac{c}{a} > 1$

The equation of a hyperbola, if the x axis coincides with the transverse axis of hyperbola, is:

$$\frac{x^2}{a^2} - \frac{y^2}{b^2} = 1$$

In parametric form:

$$x = a \cosh t \qquad y = b \sinh t \qquad \text{or} \qquad x = a \sec t \qquad y = b \tan t$$

Directrices of the hyperbola are straight lines parallel to the transverse axis at the distance from the center of $d = \dfrac{a}{e}$ (Fig. 25). For a point $M(x, y)$ of the hyperbola:

$$\frac{r_1}{d_1} = \frac{r_2}{d_2} = e$$

A tangent line to a hyperbola (Fig. 26) at $M(x_0, y_0)$ has the equation:

$$\frac{xx_0}{a^2} - \frac{yy_0}{b^2} = 1$$

The tangent line and normal line to a hyperbola are bisectors of the interior and exterior angles, respectively, between the focal radius vectors of the point of contact. The line $Ax + By + C = 0$ forms a tangent to the hyperbola if $A^2 a^2 - B^2 b^2 = C^2$.

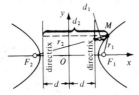

Figure 25

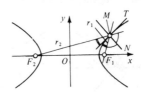

Figure 26

Asymptotes of hyperbola, as shown in Fig. 27, are straight lines that are approached by the branches of a hyperbola as the coordinates approach infinity. The slope, k, of asymptotes is represented by:

$$k = \pm \tan \delta = \pm \frac{b}{a}$$

The equation of both asymptotes is:

$$y = \pm \frac{b}{a} x$$

A point of contact M bisects the segment of a tangent TT_1 between the asymptotes, $TM = MT_1$. The area of the triangle TOT_1 between the tangents and the asymptotes equals ab for every point M. If the lines MF and MG pass parallel to the asymptotes through a point M of hyperbola, the area $OFMG = \frac{1}{4}(a^2 + b^2) = \frac{1}{4}c^2$. Conjugate hyperbolas are shown in Fig. 28 and are represented by:

$$\frac{x^2}{a^2} - \frac{y^2}{b^2} = 1 \quad \text{and} \quad \frac{y^2}{b^2} - \frac{x^2}{a^2} = 1$$

They have common asymptotes. The transverse axis of each is the conjugate axis of the other.

Diameters are chords of a given hyperbola and of its conjugate passing through the center and are bisected by the center. Two diameters with the slopes k and k' are conjugate if:

$$k' = \frac{b^2}{a^2}$$

and the conjugate diameters bisect the corresponding chords of the given hyperbola and of its conjugate (Fig. 29). If the lengths of two conjugate diameters are $2a_1$ and $2b_1$ and α and β are the acute angles between the diameters and the transverse axis ($\alpha > \beta$), then $a_1^2 - b_1^2 = a^2 - b^2$ and $ab = a_1 b_1 \sin (\alpha - \beta)$.

The radius of curvature of a hyperbola at the point $M(x_0, y_0)$ is represented by:

$$R = a^2 b^2 \left(\frac{x_0^2}{a^4} + \frac{y_0^2}{b^4} \right)^{3/2} = \frac{(r_1 r_2)^{3/2}}{ab} = \frac{p}{\sin^3 u}$$

where u represents the angle between the tangent and a radius vector of the contact point. At the vertices A and B, as shown in Fig. 24, $R = p = b^2/a$.

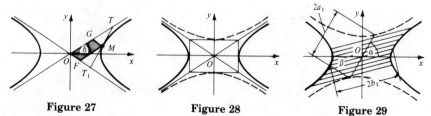

| Figure 27 | Figure 28 | Figure 29 |

The area of a segment of hyperbola, as shown in Fig. 30, is represented by the equation:

$$AMN = xy - ab \ln \left(\frac{x}{a} + \frac{y}{b} \right) = xy - ab \text{ ar cosh } \frac{x}{a}$$

The area of $OAMG = \frac{1}{4}ab + \frac{1}{2}ab \ln \dfrac{2OG}{c}$, when MG is parallel to an asymptote.

An equilateral hyperbola is a hyperbola with equal axes, $a = b$; its equation is $x^2 - y^2 = a^2$. Asymptotes of an equilateral hyperbola are perpendicular. The equation of an equilateral hyperbola (Fig. 31), with reference to its axes, is $xy = \frac{1}{2}a^2$.

Parabola. The equation of the parabola is $(y - y_0)^2 = 4a(x - x_0)$. If $(x_0, y_0) = (0, 0)$, the vertex is at the origin, as shown in Fig. 32. The focus F is on OX, the axis of the parabola, and the focus has the coordinates $(a, 0)$. The directrix is $x = -a$. The chord LL' through F is the latus rectum with length $4a$. The eccentricity is:

$$e = \frac{FP}{PM} = 1$$

The tangent to the parabola $y^2 = 4ax$ at the point (x_1, y_1) is $yy_1 = 2a(x + x_1)$. The equation of the tangent with slope m is:

$$y = mx + \frac{a}{m}$$

The normal to the parabola at the point (x_1, y_1) is $2a(y - y_1) + y_1(x - x_1) = 0$.

A diameter of the parabola is a straight line parallel to the axis. It bisects all chords parallel to the line tangent at the point at which the diameter meets the parabola.

If $P_1 T$ is tangent to the curve at (x_1, y_1), then $TQ = 2x_1$ is the subtangent, and $QN = 2a$ (a constant) is the subnormal, where $P_1 N$ is perpendicular to $P_1 T$. A parabola whose axis is parallel to OX is represented by $y^2 + 2gx + 2fy + c = 0$, where $g \neq 0$. The equation $x^2 + 2gx + 2fy + c = 0$, where $f \neq 0$, is a parabola with axis parallel to OY. A parabola oriented in reference to the tangents at the extremities of its latus rectum as axes of coordinates is, $x^{1/2} \pm y^{1/2} = b^{1/2}$, where b is the distance from the origin to each tangent.

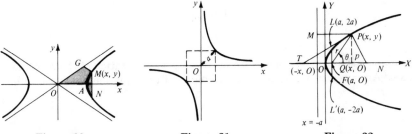

Figure 30   Figure 31   Figure 32

Polar Equations of the Conics. The polar equations are:
For an ellipse, hyperbola, or parabola:

$$r = \frac{ep}{1 \mp e \cos \theta}$$

For an ellipse or circle:

$$r = \frac{a(1 - e^2)}{1 \mp e \cos \theta}$$

For the hyperbola:

$$r = \frac{a(e^2 - 1)}{1 \mp e \cos \theta}$$

when e is the eccentricity; the directrix is vertical; the focus is at a distance p to the right or left of it, respectively; and the polar origin is taken at the focus. If the directrix is horizontal and the focus is at a distance p above or below it, respectively, the polar equations are as follows:

For an ellipse, hyperbola, or parabola:

$$r = \frac{ep}{1 \mp e \sin \theta}$$

For an ellipse or circle:

$$r = \frac{a(1 - e^2)}{1 \mp e \sin \theta}$$

For the hyperbola:

$$r = \frac{a(e^2 - 1)}{1 \mp e \sin \theta}$$

General Equation of Conic Sections. The general equation of conic sections (curves of the second degree) is:

$$ax^2 + 2bxy + cy^2 + 2dx + 2ey + f = 0$$

The equation can represent an ellipse, in particular, a circle; a hyperbola; a parabola; or a pair of straight lines, which is a degenerate curve of the second degree. The invariants of a curve of the second degree:

$$\Delta = \begin{vmatrix} a & b & d \\ b & c & e \\ d & e & f \end{vmatrix} \qquad \delta = \begin{vmatrix} a & b \\ b & c \end{vmatrix} = ac - b^2 \qquad S = a + c$$

remain unchanged by translation of the origin and rotation of the coordinate axes. After a transformation of coordinates, if the equation of the curve has the form:

$$a'x'^2 + 2b'x'y' + c'y'^2 + 2d'x' + 2e'y' + f' = 0$$

the values of Δ, δ, S computed in the new coordinates remain the same.

DEFINING PLANE CURVES USING DIFFERENTIAL CALCULUS

Plane curves, or space curves and surfaces, can be analyzed by using the methods of differential calculus. The functions involved in the equations are assumed to be continuous with continuous derivatives up to a certain required order. In dealing with geometrical objects described by their equations, distinctions are made between (a) properties that depend on the choice of a coordinate system, for example, points of intersection of the curve with the coordinate axes, the slope of a tangent line, maxima and minima, and (b) invariant properties that are not disturbed by transformations of coordinates. The latter depend only on the curve or surface itself such as points of inflection, vertices or curvature of a curve. Distinctions also are made, however, between the local properties that concern only small parts of a curve or a surface, such as curvature and linear element of a surface, and the properties of a curve or surface in the whole, such as number of vertices and length of a closed curve.

A plane curve can be defined analytically in Cartesian coordinates in the following forms:

- Implicit form $F(x, y) = 0$
- Explicit form $y = f(x)$
- Parametric form $x = x(t)$, $y = y(t)$

In polar coordinates, a curve can be defined in the form $\rho = f(\theta)$.

The positive direction of a curve in parametric form is the direction a point $Mx(t)$, $y(t)$ of the curve moves when the parameter t increases. For a curve in explicit form, the abscissa x can be taken as a parameter, $x = x$, $y = f(x)$, and the positive direction of the curve corresponds to the positive direction of the x axis. If the curve is given in polar coordinates, the angle θ can be taken as a parameter: $x = f(\theta) \cos \theta$, $y = f(\theta) \sin \theta$ and the positive direction of the curve corresponds to the increasing θ, that is, counterclockwise. For example, in Fig. 33(a), $x = t^2$, $y = t^3$; in Fig. 33(b), $y = \sin x$; and in Fig. 33(c), $\rho = a\theta$.

Plane Curves. A point (x, y) defines a plane curve if x and y are continuous functions of a variable t, as $x = x(t)$, $y = y(t)$. The elimination of t from the two equations gives $F(x, y) = 0$ or, in explicit form, $y = f(x)$. The angle τ (Fig. 34), formed by a tangent to the curve and the axis OX, can be found from:

$$\sin \tau = \frac{dy}{ds} \qquad \cos \tau = \frac{dx}{ds} \qquad \tan \tau = \frac{dy}{dx} = y'$$

where ds is the element of arc length:

$$ds = \sqrt{dx^2 + dy^2} = \sqrt{1 + y'^2}\, dx$$

In polar coordinates:

$$ds = \sqrt{dr^2 + r^2 d\theta^2} = \sqrt{\left(\frac{dr}{d\theta}\right)^2 \theta p + r^2}$$

From Fig. 34, the following can be derived:

$$\sin \psi = \frac{r d\theta}{ds} \qquad \cos \psi = \frac{dr}{ds} \qquad \tan \psi = \frac{r d\theta}{dr}$$

For the tangent to the curve $F(x, y) = 0$ at the point (x_1, y_1), the equation is:

$$\left(\frac{\partial F}{\partial x}\right)_{x=x_1,\, y=y_1} (x - x_1) + \left(\frac{\partial F}{\partial y}\right)_{x=x_1,\, y=y_1} (y - y_1) = 0$$

and for the normal to the curve $F(x, y) = 0$ at the point (x_1, y_1), the equation is:

$$\left(\frac{\partial F}{\partial y}\right)_{x=x_1,\, y=y_1} (x - x_1) - \left(\frac{\partial F}{\partial x}\right)_{x=x_1,\, y=y_1} (y - y_1) = 0$$

For the tangent to the curve $y = f(x)$ at the point (x_1, y_1), the equation is:

$$y - y_1 = \left(\frac{dy}{dx}\right)_{x=x_1} (x - x_1)$$

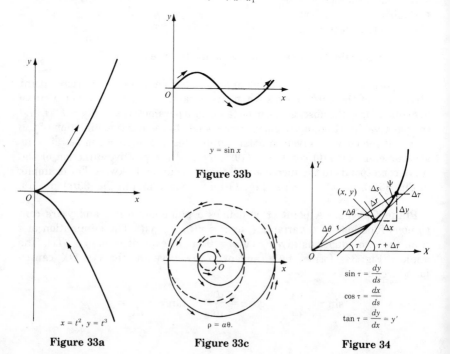

$y = \sin x$

Figure 33b

$x = t^2, \ y = t^3$

Figure 33a

$\rho = a\theta.$

Figure 33c

$$\sin \tau = \frac{dy}{ds}$$

$$\cos \tau = \frac{dx}{ds}$$

$$\tan \tau = \frac{dy}{dx} = y'$$

Figure 34

and for the normal to the curve $y = f(x)$ at the point (x_1, y_1), the equation is:

$$y - y_1 = -\frac{1}{\left(\dfrac{dy}{dx}\right)_{x=x_1}}(x - x_1)$$

At the point (x, y), the radius of curvature of the curve is:

$$\rho = \frac{ds}{dr} = \frac{\left[1 + \left(\dfrac{dy}{dx}\right)^2\right]^{3/2}}{\dfrac{d^2y}{dx^2}} = \frac{[1 + y'^2]^{3/2}}{y''}$$

The curvature of the curve at (x, y) is the reciprocal $1/\rho$. For the center of curvature for the point (x, y) on the curve, with the center of the circle of curvature tangent to the curve at (x, y) and of radius ρ, the coordinates (x_0, y_0) are:

$$x_0 = x - \rho\frac{dy}{ds} = x - y'\frac{[1 + y'^2]}{y''}$$

$$y_0 = y + \rho\frac{dx}{ds} = y + \frac{[1 + y'^2]}{y''}$$

If simultaneously:

$$F(x, y) = 0 \qquad \frac{\partial F}{\partial x} = 0 \qquad \frac{\partial F}{\partial y} = 0$$

then a curve has a singular point. For the expression:

$$D = \left(\frac{\partial^2 F}{\partial x\, \partial y}\right)^2 - \frac{\partial^2 F}{\partial x^2}\frac{\partial^2 F}{\partial y^2}$$

The curve has a double point with two real different tangents, when $D > 0$, a cusp with two coincident tangents when $D = 0$, and an isolated point with no real tangent when $D < 0$.

REFERENCE CURVES

Curtate Cycloid
$a > b$

Prolate Cycloid
$a < b$

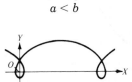

Semicubic, or Neil's, Parabola
$$y^2 = ax^3$$

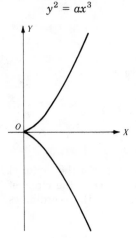

Strophoid
$$y^2 = \frac{x^2(a + x)}{a - x}$$
$$r = a(\sec\theta - \tan\theta)$$

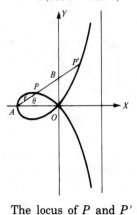

Cissoid of Diocles
$$y^2 = \frac{x^3}{a - x}$$
$$r = a(\sec\theta - \cos\theta)$$
Locus of point P such that $OP = AB$.

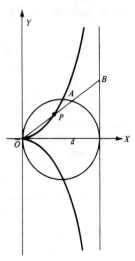

The locus of P and P' is the strophoid, if the line AB rotates about A, intersecting the y axis at B, and if $PB = BP' = OB$.

Conchoid of Nicomedes
$$(x^2 + y^2)(x - b)^2 = a^2x^2$$
$$r = b\sec\theta - a$$

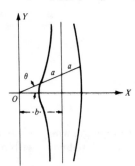

Cardioid
Limaçon in which $b = 2a$
Epicycloid in which $R = a$
$$r = 2a(1 + \cos\theta)$$
$$(x^2 + y^2 - 2ax)^2 = 4a^2(x^2 + y^2)$$

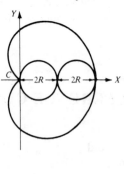

Limaçon of Pascal
$$b > 2a$$
$$r = b + 2a\cos\theta$$

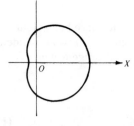

Exponential Curve
$$y = b^x$$

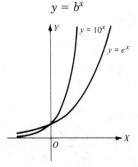

Other forms of the right-hand side of the equation, $b + 2a\sin\theta$, $b - 2a\cos\theta$, $b - 2a\sin\theta$, give curves rotated through 1, 2, 3 right angles, respectively.

Limaçon of Pascal
$b < 2a$

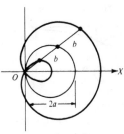

Witch of Agnesi
$$y = \frac{8a^3}{x^2 + 4a^2}$$
$x = 2a \tan \phi$
$y = 2a \cos^2 \phi$

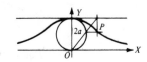

Logarithmic Curve
$y = \log_b x$

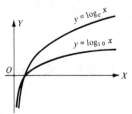

Folium of Descartes
$x^3 + y^3 - 3axy = 0$

$$r = \frac{3a \sin \theta \cos \theta}{\sin^3 \theta + \cos^3 \theta}$$

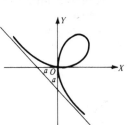

Three-leaved Roses
$r = a \cos 3\theta$

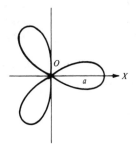

Three-leaved Roses
$r = a \sin 3\theta$

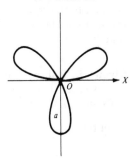

Four-leaved Roses
$r = a \sin 2\theta$

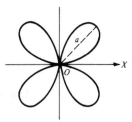

Damped Wave
$y = e^{-ax} \cos(\omega x + \theta)$

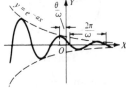

Four-leaved Roses
$r = a \cos 2\theta$

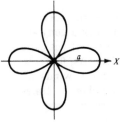

The roses, $r = a \sin n\theta$ and $r = a \cos n\theta$, have, for n even, $2n$ leaves; for n odd, n leaves.

Hypocycloid of Four Cusps, or Astroid
$b = a = \frac{1}{4}R$
$x = R \cos^3 \phi$
$y = R \sin^3 \phi$
$x^{2/3} + y^{2/3} = R^{2/3}$

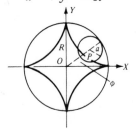

Epicycloid
$b = a$

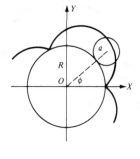

Lemniscate of Bernoulli
$$(x^2 + y^2)^2 + 2c^2(y^2 - x^2) = 0$$
$$r^2 = 2c^2 \cos 2\theta$$

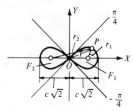

Locus of a point P, the product of whose distances from two fixed points F_1 and F_2 is equal to the square of half the distance between them, that is $r_1 \cdot r_2 = c^2$.

Circles in Polar Coordinates
$$\text{Center } (0, 0) \quad r = a$$
$$\text{Center } (a, 0) \quad r = 2a \cos \theta$$
$$\text{Center } \left(a, \frac{\pi}{2} \right) \quad r = 2a \sin \theta$$

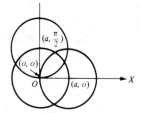

Tractrix
$$x = a \cosh^{-1} \frac{a}{y} - \sqrt{a^2 - y^2}$$

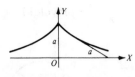

Locus of one end P of tangent line of length a as the other end Q is moved along the x axis.

Hyperbolic, or Reciprocal, Spiral
$$r\theta = a$$

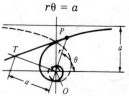

Polar subtangent $OT = -a$
A $\theta \to \infty$, $r \to 0$. The curve winds an indefinite number of times around the origin. As $\theta \to 0$, $r \to \infty$. The curve has an asymptote parallel to the polar axis at a distance a.

Logarithmic, or Equiangular, Spiral
$$r = ae^{m\theta}, m > 0$$
or
$$\ln \frac{r}{a} = m\theta$$

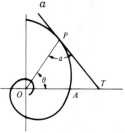

The tangent to the curve at any point makes a constant angle $\alpha (= \cot^{-1} m)$ with the radius vector. As $\theta \to -\infty$, $r \to 0$. The curve winds an indefinite number of times around the origin.

Circles in Polar Coordinates
$$r^2 + b^2 - 2rb \cos(\theta - \alpha) = a^2$$
Center at (b, α), radius a

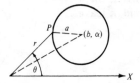

Spiral of Archimedes
$$r = a\theta$$
Polar subnormal $ON = a$
Length of arc $OP = s =$
$\frac{1}{2}a(\theta\sqrt{1 + \theta^2} + \sinh^{-1}\theta)$
For many turns, $s \approx \frac{1}{2}a\theta^2$

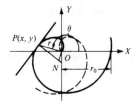

Cycloid
$$a = b$$
$$x = a(\phi - \sin \phi)$$
$$y = a(1 - \cos \phi)$$
$$x = a \cos^{-1} \frac{a - y}{a} \pm \sqrt{(2a - y)y}$$

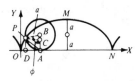

For one arch, arc length $= 8a$,
area $= 3\pi a^2$

Catenary
$$y = \frac{a}{2}(e^{x/a} + e^{-x/a}) = a \cosh \frac{x}{a}$$
For l large compared with d:
$$s \approx l\left[1 + \frac{2}{3}\left(\frac{2d}{l}\right)^2\right]$$

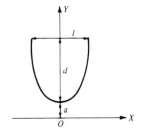

Involute of a Circle
$$x = a(\cos \phi + \phi \sin \phi)$$
$$y = a(\sin \phi - \phi \cos \phi)$$
$$\theta = \sqrt{r^2/a^2 - 1} - \tan^{-1}\sqrt{r^2/a^2 - 1}$$
(Spiral traced by the end of a taut
string unwinding from a circle)

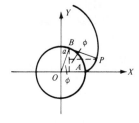

Frequency-Modulated Wave
$$y = k \cos[\phi(t)]$$

Instantaneous frequency $= \Omega(t) = \dfrac{d\phi}{dt}$

$$y = \cos \frac{\pi}{2}t^2 \qquad \Omega(t) = \pi t$$

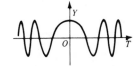

Trochoid. A trochoid is traced by a point at a distance b from the center of a circle with radius a as the circle rolls along a straight line:

$$x = a\phi - b \sin \phi \qquad y = a - b \cos \phi$$

Hypotrochoid. A hypotrochoid is traced by a point at a distance b from the center of a circle with radius a as the circle rolls inside a fixed circle with radius R:

$$x = (R - a) \cos \phi + b \cos \frac{R - a}{a} \phi \qquad y = (R - a) \sin \phi - b \sin \frac{R - a}{a} \phi$$

Epitrochoid. An epitrochoid is traced by a point at a distance b from the center of a circle with radius a as the circle rolls outside a fixed circle with radius R:

$$x = (R + a) \cos \phi - b \cos \frac{R + a}{a} \phi \qquad y = (R + a) \sin \phi - b \sin \frac{R + a}{a} \phi$$

6
Solid Analytic Geometry

COORDINATES

In a right-hand rectangular coordinate system, the position of a point $P(x, y, z)$ is fixed by distances x, y, z from perpendicular planes yz, xz, and xy, respectively, as shown in Fig. 1.

In a spherical, or polar coordinate system, a point $P(r, \theta, \phi)$ is fixed by its distance from a known point O, the origin, and its direction from O, determined by the angles θ and ϕ, as shown in Fig. 2.

In a cylindrical system, a point $P(\rho, \phi, z)$ is determined by its distance z from a given plane and by the polar coordinates (ρ, ϕ) of the projection Q of P on the plane. Among coordinates of the three systems, the following relationships hold:

$$x = r \sin \theta \cos \phi = \rho \cos \phi$$
$$y = r \sin \theta \sin \phi = \rho \sin \phi$$
$$z = r \cos \theta$$
$$\rho = \sqrt{x^2 + y^2} = r \sin \theta$$
$$\phi = \tan^{-1} \frac{y}{x}$$
$$r = \sqrt{x^2 + y^2 + z^2} = \sqrt{\rho^2 + z^2}$$
$$\theta = \tan^{-1} \frac{\sqrt{x^2 + y^2}}{z} = \tan^{-1} \frac{\rho}{z}$$

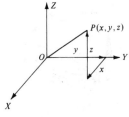

Figure 1

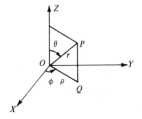

Figure 2

TRANSFORMATION OF COORDINATES

To transform rectangular coordinates, denote x, y, z as the old coordinates; x', y', z' as the new coordinates; and a, b, c as the coordinates of the new origin in the old coordinates. For a parallel translation (Fig. 3):

$$x = x' + a$$
$$x' = x - a$$
$$y = y' + b$$
$$y' = y - b$$
$$z = z' + c$$
$$z' = z - c$$

Rotation of the Axes. If the direction cosines of the new axes, as shown in Fig. 4, are denoted as follows, with respect to the old axes x, y and z:

	x'	y'	z'
x	l_1	l_2	l_3
y	m_1	m_2	m_3
z	n_1	n_2	n_3

Then

$$x = l_1 x' + l_2 y' + l_3 z'$$
$$y = m_1 x' + m_2 y' + m_3 z'$$
$$z = n_1 x' + n_2 y' + n_3 z'$$
$$x' = l_1 x + m_1 y + n_1 z$$
$$y' = l_2 x + m_2 y + n_2 z$$
$$z' = l_3 x + m_3 y + n_3 z$$

The following is a determinant of the transformation:

$$\Delta = \begin{vmatrix} l_1 & l_2 & l_3 \\ m_1 & m_2 & m_3 \\ n_1 & n_2 & n_3 \end{vmatrix}$$

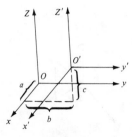

Figure 3

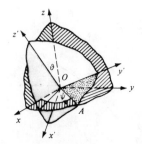

Figure 4

POINTS, LINES, AND PLANES

The distance between two points $P_1(x_1, y_1, z_1)$ and $P_2(x_2, y_2, z_2)$ is:

$$d = \sqrt{(x_2 - x_1)^2 + (y_2 - y_1)^2 + (z_2 - z_1)^2}$$

To divide the segment P_1P_2 in the ratio c_1/c_2, internally or externally:

$$x = \frac{c_2 x_1 \pm c_1 x_2}{c_2 \pm c_1}$$

$$y = \frac{c_2 y_1 \pm c_1 y_2}{c_2 \pm c_1}$$

$$z = \frac{c_2 z_1 \pm c_1 z_2}{c_2 \pm c_1}$$

The midpoint of P_1P_2 is:

$$x = \frac{x_1 + x_2}{2}$$

$$y = \frac{y_1 + y_2}{2}$$

$$z = \frac{z_1 + z_2}{2}$$

The direction cosines of a line are the cosines of the angles α, β, γ that the line or any parallel line forms with the coordinate axes. The direction cosines of the line segment $P_1(x_1, y_1, z_1)$ to $P_2(x_2, y_2, z_2)$ are:

$$\cos \alpha = \frac{x_2 - x_1}{d}$$

$$\cos \beta = \frac{y_2 - y_1}{d}$$

$$\cos \gamma = \frac{z_2 - z_1}{d}$$

If $\cos \alpha : \cos \beta : \cos \gamma = a : b : c$, then:

$$\cos \alpha = \frac{a}{\sqrt{a^2 + b^2 + c^2}}$$

$$\cos \beta = \frac{b}{\sqrt{a^2 + b^2 + c^2}}$$

$$\cos \gamma = \frac{c}{\sqrt{a^2 + b^2 + c^2}}$$

$$\cos^2 \alpha + \cos^2 \beta + \cos^2 \gamma = 1$$

The angle θ between two lines, whose direction angles are α_1, β_1, γ_1 and α_2, β_2, γ_2, respectively, is given by $\cos \theta = \cos \alpha_1 \cos \alpha_2 + \cos \beta_1 \cos \beta_2 + \cos \gamma_1 \cos \gamma_2$. A plane is represented by $Ax + By + Cz + D = 0$, where A, B, C are proportional to the direction cosines of a normal—a line perpendicular to the plane—to the plane.

The angle between two planes is the angle between their normals. The equation of a straight line through the point $P_1(x_1, y_1, z_1)$ is:

$$\frac{x - x_1}{a} = \frac{y - y_1}{b} = \frac{z - z_1}{c}$$

where a, b, c are proportional to the direction cosines of the line and are called direction numbers of the line.

A plane through the points $P_1(x_1, y_1, z_1)$, $P_2(x_2, y_2, z_2)$, and $P_3(x_3, y_3, z_3)$ has the equation:

$$\begin{vmatrix} x & y & z & 1 \\ x_1 & y_1 & z_1 & 1 \\ x_2 & y_2 & z_2 & 1 \\ x_3 & y_3 & z_3 & 1 \end{vmatrix} = 0$$

A plane whose x, y, z intercepts are respectively a, b, c (Fig. 5) is described by the equation:

$$\frac{x}{a} + \frac{y}{b} + \frac{z}{c} = 1$$

The equation of a plane in a perpendicular form, where $OP = p$ in the perpendicular distance of the plane from the origin O and the direction angles are α, β, γ, is:

$$x \cos \alpha + y \cos \beta + z \cos \gamma - p = 0$$

To transform the general form $Ax + By + Cz + D = 0$ into perpendicular form, the general form is divided by $\pm \sqrt{A^2 + B^2 + C^2}$, where the sign in front of the radical is opposite that of D.

Coefficients A, B, C are proportional to direction cosines λ, μ, ν of a line perpendicular to the plane. Thus, the expression:

$$A(x - x_1) + B(y - y_1) + C(z - z_1) = 0$$

describes a plane through $P_1(x_1, y_1, z_1)$ perpendicular to a line with direction cosines λ, μ, ν proportional to A, B, C.

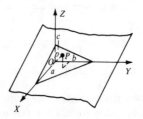

Figure 5

The perpendicular distance of a point P_1 from a plane $Ax + By + Cz + D = 0$ is given by:

$$PP_1 = \frac{Ax_1 + By_1 + Cz_1 + D}{\pm \sqrt{A^2 + B^2 + C^2}}$$

with the sign before the radical opposite to that of D.

Parallel Planes. Two planes $A_1x + B_1y + C_1z + D_1 = 0$ and $A_2x + B_2y + C_2z + D_2 = 0$ are parallel if $A_1:B_1:C_1 = A_2:B_2:C_2$. The equation:

$$A(x - x_1) + B(y - y_1) + C(z - z_1) = 0$$

describes a plane through point $P_1(x_1, y_1, z_1)$ parallel to the plane $Ax + By + Cz + D = 0$.

Between two planes, represented by $Ax + By + Cz + D = 0$ and $A_1x + B_1y + C_1z + D_1 = 0$, angle θ is the angle between two intersecting lines, each perpendicular to one of the planes, and:

$$\cos \theta = \frac{AA_1 + BB_1 + CC_1}{\pm \sqrt{(A^2 + B^2 + C^2)(A_1^2 + B_1^2 + C_1^2)}}$$

If $AA_1 + BB_1 + CC_1 = 0$, the two planes are perpendicular.

Four points lie in the same plane if:

$$\begin{vmatrix} 1 & x_1 & y_1 & z_1 \\ 1 & x_2 & y_2 & z_2 \\ 1 & x_3 & y_3 & z_3 \\ 1 & x_4 & y_4 & z_4 \end{vmatrix} = 0$$

Four planes pass through the same point if:

$$\begin{vmatrix} A_1 & B_1 & C_1 & D_1 \\ A_2 & B_2 & C_2 & D_2 \\ A_3 & B_3 & C_3 & D_3 \\ A_4 & B_4 & C_4 & D_4 \end{vmatrix} = 0$$

A straight line can be represented as the intersection of two planes by two first-degree equations:

$$\left. \begin{array}{l} A_1x + B_1y + C_1z + D_1 = 0 \\ A_2x + B_2y + C_2z + D_2 = 0 \end{array} \right\}$$

A line through two points (x_1, y_1, z_1) and (x_2, y_2, z_2) is represented by the equations:

$$\frac{x - x_1}{x_2 - x_1} = \frac{y - y_1}{y_2 - y_1} = \frac{z - z_1}{z_2 - z_1}$$

Intersection of Two Planes. The direction cosines λ, μ, ν of the line of intersection of two planes $Ax + By + Cz + D = 0$ and $A_1x + B_1y + C_1z + D_1 = 0$ are described by the ratios:

$$\lambda : \mu : \nu = \begin{vmatrix} B & C \\ B_1 & C_1 \end{vmatrix} : \begin{vmatrix} C & A \\ C_1 & A_1 \end{vmatrix} : \begin{vmatrix} A & B \\ A_1 & B_1 \end{vmatrix}$$

The equation of a plane passing through the line of intersection of two planes (Fig. 6) is:

$$A_1 x + B_1 y + C_1 z + D_1 = 0$$
$$A_2 x + B_2 y + C_2 z + D_2 = 0$$
$$A_1 x + B_1 y + C_1 z + D_1 + \lambda(A_2 x + B_2 y + C_2 z + D_2) = 0$$

SURFACES OF THE SECOND DEGREE (QUADRIC SURFACES)

In the following equations, the center of the surface, the point bisecting all chords passing through it, lies at the origin, and the coordinate axes are the axes of symmetry of the surface. The coordinate planes are planes of symmetry.

Ellipsoid. For an ellipsoid, shown in Fig. 7, the equation is:

$$\frac{x^2}{a^2} + \frac{y^2}{b^2} + \frac{z^2}{c^2} = 1$$

where a, b, c are the semiaxes. If $a = b > c$, the result is a flattened ellipsoid of revolution, or a flattened spheroid (Fig. 8), obtained by revolving an ellipse:

$$\frac{x^2}{a^2} + \frac{z^2}{c^2} = 1$$

in the xz plane about its minor axis. If $a = b < c$, the result is a lengthened ellipsoid of revolution, as shown in Fig. 9, obtained by revolving the ellipse:

$$\frac{x^2}{a^2} + \frac{z^2}{c^2} = 1$$

in the xz plane about its major axis. If $a = b = c$, a sphere results:

$$x^2 + y^2 + z^2 = a^2$$

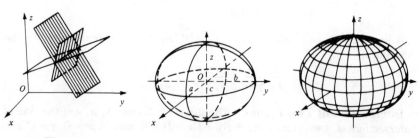

| Figure 6 | Figure 7 | Figure 8 |

Hyperboloids. A hyperboloid of one sheet (Fig. 10) is described by:

$$\frac{x^2}{a^2} + \frac{y^2}{b^2} - \frac{z^2}{c^2} = 1$$

where a and b are the real semiaxes and c is the imaginary semiaxis. A hyperboloid of two sheets (Fig. 11) is given by:

$$\frac{x^2}{a^2} + \frac{y^2}{b^2} - \frac{z^2}{c^2} = -1$$

where c is the real semiaxis and a and b are the imaginary semiaxes. For both types, the plane sections parallel to the z axis are hyperbolas, and the plane sections parallel to the xy plane are ellipses.

If $a = b$, the hyperboloid can be obtained by revolving a hyperbola with the semiaxes a and c about the axis $2c$. A hyperboloid of one sheet results from revolving the hyperbola about the real (transverse) axis, and a hyperboloid of two sheets is the result of revolving the hyperbola about the imaginary, or conjugate, axis.

Cones. A cone, represented by:

$$\frac{x^2}{a^2} + \frac{y^2}{b^2} - \frac{z^2}{c^2} = 0$$

has its vertex at the origin (Fig. 12). Its directing curve can be viewed as an ellipse with semiaxes a and b lying in a plane that is perpendicular to the z axis at a distance c from the origin.

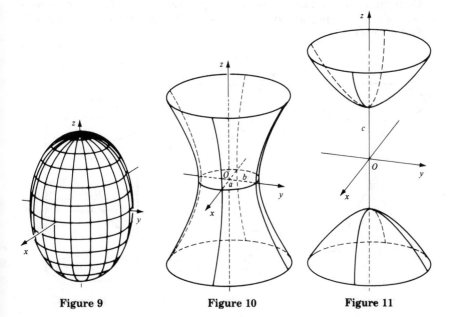

Figure 9   Figure 10   Figure 11

Paraboloids. For an elliptic paraboloid (Fig. 13):

$$z = \frac{x^2}{a^2} + \frac{y^2}{b^2}$$

Plane sections parallel to the z axis are in the form of parabolas, and sections parallel to the xy plane are ellipses. When $a = b$, a paraboloid of revolution is formed by revolving the parabola $z = x^2/a^2$ lying in the xz plane about its axis. For a hyperbolic paraboloid (Fig. 14):

$$z = \frac{x^2}{a^2} - \frac{y^2}{b^2}$$

Sections parallel to the yz plane and to the xz plane are all equal parabolas. Sections parallel to the xy plane take the form of hyperbolas or a pair of intersecting straight lines.

Cylinders. An elliptic cylinder, as shown in Fig. 15, is described by:

$$\frac{x^2}{a^2} + \frac{y^2}{b^2} = 1$$

A hyperbolic cylinder, as shown in Fig. 16, is described by:

$$\frac{x^2}{a^2} - \frac{y^2}{b^2} = 1$$

A parabolic cylinder, shown in Fig. 17, takes the form:

$$y^2 = 2px$$

Generators of Surfaces. Rectilinear generators of surfaces can be seen as straight lines lying wholly on the surface, the generators of a cone or a cylinder, for example.

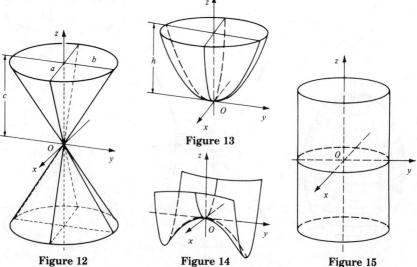

Figure 12

Figure 13

Figure 14

Figure 15

A hyperboloid of one sheet (Fig. 18):

$$\frac{x^2}{a^2} + \frac{y^2}{b^2} - \frac{z^2}{c^2} = 1$$

has two families of generators:

$$\frac{x}{a} + \frac{z}{c} = u\left(1 + \frac{y}{b}\right)$$

$$u\left(\frac{x}{a} - \frac{z}{c}\right) = 1 - \frac{y}{b}$$

and

$$\frac{x}{a} + \frac{z}{c} = v\left(1 - \frac{y}{b}\right)$$

$$v\left(\frac{x}{a} - \frac{z}{c}\right) = 1 + \frac{y}{b}$$

where u and v are arbitrary numbers.

A hyperbolic paraboloid (Fig. 19):

$$z = \frac{x^2}{a^2} - \frac{y^2}{b^2}$$

has also two families of generators:

$$\frac{x}{a} + \frac{y}{b} = u$$

$$u\left(\frac{x}{a} - \frac{y}{b}\right) = z$$

and

$$\frac{x}{a} - \frac{y}{b} = v$$

$$v\left(\frac{x}{a} + \frac{y}{b}\right) = z$$

where u and v are arbitrary numbers. Two generators pass through each point of these surfaces, one of either family.

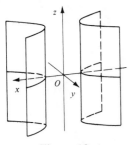

Figure 16

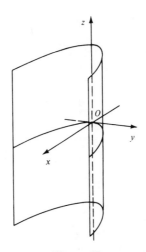

Figure 18

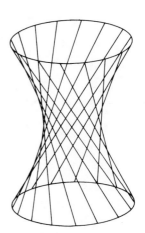

Figure 17

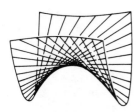

Figure 19

General Equation. The general equation of a surface of the second degree is given as:

$$a_{11}x^2 + a_{22}y^2 + a_{33}z^2 + 2a_{12}xy + 2a_{23}yz + 2a_{31}zx$$
$$+ 2a_{14}x + 2a_{24}y + 2a_{34}z + a_{44} = 0$$

Invariants of a surface of the second degree, that is, quantities that remain unchanged when the origin is translated and the coordinate axes are rotated, are:

$$\Delta = \begin{vmatrix} a_{11} & a_{12} & a_{13} & a_{14} \\ a_{21} & a_{22} & a_{23} & a_{24} \\ a_{31} & a_{32} & a_{33} & a_{34} \\ a_{41} & a_{42} & a_{43} & a_{44} \end{vmatrix}$$

$$\delta = \begin{vmatrix} a_{11} & a_{12} & a_{13} \\ a_{21} & a_{22} & a_{23} \\ a_{31} & a_{32} & a_{33} \end{vmatrix}$$

$$S = a_{11} + a_{22} + a_{33}$$
$$T = a_{22}a_{33} + a_{33}a_{11} + a_{11}a_{22} - a_{23}^2 - a_{31}^2 - a_{12}^2$$

7
Differential Calculus

BASIC CONCEPTS

Function. When variables x and y are related in such a way that for each value of x in a given domain there is a corresponding value of y, then y is a function of x. That is, x is the independent variable and y the dependent variable. Such symbols as $F(x)$, $f(x)$ and $\phi(x)$ denote functions of x, and the symbol $f(a)$ denotes the value of $f(x)$ for $x = a$.

Limits. The function $f(x)$ approaches the limit 1 as x approaches a if, within a sufficiently small interval with a as midpoint, the difference $|f(x) - 1|$ can be made arbitrarily small for all values of x except a. Symbolically, this limitation is expressed as $\lim_{x \to a} f(x) = 1$.

The symbols $\lim_{x \to a} f(x) = \infty$ or $\lim_{x \to a} f(x) = -\infty$ mean that $f(x)$ can be made arbitrarily large positively or negatively, respectively, for all values of x except a within a small interval with a as midpoint.

The symbols $\lim_{x \to \infty} f(x) = 1$ or $\lim_{x \to -\infty} f(x) = 1$ mean that the difference $|f(x) - 1|$ can be made arbitrarily small for all sufficiently large values of x, positively or negatively, respectively.

Changes in x are called increments of x and are denoted by Δx, and the corresponding changes in y are denoted by Δy. If the relationship:

$$\lim_{\Delta x \to 0} \frac{f(x + \Delta x) - f(x)}{\Delta x}$$

exists, it is called the derivative of y with respect to x and is denoted by $\frac{dy}{dx}$, $f'(x)$, or $D_x y$.

Geometric Interpretation of the Derivative. If $y = f(x)$ is represented by a graph in Cartesian coordinates, as shown in Fig. 1, then $f'(x) = \tan \alpha$, where α lies between the x axis and the line tangent to the curve in the given point, with the angle measured counterclockwise.

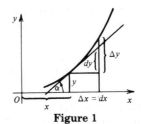

Figure 1

The derivative $f'(x)$ exists for these values of x for which the function $f(x)$ is defined and continuous, and the considered ratio has a finite limit. If, for a value x_1, the derivative does not exist, no definite tangent line exists at the corresponding point of the graph of the function, or the tangent is perpendicular to the x axis. In the latter case, the limit is infinite and is expressed as $f'(x_1) = \infty$; that is, the derivative becomes infinite. For example, the derivative does not exist for the following:

$$f(x) = \sqrt[3]{x} \qquad f'(x) = \frac{1}{3\sqrt[3]{x^2}} \qquad f'(0) = \infty$$

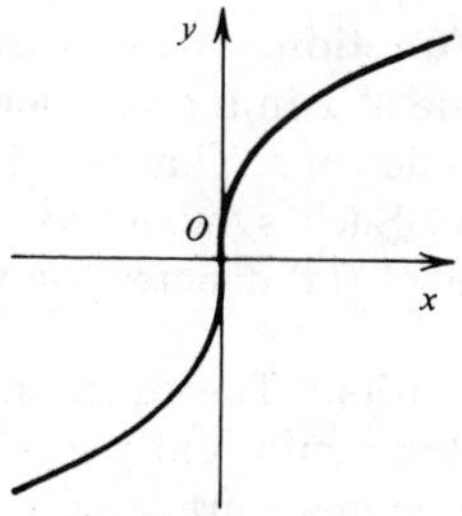

Figure 2

because the derivative becomes infinite at the point 0 (Fig. 2).

Derivative of a Function of a Function. If y is a function of a variable u and if u is a function of another variable x, then:

$$\frac{dy}{dx} = \frac{dy}{du}\frac{du}{dx}$$

Derivative of an Inverse Function. If $y = f_1(x)$ is solved for x, then the solution of $x = f_2(y)$ is termed its inverse. For example, the expression $x = \sin^{-1}y$ is the inverse of $y = \sin x$ and $x = \pm\sqrt{y}$ is the inverse of $y = x^2$. Symbolically:

$$\frac{dy}{dx} = \frac{1}{\dfrac{dx}{dy}} \quad \text{or} \quad f_2'(y) = \frac{1}{f'_1(x)}$$

Derivatives of Second and Higher Order. The derivative of the first derivative of y with respect to x is termed the second derivative of y with respect to x. If $y = f(x)$, the second derivative with respect to x is denoted variously by:

$$\frac{d^2y}{dx^2} \qquad D_{x^2}y \qquad \frac{dy'}{dx} \qquad f''(x) \qquad y'' \qquad \ddot{y}$$

Similarly, the derivative with respect to x of the second derivative is called the third derivative and may be denoted by:

$$\frac{d^3y}{dx^3} \qquad D_x^3 y \qquad f^{(3)}(x) \qquad y^{(3)}$$

For example, to find the mth derivative of x^n, note the following sequence of derivatives:

$$y' = nx^{n-1}$$
$$y'' = n(n-1)x^{n-2}$$
$$y^{(3)} = n(n-1)(n-2)x^{n-3}$$

It can be seen that:

$$y^{(m)} = n(n-1)(n-2) \cdots (n-m+1)x^{n-m}$$

Differentials. If the curve AB in Fig. 3 is defined by $y = f(x)$, and $P(x, y)$ and $Q(x + \Delta x, y + \Delta y)$ are nearby points, then as Q is moved toward P, Δx and Δy approach zero. The limiting position of the line PQ is the tangent at P. The slope of the tangent is $\dfrac{dy}{dx}$, which is the limit of the ratio $\Delta y/\Delta x$ as $\Delta x \to 0$. That is, dy represents the increment of the ordinate of the tangent at P for a given increment dx at P, whereas Δy is the increment of the ordinate to the curve AB.

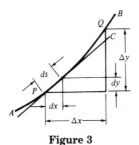

Figure 3

The increments dx and dy are termed differentials. For a function $y = f(x)$, the differential equals its derivative multiplied by the differential of the independent variable, $dy = f'(x) dx$. The length of the line PQ in Fig. 3 is given by $(\Delta s)^2 = (\Delta x)^2 + (\Delta y)^2$. Similarly, the differential length of curve is given as:

$$ds^2 = dx^2 + dy^2$$
$$ds = \sqrt{1 + y'^2} \qquad dx = \sqrt{1 + x'^2}\, dy$$

In polar coordinates:

$$ds = \sqrt{d\rho^2 + \rho^2 d\theta} = \sqrt{\rho^2 + \left(\frac{d\rho}{d\theta}\right)^2}\, d\theta$$

Implicit Functions. The expression $F(x, y) = 0$ defines y as an implicit function of x, and x as an implicit function of y. When an equation is solved for y in terms of x, $y = f(x)$, then y becomes an explicit function of x. For example, as an implicit function, $F(x, y) = x^2 + y^2 - r^2 = 0$, and as an explicit function, $y = \pm\sqrt{r^2 - x^2}$. To find $\dfrac{dy}{dx}$, differentiate $y = f(x)$ or use as an alternative method:

$$\frac{dy}{dx} = -\frac{\dfrac{\partial F}{\partial x}}{\dfrac{\partial F}{\partial y}} \quad \left(\frac{\partial F}{\partial y} \neq 0\right)$$

and

$$\frac{d^2y}{dx^2} = -\frac{\dfrac{\partial^2 F}{\partial x^2}\left(\dfrac{\partial F}{\partial y}\right)^2 - 2\dfrac{\partial^2 F}{\partial x \partial y}\dfrac{\partial F}{\partial x}\dfrac{\partial F}{\partial y} + \dfrac{\partial^2 F}{\partial y^2}\left(\dfrac{\partial F}{\partial x}\right)^2}{\left(\dfrac{\partial F}{\partial y}\right)^3} \quad \left(\frac{\partial F}{y} \neq 0\right)$$

Differentiation of Parametric Functions. If a function is given in parametric form, to find the derivatives of y with respect to x if $y = y(t)$ and $x = x(t)$ use:

$$y' = \frac{dy}{dx} = \frac{\dfrac{dy}{dt}}{\dfrac{dx}{dt}} \qquad y'' = \frac{d^2y}{dx^2} = \frac{\dfrac{dy'}{dt}}{\dfrac{dx}{dt}} \qquad y^{(n)} = \frac{d^n y}{dx^n} = \frac{\dfrac{dy^{(n-1)}}{dt}}{\dfrac{dx}{dt}}$$

To find the derivatives of y with respect to x for the ellipse $x = a\cos t$, $y = b\sin t$, use the following relationships:

$$y' = \frac{dy}{dx} = \frac{b\cos t}{-a\sin t} = -\frac{b}{a}\cot t$$

$$y'' = \frac{dy'}{dx} = \frac{\dfrac{b}{a}\csc^2 t}{-a\sin t} = -\frac{b}{a^2}\csc^3 t$$

$$y''' = \frac{dy''}{dx} = \frac{\dfrac{3b}{a^2}\csc^3 t\cot t}{-a\sin t} = -\frac{3b}{a^3}\csc^4 t\cot t$$

Logarithmic Differentiation for Products and Quotients. If:

$$y = \frac{u^l v^m}{w^n}$$

express both sides of the equation in terms of logarithms before differentiating:

$$\ln y = l \ln u + m \ln v - n \ln w$$

$$\frac{1}{y}\frac{dy}{dx} = \frac{l}{u}\frac{du}{dx} + \frac{m}{v}\frac{dv}{dx} - \frac{n}{w}\frac{dw}{dx}$$

$$\frac{dy}{dx} = y\left(\frac{l}{u}\frac{du}{dx} + \frac{m}{v}\frac{dv}{dx} - \frac{n}{w}\frac{dw}{dx}\right)$$

For example, to find $\dfrac{dy}{dx}$ if $y = \dfrac{\sqrt{x^2 - 25}}{(x-1)^3(x+5)^2}$, use the following relationships:

$$\ln y = \tfrac{1}{2}\ln(x^2 - 25) - 3\ln(x-1) - 2\ln(x+5)$$

$$\frac{1}{y}\frac{dy}{dx} = \frac{2x}{2(x^2 - 25)} - \frac{3}{x-1} - \frac{2}{x+5}$$

$$\frac{dy}{dx} = \frac{y(-4x^2 + 11x + 65)}{(x^2 - 25)(x-1)}$$

INDETERMINATE FORMS

If a function $f(x)$ for $x = a$, where a can also be ∞, has no determined value but appears in a meaningless form, such as $\dfrac{0}{0}, \dfrac{\infty}{\infty}, \ 0\cdot\infty, \ \infty - \infty, \ 0^0, \ \infty^0, \ 0^\infty$

or 1^∞, then the $\lim f(x)$ may have a definite value. To determine this limiting value, if it exists, the following rules can be applied.

L'Hôpital's Rule for Indeterminate Forms. If $f(x)/g(x)$ approaches $0/0$ or ∞/∞ as $x \to a$ and if $f(x)$ and $g(x)$ have derivatives of all orders up to n, then the limit, if it exists, of $f(x)/g(x)$ equals the first of the following limits that is not indeterminate:

$$\lim\left[\frac{f'(x)}{g'(x)}\right]_{x\to a}; \lim\left[\frac{f''(x)}{g''(x)}\right]_{x\to a}; \cdots; \lim\left[\frac{f^{(n)}(x)}{g^{(n)}(x)}\right]_{x\to a}$$

If the first of these limits becomes infinite, then $f(x)/g(x)$ also becomes infinite. For example, to evaluate $\lim[(x^2 - 4)/(x^2 + x - 6)]_{x\to 2},$ substitute $x = 2$ in this function. Because it takes the form $0/0$, apply l'Hôpital's rule; differentiate numerator and denominator:

$$\lim\left[\frac{x^2 - 4}{x^2 + x - 6}\right]_{x\to 2} = \left[\frac{2x}{2x+1}\right]_{x\to 2} = \frac{4}{5}$$

In an evaluation of $\lim[(x + \log x)/x \log x]_{x\to\infty}$, as x increases without bound, the function approaches ∞/∞. Differentiate numerator and denominator:

$$\lim\left[\frac{x + \log x}{x \log x}\right]_{x\to\infty} = \left[\frac{1 + 1/x}{\log x + 1}\right]_{x\to\infty} = 0$$

As $x \to \infty$, the numerator approaches 1, but the denominator approaches ∞; thus, the limit is zero.

Evaluation of Form $0 \cdot \infty$. If, as $x \to a$, $f(x)g(x) \to 0 \cdot \infty$, place the product in the form:

$$\frac{f(x)}{1/g(x)} \quad \text{or} \quad \frac{g(x)}{1/f(x)}$$

so that it approaches $0/0$ or ∞/∞. Then find the limit, if one exists, by l'Hôpital's rule.

Evaluation of Form $\infty - \infty$. If, as $x \to a$ and $f(x) - g(x) \to \infty - \infty$, transform the function into one of the forms $0/0$ or ∞/∞. Then find the limit by l'Hôpital's rule.

To determine $\lim (\csc \theta - \cot \theta)$ as $\theta \to 0$ from the positive side, substitute $\theta = 0$ in this function; it takes the form $\infty - \infty$. Rewrite it in the form:

$$\csc \theta - \cot \theta = \frac{1}{\sin \theta} - \frac{\cos \theta}{\sin \theta} = \frac{1 - \cos \theta}{\sin \theta}$$

The function on the right approaches $0/0$ as $\theta \to 0$. Differentiating the numerator and denominator with $\theta \to 0^+$ obtains:

$$\lim[\csc \theta - \cot \theta]_{\theta \to 0^+} = \left[\frac{\sin \theta}{\cos \theta}\right]_{\theta \to 0^+} = 0$$

Evaluation of Forms 0^0, 1^∞, ∞^0. If, as $x \to a$, $y = f(x)^{y(x)} \to 0^0$, 1^∞, or ∞^0, the logarithm of both sides of the equation can be used to reduce the expression:

$$\log_e y = g(x) \log_e f(x)$$

Thus, the expression approaches $0 \cdot \infty$ as $x \to a$ and can be rewritten as:

$$\log_e y = \frac{\log_e f(x)}{1/g(x)}$$

L'Hôpital's rule can be applied to find the limit of $\log_e y$. If this limit is z, then $y = e^z$.

DIFFERENTIATION FORMULAS

Basic differentiation formulas for algebraic and transcendental functions are as follows (Functions of x are represented by u, v, w; a and n are constants; and e is the base of the natural or Napierian logarithms; $e = 2.7183^-$):

Algebraic functions

$$\frac{d}{dx} a = 0 \qquad\qquad \frac{d}{dx}(u + v + w + \cdots) = \frac{du}{dx} + \frac{dv}{dx} + \frac{dw}{dx} + \cdots$$

$$\frac{d}{dx}\,au = a\,\frac{du}{dx}$$

$$\frac{d}{dx}\,uv = u\,\frac{dv}{dx} + v\,\frac{du}{dx}$$

$$\frac{d}{dx}\,(uvw\cdots) = \left(\frac{1}{u}\,\frac{du}{dx} + \frac{1}{v}\,\frac{dv}{dx} + \frac{1}{w}\,\frac{dw}{dx} + \cdots\right)(uvw\cdots)$$

$$\frac{d}{dx}\left(\frac{u}{v}\right) = \frac{v\,\dfrac{du}{dx} - u\,\dfrac{dv}{dx}}{v^2}$$

$$\frac{d}{dx}\,u^n = nu^{n-1}\,\frac{du}{dx}$$

Transcendental functions

$$\frac{d}{dx}\,\log_e u = \frac{1}{u}\,\frac{du}{dx}$$

$$\frac{d}{dx}\,\log_{10} u = \frac{1}{u}\,\frac{du}{dx}\,\log_{10} e = (0.4343)\,\frac{1}{u}\,\frac{du}{dx}$$

$$\frac{d}{dx}\,e^u = e^u\,\frac{du}{dx}$$

$$\frac{d}{dx}\,u^v = vu^{v-1}\,\frac{du}{dx} + u^v\,\frac{dv}{dx}\,\log_e u$$

$$\frac{d}{dx}\,f(u) = \frac{df(u)}{du}\cdot\frac{du}{dx}$$

$$\frac{d^2 f(u)}{dx^2} = \frac{df(u)}{du}\cdot\frac{d^2 u}{dx^2} + \frac{d^2 f(u)}{du^2}\left(\frac{du}{dx}\right)^2$$

$$\frac{d}{dx}\,\sin u = \cos u\,\frac{du}{dx}$$

$$\frac{d}{dx}\,\cos u = -\sin u\,\frac{du}{dx}$$

$$\frac{d}{dx}\,\tan u = \sec^2 u\,\frac{du}{dx}$$

$$\frac{d}{dx}\,\cot u = -\csc^2 u\,\frac{du}{dx}$$

$$\frac{d}{dx}\,\sec u = \sec u\,\tan u\,\frac{du}{dx}$$

$$\frac{d}{dx}\,\csc u = -\csc u\,\cot u\,\frac{du}{dx}$$

$$\frac{d}{dx}\,\sin^{-1} u = \frac{1}{\sqrt{1 - u^2}}\,\frac{du}{dx}\left(-\frac{\pi}{2} \leq \sin^{-1} u \leq \frac{\pi}{2}\right)$$

$$\frac{d}{dx}\cos^{-1}u = \frac{1}{\sqrt{1-u^2}}\frac{du}{dx}\ (0 \le \cos^{-1}u \le \pi)$$

$$\frac{d}{dx}\tan^{-1}u = \frac{1}{1+u^2}\frac{du}{dx}$$

$$\frac{d}{dx}\cot^{-1}u = -\frac{1}{1+u^2}\frac{du}{dx}$$

$$\frac{d}{dx}\sec^{-1}u = \frac{1}{u\sqrt{u^2-1}}\frac{du}{dx}\ *$$

$$\frac{d}{dx}\csc^{-1}u = -\frac{1}{u\sqrt{u^2-1}}\frac{du}{dx}\ *$$

$$\frac{d}{dx}\sinh u = \cosh u\frac{du}{dx}$$

$$\frac{d}{dx}\cosh u = \sinh u\frac{du}{dx}$$

$$\frac{d}{dx}\tanh u = \operatorname{sech}^2 u\frac{du}{dx}$$

$$\frac{d}{dx}\coth u = -\operatorname{csch}^2 u\frac{du}{dx}$$

$$\frac{d}{dx}\operatorname{sech} u = -\operatorname{sech} u\tanh u\frac{du}{dx}$$

$$\frac{d}{dx}\operatorname{csch} u = -\operatorname{csch} u\coth u\frac{du}{dx}$$

$$\frac{d}{dx}\sinh^{-1}u = \frac{1}{\sqrt{u^2+1}}\frac{du}{dx}$$

$$\frac{d}{dx}\cosh^{-1}u = \frac{1}{\sqrt{u^2-1}}\frac{du}{dx}$$

$$\frac{d}{dx}\tanh^{-1}u = \frac{1}{1-u^2}\frac{du}{dx}$$

$$\frac{d}{dx}\coth^{-1}u = \frac{1}{1-u^2}\frac{du}{dx}$$

$$\frac{d}{dx}\operatorname{sech}^{-1}u = -\frac{1}{u\sqrt{1-u^2}}\frac{du}{dx}$$

$$\frac{d}{dx}\operatorname{csch}^{-1}u = -\frac{1}{u\sqrt{u^2+1}}\frac{du}{dx}$$

PARTIAL DERIVATIVES

If three variables $f(x, y)$, x, y are related in such a way that for each set of values of x and y in a given domain there exists a corresponding value of $f(x, y)$, then $f(x, y)$ is a function of x and y. If x is the only variable and y is a constant, then the derivative of $f(x, y)$ with respect to x becomes the partial derivative of f with respect to x and is given as:

$$\frac{\partial f}{\partial x} = f_x = \lim_{\Delta x \to 0}\frac{f(x + \Delta x, y) - f(x, y)}{\Delta x}$$

Similarly, the partial derivative of f with respect to y is obtained when y varies and x is constant:

$$\frac{\partial f}{\partial y} = f_y = \lim_{\Delta y \to 0}\frac{f(x, y + \Delta y) - f(x, y)}{\Delta y}$$

Partial Derivatives of Second or Higher Order. If $\frac{\partial f}{\partial x}$ and $\frac{\partial f}{\partial y}$ are again differentiable, the partial derivatives of the second order may be found:

*For angles in the first and third quadrants. Use the opposite sign in the second and fourth quadrants

$$\frac{\partial}{\partial x}\left(\frac{\partial f}{\partial x}\right) = \frac{\partial^2 f}{\partial x^2} = f_{xx} \qquad \frac{\partial}{\partial y}\left(\frac{\partial f}{\partial y}\right) = \frac{\partial^2 f}{\partial y^2} = f_{yy}$$

$$\frac{\partial}{\partial x}\left(\frac{\partial f}{\partial y}\right) = \frac{\partial^2 f}{\partial x \partial y} = f_{yx} \qquad \frac{\partial}{\partial y}\left(\frac{\partial f}{\partial x}\right) = \frac{\partial^2 f}{\partial y \partial x} = f_{xy}$$

When the derivatives are continuous, the order of differentiation is immaterial, that is:

$$\frac{\partial^2 f}{\partial y \partial x} = \frac{\partial^2 f}{\partial x \partial y}$$

The third and higher partial derivatives of $f(x, y)$ may be determined in a similar manner. If continuous, the third partial derivatives are the following four:

$$\frac{\partial}{\partial x}\left(\frac{\partial^2 f}{\partial x^2}\right) = \frac{\partial^3 f}{\partial x^3} \qquad \frac{\partial}{\partial x}\left(\frac{\partial^2 f}{\partial y^2}\right) = \frac{\partial}{\partial y}\left(\frac{\partial^2 f}{\partial x \partial y}\right) = \frac{\partial^2}{\partial y^2}\left(\frac{\partial f}{\partial x}\right) = \frac{\partial^3 f}{\partial x \partial y^2}$$

$$\frac{\partial}{\partial y}\left(\frac{\partial^2 f}{\partial y^2}\right) = \frac{\partial^3 f}{\partial y^3} \qquad \frac{\partial}{\partial y}\left(\frac{\partial^2 f}{\partial x^2}\right) = \frac{\partial}{\partial x}\left(\frac{\partial^2 f}{\partial x \partial y}\right) = \frac{\partial^2}{\partial x^2}\left(\frac{\partial f}{\partial y}\right) = \frac{\partial^3 f}{\partial x^2 \partial y}$$

Functions of N Variables. The partial derivative formulas may be generalized to the form that has f as a function of more than two variables; that is, there corresponds a value of $f(x, y, z, \cdots)$ to every set of values of $x, y, z, \cdots$.

If the increments $\Delta x, \Delta y, \Delta z, \cdots$ are assigned to the variables $x, y, z, \cdots$ in the function $f(x, y, z, \cdots)$, the total increment of f is:

$$\Delta f = f(x + \Delta x, y + \Delta y, z + \Delta z, \cdots) - f(x, y, z, \cdots)$$

The total differential of f becomes:

$$df = \frac{\partial f}{\partial x}dx + \frac{\partial f}{\partial y}dy + \frac{\partial f}{\partial z}dz + \cdots$$

The second total differential of f becomes:

$$d^2 f = \frac{\partial^2 f}{\partial x^2}(dx)^2 + \frac{\partial^2 f}{\partial y^2}(dy)^2 + \frac{\partial^2 f}{\partial z^2}(dz)^2 + \cdots + 2\frac{\partial^2 f}{\partial x \partial y}dx\,dy + \cdots$$

The general form is:

$$d^n f = \left(\frac{\partial}{\partial x}dx + \frac{\partial}{\partial y}dy + \frac{\partial}{\partial z}dz + \cdots\right)^n f(x, y, z, \cdots)$$

Exact Differential. For the expression $P(x, y)\,dx + Q(x, y)\,dy$ to be the exact or complete differential of a function of two variables, the following condition is necessary:

$$\frac{\partial Q}{\partial x} = \frac{\partial P}{\partial y}$$

For three variables, $P\,dx + Q\,dy + R\,dz$, the required conditions are:

$$\frac{\partial Q}{\partial z} = \frac{\partial R}{\partial y}$$

$$\frac{\partial R}{\partial x} = \frac{\partial P}{\partial z}$$

$$\frac{\partial P}{\partial y} = \frac{\partial Q}{\partial x}$$

Composite Functions. If $u = f(x, y, z, \cdots w)$, and $x, y, z, \cdots w$ are functions of a single variable t, then:

$$\frac{du}{dt} = \frac{\partial u}{\partial x}\frac{dx}{dt} + \frac{\partial u}{\partial y}\frac{dy}{dt} + \cdots + \frac{\partial u}{\partial w}\frac{dw}{dt}$$

This expression represents the total derivative of u with respect to t.

INFINITE SERIES

If $a_1, a_2, \ldots a_n, \ldots$ is a number sequence formed according to some rule, the indicated sum is an infinite series:

$$\sum_{n=1}^{\infty} a_n = a_1 + a_2 + \cdots + a_n + \cdots$$

If the partial sums s_n, in the expression $s_n = a_1 + a_2 + \cdots + a_n$, approach a limit S as $n \to \infty$, the series is convergent; S is the sum of the series, or its value. A series that does not converge is divergent.

If the series of absolute values $|a_1| + |a_2| + \cdots + |a_n| + \cdots$ is convergent, then the infinite series above is absolutely convergent. If the series converges, but not absolutely, it is conditionally convergent. An absolutely convergent series does not change in sum by rearrangement of its terms. The convergence of a series can be verified by testing.

Comparison Test. For a series of positive terms, such as $c_1 + c_2 + \cdots + c_n + \cdots$, for which $a_n \leq c_n$ for every n from some term onward, the infinite series converges. If there is a divergent series of positive terms $d_1 + d_2 + \cdots + d_n + \cdots$, for which $a_n \geq d_n$ for every n from some term onward, then the infinite series diverges. A useful comparison series is the geometric series $a + ar + ar^2 + \cdots + ar^{n-1} + \cdots$, which converges for $|r| < 1$ and diverges for $|r| \geq 1$.

Ratio Test.   In the expression:

$$L = \lim_{n \to \infty} \left| \frac{a_n + 1}{a_n} \right|$$

if $L < 1$, the infinite series converges absolutely; if L does not exist or if $L > 1$, the series diverges; if $L = 1$, the test fails.

Root Test.   For the expression:

$$L = \lim_{n \to \infty} |a_n|^{1/n}$$

if $L < 1$, the infinite series converges; if $L > 1$, the series diverges; if $L = 1$, the test fails.

Integral Test.   For the function $f(n) = a_n$, if $f(x)$ is positive and non-increasing for $x > k$, then the infinite series converges or diverges with the improper integral $\int_k^\infty f(x)\, dx$.

Raabe's Test.   For the expression:

$$L = \lim_{n \to \infty} n \left(\frac{a_n}{a_n + 1} - 1 \right)$$

if $L > 1$, the infinite series converges; if $L < 1$, the infinite series diverges; if $L = 1$, the test fails.

Convergence of an Alternating Series.   In an alternating series:

$$a_1 - a_2 + a_3 - + \cdots + (-1)^{n+1} a_n + \cdots$$

the terms are alternately positive and negative. The series converges if, from some term onward, $|a_{n+1}| \leq |a_n|$ and $a_n \to 0$ as $n \to \infty$. The sum of the first n terms differs numerically from the sum of the series by less than $|a_{n+1}|$.

EXPANSION OF A FUNCTION INTO A POWER SERIES

A power series takes the form:

$$\sum_{n=0}^{\infty} a_n x^n = a_0 + a_1 x + a_2 x^2 + \cdots + a_n x^n + \cdots$$

If $\lim_{n \to \infty} \left| \frac{a_{n-1}}{a_n} \right| = r$, the series converges absolutely for all values of x in the interval $-r < x < r$. For $|x| = r$, one of the convergence tests for a series of numerical terms must be used. For example, for a series in the form:

$$1 - \frac{x}{1 \cdot 2} + \frac{x^2}{2 \cdot 2^2} - \frac{x^3}{3 \cdot 2^3} + \cdots + (-1)^n \frac{x^n}{n \cdot 2^n} + \cdots$$

since $\lim_{n \to \infty} \dfrac{n \cdot 2^n}{(n-1)2^{n-1}} = 2$, the interval of convergence is $-2 < x < 2$. For $x = 2$, the series is a convergent alternating series. For $x = -2$, it is a divergent p-series.

Taylor's Series. A function $y = f(x)$, continuous and with all derivatives at $x = a$, can be expressed as:

$$f(x) = f(a) + \frac{f'(a)}{1!}(x-a) + \frac{f''(a)}{2!}(x-a)^2 + \cdots + \frac{f^{(n-1)}(a)}{(n-1)!}(x-a)^{n-1} + \cdots$$

The expression for the remainder after n terms is:

$$R_n = \frac{f^{(n)}(\xi)}{n!}(x-a)^n \qquad \xi = a + \theta(x-a) \qquad 0 < \theta < 1$$

Another form of Taylor's series is:

$$f(x+h) = f(x) + \frac{h}{1!}f'(x) + \frac{h^2}{2!}f''(x) + \cdots + \frac{h^{n-1}}{(n-1)!}f^{(n-1)}(x) + \cdots$$

where the remainder after n terms is:

$$R_n = \frac{h^n}{n!}f^{(n)}(\xi) \qquad \xi = x + \theta h \qquad 0 < \theta < 1$$

Maclaurin's Series. The formula for expansion of a function $f(x)$ in powers of x, obtained from Taylor's series for $a = 0$, is:

$$f(x) = f(0) + \frac{f'(0)}{1!}x + \frac{f''(0)}{2!}x^2 + \cdots + \frac{f^{(n-1)}(0)}{(n-1)!}x^{n-1} + \cdots$$

where the remainder after n terms is:

$$R_n = \frac{f^{(n)}(\xi)}{n!}x^n \qquad \xi = \theta x \qquad 0 < \theta < 1$$

A Taylor's or Maclaurin's series represents a function in an interval only when $R_n \to 0$ as $n \to \infty$. For example, to expand e^{ax} in powers of x, let:

$$f(x) = e^{ax} \quad f'(x) = ae^{ax} \quad f''(x) = a^2 e^{ax} \quad f'''(x) = a^3 e^{ax}, \cdots$$
$$f(0) = 1 \quad f'(0) = a \quad f''(0) = a^2 \quad f'''(0) = a^3, \cdots$$

$$f(x) = e^{ax} = 1 + \frac{a}{1!}x + \frac{a^2}{2!}x^2 + \frac{a^3}{3!}x^3 + \cdots$$

Because:

$$\lim_{n \to \infty} \frac{\dfrac{a^{n-1}}{(n-1)!}}{\dfrac{a^n}{n!}} = \lim_{n \to \infty} \frac{n}{a} = \infty$$

the series converges for all values of x.

Taylor's series for a function of two variables is expressed in the following:

$$f(x + h, y + k) = f(x, y) + \frac{1}{1!}\left(h\frac{\partial}{\partial x} + k\frac{\partial}{\partial y}\right) f(x, y) +$$

$$\frac{1}{2!}\left(h\frac{\partial}{\partial x} + k\frac{\partial}{\partial y}\right)^2 f(x, y) + \cdots +$$

$$\frac{1}{(n-1)!}\left(h\frac{\partial}{\partial x} + k\frac{\partial}{\partial y}\right)^{n-1} f(x, y) + \cdots$$

where the remainder is:

$$R_n = \frac{1}{n!}\left(h\frac{\partial}{\partial x} + k\frac{\partial}{\partial y}\right)^n f(x + \theta h, y + \theta k) \qquad 0 < \theta < 1$$

Fourier Series. If a function $f(x)$ varies over an interval of length $2l$ and can be expressed as the difference of two nondecreasing or nonincreasing bounded functions, then:

$$f(x) = \frac{a_0}{2} + \sum_{n=1}^{\infty}\left(a_n \cos\frac{n\pi x}{l} + b_n \sin\frac{n\pi x}{l}\right) =$$

$$\frac{a_0}{2} + a_1 \cos\frac{\pi x}{l} + a_a \cos\frac{2\pi x}{l} + \cdots +$$

$$b_1 \sin\frac{\pi x}{l} + b_2 \sin\frac{2\pi x}{l} + \cdots\Big)$$

for which

$$a_n = \frac{1}{l}\int_k^{k+2l} f(x) \cos\frac{n\pi x}{l} dx$$

$$b_n = \frac{1}{l}\int_k^{k+2l} f(x) \sin\frac{n\pi x}{l} dx$$

$$n = 0, 1, 2, \cdots$$

In exponential form, the function is:

$$f(x) = \sum_{n=-\infty}^{\infty} c_n e^{\frac{in\pi x}{l}}$$

$$c_n = \frac{1}{2l}\int_k^{k+2l} f(x) e^{\frac{-in\pi x}{l}} dx$$

$$n = \cdots, -2, -1, 0, 1, 2, \cdots$$

At a point of discontinuity, a Fourier series produces the value at the midpoint of the jump. For example, when e^x is expanded in the interval 0 to 2π:

$$a_0 = \frac{1}{\pi}\int_0^{2\pi} e^x dx = \frac{1}{\pi}(e^{2\pi} - 1)$$

$$a_n = \frac{1}{\pi}\int_0^{2\pi} e^x \cos nx\, dx = \frac{e^{2\pi} - 1}{\pi(n^2 + 1)}$$

$$b_n = - \frac{n(e^{2\pi} - 1)}{\pi(n^2 + 1)}$$

Thus:

$$e^x = \frac{1}{\pi}(e^{2\pi} - 1)\left[\frac{1}{2} + \frac{1}{1^2 + 1}\cos x + \frac{1}{2^2 + 1}\cos 2x + \frac{1}{3^2 + 1}\cos 3x + \cdots\right]$$

$$- \frac{1}{\pi}(e^{2\pi} - 1)\left[\frac{1}{1^2 + 1}\sin x + \frac{2}{2^2 + 1}\sin 2x + \frac{3}{3^2 + 1}\sin 3x + \cdots\right]$$

Only in the interval from 0 to 2π does the expansion have validity; beyond that interval, the series repeats itself, as a result of the periodic behavior of $\sin nx$ and $\cos nx$. In a Fourier series, if $f(-x) = f(x)$, it is an even function. Then:

$$a_n = \frac{2}{l} \int_0^l f(x) \cos \frac{n\pi x}{l}\, dx \qquad n = 0, 1, 2, \cdots$$

and

$$b_n = 0$$

If $f(-x) = -f(x)$, it is an odd function, $a_n = 0$, and:

$$b_n = \frac{2}{l} \int_0^l f(x) \sin \frac{n\pi x}{l}\, dx,\, n = 0, 1, 2, \cdots$$

For example, if the function $f(x) = x$ is expanded in a cosine series in the interval $(0, \pi)$:

$$\frac{1}{2}a_0 = \frac{1}{\pi} \int_0^\pi x\, dx = \frac{\pi}{2}$$

and

$$a_n = \frac{2}{\pi} \int_0^\pi x \cos nx\, dx = \frac{2}{\pi}\left\{\left[\frac{x \sin nx}{n}\right]_0^\pi - \int_0^\pi \frac{\sin nx}{n}\, dx\right\}$$

$$= \frac{2}{\pi}\left[\frac{1}{n^2}\cos nx\right]_0^\pi = \frac{2}{\pi n^2}(\cos n\pi - 1)$$

Thus:

$$x = \frac{\pi}{2} - \frac{4}{\pi}\left[\cos x + \frac{\cos 3x}{3^2} + \frac{\cos 5x}{5^2} + \cdots\right] (0 < x < \pi)$$

For $x = 0$, the sum of the series is 0, and for $x = \pi$, the sum of the series is π.

Expansion of functions into power series

Function	Series expansion	Domain of convergence
	$(\log = \log_e)$	
$(a + x)^n$ ......$a^n + na^{n-1}x + \dfrac{n(n-1)}{2!}a^{n-2}x^2$ $+ \dfrac{n(n-1)(n-2)}{3!}a^{n-3}x^3 + \cdots$		$(x^2 < a^2)$
e^x............$1 + x + \dfrac{x^2}{2!} + \dfrac{x^3}{3!} + \dfrac{x^4}{4!} + \cdots$		$(-\infty < x < \infty)$
a^x............$1 + x \log a + \dfrac{(x \log a)^2}{2!} +$ $\dfrac{(x \log a)^3}{3!} + \cdots$		$(-\infty < x < \infty)$
e^{-x^2}..........$1 - x^2 + \dfrac{x^4}{2!} - \dfrac{x^6}{3!} + \dfrac{x^8}{4!} - \cdots$		$(-\infty < x < \infty)$
$e^{\sin x}$ ....$1 + x + \dfrac{x^2}{2!} - \dfrac{3x^4}{4!} - \dfrac{8x^5}{5!} - \dfrac{3x^6}{6!} - \dfrac{56x^7}{7!} + \cdots$		$(-\infty < x < \infty)$
$e^{\cos x}$ ....$e\left(1 - \dfrac{x^2}{2!} + \dfrac{4x^4}{4!} - \dfrac{31x^6}{6!} + \cdots\right)$		$(-\infty < x < \infty)$
$e^{\tan x}$ ....$1 + x + \dfrac{x^2}{2!} + \dfrac{3x^3}{3!} + \dfrac{9x^4}{4!} + \dfrac{37x^5}{5!} + \cdots$		$\left(-\dfrac{\pi}{2} < x < \dfrac{\pi}{2}\right)$
$\log x$ ....$\dfrac{x-1}{x} + \dfrac{1}{2}\left(\dfrac{x-1}{x}\right)^2 + \dfrac{1}{3}\left(\dfrac{x-1}{x}\right)^3 + \cdots$		$\left(x > \dfrac{1}{2}\right)$
$\log x$ ....$2\left[\dfrac{x-1}{x+1} + \dfrac{1}{3}\left(\dfrac{x-1}{x+1}\right)^3 + \dfrac{1}{5}\left(\dfrac{x-1}{x+1}\right)^5 + \cdots\right]$		$(x > 0)$
$\log(1 + x)$......$x - \dfrac{x^2}{2} + \dfrac{x^3}{3} - \dfrac{x^4}{4} + \cdots$		$(-1 < x < 1)$
$\log\left(\dfrac{1+x}{1-x}\right)$...$2\left[x + \dfrac{x^3}{3} + \dfrac{x^5}{5} + \dfrac{x^7}{7} + \cdots\right]$		$(-1 < x < 1)$
$\log\left(\dfrac{x+1}{x-1}\right)$...$2\left[\dfrac{1}{x} + \dfrac{1}{3x^3} + \dfrac{1}{5x^5} + \cdots\right]$		$(x^2 > 1)$
$\log \sin x$.......$\log x - \dfrac{x^2}{6} - \dfrac{x^4}{180} - \dfrac{x^6}{2835} - \cdots$		$(-\pi < x < \pi)$
$\log \cos x$.......$-\dfrac{x^2}{2} - \dfrac{x^4}{12} - \dfrac{x^6}{45} - \dfrac{17x^8}{2520} - \cdots$		$\left(-\dfrac{\pi}{2} < x < \dfrac{\pi}{2}\right)$
$\log \tan x$.......$\log x + \dfrac{x^2}{3} + \dfrac{7x^4}{90} + \dfrac{62x^6}{2835} + \cdots$		$\left(-\dfrac{\pi}{2} < x < \dfrac{\pi}{2}\right)$
$\sin x$ ....$x - \dfrac{x^3}{3!} + \dfrac{x^5}{5!} - \dfrac{x^7}{7!} + \cdots$		$(-\infty < x < \infty)$

(continued)

Expansion of functions into power series (continued)

Function	Series expansion	Domain of convergence
$\cos x$	$1 - \dfrac{x^2}{2!} + \dfrac{x^4}{4!} - \dfrac{x^6}{6!} + \cdots$	$(-\infty < x < \infty)$
$\tan x$	$x + \dfrac{x^3}{3} + \dfrac{2x^5}{15} + \dfrac{17x^7}{315} + \dfrac{62x^9}{2835} + \cdots$	$\left(-\dfrac{\pi}{2} < x < \dfrac{\pi}{2}\right)$
$\cot x$	$\dfrac{1}{x} - \dfrac{x}{3} - \dfrac{x^3}{45} - \dfrac{2x^5}{945} - \dfrac{x^7}{4275} - \cdots$	$(-\pi < x < \pi)$
$\sec x$	$1 + \dfrac{x^2}{2!} + \dfrac{5x^4}{4!} + \dfrac{61x^6}{6!} + \cdots$	$\left(-\dfrac{\pi}{2} < x < \dfrac{\pi}{2}\right)$
$\csc x$	$\dfrac{1}{x} + \dfrac{x}{3!} + \dfrac{7x^3}{3 \cdot 5!} + \dfrac{31x^5}{3 \cdot 7!} + \cdots$	$(-\pi < x < \pi)$
$\sin^{-1}x$	$x + \dfrac{x^3}{2 \cdot 3} + \dfrac{3x^5}{2 \cdot 4 \cdot 5} + \dfrac{3 \cdot 5x^7}{2 \cdot 4 \cdot 6 \cdot 7} + \cdots$	$(-1 \leqq x \leqq 1)$
$\cos^{-1}x$	$\dfrac{\pi}{2} - \sin^{-1}x$	
$\tan^{-1}x$	$\dfrac{\pi}{2} - \dfrac{1}{x} + \dfrac{1}{3x^3} - \dfrac{1}{5x^5} + \cdots$	$(x^2 \geqq 1)$
	$x - \dfrac{x^3}{3} + \dfrac{x^5}{5} - \dfrac{x^7}{7} + \cdots$	$(-1 \leqq x \leqq 1)$
$\cot^{-1}x$	$\dfrac{\pi}{2} - \tan^{-1}x$	
$\sec^{-1}x$	$\dfrac{\pi}{2} - \dfrac{1}{x} - \dfrac{1}{2 \cdot 3x^3} - \dfrac{3}{2 \cdot 4 \cdot 5x^5} - \dfrac{3 \cdot 5}{2 \cdot 4 \cdot 6 \cdot 7x^7} - \cdots$	$(x^2 > 1)$
$\csc^{-1}x$	$\dfrac{\pi}{2} - \sec^{-1}x$	
$\sinh x$	$x + \dfrac{x^3}{3!} + \dfrac{x^5}{5!} + \dfrac{x^7}{7!} + \cdots$	$(-\infty < x < \infty)$
$\cosh x$	$1 + \dfrac{x^2}{2!} + \dfrac{x^4}{4!} + \dfrac{x^6}{6!} + \dfrac{x^8}{8!} + \cdots$	$(-\infty < x < \infty)$
$\tanh x$	$x - \dfrac{x^3}{3} + \dfrac{2x^5}{15} - \dfrac{17x^7}{315} + \cdots$	$\left(-\dfrac{\pi}{2} < x < \dfrac{\pi}{2}\right)$
$\coth x$	$\dfrac{1}{x} + \dfrac{x}{3} - \dfrac{x^3}{45} + \dfrac{2x^5}{945} - \dfrac{x^7}{4725} + \cdots$	$(-\pi < x < \pi)$
$\operatorname{sech} x$	$1 - \dfrac{x^2}{2!} + \dfrac{5x^4}{4!} - \dfrac{61x^6}{6!} + \dfrac{1385x^8}{8!} - \cdots$	$\left(-\dfrac{\pi}{2} < x < \dfrac{\pi}{2}\right)$

(continued)

Expansion of functions into power series (continued)

Function	Series expansion	Domain of convergence
csch x	$\dfrac{1}{x} - \dfrac{x}{6} + \dfrac{7x^3}{360} - \dfrac{31x^5}{15{,}120} + \cdots$	$(-\pi < x < \pi)$
sinh^{-1}x	$x - \dfrac{x^3}{2 \cdot 3} + \dfrac{3x^5}{2 \cdot 4 \cdot 5} - \dfrac{3 \cdot 5x^7}{2 \cdot 4 \cdot 6 \cdot 7} + \cdots$	$(-1 < x < 1)$
sinh^{-1}x	$\log 2x + \dfrac{1}{2 \cdot 2x^2} - \dfrac{3}{2 \cdot 4 \cdot 4x^4} +$ $\dfrac{3 \cdot 5}{2 \cdot 4 \cdot 6 \cdot 6 \cdot x^6} + \cdots$	$(x^2 > 1)$
cosh^{-1}x	$\pm \left(\log 2x - \dfrac{1}{2 \cdot 2x^2} - \dfrac{1 \cdot 3}{2 \cdot 4 \cdot 4x^4} - \right.$ $\left. \dfrac{1 \cdot 3 \cdot 5}{2 \cdot 4 \cdot 6 \cdot 6x^6} - \cdots \right)$	$(x > 1)$
tanh^{-1}x	$x + \dfrac{x^3}{3} + \dfrac{x^5}{5} + \dfrac{x^7}{7} + \cdots$	$(-1 < x < 1)$
coth^{-1}x	$\dfrac{1}{x} + \dfrac{1}{3x^3} + \dfrac{1}{5x^5} + \dfrac{1}{7x^7} + \cdots$	$(x^2 > 1)$
sech^{-1}x	$\pm \left(\log \dfrac{2}{x} - \dfrac{1}{2 \cdot 2}x^2 - \dfrac{1 \cdot 3}{2 \cdot 4 \cdot 4}x - \right.$ $\left. \dfrac{1 \cdot 3 \cdot 5}{2 \cdot 4 \cdot 6 \cdot 6}x^6 - \cdots \right)$	$(0 < x < 1)$
csch^{-1}x	$\dfrac{1}{x} - \dfrac{1}{2 \cdot 3x^3} + \dfrac{3}{2 \cdot 4 \cdot 5x^5} -$ $\dfrac{3 \cdot 5}{2 \cdot 4 \cdot 6 \cdot 7x^7} + \cdots$	$(x^2 > 1)$

FINDING MAXIMA AND MINIMA

Function of One Variable. A maximum or a minimum of a function $y = f(x)$ is its value $f(x_0)$ for which the following inequalities hold:

$$f(x_0 + h) < f(x_0) \quad \text{(for a maximum)}$$

and

$$f(x_0 + h) > f(x_0) \quad \text{(for a minimum)}$$

for arbitrary small values of h, positive or negative. Thus the value $f(x_0)$ at a maximum or minimum is greater or less than all neighboring values of the function.

For a continuous function, a maximum or minimum can occur only at the points where the derivative either is equal to zero or does not exist, in particular, is infinite. In mathematical analysis, maxima and minima also are known as turning values or extrema.

Geometric Significance. At points of the graph corresponding to a maximum (M) or a minimum (m), the tangent either is parallel to the x axis (Fig. 4a), parallel to the y axis (Fig. 4b), or does not exist (Fig. 4c).

This condition is not sufficient; however, it is satisfied at the points A, B, C in Fig. 5, but these points are not points of maximum or minimum.

Maxima and minima of a continuous function alternate when a minimum lies between two successive maxima and a maximum lies between two minima.

To locate possible extreme points, solve the equation $f'(x) = 0$. A solution $x = a$ gives a maximum or minimum value of $f(x)$ only if the derivative is positive or negative for $x < a$ and negative or positive for $x > a$. If the derivative does not change sign, $x = a$ produces a point of inflection.

A solution $x = a$ can be tested further by using the higher derivatives of $f(x)$. For example, if $f^{(n)}(x)$ is the first derivative that does not equal zero for $x = a$, $f^{(n)}(x)$ is the first derivative that does not equal zero for $x = a$, $f^{(n)}(a) \neq 0$, and if n is even, there is a maximum, M in Fig. 4(a), if $f^{(n)}(a) < 0$, and a minimum (m) in Fig. 4(a), if $f^{(n)}(a) > 0$. If n is odd, there is a point of inflection (Fig. 5).

Function of Two or More Variables. A function $f(x, y)$ has a relative maximum or minimum at a point $(x, y) = (a, b)$ if at every point in some neighborhood of (a, b) the values of $f(x, y)$ are all less than or greater than

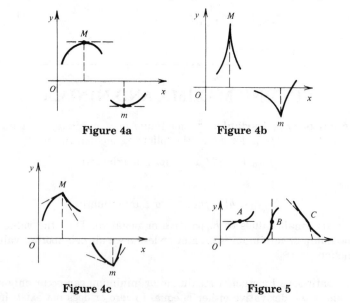

Figure 4a   Figure 4b

Figure 4c   Figure 5

$f(a, b)$. If the first partial derivatives exist at a relative extreme, it is necessary that:

$$\frac{\partial f}{\partial x} = \frac{\partial f}{\partial y} = 0$$

If at the point (a, b):

$$\frac{\partial^2 f}{\partial x^2} \frac{\partial^2 f}{\partial y^2} - \left(\frac{\partial^2 f}{\partial x \partial y}\right)^2 > 0$$

then $f(a, b)$ becomes an extreme value, which is a maximum if:

$$\frac{\partial^2 f}{\partial x^2} < 0 \left(\text{thus, } \frac{\partial^2 f}{\partial y^2} < 0\right)$$

and a minimum if:

$$\frac{\partial^2 f}{\partial x^2} > 0$$

If:

$$\frac{\partial^2 f}{\partial x^2} \frac{\partial^2 f}{\partial y^2} - \left(\frac{\partial^2 f}{\partial x \partial y}\right)^2 < 0$$

then $f(x, y)$ has no extreme value but a saddle point. If:

$$\frac{\partial^2 f}{\partial x^2} \frac{\partial^2 f}{\partial y^2} - \left(\frac{\partial^2 f}{\partial x \partial y}\right)^2 = 0$$

the test produces no information.

For a function of several variables $f(x, y, z, \ldots)$, necessary conditions for an extreme value are:

$$\frac{\partial f}{\partial x} = \frac{\partial f}{\partial y} = \frac{\partial f}{\partial z} = \cdots = 0$$

PRINCIPAL THEOREMS OF DIFFERENTIAL CALCULUS

Fermat's Theorem. If a function $y = f(x)$, defined in a connected domain, assumes a greatest or least value at a point, $x = c$, which is not an end point of the interval, that is:

$$f(c) < f(x) \qquad \text{or} \qquad f(c) > f(x)$$

and if the function possesses a finite derivative at points c, then this derivative is zero:

$$f'(c) = 0$$

At points A and B of the graph of functions satisfying this condition, as shown in Fig. 6, the tangent is parallel to the x axis. Fermat's theorem establishes only a necessary condition for a greatest and a least value of the function. It is not sufficient; however, at point A in Fig. 7, $f'(x) = 0$, but the function does not assume a greatest or least value at this point.

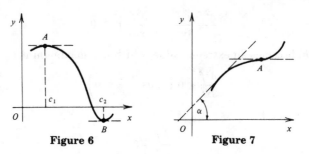

| Figure 6 | Figure 7 |

Thus, the assumption of Fermat's theorem of a finite derivative is essential: the function in Fig. 8(d) assumes a greatest value at the point E, but the derivative is not zero.

Rolle's Theorem. If a function $y = f(x)$ is continuous in a closed interval (a, b), has a continuous derivative within the interval, and vanishes at the interval end points, that is:

$$f(a) = 0 \qquad f(b) = 0 \qquad (a < b)$$

then at least one point c exists between a and b, characterized by:

$$f'(c) = 0 \qquad (a < c < b)$$

If the graph of the function $y = f(x)$ is a continuous curve with a tangent that varies continuously, and if the curve intersects the x axis at the points A and B, then at least one point C exists between A and B in such a manner that the tangent at C is parallel to the x axis (Fig. 8a).

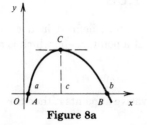

Figure 8a

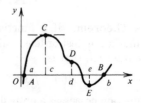

Figure 8b

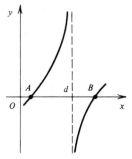

Figure 8c

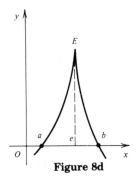

Figure 8d

More such points (the points C, D, E in Fig. 8b) may exist. That the function and its derivative are continuous is an essential assumption. The function shown in Fig. 8(c) has a discontinuity at $x = d$, and the derivative of the function in Fig. 8(d) has a discontinuity at $x = e$. At point C with $f'(x) = 0$ does not exist in each case.

Theorem of the Mean. If a function $f(x)$ is continuous in the closed interval $a \leq x \leq b$ and has a continuous derivative in this interval, then there exists a value x_1 of x between a and b for which:

$$f(b) - f(a) = (b - a)f'(x_1)$$

where $f'(x_1)$ is the value of the derivative of $f(x)$ at x_1. Cauchy's formula, an extended theorem of the mean, states that:

$$\frac{f(b) - f(a)}{g(b) - g(a)} = \frac{f'(x_1)}{g'(x_1)} \qquad a < x_1 < b$$

where g is any other continuous function that has derivatives in the interval $a \leq x \leq b$.

8
Integral Calculus

INDEFINITE INTEGRALS

Integration is the process of finding a function when its differential is known. The operation is indicated in symbols by:

$$\int f(x)\,dx = F(x) + C$$

with the left-hand side of the equation called an indefinite integral, and $f(x)$ the integrand. The expression is read as the integral of $f(x)\,dx$.

$F(x)$ is any function whose derivative is $f(x)$; C is a constant. Because the derivative of a constant is zero, all functions differing only by a constant have the same derivative. $F(x)$ plus any constant is called an integral of $f(x)$.

Because of the indeterminacy of C, an infinite number of $F(x) + C$ is possible, differing by their relative position to X axis only. The graph in Fig. 1 illustrates the meaning of C for a given function.

Basic Properties of Integrals. For any function u of the variable x, with the differential of du:

$$\int du = u + C$$

$$\int \frac{du}{dx}\,dx = u + C$$

$$\frac{d}{dx} \int u\,dx = u + C$$

where C is a constant. A constant factor can be moved outside the integral sign.

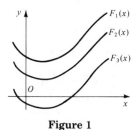

Figure 1

If k is a constant, for example:

$$\int k\, du = k \int du$$

The integral of the algebraic sum of a finite number of functions is the algebraic sum of the integrals of the functions. If u, v, and w are functions of a single variable, for example:

$$\int (du + dv - dw) = \int du + \int dv - \int dw$$

Standard Elementary Integrals:

$$\int dx = x + C$$

$$\int u^n\, du = \frac{u^{n+1}}{n+1} + C \qquad n \neq -1$$

$$\int \frac{du}{u} = \log_e u + C = \log_e cu$$

$$\int e^u\, du = e^u + C$$

$$\int a^u\, du = \frac{a^u}{\log_e a} + C$$

$$\int \sin u\, du = -\cos u + C$$

$$\int \cos u\, du = \sin u + C$$

$$\int \tan u\, du = \log_e \sec u + C$$

$$\int \cot u\, du = \log_e \sin u + C$$

$$\int \sec u\, du = \log_e (\sec u + \tan u)C$$

$$\int \csc u\, du = \log_e (\csc u - \cot u)C$$

$$\int \sec^2 u\, du = \tan u + C$$

$$\int \csc^2 u\, du = -\cot u + C$$

$$\int \sec u \tan u\, du = \sec u + C$$

$$\int \csc u \cot u\, du = -\csc u + C$$

$$\int \frac{du}{u^2 + a^2} = \frac{1}{a} \arctan \frac{u}{a} + C$$

$$\int \frac{du}{u^2 - a^2} = \frac{1}{2a} \log_e \frac{a-u}{a+u} C$$

$$\int \frac{du}{a^2 - u^2} = \frac{1}{2a} \log_e \frac{a+u}{a-u} C$$

$$\int \frac{du}{\sqrt{u^2 \pm a^2}} = \log_e (u + \sqrt{u^2 \pm a^2}) C$$

$$\int \frac{du}{\sqrt{a^2 - u^2}} = \arcsin \frac{u}{a} + C$$

$$\int \sqrt{a^2 - u^2}\, du = \frac{u}{2} \sqrt{a^2 - u^2} + \frac{a^2}{2} \arcsin \frac{u}{a} + C$$

$$\int \sqrt{u^2 \pm a^2}\, du = \frac{u}{2} \sqrt{u^2 \pm a^2} \pm \frac{a^2}{2} \log_e(u + \sqrt{u^2 \pm a^2})C$$

$\int \sinh u\, du = \cosh u + C$

$\int \cosh u\, du = \sinh u + C$

$\int \tanh u\, du = \log_e \cosh u + C$

$\int \coth u\, du = \log_e|\sinh u| + C$

Integration Methods. The first step in integration is to simplify the integral, if necessary. If the integrand is a sum of functions, it may be rewritten as the sum of the integrals of the functions. When the integrand is a rational fraction with numerator of degree equal to or greater than that of the denominator, it may be transformed until the remainder is of lower degree than the denominator. The remainder may be broken into partial fractions for further simplification. Substitution of another variable for part of the integrand may simplify integration.

The original or simplified integrand can be compared with the standard elementary forms or with solutions in more elaborate tables of integrals, such as presented at the end of this chapter. If the solution does not appear with inspection, algebraic or trigonometric manipulation may be used to put the integral in a recognizable form for solution with a table. Substitution of another variable may also be tried.

If an integral contains:	Try substituting:
$f(\sqrt{a^2 - u^2})$	$u = a \sin \theta$
$f(\sqrt{a^2 + u^2})$	$u = a \tan \theta$
$f(\sqrt{u^2 - a^2})$	$u = a \sec \theta$
$f(x^{p/q})$	$x = z^n$

where n is the least common denominator of the fractional exponents of x.

If an integral contains:	Try substituting:
$f[x, (a + bx)^{p/q}]$	$a + bx = z^n$

where n represents the least common denominator of the fractional exponents of $a + bx$. For integrals in the form:

$$x^m (a + bx^n)^{p/q}$$

where $q > 0$, $n \neq 0$, and m, n, p, q are integers, try:

$$z^q = a + bx^n \text{ if } \frac{m + 1}{n} \text{ is zero or an integer}$$

or

$$z^q x^n = a + bx^n \text{ if } \frac{m+1}{n} + \frac{p}{q} \text{ is zero or an integer.}$$

Thus, the fundamental rules of integration are those properties of indefinite integrals that enable transformation of the integral of a given function to the integrals of other functions.

Integration by Parts. If u and v are functions of a single variable:

$$\int u \, dv = uv - \int v \, du$$

Hence, $u \, dv$ can be integrated if $v \, du$ can be integrated.

Integration by Series. If the integrand can be expressed as a uniformly convergent series of powers of x, within its interval of convergence, and if term-by-term integration of this series also produces a uniformly convergent series, the sum of this series is also the value of the integral.

Integration of Trigonometric Functions. A trigonometric integrand may be reduced to a standard form in several ways.

If an integral contains $f(\sin \theta, \cos \theta)$, substitution of $\theta = 2 \arctan x$ may be used, so that $x = \tan (\theta/2)$, $\sin \theta = 2x/(1 + x^2)$, $\cos \theta = (1 - x^2)/(1 + x^2)$ and $d\theta = 2 dx/(1 + x^2)$.

If an integral has the form:

$$\int \sin^{2m+1} \theta \cos^n \theta \, d\theta,$$

where m is any integer or zero, the integrand may be rewritten in the form:

$$\sin^{2m} \theta \cos^n \theta \sin \theta = (1 - \cos^2 \theta)^m \cos^n \theta \sin \theta$$

After multiplication, the integrand becomes a sum of powers of $\cos \theta$ multiplied by $\sin \theta$; it then can be integrated term by term.

For an integral in the form:

$$\int \sin^p \theta \cos^{2r+1} \theta \, d\theta,$$

where r is any integer or zero, the integrand can be rewritten as:

$$\sin^p \theta \cos^{2r} \theta \cos \theta = \sin^p \theta (1 - \sin^2 \theta)^r \cos \theta$$

After multiplication, the integrand becomes a sum of powers of $\sin \theta$ multiplied by $\cos \theta$; it then can be integrated term by term.

For an integral in the form:

$$\int \sin^{2m} \theta \cos^{2n} \theta \, d\theta$$

where m and n are integers or zero, use the identities:

$$\sin^2\theta = \tfrac{1}{2}(1 - \cos 2\theta)$$
$$\cos^2\theta = \tfrac{1}{2}(1 + \cos 2\theta)$$

$$\sin\theta\cos\theta = \frac{\sin 2\theta}{2}$$

For an integral in the form:

$$\int \tan^m\theta\,\sec^n\theta\,d\theta \qquad \text{or} \qquad \int \cot^m\theta\,\csc^n\theta\,d\theta$$

the identities $\sec^2\theta = 1 + \tan^2\theta$ or $\csc^2\theta = 1 + \cot^2\theta$ may be tried. The form:

$$\int \sin^m\theta\,\cos^n\theta\,d\theta$$

also may be integrated by the use of reduction formulas, which contain an integral of lower degree in $\sin\theta$ or $\cos\theta$. Successive reduction may produce the required integral.

Integration of Rational Fractions. If the quotient of two polynomials:

$$R(x) = \frac{P_n(x)}{P_d(x)}$$

is not a proper fraction, $R(x)$ can be changed, by dividing, to the sum of integrable polynomial and a proper fraction. If the proper fraction cannot be integrated by reference to a table of integrals, resolve it, if possible, into partial fractions. These can be integrated from a table.

Integration of Irrational Functions. Irrational functions are not always integrable in terms of elementary functions. In simplest cases, integrals of irrational functions can be reduced to those of rational functions by means of the following substitutions:

Form	Substitution
$f[(ax + b)^{p/q}]dx$	let $ax + b = y^q$
$f[(ax + b)^{p/q}(ax + b)^{r/s}]dx$	let $ax + b = y^n$, where n is the Least Common Multiple (LCM) of q, s
$f[x, \sqrt{x^3 + ax + b}]dx$	let $\sqrt{x^2 + ax + b} = y - x$
$f[x, \sqrt{-x^2 + ax + b}]dx$	let $\sqrt{-x^2 + ax + b} = \sqrt{(\alpha - x)(\beta + x)}$ $= (\alpha - x)y$ or $= (\beta + x)y$
$f[\sin x, \cos x]dx$	let $\tan\frac{x}{2} = y$
$f[x, \sqrt{a^2 - x^2}]dx$	let $x = a\sin y$
$f[x, \sqrt{x^2 - a^2}]dx$	let $x = a\sec y$ or $x = a\cosh y$
$f[x, \sqrt{x^2 + a^2}]dx$	let $x = a\tan y$ or $x = a\sinh y$

Elliptic Integrals. Integrals such as:

$$\int R\left(x, \sqrt{ax^3 + bx^2 + cx + \partial}\right) dx$$

and

$$\int R\left(x, \sqrt{ax^4 + bx^3 + cx^2 + \partial x + e}\right) dx$$

cannot, in general, be expressed in terms of elementary functions. In such cases, they are called elliptic integrals.

Integrals of this type, which are not expressable in terms of elementary functions, can be reduced by transformation to elementary functions and to the following types of integrals:

$$\int \frac{dt}{\sqrt{(1 - t^2)(1 - k^2 t^2)}}$$

$$\int \frac{t^2 \, dt}{\sqrt{(1 - t^2)(1 - k^2 t)^2}}$$

$$\int \frac{dt}{(1 + ht^2)\sqrt{(1 - t^2)(1 - k^2 t^2)}}$$

where $0 < k < 1$. By substituting $t = \sin \varphi \, (0 < \varphi < \frac{1}{2}\pi)$, these transformed integrals can be reduced to the following form of Legendre:

$$\int \frac{d\varphi}{\sqrt{1 - k^2 \sin^2 \varphi}} \quad \text{(elliptic integral of the 1st kind)}$$

$$\int \sqrt{1 - k^2 \sin^2 \varphi} \, d\varphi \quad \text{(elliptic integral of the 2nd kind)}$$

$$\int \frac{d\varphi}{(1 + h \sin^2 \varphi)\sqrt{1 - k^2 \sin^2 \varphi}} \quad \text{(elliptic integral of the 3rd kind)}$$

The corresponding definite integrals with the lower limit of integration equal to zero are denoted as follows:

(I) $$\int_0^\varphi \frac{d\psi}{\sqrt{1 - k^2 \sin^2 \psi}} = F(k, \varphi)$$

(II) $$\int_0^\varphi \sqrt{1 - k^2 \sin^2 \psi} \, d\psi = E(k, \varphi)$$

(III) $$\int_0^\varphi \frac{d\psi}{(1 + h \sin^2 \psi)\sqrt{1 - k^2 \sin^2 \psi}} = \Pi(h, k, \varphi)$$

where $k < 1$.

These are incomplete elliptic integrals of the first, second, and third kind, respectively. When $\varphi = \frac{1}{2}\pi$, (I) and (II) are called complete elliptic integrals and denoted by:

$$K = F\left(k, \frac{\pi}{2}\right) = \int_0^{\pi/2} \frac{d\psi}{\sqrt{1 - k^2 \sin^2 \psi}}$$

$$E = E\left(k, \frac{\pi}{2}\right) = \int_0^{\pi/2} \sqrt{1 - k^2 \sin^2 \psi} \; d\psi$$

DEFINITE INTEGRALS

Definitions. If $f(x)$ is continuous in the closed interval $[a, b]$ and this interval is divided into n equal parts by the points $a, x_1, x_2, \ldots, x_{n-1}, b$ in such a way that $\Delta x = (b - a)/n$, then the definite integral of $f(x)$ with respect to x between the limits $x = a$ to $x = b$, is expressed as:

$$\int_a^b f(x) \; dx = \lim_{n \to \infty} \sum_1^n f(X_i) \; \Delta x = \left[\int f(x) \; dx \right]_a^b = [F(x)]_a^b = F(b) - F(a)$$

where $F(x)$ is a function and $f(x)$ is the derivative of the function with respect to x. The numbers a and b are called, respectively, the lower and upper limits of integration, and $[a, b]$ is called the range of integration. Geometrically, the definite integral of $f(x)$ with respect to x, between limits $x = a$ to $x = b$, is the area bounded by $f(x)$, the X axis, and the verticals through the end points of a and b. Figure 2 shows the division of intervals and the area boundaries of a generalized definite integral.

Rules of Limits:

$$\int_a^b = - \int_b^a$$

$$\int_a^b + \int_b^c = \int_a^c$$

$$\int_a^c - \int_b^c = \int_a^b$$

$$\int_a^a = 0$$

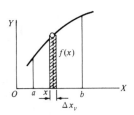

Figure 2

FUNDAMENTAL PROPERTIES

The integral of an algebraic sum of several functions is equal to the sum of the integrals of these functions:

$$\int_a^b (f(x) + \varphi(x) - \psi(x))\,dx = \int_a^b f(x)\,dx + \int_a^b \varphi(x)\,dx - \int_a^b \psi(x)\,dx$$

A constant factor can be brought out from under the integral sign:

$$\int_a^b cf(x)\,dx = c\int_a^b f(x)\,dx$$

Mean Value Theorem. If the function $f(x)$ is continuous in the interval $[a, b]$, then there exists at least one point ξ inside the interval $[a, b]$, such that:

$$\int_a^b f(x)\,dx = (b - a)\,f(\xi)$$

The geometric significance of this theorem is shown in Fig. 3; a point ξ exists between a and b that defines the area of $ABCD$ equal to the area of the rectangle $AB'C'D$.

For the integral of a product of two functions $f(x)$ and $\varphi(x)$, where $f(x)$ is continuous and $\varphi(x)$ has a constant sign in the interval $[a, b]$, there exists inside the interval $[a, b]$ at least one number ξ for which:

$$\int_a^b f(x)\varphi(x)\,dx = f(\xi)\int_a^b \varphi(x)\,dx$$

Estimation of the Integral. The value of a definite integral is contained between the products of the least and the greatest value of the integrand multiplied by the length of the interval of integration:

$$m(b - a) \le \int_a^b f(x)\,dx \le M(b - a)$$

where m is the least and M is the greatest value of $f(x)$ in the interval $[a, b]$. The significance of this theorem is illustrated in Fig. 4.

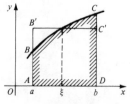

Figure 3

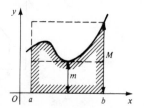

Figure 4

EVALUATION OF DEFINITE INTEGRALS

The fundamental method of evaluating definite integrals is based on re-placing the definite integral by an indefinite integral:

$$\int_a^b f(x)\,dx = \left[\int f(x)\,dx\right]_a^b$$

In this case, to evaluate the definite integral, a primitive function of $f(x)$ should be found. Definite and indefinite integrals can be transformed one into another by the following rules.

Substitution. By introducing an auxiliary function $x = \varphi(t)$, where the new variable t is a single-valued function $t = \psi(x)$ of x in the interval $[a, b]$, the integral can be transformed into the form:

$$\int_a^b f(x)\,dx = \int_{\psi(a)}^{\psi(b)} f(\varphi(t))\,\varphi'(t)\,dt$$

Using this formula, the inverse substitution in evaluating the indefinite integral can be avoided. For example:

$$\int_0^a \sqrt{a^2 - x^2}\,dx = \int_{\text{arc sin } 0}^{\text{arc sin } 1} a^2\sqrt{1 - \sin^2 t}\,d\sin t = a^2 \int_0^{\pi/2} \cos^2 t\,dt$$

$$= a^2 \int_0^{\pi/2} \frac{1}{2}(1 + \cos 2t)\,dt = \frac{a^2}{2}[t]_0^{\pi/2} + \frac{a^2}{4}\int_0^\pi \cos z\,dz$$

$$= \frac{\pi a^2}{4} + \frac{a^2}{4}[\sin z]_0^\pi = \frac{\pi a^2}{4}$$

Integration by Parts. The expression $f(x)\,dx$ can be written in an arbitrary way, in the form $u\,dv$; du can be found by differentiation and v by integration. The definite integral this way can be transformed into the form:

$$\int_a^b f(x)\,dx = \int_a^b u\,dv = [uv]_a^b - \int_a^b v\,du$$

For example:

$$\int_0^1 x\,e^x\,dx = [xe^x]_0^1 - \int_0^1 e^x\,dx = e - (e - 1) = 1$$

Integration by Expansion into a Series. If $f(x)$ is represented in the interval of integration by a uniformly convergent series of functions:

$$f(x) = \varphi_1(x) + \varphi_2(x) + \cdots + \varphi_n(x) + \cdots$$

then the following relationship holds:

$$\int f(x)\,dx = \int \varphi_1(x)\,dx + \int \varphi_2(x)\,dx + \cdots + \int \varphi_n(x)\,dx + \cdots$$

Thus, the definite integral can be represented as a convergent series of numbers:

$$\int_a^b f(x)\,dx = \int_a^b \varphi_1(x)\,dx + \int_a^b \varphi_2(x)\,dx + \cdots + \int_a^b \varphi_n(x)\,dx + \cdots$$

If the functions $\varphi_1(x)$ can be easily integrated, as with an expansion of $f(x)$ into a power series uniformly convergent in the interval $[a, b]$, then the integral $\int_a^b f(x)\,dx$ can be evaluated with an arbitrary accuracy.

Improper Integrals. If one limit is infinite, then:

$$\int_a^\infty f(x)\,dx = \lim_{b \to \infty} \int_a^b f(x)\,dx$$

The integral exists, or converges, if there exist numbers $k > 1$ and M independent of x in a relationship $x^k|f(x)| < M$ for arbitrarily large values of x. If $x|f(x)| > m$, an arbitrary positive number, for sufficiently large values of x, the interval diverges. For example, the integral:

$$\int_0^\infty \frac{x\,dx}{(x + x^2)^{1/2}}$$

exists because, for $k = 2$ and $M = 1$, $x^2 \left| \dfrac{x}{(x + x^2)^{1/2}} \right| = \left(\dfrac{x^2}{x + x^2} \right)^{1/2} < 1,$

regardless of how large x becomes. If the integrand is infinite at the upper limit, then:

$$\int_a^b f(x)\,dx = \lim_{\epsilon \to 0} \int_a^{b-\epsilon} f(x)\,dx, \text{ with } 0 < \epsilon < (b - a)$$

The integral exists if numbers $k < 1$ and M independent of x exist in the relationship $(b - x)^k|f(x)| < M$ for $a \le x < b$. If there is a number $k \ge 1$ and a number m such that $(b - x)^k|f(x)| > m$ for $a \le x < b$, the integral diverges. For example, the integral:

$$\int_0^1 \frac{dx}{1 - x}$$

diverges, because for $k = 1$ and $m = \frac{1}{2}$, $\dfrac{1 - x}{1 - x} = 1 > \frac{1}{2}$.

The tests are analogous if the integrand is infinite at the lower limit. If the integrand is infinite at an intermediate point, the point is used to divide the interval into two subintervals and the above tests are applied.

Multiple Integrals. Let $f(x, y)$ be defined in the region R of the xy plane. Divide R into subregions $\Delta R_1, \Delta R_2, \ldots, \Delta R_n$ of areas $\Delta A_1, \Delta A_2, \ldots, \Delta A_n$. Let (ξ_i, η_i) be any point in ΔR_i. If the sum:

$$\sum_{i=1}^n f(\xi_i, \eta_i)\,\Delta A_i$$

has a limit as $n > \infty$ and the maximum diameter of the subregions ΔR_i approaches 0, then:

$$\int_R f(x, y)\, dA = \lim_{n \to \infty} \sum_{i=1}^{n} f(\xi_i, \eta_i)\, \Delta A_i$$

The double integral is evaluated by two successive single integrations. It is first evaluated with respect to y holding x constant, between variable limits of integration, and then with respect to x between constant limits, as shown in Fig. 5. If $f(x, y)$ is continuous, the order of integration can be reversed:

$$\int_R f(x, y)\, dA = \int_a^b \int_{y_1(x)}^{y_2(x)} f(x, y)\, dy\, dx = \int_c^d \int_{x_1(y)}^{x_2(y)} f(x, y)\, dx\, dy$$

In polar coordinates:

$$\int_R F(r, \theta)\, dA = \int_\alpha^\beta \int_{r_1(\theta)}^{r_2(\theta)} F(r, \theta)\, r\, dr\, d\theta = \int_k^l \int_{\theta_1(r)}^{\theta_2(r)} F(r, \theta)\, r\, d\theta\, dr$$

Similarly, triple integrals are evaluated by three single integrations. In rectangular coordinates:

$$\int_R f(x, y, z)\, dV = \iiint f(x, y, z)\, dx\, dy\, dz$$

In spherical coordinates:

$$\int_R F(r, \theta, \phi)\, dV = \iiint F(r, \theta, \phi)\, r^2 \sin \theta\, dr\, d\theta\, d\phi$$

In cylindrical coordinates:

$$\int_R G(\rho, \phi, z)\, dv = \iiint G(\rho, \phi, z)\, \rho\, d\rho\, d\phi\, dz$$

Integrals Depending on a Parameter. The definite integral:

$$\int_a^b f(x, y)\, dx = F(y)$$

is a function of the variable y called a parameter.

The function $F(y)$ often is not an elementary function. The integral may be an ordinary integral, an improper integral or an integral of a discontinuous function $f(x, y)$. For example:

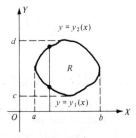

Figure 5

$$\Gamma(y) = \int_0^\infty x^{y-1} e^{-x} dx$$

with the integral convergent for $y > 0$. This is the Gamma function or Euler's integral of the second kind.

Differentiation Under the Integral Sign.   If the function:

$$\int_a^b f(x, y)\, dx = F(y)$$

is defined in the interval $c \leq y \leq e$ and the function $f(x, y)$ is continuous in the rectangle $a \leq x \leq b$, $c \leq y \leq e$ with a continuous partial derivative $\dfrac{\partial f}{\partial y}$ in this domain, then, for every y in the interval $[c, e]$, there is:

$$\frac{d}{dy} \int_a^b f(x, y)\, dx = \int_a^b \frac{\partial f(x, y)}{\partial y}\, dx$$

For example, in an arbitrary interval, for $y > 0$:

$$\frac{d}{dy} \int_0^1 \arctan \frac{x}{y}\, dx = \int_0^1 \frac{\partial}{\partial y} \left(\arctan \frac{x}{y} \right) dx =$$

$$- \int_0^1 \frac{x}{x^2 + y^2}\, dx = \tfrac{1}{2} \ln \frac{y^2}{1 + y^2}$$

Expressed another way:

$$\int_0^1 \arctan \frac{x}{y}\, dx = \arctan \frac{1}{y} + \frac{1}{2} y \ln \frac{y^2}{1 + y^2}$$

$$\frac{d}{dy} \left(\arctan \frac{1}{y} + \frac{1}{2} y \ln \frac{1}{1 + y^2} \right) = \frac{1}{2} \ln \frac{y^2}{1 + y^2}$$

Integration Under the Integral Sign.   If the function:

$$\int_a^b f(x, y)\, dx = F(y)$$

is defined in the interval $[c, e]$ and the function $f(x, y)$ is continuous in the rectangle $a \leq x \leq b$, $c \leq y \leq e$, then:

$$\int_c^e \left(\int_a^b f(x, y)\, dx \right) dy = \int_a^b \left(\int_c^e f(x, y)\, dy \right) dx$$

LINE, SURFACE, AND VOLUME INTEGRALS

Line Integrals.   The functions $P(x, y)$ and $Q(x, y)$ are continuous at all points of a continuous curve C joining the points A and B in the xy plane as shown in Fig. 6. The curve C is divided into n arbitrary parts Δs_v by the points (x_ν, y_ν) and (ξ_ν, η_ν) is an arbitrary point on Δs_ν. The increments Δx_ν and Δy_ν are projections of ΔS_ν on the x and the y axes. The line integral is:

$$\int_A^B [P(x, y)\,dx + Q(x, y)\,dy] =$$

$$\lim_{\substack{n \to \infty \\ \max \Delta x_\nu,\, \Delta y_\nu \to 0}} \sum_{\nu-1}^n [P(\xi_\nu, \eta_\nu)\Delta x_\nu + Q(\xi_\nu, \eta_\nu)\Delta y_\nu]$$

If the equation of the curve C is $y = f(x)$, $x = \phi(y)$, or the parametric equations $x = x(t)$, $y = y(t)$, the line integral may be evaluated as a definite integral in variable x, y, or t, respectively. A line integral in xyz:

$$\int_A^B [P(x, y, z)\,dx + Q(x, y, z)\,dy + R(x, y, z)\,dz]$$

is similarly defined. The work done by a constant force F, acting on a particle moving a distance s along a straight line inclined at angle θ to the force, is $W = Fs\cos\theta$. If the path is defined as a curve C and the force is variable, the differential of work is $dW = F\cos\theta\,ds$, where ds is the differential of path. Then:

$$W = \int dW = \int_C F\cos\theta\,ds = \int_C (X\,dx + Y\,dy)$$

where X and Y are the x and y components of F, as shown in Fig. 7.

Surface Areas by Integration. If a plane curve is rotated about an axis in its plane, the area of the surface of revolution is given by:

$$S = 2\pi \int_a^b y\,ds$$

where

$$y = \text{distance from axis to curve}$$
$$ds = \text{differential of length of arc}$$

For example, the surface area generated by rotating the hypocycloid $x^{2/3} + y^{2/3} = a^{2/3}$ about the x axis is found by computing the area from $x = 0$ to $x = a$ and multiplying by 2:

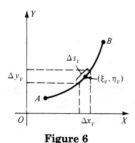

Figure 6

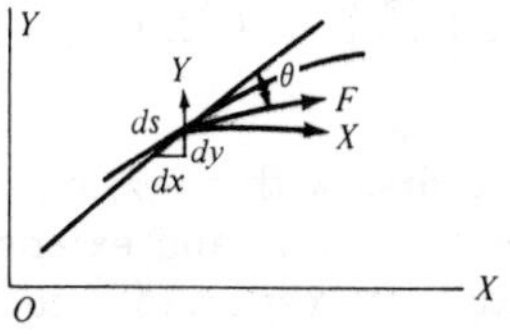

Figure 7

$$y = (a^{2/3} - x^{2/3})^{3/2} \qquad y' = -\frac{y^{1/3}}{x^{1/3}} \qquad 1 + y'^2 = 1 + \frac{y^{2/3}}{x^{2/3}} = \frac{a^{2/3}}{x^{2/3}}$$

$$ds = (1 + y'^2)^{1/2} \qquad dx = \frac{a^{1/3}}{x^{1/3}}\, dx$$

$$S = 4\pi \int_0^a (a^{2/3} - x^{2/3})^{3/2} \left(\frac{a^{1/3}}{x^{1/3}}\right) dx$$

To integrate, let $z^2 = a^{2/3} - x^{2/3}$. Then $2z\, dz = -2/3x^{-1/3}\, dx$ and $dx = -3zx^{1/3}\, dz$. When $x = 0$, $z = a^{1/3}$; when $x = a$, $z = 0$:

$$S = 4\pi a^{1/3} \int_{a^{1/3}}^0 z^3 x^{-1/3} (-3zx^{1/3}\, dz)$$

$$= 12\pi a^{1/3} \int_0^{a^{1/3}} z^4\, dz$$

$$= 12\pi a^{1/3} [1/5z^5]_0^{a^{1/3}}$$

$$= \frac{12\pi a^2}{5}$$

The area of any curved surface in rectangular coordinates is given by:

$$A = \iint_S \left[1 + \left(\frac{\partial z}{\partial x}\right)^2 + \left(\frac{\partial z}{\partial y}\right)^2\right]^{1/2} dy\, dx$$

$$= \iint_S \left[1 + \left(\frac{\partial y}{\partial x}\right)^2 + \left(\frac{\partial y}{\partial z}\right)^2\right]^{1/2} dz\, dx$$

$$= \iint_S \left[1 + \left(\frac{\partial x}{\partial y}\right)^2 + \left(\frac{\partial x}{\partial z}\right)^2\right]^{1/2} dz\, dy$$

For example, the area of the surface of the sphere $x^2 + y^2 + z^2 = r^2$ is formed by computing the area in the first octant, then multiplying by 8:

$$\frac{\partial z}{\partial x} = -\frac{x}{z}$$

$$\frac{\partial z}{\partial y} = -\frac{y}{z}$$

$$1 + \left(\frac{\partial z}{\partial x}\right)^2 + \left(\frac{\partial z}{\partial y}\right)^2 = 1 + \frac{x^2}{z^2} + \frac{y^2}{z^2} = \frac{z^2 + x^2 + y^2}{z^2} = \frac{r^2}{r^2 - x^2 - y^2}$$

Integrate first with respect to y, holding x constant, to find the area of an increment dx wide and extending from the xz plane to the xy plane. Then integrate with respect to x, to add the increments from $x = 0$ to $x = r$:

$$A = 8 \int_0^r \int_0^{\sqrt{r^2-x^2}} \left[\frac{r^2}{r^2 - x^2 - y^2} \right]^{1/2} dy\, dx$$

$$= 8r \int_0^r \left[\arcsin \frac{y}{\sqrt{r^2 - x^2}} \right]_0^{\sqrt{r^2-x^2}} dx$$

$$= 8r \int_0^r \frac{\pi}{2} dx = 4\pi r [x]_0^r = 4\pi r^2$$

Volumes by Integration. When a plane curve is rotated about an axis in its plane, the volume of the solid generated is:

$$V = \pi \int_a^b y^2\, dx$$

where

$$y = \text{distance from axis to curve}$$
$$dx = \text{differential length along axis}$$

The integration is equivalent to adding circular cross sections of thickness dx.

A volume of revolution also is given by:

$$V = 2\pi \int_{r_1}^r rh\, dr$$

where

$$r = \text{distance from axis to curve}$$
$$h = \text{length of element of volume normal to } r$$

The integration is equivalent to adding cylinders of thickness dr.

In polar coordinates, a volume of revolution is given by:

$$V = 2\pi \int_\alpha^\beta \int_c^d r^2 \sin\theta\, dr\, d\theta$$

The volume of a solid in rectangular coordinates generally is given by:

$$V = \int_a^b \int_m^n f(x, y)\, dy\, dx = \int_c^d \int_p^q f(x, y)\, dx\, dy$$

where m and n denote functions of x, and p and q denote functions of y.

In cylindrical coordinates, volume is given by:

$$V = \int_\alpha^\beta \int_a^b f(r, \theta) r\, dr\, d\theta = \int_c^d \int_\gamma^\delta f(r, \theta) r\, d\theta\, dr$$

where a and b denote functions of r, and γ and δ denote functions of θ.

Volume can also be calculated by triple integration:

$$V = \iiint\limits_V dV = \int_a^b \int_m^n \int_u^v dz\, dy\, dx$$

where u and v denote functions of y, and m and n denote functions of x.

Green's Theorem. If $P(x, y)$ and $Q(x, y)$ are continuous functions with continuous partial derivatives $\dfrac{\partial P}{\partial y}$ and $\dfrac{\partial Q}{\partial z}$ in a simply connected region R bounded by a simple closed curve C, then:

$$\iint\limits_R \left(\frac{\partial Q}{\partial x} - \frac{\partial P}{\partial y}\right) dx\, dy = \int_C (P\, dx + Q\, dy)$$

A simply connected region is defined as one in which any closed curve in the region can be reduced to a point without passing outside the region.

Stokes' Theorem. If $P(x, y, z)$, $Q(x, y, z)$, $R(x, y, z)$ are continuous functions having continuous first partial derivatives, and if S is a region that is bounded by a simple closed curve C and part of a surface $z = f(x, y)$, continuous with continuous first partial derivatives, then:

$$\iint\limits_S \left[\left(\frac{\partial R}{\partial y} - \frac{\partial Q}{\partial z}\right) dy\, dz + \left(\frac{\partial P}{\partial z} - \frac{\partial R}{\partial x}\right) dz\, dx + \left(\frac{\partial Q}{\partial x} - \frac{\partial P}{\partial y}\right) dx\, dy \right] =$$

$$\int_C (P\, dx + Q\, dy + R\, dz)$$

The signs are determined by a viewpoint in the direction of the normal resulting in the integration around C taken in the positive direction.

APPLICATIONS OF INTEGRATION

Length of Arc. For an arc of a plane curve $y = f(x)$, the length s from the point (a, b) to the point (c, d) is expressed as:

$$s = \int_a^c \sqrt{1 + \left(\frac{dy}{dx}\right)^2}\, dx = \int_b^d \sqrt{1 + \left(\frac{dx}{dy}\right)^2}\, dy$$

In polar coordinates, with $r = f(\theta)$, the length of the arc from the point (r_1, θ_1) to the point (r_2, θ_2) becomes:

$$s = \int_{\theta_1}^{\theta_2} \sqrt{r^2 + \left(\frac{dr}{d\theta}\right)^2}\, d\theta = \int_{r_1}^{r_2} \sqrt{1 + r^2 \left(\frac{d\theta}{dr}\right)^2}\, dr$$

In three dimensions, with the curve represented by the equations $y = f_1(x)$ and $z = f_2(x)$, the length of arc from $x_1 = a$ to $x_2 = b$ is:

$$s = \int_a^b \sqrt{1 + \left(\frac{dy}{dx}\right)^2 + \left(\frac{dz}{dx}\right)^2}\, dx$$

Areas of Plane Figures. For the curve $y = f(x)$, the area bounded by $f(x)$, the x axis, and the ordinates $x = a$ and $x = b$ is given by:

$$A = \int_a^b y \, dx$$

The area above the x axis is represented as positive, that below the x axis is negative. In polar coordinates, the area under a curve is:

$$A = \frac{1}{2} \int_\alpha^\beta \rho^2 d\theta$$

In rectangular coordinates, the area under a curve is also determined by the double integral:

$$A = \iint_A dA = \iint dx \, dy$$

In polar coordinates, the double integral becomes:

$$A = \iint \rho \, d\rho \, d\theta$$

The area bounded by a closed curve C also can be determined by the line integral:

$$A = \frac{1}{2} \int_C (-y \, dx + x \, dy)$$

Area of a Surface. The formula for area of a surface formed by revolution of a curve $y = f(x)$ about the x axis, as shown in Fig. 8a, is determined by:

$$S = 2\pi \int_a^b y \, dl = 2\pi \int_a^b y \sqrt{1 + \left(\frac{dy}{dx}\right)^2} \, dx$$

The area of a surface formed by revolution of a curve $x = g(y)$ about the y axis, as shown in Fig. 8b, is determined by:

$$S = 2\pi \int_\alpha^\beta x \, dl = 2\pi \int_\alpha^\beta x \sqrt{\left(\frac{dx}{dy}\right)^2 + 1} \, dy$$

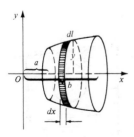

Figure 8a

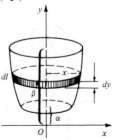

Figure 8b

Volume. The formula for the interior volume of a surface of revolution, about the x axis, as shown in Fig. 8a, is determined by:

$$V = \pi \int_a^b y^2 \, dx$$

The volume of a surface of revolution about the y axis, as shown in Fig. 8b, is given by:

$$V = \pi \int_\alpha^\beta x^2 \, dy$$

For the volume of a solid, when the area of its plane section perpendicular to the x axis is given as a function $S = f(x)$, as shown in Fig. 9, the formula is:

$$V = \int_a^b f(x) \, dx$$

Work. The work represented by the force F acting from the point $x = a$ to $x = b$ of the x axis, when the force is a function $F = f(x)$, is given by the formula:

$$A = \int_a^b F \, dx$$

Fluid Pressure. For a fluid with specific gravity γ, the pressure on one side of a vertical plate immersed in the fluid can be determined by the following formula, when the distance x of the points of the plate from the level of the fluid varies from a to b, and where y is the length of a horizontal section of the plate ($y = f(x)$), as shown in Fig. 10:

$$P = \int_a^b \gamma x y \, dx$$

Center of Pressure. The depth $\bar{y}$ of the center of pressure against a surface vertical to the liquid surface between the depths a and b is:

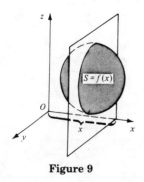

Figure 9

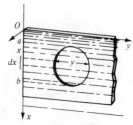

Figure 10

$$\bar{y} = \frac{\int_{y=a}^{y=b} \gamma y^2 \, dA}{\int_{y=a}^{y=b} \gamma y \, dA}$$

Moment of Inertia. The moment of inertia of an arc of a homogeneous curve $y = f(x)$, with $a \le x \le b$, with respect to the y axis is given by the formula:

$$I_y = \delta \int_a^b x^2 \, dl = \delta \int_a^b x^2 \sqrt{1 + (y')^2} \, dx$$

where δ is the linear density of the arc.

The moment of inertia of a plane figure, as shown in Fig. 11, with respect to the y axis is given by:

$$I_y = \int_a^b x^2 y \, dx$$

where y is the length of a section parallel to the y axis and δ is the surface density of the figure.

Center of Gravity. The center of gravity C of an arc of a homogeneous plane curve $y = f(x)$, with $a \le x \le b$, as shown in Fig. 12a, has the coordinates:

$$x_C = \frac{\int_a^b x \sqrt{1 + y'^2} \, dx}{L}$$

$$y_C = \frac{\int_a^b y \sqrt{1 + y'^2} \, dx}{L}$$

where L is the length of the arc. The center of gravity of a closed curve, as

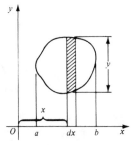

Figure 11

shown in Fig. 12b, has coordinates:

$$x_C = \frac{\int_a^b x(\sqrt{1 + |y_1'|^2} + \sqrt{1 + |y_2'|^2})\,dx}{L}$$

$$y_C = \frac{\int_a^b (y_1\sqrt{1 + |y_1'|^2} + y_2\sqrt{1 + |y_2'|^2})\,dx}{L}$$

where $y_1 = f_1(x)$ and $y_2 = f_2(x)$ are the equations of the upper and lower part of the bounding curve and L is the length of the entire curve.

For a homogeneous curvilinear trapezoid, as shown in Fig. 12c, the center of gravity C has the coordinates:

$$x_C = \frac{\int_a^b xy\,dx}{S}$$

$$y_C = \frac{\frac{1}{2}\int_a^b y^2\,dx}{S}$$

where S is the area of the trapezoid and $y = f(x)$ is the equation of the curve AB. For an arbitrary plane figure, as shown in Fig. 12d, the center of gravity has the coordinates:

$$x_C = \frac{\int_a^b x(y_1 - y_2)\,dx}{S}$$

$$y_C = \frac{\frac{1}{2}\int_a^b (y_1^2 - y_2^2)\,dx}{S}$$

where $y_1 = f_1(x)$ and $y_2 = f_2(x)$ are the equations of the upper and lower portions of the bounding curve and S is the area.

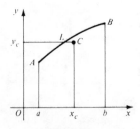

Figure 12a

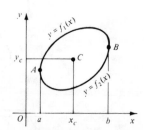

Figure 12b

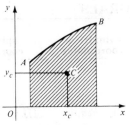

Figure 12c

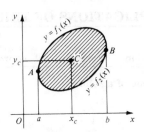

Figure 12d

APPLICATIONS OF DOUBLE INTEGRALS

Notation Formula	In Cartesian coordinates	In polar coordinates

Area of a plane figure

$$S \ldots \int_S dS \qquad\qquad \iint dydx \qquad\qquad\qquad \iint \rho\, d\rho d\varphi$$

Area of a surface

$$\Sigma \ldots \int_S \frac{dS}{\cos\gamma} \quad \iint \sqrt{1 + \left(\frac{\partial z}{\partial x}\right)^2 + \left(\frac{\partial z}{\partial y}\right)^2}\, dydx \quad \iint \sqrt{\rho^2 + \rho^2 \left(\frac{\partial z}{\partial \rho}\right)^2 + \left(\frac{\partial z}{\partial \varphi}\right)^2}\, d\rho d\varphi$$

Volume of a cylinder

$$V \ldots \int_S z\, dS \qquad\qquad \iint z\, dydx \qquad\qquad\qquad \iint z\rho\, d\rho d\varphi$$

Moment of inertia(a)

$$I_x \ldots \int_S y^2\, dS \qquad\qquad \iint y^2\, dydx \qquad\qquad\qquad \iint \rho^3 \sin^2\varphi\, d\rho d\varphi$$

Moment of inertia(b)

$$I_0 \ldots \int_S \rho^3\, dS \qquad\qquad \iint (x^2 + y^2)\, dydx \qquad\qquad\qquad \iint \rho^3\, d\rho d\varphi$$

Mass of a plane figure(c)

$$M \ldots \int_S \delta\, dS \qquad\qquad \iint \delta\, dydx \qquad\qquad\qquad \iint \delta\rho\, d\rho d\varphi$$

$$x_C \ldots \frac{\int_S x\, dS}{S} \qquad\qquad \frac{\iint x\, dydx}{\iint dydx} \qquad\qquad\qquad \frac{\iint \rho^2 \cos\varphi\, d\rho d\varphi}{\iint \rho\, d\rho d\varphi}$$

Coordinates of the center of gravity(d)

$$y_C \ldots \frac{\int_S y\, dS}{S} \qquad\qquad \frac{\iint y\, dydx}{\iint dydx} \qquad\qquad\qquad \frac{\iint \rho^2 \sin\varphi\, d\rho d\varphi}{\iint \rho\, d\rho d\varphi}$$

(a) Of a plane figure with respect to the x axis. (b) Of a plane figure with respect to a pole O. (c) With surface density δ given as a function of a point. (d) Of a plane homogeneous figure

APPLICATIONS OF TRIPLE INTEGRALS

Notation	Formula	In Cartesian coordinates	In cylindrical coordinates	In spherical coordinates
Volume of a solid				
V	$\int_V dV$	$\iiint dz\,dy\,dx$	$\iiint \rho\,dz\,d\rho\,d\varphi$	$\iiint r^3 \sin\theta\,dr\,d\theta\,d\varphi$
Moment of inertia(a)				
I_z	$\int_V \rho^2\,dV$	$\iiint (x^2+y^2)\,dz\,dy\,dx$	$\iiint \rho^3\,dz\,d\rho\,d\varphi$	$\iiint r^4 \sin^3\theta\,dr\,d\theta\,d\varphi$
Mass of a solid(b)				
M	$\int_V \delta\,dV$	$\iiint \delta\,dz\,dy\,dx$	$\iiint \delta\rho\,dz\,d\rho\,d\varphi$	$\iiint \delta r^3 \sin\theta\,dr\,d\theta\,d\varphi$
x_C	$\dfrac{\int_V y\,dV}{V}$	$\dfrac{\iiint y\,dz\,dy\,dx}{\iiint dz\,dy\,dx}$		
Coordinates of the center of gravity(c)				
y_C	$\dfrac{\int_V y\,dV}{V}$	$\dfrac{\iiint y\,dz\,dy\,dx}{\iiint dz\,dy\,dx}$		
z_C	$\dfrac{\int_V z\,dV}{V}$	$\dfrac{\iiint z\,dz\,dy\,dx}{\iiint dz\,dy\,dx}$		

(a) Of a solid with respect to the z axis. (b) With density δ given as a function of a point. (c) Of a homogeneous solid.

9
Table of Integrals

INDEFINITE INTEGRALS

The constant of integration should be added to the result in each case. The letter x represents any variable, and u is any function of x. Arbitrary constants are denoted as a, b; and $\log_e u \equiv \log u$, unless otherwise stated. Angles are in radians. In general, symbols for inverse relations are principal values and $\sqrt{}$ has the positive value. When an integration gives a constant A times the logarithm of a negative number N, use $A \log |N|$.

INTEGRALS WITH $(ax + b)$

1. $\displaystyle\int (ax+b)^n\,dx = \frac{1}{a(n+1)}(ax+b)^{n+1} \qquad (n \neq -1)$

2. $\displaystyle\int \frac{dx}{ax+b} = \frac{1}{a}\log_e(ax+b)$

3. $\displaystyle\int \frac{dx}{(ax+b)^2} = -\frac{1}{a(ax+b)}$

4. $\displaystyle\int \frac{dx}{(ax+b)^3} = -\frac{1}{2a(ax+b)^2}$

5. $\displaystyle\int x(ax+b)^n\,dx = \frac{1}{a^2(n+2)}(ax+b)^{n+2} - \frac{b}{a^2(n+1)}(ax+b)^{n+1}$

$$(n \neq -1, -2)$$

6. $\displaystyle\int \frac{x\,dx}{ax+b} = \frac{x}{a} - \frac{b}{a^2}\log(ax+b)$

7. $\displaystyle\int \frac{x\,dx}{(ax+b)^2} = \frac{b}{a^2(ax+b)} + \frac{1}{a^2}\log(ax+b)$

8. $\displaystyle\int \frac{x\,dx}{(ax+b)^3} = \frac{b}{2a^2(ax+b)^2} - \frac{1}{a^2(ax+b)}$

9. $\displaystyle\int x^2(ax+b)^n\,dx = \frac{1}{a^3}\left[\frac{(ax+b)^{n+3}}{n+3} - \right.$

$$\left. 2b\frac{(ax+b)^{n+2}}{n+2} + b^2\frac{(ax+b)^{n+1}}{n+1}\right] \qquad (n \neq -1, -2, -3)$$

10. $\displaystyle\int \frac{x^2\,dx}{ax+b} = \frac{1}{a^3}\left[\frac{1}{2}\,(ax+b)^2 - 2b\,(ax+b) + b^2 \log\,(ax+b)\right]$

11. $\displaystyle\int \frac{x^2\,dx}{(ax+b)^2} = \frac{1}{a^3}\left[ax+b - 2b\log\,(ax+b) - \frac{b^2}{ax+b}\right]$

12. $\displaystyle\int \frac{x^2\,dx}{(ax+b)^3} = \frac{1}{a^3}\left[\log\,(ax+b) + \frac{2b}{ax+b} - \frac{b^2}{2\,(ax+b)^2}\right]$

13. $\displaystyle\int x^m\,(ax+b)^n\,dx$

$$= \frac{1}{a\,(m+n+1)}\left[x^m\,(ax+b)^{n+1} - mb\int x^{m-1}\,(ax+b)^n\,dx\right]$$

$$= \frac{1}{m+n+1}\left[x^{m+1}\,(ax+b)^n + nb\int x^m\,(ax+b)^{n-1}\,dx\right]$$

$$(m>0,\ m+n+1 \neq 0)$$

14. $\displaystyle\int \frac{dx}{x\,(ax+b)} = \frac{1}{b}\log\frac{x}{ax+b}$

15. $\displaystyle\int \frac{dx}{x^2\,(ax+b)} = -\frac{1}{bx} + \frac{a}{b^2}\log\frac{ax+b}{x}$

16. $\displaystyle\int \frac{dx}{x^3\,(ax+b)} = \frac{2ax-b}{2b^2x^2} + \frac{a^2}{b^3}\log\frac{x}{ax+b}$

17. $\displaystyle\int \frac{dx}{x\,(ax+b)^2} = \frac{1}{b\,(ax+b)} - \frac{1}{b^2}\log\frac{ax+b}{x}$

18. $\displaystyle\int \frac{dx}{x\,(ax+b)^3} = \frac{1}{b^3}\left[\frac{1}{2}\left(\frac{ax+2b}{ax+b}\right)^2 + \log\frac{x}{ax+b}\right]$

19. $\displaystyle\int \frac{dx}{x^2\,(ax+b)^2} = -\frac{b+2ax}{b^2x\,(ax+b)} + \frac{2a}{b^3}\log\frac{ax+b}{x}$

20. $\displaystyle\int \sqrt{ax+b}\,dx = \frac{2}{3a}\sqrt{(ax+b)^3}$

21. $\displaystyle\int x\sqrt{ax+b}\,dx = \frac{2\,(3ax-2b)}{15a^2}\sqrt{(ax+b)^3}$

22. $\displaystyle\int x^2\sqrt{ax+b}\,dx = \frac{2\,(15a^2x^2 - 12abx + 8b^2)\sqrt{(ax+b)^3}}{105a^3}$

23. $\displaystyle\int x^3\sqrt{ax+b}\,dx = \frac{2\,(35a^3x^3 - 30a^2bx^2 + 24ab^2x - 16b^3)\sqrt{(ax+b)^3}}{315a^4}$

24. $\displaystyle\int x^n\sqrt{ax+b}\,dx = \frac{2}{a^{n+1}}\int u^2(u^2-b)^n\,du \qquad (u = \sqrt{ax+b})$

25. $\displaystyle\int \frac{\sqrt{ax+b}}{x}\,dx = 2\sqrt{ax+b} + b\int \frac{dx}{x\sqrt{ax+b}}$

26. $\displaystyle\int \frac{dx}{\sqrt{ax+b}} = \frac{2\sqrt{ax+b}}{a}$

27. $\displaystyle\int \frac{x\,dx}{\sqrt{ax+b}} = \frac{2(ax-2b)}{3a^2}\sqrt{ax+b}$

28. $\displaystyle\int \frac{x^2\,dx}{\sqrt{ax+b}} = \frac{2(3a^2x^2 - 4abx + 8b^2)}{15a^3}\sqrt{ax+b}$

29. $\displaystyle\int \frac{x^3\,dx}{\sqrt{ax+b}} = \frac{2(5a^3x^3 - 6a^2bx^2 + 8ab^2x - 16b^3)}{35a^4}\sqrt{ax+b}$

30. $\displaystyle\int \frac{x^n\,dx}{\sqrt{ax+b}} = \frac{2}{a^{n+1}}\int (u^2 - b)^n\,du \qquad (u = \sqrt{ax+b})$

31. $\displaystyle\int \frac{dx}{x\sqrt{ax+b}} = \frac{1}{\sqrt{b}}\log \frac{\sqrt{ax+b} - \sqrt{b}}{\sqrt{ax+b} + \sqrt{b}} \qquad\qquad (b > 0)$

32. $\displaystyle\int \frac{dx}{x\sqrt{ax+b}} = \begin{cases} \dfrac{2}{\sqrt{-b}}\tan^{-1}\sqrt{\dfrac{ax+b}{-b}} & (b < 0) \\[2ex] \dfrac{-2}{\sqrt{b}}\tanh^{-1}\sqrt{\dfrac{ax+b}{b}} & (b > 0) \end{cases}$

33. $\displaystyle\int \frac{dx}{x^2\sqrt{ax+b}} = -\frac{\sqrt{ax+b}}{bx} - \frac{a}{2b}\int \frac{dx}{x\sqrt{ax+b}}$

34. $\displaystyle\int \frac{dx}{x^3\sqrt{ax+b}} = -\frac{\sqrt{ax+b}}{2bx^2} + \frac{3a\sqrt{ax+b}}{4b^2x} + \frac{3a^2}{8b^2}\int \frac{dx}{x\sqrt{ax+b}}$

35. $\displaystyle\int \frac{dx}{x^n(ax+b)^m} = -\frac{1}{b^{m+n-1}}\int \frac{(u-a)^{m+n-2}\,du}{u^m} \qquad \left(u = \frac{ax+b}{x}\right)$

36. $\displaystyle\int (ax+b)^{\pm(n/2)}\,dx = \frac{2(ax+b)^{(2\pm n)/2}}{a(2\pm n)}$

37. $\displaystyle\int x(ax+b)^{\pm(n/2)}\,dx = \frac{2}{a^2}\left[\frac{(ax+b)^{(4\pm n)/2}}{4\pm n} - \frac{b(ax+b)^{(2\pm n)/2}}{2\pm n}\right]$

38. $\displaystyle\int \frac{dx}{x(ax+b)^{n/2}} = \frac{1}{b}\int \frac{dx}{x(ax+b)^{(n-2)/2}} - \frac{a}{b}\int \frac{dx}{(ax+b)^{n/2}}$

39. $\displaystyle\int \frac{x^m\,dx}{\sqrt{ax+b}} = \frac{2x^m\sqrt{ax+b}}{(2m+1)a} - \frac{2mb}{(2m+1)a}\int \frac{x^{m-1}\,dx}{\sqrt{ax+b}}$

40. $\displaystyle\int \frac{dx}{x^n\sqrt{ax+b}} = \frac{-\sqrt{ax+b}}{(n-1)bx^{n-1}} - \frac{(2n-3)a}{(2n-2)b}\int \frac{dx}{x^{n-1}\sqrt{ax+b}}$

41. $\int \dfrac{(ax + b)^{n/2}}{x} dx = a \int (ax + b)^{(n-2)/2} dx + b \int \dfrac{(ax + b)^{(n-2)/2}}{x} dx$

42. $\int \dfrac{dx}{(ax + b)(cx + d)} = \dfrac{1}{bc - ad} \log \dfrac{cx + d}{ax + b}$ $\qquad (bc - ad \neq 0)$

43. $\int \dfrac{dx}{(ax + b)^2(cx + d)} = \dfrac{1}{bc - ad} \left(\dfrac{1}{ax + b} + \dfrac{c}{bc - ad} \log \dfrac{cx + d}{ax + b} \right)$

$\qquad (bc - ad \neq 0)$

44. $\int (ax + b)^n (cx + d)^m dx = \dfrac{1}{(m + n + 1)a} \left[(ax + b)^{n+1}(cx + d)^m - \right.$

$\left. m(bc - ad) \int (ax + b)^n (cx + d)^{m-1} dx \right]$

45. $\int \dfrac{dx}{(ax + b)^n (cx + d)^m} = \dfrac{-1}{(m - 1)(bc - ad)} \left[\dfrac{1}{(ax + b)^{n-1}(cx + d)^{m-1}} + \right.$

$\left. a(m + n - 2) \int \dfrac{dx}{(ax + b)^n (cx + d)^{m-1}} \right] \quad (m > 1, n > 0, bc - ad \neq 0)$

46. $\int \dfrac{(ax + b)^n}{(cx + d)^m} dx = - \dfrac{1}{(m - 1)(bc - ad)} \left[\dfrac{(ax + b)^{n+1}}{(cx + d)^{m-1}} + \right.$

$\left. (m - n - 2)a \int \dfrac{(ax + b)^n dx}{(cx + d)^{m-1}} \right] = \dfrac{-1}{(m - n - 1)c} \left[\dfrac{(ax + b)^n}{(cx + d)^{m-1}} + \right.$

$\left. n(bc - ad) \int \dfrac{(ax + b)^{n-1}}{(cx + d)^m} dx \right]$

47. $\int \dfrac{x \, dx}{(ax + b)(cx + d)} = \dfrac{1}{bc - ad} \left[\dfrac{b}{a} \log (ax + b) - \dfrac{d}{c} \log (cx + d) \right]$

$\qquad (bc - ad \neq 0)$

48. $\int \dfrac{x \, dx}{(ax + b)^2(cx + d)} = \dfrac{1}{bc - ad} \left[- \dfrac{b}{a(ax + b)} - \dfrac{d}{bc - ad} \log \dfrac{cx + d}{ax + b} \right]$

$\qquad (bc - ad \neq 0)$

49. $\int \dfrac{cx + d}{\sqrt{ax + b}} dx = \dfrac{2}{3a^2} (3ad - 2bc + acx) \sqrt{ax + b}$

50. $\int \dfrac{\sqrt{ax + b}}{cx + d} dx = \dfrac{2\sqrt{ax + b}}{c} - \dfrac{2}{c} \sqrt{\dfrac{ad - bc}{c}} \tan^{-1} \sqrt{\dfrac{c(ax + b)}{ad - bc}}$

$\qquad (c > 0, ad > bc)$

51. $\int \dfrac{\sqrt{ax + b}}{cx + d} dx = \dfrac{2\sqrt{ax + b}}{c} + \dfrac{1}{c} \sqrt{\dfrac{bc - ad}{c}} \log \dfrac{\sqrt{c(ax + b)} - \sqrt{bc - ad}}{\sqrt{c(ax + b)} + \sqrt{bc - ad}}$

$\qquad (c > 0, bc > ad)$

$$52. \int \frac{dx}{(cx + d)\sqrt{ax + b}} = \frac{2}{\sqrt{c}\sqrt{ad - bc}} \tan^{-1} \sqrt{\frac{c(ax + b)}{ad - bc}}$$

$$(c > 0, ad > bc)$$

$$53. \int \frac{dx}{(cx + d)\sqrt{ax + b}} =$$

$$\frac{1}{\sqrt{c}\sqrt{bc - ad}} \log \frac{\sqrt{c(ax + b)} - \sqrt{bc - ad}}{\sqrt{c(ax + b)} + \sqrt{(bc - ad)}}, \qquad (c > 0, bc > ad)$$

INTEGRALS WITH $ax^2 + c$, $ax^n + c$, $x^2 \pm p^2$, AND $p^2 - x^2$

$$54. \int \frac{dx}{p^2 + x^2} = \frac{1}{p} \tan^{-1} \frac{x}{p} \qquad \text{or} \qquad -\frac{1}{p} \cot^{-1} \frac{x}{p}$$

$$55. \int \frac{dx}{p^2 - x^2} = \frac{1}{2p} \log \frac{p + x}{p - x} \qquad \text{or} \qquad \frac{1}{p} \tanh^{-1} \frac{x}{p}$$

$$56. \int \frac{dx}{ax^2 + c} = \frac{1}{\sqrt{ac}} \tan^{-1} \left(x \sqrt{\frac{a}{c}} \right) \qquad\qquad (a, c > 0)$$

$$57. \int \frac{dx}{ax^2 + c} = \begin{cases} \dfrac{1}{2\sqrt{-ac}} \log \dfrac{x\sqrt{a} - \sqrt{-c}}{x\sqrt{a} + \sqrt{-c}} & (a > 0, c < 0) \\[4mm] \dfrac{1}{2\sqrt{-ac}} \log \dfrac{\sqrt{c} + x\sqrt{-a}}{\sqrt{c} - x\sqrt{-a}} & (a < 0, c > 0) \end{cases}$$

$$58. \int \frac{dx}{(ax^2 + c)^n} = \frac{1}{2(n - 1)c} \frac{x}{(ax^2 + c)^{n-1}} + \frac{2n - 3}{2(n - 1)c} \int \frac{dx}{(ax^2 + c)^{n-1}} \, (n > 1)$$

$$59. \int x(ax^2 + c)^n \, dx = \frac{1}{2a} \frac{(ax^2 + c)^{n+1}}{n + 1} \qquad\qquad (n \neq -1)$$

$$60. \int \frac{x}{ax^2 + c} \, dx = \frac{1}{2a} \log (ax^2 + c)$$

$$61. \int \frac{dx}{x(ax^2 + c)} = \frac{1}{2c} \log \frac{x^2}{ax^2 + c}$$

$$62. \int \frac{dx}{x^2(ax^2 + c)} = -\frac{1}{cx} - \frac{a}{c} \int \frac{dx}{ax^2 + c}$$

$$63. \int \frac{x^2 \, dx}{ax^2 + c} = \frac{x}{a} - \frac{c}{a} \int \frac{dx}{ax^2 + c}$$

$$64. \int \frac{x^n \, dx}{ax^2 + c} = \frac{x^{n-1}}{a(n - 1)} - \frac{c}{a} \int \frac{x^{n-2} \, dx}{ax^2 + c} \qquad\qquad (n \neq 1)$$

$$65. \int \frac{x^2 \, dx}{(ax^2 + c)^n} = -\frac{1}{2(n - 1)a} \frac{x}{(ax^2 + c)^{n-1}} + \frac{1}{2(n - 1)a} \int \frac{dx}{(ax^2 + c)^{n-1}}$$

66. $\displaystyle\int \frac{dx}{x^2(ax^2+c)^n} = \frac{1}{c}\int \frac{dx}{x^2(ax^2+c)^{n-1}} - \frac{a}{c}\int \frac{dx}{(ax^2+c)^n}$

67. $\displaystyle\int \sqrt{x^2 \pm p^2}\, dx = \frac{1}{2}[x\sqrt{x^2 \pm p^2} \pm p^2 \log(x + \sqrt{x^2 \pm p^2})]$

68. $\displaystyle\int \sqrt{p^2 - x^2}\, dx = \frac{1}{2}\left(x\sqrt{p^2 - x^2} + p^2 \sin^{-1}\frac{x}{p}\right)$

69. $\displaystyle\int \frac{dx}{\sqrt{x^2 \pm p^2}} = \log(x + \sqrt{x^2 \pm p^2})$

70. $\displaystyle\int \frac{dx}{\sqrt{p^2 - x^2}} = \sin^{-1}\frac{x}{p} \quad \text{or} \quad -\cos^{-1}\frac{x}{p}$

71. $\displaystyle\int \sqrt{ax^2 + c}\, dx = \frac{x}{2}\sqrt{ax^2 + c} + \frac{c}{2\sqrt{a}}\log(x\sqrt{a} + \sqrt{ax^2 + c}) \qquad (a > 0)$

72. $\displaystyle\int \sqrt{ax^2 + c}\, dx = \frac{x}{2}\sqrt{ax^2 + c} + \frac{c}{2\sqrt{-a}}\sin^{-1}\left(x\sqrt{\frac{-a}{c}}\right) \qquad (a < 0)$

73. $\displaystyle\int \frac{dx}{\sqrt{ax^2 + c}} = \frac{1}{\sqrt{a}}\log(x\sqrt{a} + \sqrt{ax^2 + c}) \qquad (a > 0)$

74. $\displaystyle\int \frac{dx}{\sqrt{ax^2 + c}} = \frac{1}{\sqrt{-a}}\sin^{-1}\left(x\sqrt{\frac{-a}{c}}\right) \qquad (a < 0)$

75. $\displaystyle\int x\sqrt{ax^2 + c}\, dx = \frac{1}{3a}(ax^2 + c)^{3/2}$

76. $\displaystyle\int x^2\sqrt{ax^2 + c}\, dx = \frac{x}{4a}\sqrt{(ax^2 + c)^3} - \frac{cx}{8a}\sqrt{ax^2 + c} -$
$$\frac{c^2}{8\sqrt{a^3}}\log(x\sqrt{a} + \sqrt{ax^2 + c}) \quad (a > 0)$$

77. $\displaystyle\int x^2\sqrt{ax^2 + c}\, dx = \frac{x}{4a}\sqrt{(ax^2 + c)^3} - \frac{cx}{8a}\sqrt{ax^2 + c} -$
$$\frac{c^2}{8a\sqrt{-a}}\sin^{-1}\left(x\sqrt{\frac{-a}{c}}\right) \quad (a < 0)$$

78. $\displaystyle\int \frac{x\, dx}{\sqrt{ax^2 + c}} = \frac{1}{a}\sqrt{ax^2 + c}$

79. $\displaystyle\int \frac{x^2\, dx}{\sqrt{ax^2 + c}} = \frac{x}{a}\sqrt{ax^2 + c} - \frac{1}{a}\int \sqrt{ax^2 + c}\, dx$

80. $\displaystyle\int \frac{\sqrt{ax^2 + c}}{x}\, dx = \sqrt{ax^2 + c} + \sqrt{c}\,\log\frac{\sqrt{ax^2 + c} - \sqrt{c}}{x} \qquad (c > 0)$

81. $\displaystyle\int \frac{\sqrt{ax^2 + c}}{x}\, dx = \sqrt{ax^2 + c} - \sqrt{-c}\, \tan^{-1} \frac{\sqrt{ax^2 + c}}{\sqrt{-c}}$ $(c < 0)$

82. $\displaystyle\int \frac{dx}{x\sqrt{p^2 \pm x^2}} = -\frac{1}{p}\log \frac{p + \sqrt{p^2 \pm x^2}}{x}$

83. $\displaystyle\int \frac{dx}{x\sqrt{x^2 - p^2}} = \frac{1}{p}\cos^{-1}\frac{p}{x}$ or $-\frac{1}{p}\sin^{-1}\frac{p}{x}$

84. $\displaystyle\int \frac{dx}{x\sqrt{ax^2 + c}} = \frac{1}{\sqrt{c}}\log \frac{\sqrt{ax^2 + c} - \sqrt{c}}{x}$ $(c > 0)$

85. $\displaystyle\int \frac{dx}{x\sqrt{ax^2 + c}} = \frac{1}{\sqrt{-c}}\sec^{-1}\left(x\sqrt{-\frac{a}{c}}\right)$ $(c < 0)$

86. $\displaystyle\int \frac{dx}{x^2\sqrt{ax^2 + c}} = -\frac{\sqrt{ax^2 + c}}{cx}$

87. $\displaystyle\int \frac{x^n\, dx}{\sqrt{ax^2 + c}} = \frac{x^{n-1}\sqrt{ax^2 + c}}{na} - \frac{(n-1)c}{na}\int \frac{x^{n-2}\, dx}{\sqrt{ax^2 + c}}$ $(n > 0)$

88. $\displaystyle\int x^n\sqrt{ax^2 + c}\, dx = \frac{x^{n-1}(ax^2 + c)^{3/2}}{(n+2)a} - \frac{(n-1)c}{(n+2)a}\int x^{n-2}\sqrt{ax^2 + c}\, dx$

     $(n > 0)$

89. $\displaystyle\int \frac{\sqrt{ax^2 + c}}{x^n}\, dx = -\frac{(ax^2 + c)^{3/2}}{c(n-1)x^{n-1}} - \frac{(n-4)a}{(n-1)c}\int \frac{\sqrt{ax^2 + c}}{x^{n-2}}\, dx$ $(n > 1)$

90. $\displaystyle\int \frac{dx}{x^n\sqrt{ax^2 + c}} = -\frac{\sqrt{ax^2 + c}}{c(n-1)x^{n-1}} - \frac{(n-2)a}{(n-1)c}\int \frac{dx}{x^{n-2}\sqrt{ax^2 + c}}$ $(n > 1)$

91. $\displaystyle\int (ax^2 + c)^{3/2}\, dx = \frac{x}{8}(2ax^2 + 5c)\sqrt{ax^2 + c} + \frac{3c^2}{8\sqrt{a}}\log\left(x\sqrt{a} + \sqrt{ax^2 + c}\right)$

     $(a > 0)$

92. $\displaystyle\int (ax^2 + c)^{3/2}\, dx = \frac{x}{8}(2ax^2 + 5c)\sqrt{ax^2 + c} + \frac{3c^2}{8\sqrt{-a}}\sin^{-1}\left(x\sqrt{\frac{-a}{c}}\right)$

     $(a < 0)$

93. $\displaystyle\int \frac{dx}{(ax^2 + c)^{3/2}} = \frac{x}{c\sqrt{ax^2 + c}}$

94. $\displaystyle\int x(ax^2 + c)^{3/2}\, dx = \frac{1}{5a}(ax^2 + c)^{5/2}$

95. $\displaystyle\int x^2(ax^2 + c)^{3/2}\, dx = \frac{x^3}{6}(ax^2 + c)^{3/2} + \frac{c}{2}\int x^2\sqrt{ax^2 + c}\, dx$

96. $\displaystyle\int x^n(ax^2 + c)^{3/2}\, dx = \frac{x^{n+1}(ax^2 + c)^{3/2}}{n+4} + \frac{3c}{n+4}\int x^n\sqrt{ax^2 + c}\, dx$

97. $\displaystyle\int \frac{x\,dx}{(ax^2 + c)^{3/2}} = -\frac{1}{a\sqrt{ax^2 + c}}$

98. $\displaystyle\int \frac{x^2\,dx}{(ax^2 + c)^{3/2}} = -\frac{x}{a\sqrt{ax^2 + c}} + \frac{1}{a\sqrt{a}}\log\left(x\sqrt{a} + \sqrt{ax^2 + c}\right)$ $\qquad (a > 0)$

99. $\displaystyle\int \frac{x^2\,dx}{(ax^2 + c)^{3/2}} = -\frac{x}{a\sqrt{ax^2 + c}} + \frac{1}{a\sqrt{-a}}\sin^{-1}\left(x\sqrt{\frac{-a}{c}}\right)$ $\qquad (a < 0)$

100. $\displaystyle\int \frac{x^3\,dx}{(ax^2 + c)^{3/2}} = -\frac{x^2}{a\sqrt{ax^2 + c}} + \frac{2}{a^2}\sqrt{ax^2 + c}$

101. $\displaystyle\int \frac{dx}{x(ax^n + c)} = \frac{1}{cn}\log\frac{x^n}{ax^n + c}$

102. $\displaystyle\int \frac{dx}{(ax^n + c)^m} = \frac{1}{c}\int \frac{dx}{(ax^n + c)^{m-1}} - \frac{a}{c}\int \frac{x^n\,dx}{(ax^n + c)^m}$

103. $\displaystyle\int \frac{dx}{x\sqrt{ax^n + c}} = \frac{1}{n\sqrt{c}}\log\frac{\sqrt{ax^n + c} - \sqrt{c}}{\sqrt{ax^n + c} + \sqrt{c}}$ $\qquad (c > 0)$

104. $\displaystyle\int \frac{dx}{x\sqrt{ax^n + c}} = \frac{2}{n\sqrt{-c}}\sec^{-1}\sqrt{\frac{-ax^n}{c}}$ $\qquad (c < 0)$

105. $\displaystyle\int x^{m-1}(ax^n + c)^p\,dx$

$\displaystyle = \frac{1}{m + np}\left[x^m(ax^n + c)^p + npc\int x^{m-1}(ax^n + c)^{p-1}\,dx\right]$

$\displaystyle = \frac{1}{cn(p + 1)}\left[-x^m(ax^n + c)^{p+1} + (m + np + n)\int x^{m-1}(ax^n + c)^{p+1}\,dx\right]$

$\displaystyle = \frac{1}{a(m + np)}\left[x^{m-n}(ax^n + c)^{p+1} - (m - n)c\int x^{m-n-1}(ax^n + c)^p\,dx\right]$

$\displaystyle = \frac{1}{mc}\left[x^m(ax^n + c)^{p+1} - (m + np + n)a\int x^{m+n-1}(ax^n + c)^p\,dx\right]$

106. $\displaystyle\int \frac{x^m\,dx}{(ax^n + c)^p} = \frac{1}{a}\int \frac{x^{m-n}\,dx}{(ax^n + c)^{p-1}} - \frac{c}{a}\int \frac{x^{m-n}\,dx}{(ax^n + c)^p}$

107. $\displaystyle\int \frac{dx}{x^m(ax^n + c)^p} = \frac{1}{c}\int \frac{dx}{x^m(ax^n + c)^{p-1}} - \frac{a}{c}\int \frac{dx}{x^{m-n}(ax^n + c)^p}$

INTEGRALS WITH $(ax^2 + bx + c)$

108. $\displaystyle\int \frac{dx}{ax^2 + bx + c} = \frac{1}{\sqrt{b^2 - 4ac}}\log\frac{2ax + b - \sqrt{b^2 - 4ac}}{2ax + b + \sqrt{b^2 - 4ac}}$ $\qquad (b^2 > 4ac)$

109. $\displaystyle\int \frac{dx}{ax^2 + bx + c} = \frac{2}{\sqrt{4ac - b^2}}\tan^{-1}\frac{2ax + b}{\sqrt{4ac - b^2}}$ $\qquad (b^2 < 4ac)$

110. $\displaystyle\int \frac{dx}{ax^2 + bx + c} = -\frac{2}{2ax + b}$ $\qquad (b^2 = 4ac)$

111. $\displaystyle\int \frac{dx}{(ax^2 + bx + c)^{n+1}} = \frac{2ax + b}{n(4ac - b^2)(ax^2 + bx + c)^n} +$

$$\frac{2(2n-1)a}{n(4ac - b^2)} \int \frac{dx}{(ax^2 + bx + c)^n}$$

112. $\displaystyle\int \frac{x\,dx}{ax^2 + bx + c} = \frac{1}{2a} \log(ax^2 + bx + c) - \frac{b}{2a} \int \frac{dx}{ax^2 + bx + c}$

113. $\displaystyle\int \frac{x^2\,dx}{ax^2 + bx + c} = \frac{x}{a} - \frac{b}{2a^2} \log(ax^2 + bx + c) + \frac{b^2 - 2ac}{2a^2} \int \frac{dx}{ax^2 + bx + c}$

114. $\displaystyle\int \frac{x^n\,dx}{ax^2 + bx + c} = \frac{x^{n-1}}{(n-1)a} - \frac{c}{a} \int \frac{x^{n-2}\,dx}{ax^2 + bx + c} - \frac{b}{a} \int \frac{x^{n-1}\,dx}{ax^2 + bx + c}$

115. $\displaystyle\int \frac{x\,dx}{(ax^2 + bx + c)^{n+1}} = \frac{-(2c + bx)}{n(4ac - b^2)(ax^2 + bx + c)^n} -$

$$\frac{b(2n-1)}{n(4ac - b^2)} \int \frac{dx}{(ax^2 + bx + c)^n}$$

116. $\displaystyle\int \frac{x^m\,dx}{(ax^2 + bx + c)^{n+1}} = -\frac{x^{m-1}}{a(2n - m + 1)(ax^2 + bx + c)^n} -$

$$\frac{n - m + 1}{2n - m + 1}\frac{b}{a} \int \frac{x^{m-1}\,dx}{(ax^2 + bx + c)^{n+1}} + \frac{m-1}{2n - m + 1}\frac{c}{a} \int \frac{x^{m-2}\,dx}{(ax^2 + bx + c)^{n+1}}$$

117. $\displaystyle\int \frac{dx}{x(ax^2 + bx + c)} = \frac{1}{2c} \log\left(\frac{x^2}{ax^2 + bx + c}\right) - \frac{b}{2c} \int \frac{dx}{ax^2 + bx + c}$

118. $\displaystyle\int \frac{dx}{x^2(ax^2 + bx + c)} = \frac{b}{2c^2} \log\left(\frac{ax^2 + bx + c}{x^2}\right) - \frac{1}{cx} +$

$$\left(\frac{b^2}{2c^2} - \frac{a}{c}\right) \int \frac{dx}{ax^2 + bx + c}$$

119. $\displaystyle\int \frac{dx}{x^m(ax^2 + bx + c)^{n+1}} = -\frac{1}{(m-1)cx^{m-1}(ax^2 + bx + c)^n} -$

$$\frac{n + m - 1}{m - 1}\frac{b}{c} \int \frac{dx}{x^{m-1}(ax^2 + bx + c)^{n+1}} -$$

$$\frac{2n + m - 1}{m - 1}\frac{a}{c} \int \frac{dx}{x^{m-2}(ax^2 + bx + c)^{n+1}}$$

120. $\displaystyle\int \frac{dx}{x(ax^2 + bx + c)^n} = \frac{1}{2c(n-1)(ax^2 + bx + c)^{n-1}} -$

$$\frac{b}{2c} \int \frac{dx}{(ax^2 + bx + c)^n} + \frac{1}{c} \int \frac{dx}{x(ax^2 + bx + c)^{n-1}}$$

121. $\int \dfrac{dx}{\sqrt{ax^2 + bx + c}} = \dfrac{1}{\sqrt{a}} \log \left(2ax + b + 2\sqrt{a}\sqrt{ax^2 + bx + c}\right)$ $(a > 0)$

122. $\int \dfrac{dx}{\sqrt{ax^2 + bx + c}} = \dfrac{1}{\sqrt{-a}} \sin^{-1} \dfrac{-2ax - b}{\sqrt{b^2 - 4ac}}$ $(a < 0)$

123. $\int \dfrac{x\,dx}{\sqrt{ax^2 + bx + c}} = \dfrac{\sqrt{ax^2 + bx + c}}{a} - \dfrac{b}{2a} \int \dfrac{dx}{\sqrt{ax^2 + bx + c}}$

124. $\int \dfrac{x^n\,dx}{\sqrt{ax^2 + bx + c}} = \dfrac{x^{n-1}}{an} \sqrt{ax^2 + bx + c} \; -$

$\dfrac{b(2n - 1)}{2an} \int \dfrac{x^{n-1}\,dx}{\sqrt{ax^2 + bx + c}} - \dfrac{c(n - 1)}{an} \int \dfrac{x^{n-2}\,dx}{\sqrt{ax^2 + bx + c}}$

125. $\int \sqrt{ax^2 + bx + c}\,dx = \dfrac{2ax + b}{4a} \sqrt{ax^2 + bx + c} \; +$

$\dfrac{4ac - b^2}{8a} \int \dfrac{dx}{\sqrt{ax^2 + bx + c}}$

126. $\int x\sqrt{ax^2 + bx + c}\,dx = \dfrac{(ax^2 + bx + c)^{3/2}}{3a} - \dfrac{b}{2a} \int \sqrt{ax^2 + bx + c}\,dx$

127. $\int x^2\sqrt{ax^2 + bx + c}\,dx = \left(x - \dfrac{5b}{6a}\right) \dfrac{(ax^2 + bx + c)^{3/2}}{4a} \; +$

$\dfrac{5b^2 - 4ac}{16a^2} \int \sqrt{ax^2 + bx + c}\,dx$

128. $\int \dfrac{dx}{x\sqrt{ax^2 + bx + c}} = -\dfrac{1}{\sqrt{c}} \log \left(\dfrac{\sqrt{ax^2 + bx + c} + \sqrt{c}}{x} + \dfrac{b}{2\sqrt{c}}\right)$ $(c > 0)$

129. $\int \dfrac{dx}{x\sqrt{ax^2 + bx + c}} = \dfrac{1}{\sqrt{-c}} \sin^{-1} \dfrac{bx + 2c}{x\sqrt{b^2 - 4ac}}$ $(c < 0)$

130. $\int \dfrac{dx}{x\sqrt{ax^2 + bx}} = -\dfrac{2}{bx} \sqrt{ax^2 + bx}$ $(c = 0)$

131. $\int \dfrac{dx}{x^n\sqrt{ax^2 + bx + c}} = -\dfrac{\sqrt{ax^2 + bx + c}}{c(n - 1)x^{n-1}} \; +$

$\dfrac{b(3 - 2n)}{2c(n - 1)} \int \dfrac{dx}{x^{n-1}\sqrt{ax^2 + bx + c}} + \dfrac{a(2 - n)}{c(n - 1)} \int \dfrac{dx}{x^{n-2}\sqrt{ax^2 + bx + c}}$

132. $\int \dfrac{dx}{(ax^2 + bx + c)^{3/2}} = -\dfrac{2(2ax + b)}{(b^2 - 4ac)\sqrt{ax^2 + bx + c}}$ $(b^2 \neq 4ac)$

133. $\int \dfrac{dx}{(ax^2 + bx + c)^{3/2}} = -\dfrac{1}{2\sqrt{a^3}(x + b/2a)^2}$ $(b^2 = 4ac)$

INTEGRALS WITH MISCELLANEOUS ALGEBRAIC EXPRESSIONS

134. $\displaystyle \int \sqrt{2px - x^2}\, dx = \frac{1}{2}\left[(x - p)\sqrt{2px - x^2} + p^2 \sin^{-1}\frac{x - p}{p} \right]$

135. $\displaystyle \int \frac{dx}{\sqrt{2px - x^2}} = \cos^{-1}\frac{p - x}{p}$

136. $\displaystyle \int \frac{dx}{\sqrt{ax + b}\,\sqrt{cx + d}} = \frac{2}{\sqrt{-ac}}\tan^{-1}\sqrt{\frac{-c(ax + b)}{a(cx + d)}}$

$\displaystyle \qquad\qquad\qquad\qquad = \frac{2}{\sqrt{ac}}\tanh^{-1}\sqrt{\frac{c(ax + b)}{a(cx + d)}}$

137. $\displaystyle \int \sqrt{ax + b}\,\sqrt{cx + d}\, dx = \frac{(2acx + bc + ad)\sqrt{ax + b}\,\sqrt{cx + d}}{4ac} -$

$\displaystyle \qquad\qquad\qquad\qquad \frac{(ad - bc)^2}{8ac}\int \frac{dx}{\sqrt{ax + b}\,\sqrt{cx + d}}$

138. $\displaystyle \int \sqrt{\frac{cx + d}{ax + b}}\, dx = \frac{\sqrt{ax + b}\,\sqrt{cx + d}}{a} + \frac{ad - bc}{2a}\int \frac{dx}{\sqrt{ax + b}\,\sqrt{cx + d}}$

139. $\displaystyle \int \sqrt{\frac{x + b}{x + d}}\, dx = \sqrt{x + d}\,\sqrt{x + b} + (b - d)\log\left(\sqrt{x + d} + \sqrt{x + b}\right)$

140. $\displaystyle \int \sqrt{\frac{1 + x}{1 - x}}\, dx = \sin^{-1}x - \sqrt{1 - x^2}$

141. $\displaystyle \int \sqrt{\frac{p - x}{q + x}}\, dx = \sqrt{p - x}\,\sqrt{q + x} + (p + q)\sin^{-1}\sqrt{\frac{x + q}{p + q}}$

142. $\displaystyle \int \sqrt{\frac{p + x}{q - x}}\, dx = -\sqrt{p + x}\,\sqrt{q - x} - (p + q)\sin^{-1}\sqrt{\frac{q - x}{p + q}}$

143. $\displaystyle \int \frac{dx}{\sqrt{x - p}\,\sqrt{q - x}} = 2\sin^{-1}\sqrt{\frac{x - p}{q - p}}$

INTEGRALS WITH THE SINE FUNCTION WHERE $(a \neq 0)$

144. $\displaystyle \int \sin ax\, dx = -\frac{1}{a}\cos ax$

145. $\displaystyle \int \sin^2 ax\, dx = \frac{1}{2}x - \frac{1}{4a}\sin 2ax$

146. $\displaystyle \int \sin^3 ax\, dx = -\frac{1}{a}\cos ax + \frac{1}{3a}\cos^3 ax$

147. $\displaystyle \int \sin^4 ax\, dx = \frac{3}{8}x - \frac{1}{4a}\sin 2ax + \frac{1}{32a}\sin 4ax$

148. $\displaystyle\int \sin^n ax\, dx = -\frac{\sin^{n-1} ax \cos ax}{na} + \frac{n-1}{n} \int \sin^{n-2} ax\, dx$ $\qquad (n > 0)$

149. $\displaystyle\int x \sin ax\, dx = \frac{\sin ax}{a^2} - \frac{x \cos ax}{a}$

150. $\displaystyle\int x^2 \sin ax\, dx = \frac{2x}{a^2} \sin ax - \left(\frac{x^2}{a} - \frac{2}{a^3}\right) \cos ax$

151. $\displaystyle\int x^3 \sin ax\, dx = \left(\frac{3x^2}{a^2} - \frac{6}{a^4}\right) \sin ax - \left(\frac{x^3}{a} - \frac{6x}{a^3}\right) \cos ax$

152. $\displaystyle\int x^n \sin ax\, dx = -\frac{x^n}{a} \cos ax + \frac{n}{a} \int x^{n-1} \cos ax\, dx$

153. $\displaystyle\int \frac{\sin ax}{x}\, dx = ax - \frac{(ax)^3}{3 \cdot 3!} + \frac{(ax)^5}{5 \cdot 5!} - \frac{(ax)^7}{7 \cdot 7!} + \cdots$

154. $\displaystyle\int \frac{\sin ax}{x^2}\, dx = -\frac{\sin ax}{x} + a \int \frac{\cos ax\, dx}{x}$

155. $\displaystyle\int \frac{\sin ax}{x^n}\, dx = -\frac{1}{n-1} \frac{\sin ax}{x^{n-1}} + \frac{a}{n-1} \int \frac{\cos ax}{x^{n-1}}\, dx$

156. $\displaystyle\int \frac{dx}{\sin ax} = \int \operatorname{cosec} ax\, dx = \frac{1}{a} \log_e \tan \frac{ax}{2} = \frac{1}{a} \log_e (\operatorname{cosec} ax - \cot ax)$

157. $\displaystyle\int \frac{dx}{\sin^2 ax} = -\frac{1}{a} \cot ax$

158. $\displaystyle\int \frac{dx}{\sin^3 ax} = -\frac{\cos ax}{2a \sin^2 ax} + \frac{1}{2a} \log_e \tan \frac{ax}{2}$

159. $\displaystyle\int \frac{dx}{\sin^n ax} = -\frac{1}{a(n-1)} \frac{\cos ax}{\sin^{n-1} ax} + \frac{n-2}{n-1} \int \frac{dx}{\sin^{n-2} ax}$ $\qquad (n > 1)$

160. $\displaystyle\int \frac{x\, dx}{\sin ax} = \frac{1}{a^2}\left[ax + \frac{(ax)^3}{3 \cdot 3!} + \frac{7(ax)^5}{3 \cdot 5 \cdot 5!} + \frac{31(ax)^7}{3 \cdot 7 \cdot 7!} + \frac{127(ax)^9}{3 \cdot 5 \cdot 9!} + \cdots \right]$

161. $\displaystyle\int \frac{x\, dx}{\sin^2 ax} = -\frac{x}{a} \cot ax + \frac{1}{a^2} \log_e \sin ax$

162. $\displaystyle\int \frac{x\, dx}{\sin^n ax} = -\frac{x \cos ax}{(n-1)a \sin^{n-1} ax} - \frac{1}{(n-1)(n-2)a^2 \sin^{n-2} ax} +$

$\qquad\qquad\qquad\qquad \frac{n-2}{n-1} \int \frac{x\, dx}{\sin^{n-2} ax}$ $\qquad (n > 2)$

163. $\displaystyle\int \frac{dx}{1 + \sin ax} = -\frac{1}{a} \tan \left(\frac{\pi}{4} - \frac{ax}{2} \right)$

164. $\displaystyle\int \frac{dx}{1 - \sin ax} = \frac{1}{a} \tan\left(\frac{\pi}{4} + \frac{ax}{2}\right)$

165. $\displaystyle\int \frac{x\,dx}{1 + \sin ax} = -\frac{x}{a} \tan\left(\frac{\pi}{4} - \frac{ax}{2}\right) + \frac{2}{a^2} \log_e \cos\left(\frac{\pi}{4} - \frac{ax}{2}\right)$

166. $\displaystyle\int \frac{x\,dx}{1 - \sin ax} = \frac{x}{a} \cot\left(\frac{\pi}{4} - \frac{ax}{2}\right) + \frac{2}{a^2} \log_e \sin\left(\frac{\pi}{4} - \frac{ax}{2}\right)$

167. $\displaystyle\int \frac{\sin ax\,dx}{1 \pm \sin ax} = \pm x + \frac{1}{a} \tan\left(\frac{\pi}{4} \mp \frac{ax}{2}\right)$

168. $\displaystyle\int \frac{dx}{\sin ax\,(1 \pm \sin ax)} = \frac{1}{a} \tan\left(\frac{\pi}{4} \mp \frac{ax}{2}\right) + \frac{1}{a} \log_e \tan \frac{ax}{2}$

169. $\displaystyle\int \frac{dx}{(1 + \sin ax)^2} = -\frac{1}{2a} \tan\left(\frac{\pi}{4} - \frac{ax}{2}\right) - \frac{1}{6a} \tan^3\left(\frac{\pi}{4} - \frac{ax}{2}\right)$

170. $\displaystyle\int \frac{dx}{(1 - \sin ax)^2} = \frac{1}{2a} \cot\left(\frac{\pi}{4} - \frac{ax}{2}\right) + \frac{1}{6a} \cot^3\left(\frac{\pi}{4} - \frac{ax}{2}\right)$

171. $\displaystyle\int \frac{\sin ax\,dx}{(1 + \sin ax)^2} = -\frac{1}{2a} \tan\left(\frac{\pi}{4} - \frac{ax}{2}\right) + \frac{1}{6a} \tan^3\left(\frac{\pi}{4} - \frac{ax}{2}\right)$

172. $\displaystyle\int \frac{\sin ax\,dx}{(1 - \sin ax)^2} = -\frac{1}{2a} \cot\left(\frac{\pi}{4} - \frac{ax}{2}\right) + \frac{1}{6a} \cot^3\left(\frac{\pi}{4} - \frac{ax}{2}\right)$

173. $\displaystyle\int \frac{dx}{1 + \sin^2 ax} = \frac{1}{2\sqrt{2a}} \arcsin\left(\frac{3\sin^2 ax - 1}{\sin^2 ax + 1}\right)$

174. $\displaystyle\int \frac{dx}{1 - \sin^2 ax} = \int \frac{dx}{\cos^2 ax} = \frac{1}{a} \tan ax$

175. $\displaystyle\int \sin ax \sin bx\,dx = \frac{\sin(a - b)x}{2(a - b)} - \frac{\sin(a + b)x}{2(a + b)}$

$(|a| \neq |b|;\ \text{for}\ |a| = |b|,\ \text{see } 145)$

176. $\displaystyle\int \frac{dx}{b + c \sin ax} = \frac{2}{a\sqrt{b^2 - c^2}} \arctan \frac{b \tan(ax/2) + c}{\sqrt{b^2 - c^2}} = \qquad (b^2 > c^2)$

$\displaystyle \frac{1}{a\sqrt{c^2 - b^2}} \log_e \frac{b \tan(ax/2) + c - \sqrt{c^2 - b^2}}{b \tan(ax/2) + c + \sqrt{c^2 - b^2}} \qquad (b^2 < c^2)$

177. $\displaystyle\int \frac{\sin ax\,dx}{b + c \sin ax} = \frac{x}{c} - \frac{b}{c} \int \frac{dx}{b + c \sin ax}$

178. $\displaystyle\int \frac{dx}{\sin ax\,(b + c \sin ax)} = \frac{1}{ab} \log_e \tan \frac{ax}{2} - \frac{c}{b} \int \frac{dx}{b + c \sin ax}$

179. $\displaystyle\int \frac{dx}{(b + c \sin ax)^2} = \frac{c \cos ax}{a(b^2 - c^2)(b + c \sin ax)} + \frac{b}{b^2 - c^2} \int \frac{dx}{b + c \sin ax}$

180. $\displaystyle\int \frac{\sin ax\,dx}{(b + c\sin ax)^2} = \frac{b\cos ax}{a(c^2 - b^2)(b + c\sin ax)} + \frac{c}{c^2 - b^2}\int \frac{dx}{b + c\sin ax}$

181. $\displaystyle\int \frac{dx}{b^2 + c^2\sin^2 ax} = \frac{1}{ab\sqrt{b^2 + c^2}}\arctan\frac{\sqrt{b^2 + c^2}\,\tan ax}{b}$ $(b > 0)$

182. $\displaystyle\int \frac{dx}{b^2 - c^2\sin^2 ax} = \frac{1}{ab\sqrt{b^2 - c^2}}\arctan\frac{\sqrt{b^2 - c^2}\,\tan ax}{b} =$

$(b^2 > c^2, b > 0)$

$\displaystyle\frac{1}{2ab\sqrt{c^2 - b^2}}\log_e\frac{\sqrt{c^2 - b^2}\,\tan ax + b}{\sqrt{c^2 - b^2}\,\tan ax - b}$ $(c^2 > b^2, b > 0)$

INTEGRALS WITH THE COSINE FUNCTION WHERE $(a \neq 0)$

183. $\displaystyle\int \cos ax\,dx = \frac{1}{a}\sin ax$

184. $\displaystyle\int \cos^2 ax\,dx = \frac{1}{2}x + \frac{1}{4a}\sin 2ax$

185. $\displaystyle\int \cos^2 ax\,dx = \frac{1}{a}\sin ax - \frac{1}{3a}\sin^3 ax$

186. $\displaystyle\int \cos^4 ax\,dx = \frac{3}{8}x + \frac{1}{4a}\sin 2ax + \frac{1}{32a}\sin 4ax$

187. $\displaystyle\int \cos^n ax\,dx = \frac{\cos^{n-1} ax\sin ax}{na} + \frac{n-1}{n}\int \cos^{n-2} ax\,dx$

188. $\displaystyle\int x\cos ax\,dx = \frac{\cos ax}{a^2} + \frac{x\sin ax}{a}$

189. $\displaystyle\int x^2\cos ax\,dx = \frac{2x}{a^2}\cos ax + \left(\frac{x^2}{a} - \frac{2}{a^3}\right)\sin ax$

190. $\displaystyle\int x^3\cos ax\,dx = \left(\frac{3x^2}{a^2} - \frac{6}{a^4}\right)\cos ax + \left(\frac{x^3}{a} - \frac{6x}{a^3}\right)\sin ax$

191. $\displaystyle\int x^n\cos ax\,dx = \frac{x^n\sin ax}{a} - \frac{n}{a}\int x^{n-1}\sin ax\,dx$ $(n > 0)$

192. $\displaystyle\int \frac{\cos ax}{x}\,dx = \log_e(ax) - \frac{(ax)^2}{2\cdot 2!} + \frac{(ax)^4}{4\cdot 4!} - \frac{(ax)^6}{6\cdot 6!} + \cdots$

193. $\displaystyle\int \frac{\cos ax}{x^2}\,dx = -\frac{\cos ax}{x} - a\int \frac{\sin ax\,dx}{x}$

194. $\displaystyle\int \frac{\cos ax}{x^n}\,dx = -\frac{\cos ax}{(n-1)x^{n-1}} - \frac{a}{n-1}\int \frac{\sin ax\,dx}{x^{n-1}}$ $(n \neq 1)$

195. $\displaystyle\int \frac{dx}{\cos ax} = \frac{1}{a} \log_e \tan\left(\frac{ax}{2} + \frac{\pi}{4}\right) = \frac{1}{a} \log_e (\sec ax + \tan ax)$

196. $\displaystyle\int \frac{dx}{\cos^2 ax} = \frac{1}{a} \tan ax$

197. $\displaystyle\int \frac{dx}{\cos^3 ax} = \frac{\sin ax}{2a \cos^2 ax} + \frac{1}{2a} \log_e \tan\left(\frac{\pi}{4} + \frac{ax}{2}\right)$

198. $\displaystyle\int \frac{dx}{\cos^n ax} = \frac{1}{a(n-1)} \frac{\sin ax}{\cos^{n-1} ax} + \frac{n-2}{n-1} \int \frac{dx}{\cos^{n-2} ax}$ $\qquad (n > 1)$

199. $\displaystyle\int \frac{x\, dx}{\cos ax} = \frac{1}{a^2}\left[\frac{(ax)^2}{2} + \frac{(ax)^4}{4 \cdot 2!} + \frac{5(ax)^6}{6 \cdot 4!} + \frac{61(ax)^8}{8 \cdot 6!} + \frac{1{,}385(ax)^{10}}{10 \cdot 8!} + \cdots\right]$

200. $\displaystyle\int \frac{x\, dx}{\cos^2 ax} = \frac{x}{a} \tan ax + \frac{1}{a^2} \log_e \cos ax$

201. $\displaystyle\int \frac{x\, dx}{\cos^n ax} = \frac{x \sin ax}{(n-1)a \cos^{n-1} ax} - \frac{1}{(n-1)(n-2)a^2 \cos^{n-2} ax} +$

$\displaystyle\qquad\qquad \frac{n-2}{n-1} \int \frac{x\, dx}{\cos^{n-2} ax} \qquad (n > 2)$

202. $\displaystyle\int \frac{dx}{1 + \cos ax} = \frac{1}{a} \tan \frac{ax}{2}$

203. $\displaystyle\int \frac{dx}{1 - \cos ax} = -\frac{1}{a} \cot \frac{ax}{2}$

204. $\displaystyle\int \frac{x\, dx}{1 + \cos ax} = \frac{x}{a} \tan \frac{ax}{2} + \frac{2}{a^2} \log_e \cos \frac{ax}{2}$

205. $\displaystyle\int \frac{x\, dx}{1 - \cos ax} = -\frac{x}{a} \cot \frac{ax}{2} + \frac{2}{a^2} \log_e \sin \frac{ax}{2}$

206. $\displaystyle\int \frac{\cos ax\, dx}{1 + \cos ax} = x - \frac{1}{a} \tan \frac{ax}{2}$

207. $\displaystyle\int \frac{\cos ax\, dx}{1 - \cos ax} = -x - \frac{1}{a} \cot \frac{ax}{2}$

208. $\displaystyle\int \frac{dx}{\cos ax\,(1 + \cos ax)} = \frac{1}{a} \log_e \tan\left(\frac{\pi}{4} + \frac{ax}{2}\right) - \frac{1}{a} \tan \frac{ax}{2}$

209. $\displaystyle\int \frac{dx}{\cos ax\,(1 - \cos ax)} = \frac{1}{a} \log_e \tan\left(\frac{\pi}{4} + \frac{ax}{2}\right) - \frac{1}{a} \cot \frac{ax}{2}$

210. $\displaystyle\int \frac{dx}{(1 + \cos ax)^2} = \frac{1}{2a} \tan \frac{ax}{2} + \frac{1}{6a} \tan^3 \frac{ax}{2}$

211. $\displaystyle\int \frac{dx}{(1 - \cos ax)^2} = -\frac{1}{2a} \cot \frac{ax}{2} - \frac{1}{6a} \cot^3 \frac{ax}{2}$

212. $\int \dfrac{\cos ax\,dx}{(1+\cos ax)^2} = \dfrac{1}{2a}\tan\dfrac{ax}{2} - \dfrac{1}{6a}\tan^3\dfrac{ax}{2}$

213. $\int \dfrac{\cos ax\,dx}{(1-\cos ax)^2} = \dfrac{1}{2a}\cot\dfrac{ax}{2} - \dfrac{1}{6a}\cot^3\dfrac{ax}{2}$

214. $\int \dfrac{dx}{1+\cos^2 ax} = \dfrac{1}{2\sqrt{2a}}\arcsin\left(\dfrac{1-3\cos^2 ax}{1+\cos^2 ax}\right)$

215. $\int \dfrac{dx}{1-\cos^2 ax} = \int \dfrac{dx}{\sin^2 ax} = -\dfrac{1}{a}\cot ax$

216. $\int \cos ax \cos bx\,dx = \dfrac{\sin(a-b)x}{2(a-b)} + \dfrac{\sin(a+b)x}{2(a+b)}$

$(|a|\neq|b|;$ for $|a|=|b|,$ see 184$)$

217. $\int \dfrac{dx}{b+c\cos ax} = \dfrac{2}{a\sqrt{b^2-c^2}}\arctan\dfrac{(b-c)\tan(ax/2)}{\sqrt{b^2-c^2}} =$ $(b^2>c^2)$

$\dfrac{1}{a\sqrt{c^2-b^2}}\log_e\dfrac{(c-b)\tan(ax/2)+\sqrt{c^2-b^2}}{(c-b)\tan(ax/2)-\sqrt{c^2-b^2}}$ $(b^2<c^2)$

218. $\int \dfrac{\cos ax\,dx}{b+c\cos ax} = \dfrac{x}{c} - \dfrac{b}{c}\int\dfrac{dx}{b+c\cos ax}$

219. $\int \dfrac{dx}{\cos ax\,(b+c\cos ax)} = \dfrac{1}{ab}\log_e\tan\left(\dfrac{ax}{2}+\dfrac{\pi}{4}\right) - \dfrac{c}{b}\int\dfrac{dx}{b+c\cos ax}$

220. $\int \dfrac{dx}{(b+c\cos ax)^2} = \dfrac{c\sin ax}{a(c^2-b^2)(b+c\cos ax)} - \dfrac{b}{c^2-b^2}\int\dfrac{dx}{b+c\cos ax}$

221. $\int \dfrac{\cos ax\,dx}{(b+c\cos ax)^2} = \dfrac{b\sin ax}{a(b^2-c^2)(b+c\cos ax)} - \dfrac{c}{b^2-c^2}\int\dfrac{dx}{b+c\cos ax}$

222. $\int \dfrac{dx}{b^2+c^2\cos^2 ax} = \dfrac{1}{ab\sqrt{b^2+c^2}}\arctan\dfrac{b\tan ax}{\sqrt{b^2+c^2}}$ $(b>0)$

223. $\int \dfrac{dx}{b^2-c^2\cos^2 ax} = \dfrac{1}{ab\sqrt{b^2-c^2}}\arctan\dfrac{b\tan ax}{\sqrt{b^2-c^2}} =$ $(b^2>c^2,b>0)$

$\dfrac{1}{2ab\sqrt{c^2-b^2}}\log_e\dfrac{b\tan ax-\sqrt{c^2-b^2}}{b\tan ax+\sqrt{c^2-b^2}}$ $(c^2>b^2,b>0)$

INTEGRALS WITH SINE AND COSINE WHERE $(a\neq0)$

224. $\int \sin ax \cos ax\,dx = \dfrac{1}{2a}\sin^2 ax$

225. $\int \sin^2 ax \cos^2 ax\,dx = \dfrac{x}{8} - \dfrac{\sin 4ax}{32a}$

226. $\int \sin^n ax \cos ax \, dx = \dfrac{1}{a(n+1)} \sin^{n+1} ax$ $(n \neq -1)$

227. $\int \sin ax \cos^n ax \, dx = -\dfrac{1}{a(n+1)} \cos^{n+1} ax$ $(n \neq -1)$

228. $\int \sin^n ax \cos^m ax \, dx = -\dfrac{\sin^{n-1} ax \cos^{m+1} ax}{a(n+m)} +$

$\dfrac{n-1}{n+m} \int \sin^{n-2} ax \cos^m ax \, dx =$ $(m, n > 0)$

$\dfrac{\sin^{n+1} ax \cos^{m-1} ax}{a(n+m)} + \dfrac{m-1}{n+m} \int \sin^n ax \cos^{m-2} ax \, dx$ $(m, n > 0)$

229. $\int \dfrac{dx}{\sin ax \cos ax} = \dfrac{1}{a} \log_e \tan ax$

230. $\int \dfrac{dx}{\sin^2 ax \cos ax} = \dfrac{1}{a} \left[\log_e \tan \left(\dfrac{\pi}{4} + \dfrac{ax}{2} \right) - \dfrac{1}{\sin ax} \right]$

231. $\int \dfrac{dx}{\sin ax \cos^2 ax} = \dfrac{1}{a} \left(\log_e \tan \dfrac{ax}{2} + \dfrac{1}{\cos ax} \right)$

232. $\int \dfrac{dx}{\sin^3 ax \cos ax} = \dfrac{1}{a} \left(\log_e \tan ax - \dfrac{1}{2 \sin^2 ax} \right)$

233. $\int \dfrac{dx}{\sin ax \cos^3 ax} = \dfrac{1}{a} \left(\log_e \tan ax + \dfrac{1}{2 \cos^2 ax} \right)$

234. $\int \dfrac{dx}{\sin^2 ax \cos^2 ax} = -\dfrac{2}{a} \cot 2ax$

235. $\int \dfrac{dx}{\sin^2 ax \cos^3 ax} = \dfrac{1}{a} \left[\dfrac{\sin ax}{2 \cos^2 ax} - \dfrac{1}{\sin ax} + \dfrac{3}{2} \log_e \tan \left(\dfrac{\pi}{4} + \dfrac{ax}{2} \right) \right]$

236. $\int \dfrac{dx}{\sin^3 ax \cos^2 ax} = \dfrac{1}{a} \left(\dfrac{1}{\cos ax} - \dfrac{\cos ax}{2 \sin^2 ax} + \dfrac{3}{2} \log_e \tan \dfrac{ax}{2} \right)$

237. $\int \dfrac{dx}{\sin ax \cos^n ax} = \dfrac{1}{a(n-1) \cos^{n-1} ax} + \int \dfrac{dx}{\sin ax \cos^{n-2} ax}$

$(n \neq 1, \text{see } 231, 233)$

238. $\int \dfrac{dx}{\sin^n ax \cos ax} = -\dfrac{1}{a(n-1) \sin^{n-1} ax} + \int \dfrac{dx}{\sin^{n-2} ax \cos ax}$

$(n \neq 1, \text{see } 230, 232)$

239. $\displaystyle\int \frac{dx}{\sin^n ax \cos^m ax} = -\frac{1}{a(n-1)} \cdot \frac{1}{\sin^{n-1} ax \cos^{m-1} ax} +$

$$\frac{n+m-2}{n-1} \int \frac{dx}{\sin^{n-2} ax \cos^m ax} = (m > 0, n > 1)$$

$$\frac{1}{a(m-1)} \cdot \frac{1}{\sin^{n-1} ax \cos^{m-1} ax} +$$

$$\frac{n+m-2}{m-1} \int \frac{dx}{\sin^n ax \cos^{m-2} ax} \quad (n > 0, m > 1)$$

240. $\displaystyle\int \frac{\sin ax \, dx}{\cos^2 ax} = \frac{1}{a \cos ax}$

241. $\displaystyle\int \frac{\sin ax \, dx}{\cos^3 ax} = \frac{1}{2a \cos^2 ax} = \frac{1}{2a} \tan^2 ax + C_1$

242. $\displaystyle\int \frac{\sin ax \, dx}{\cos^n ax} = \frac{1}{a(n-1) \cos^{n-1} ax}$

243. $\displaystyle\int \frac{\sin^2 ax \, dx}{\cos ax} = -\frac{1}{a} \sin ax + \frac{1}{a} \log_e \tan \left(\frac{\pi}{4} + \frac{ax}{2} \right)$

244. $\displaystyle\int \frac{\sin^2 ax \, dx}{\cos^3 ax} = \frac{1}{a} \left[\frac{\sin ax}{2 \cos^2 ax} - \frac{1}{2} \log_e \tan \left(\frac{\pi}{4} + \frac{ax}{2} \right) \right]$

245. $\displaystyle\int \frac{\sin^2 ax \, dx}{\cos^n ax} = \frac{\sin ax}{a(n-1) \cos^{n-1} ax} - \frac{1}{n-1} \int \frac{dx}{\cos^{n-2} ax}$

$$(n \neq 1, \text{ see } 195, 196, 198)$$

246. $\displaystyle\int \frac{\sin^3 ax \, dx}{\cos ax} = -\frac{1}{a} \left(\frac{\sin^2 ax}{2} + \log_e \cos ax \right)$

247. $\displaystyle\int \frac{\sin^3 ax \, dx}{\cos^2 ax} = \frac{1}{a} \left(\cos ax + \frac{1}{\cos ax} \right)$

248. $\displaystyle\int \frac{\sin^3 ax \, dx}{\cos^n ax} = \frac{1}{a} \left[\frac{1}{(n-1) \cos^{n-1} ax} - \frac{1}{(n-3) \cos^{n-3} ax} \right]$

$$(n \neq 1, n \neq 3)$$

249. $\displaystyle\int \frac{\sin^n ax}{\cos ax} \, dx = -\frac{\sin^{n-1} ax}{a(n-1)} + \int \frac{\sin^{n-2} ax \, dx}{\cos ax} \qquad (n \neq 1)$

250. $\displaystyle\int \frac{\sin^n ax}{\cos^m ax} \, dx = \frac{\sin^{n+1} ax}{a(m-1) \cos^{m-1} ax} - \frac{n-m+2}{m-1} \int \frac{\sin^n ax}{\cos^{m-2} ax} \, dx =$

$$(m \neq 1)$$

$$-\frac{\sin^{n-1} ax}{a(n-m) \cos^{m-1} ax} + \frac{n-1}{n-m} \int \frac{\sin^{n-2} ax \, dx}{\cos^m ax} = (m \neq n)$$

$$\frac{\sin^{n-1} ax}{a(m-1) \cos^{m-1} ax} - \frac{n-1}{m-1} \int \frac{\sin^{n-1} ax \, dx}{\cos^{m-2} ax} \qquad (m \neq 1)$$

251. $\displaystyle\int \frac{\cos ax \, dx}{\sin^2 ax} = -\frac{1}{a \sin ax}$

252. $\displaystyle\int \frac{\cos ax \, dx}{\sin^3 ax} = -\frac{1}{2a \sin^2 ax}$

253. $\displaystyle\int \frac{\cos ax \, dx}{\sin^n ax} = -\frac{1}{a(n-1)\sin^{n-1} ax}$ $\quad (n \neq 1)$

254. $\displaystyle\int \frac{\cos^2 ax \, dx}{\sin ax} = \frac{1}{a}\left(\cos ax + \log_e \tan \frac{ax}{2}\right)$

255. $\displaystyle\int \frac{\cos^2 ax \, dx}{\sin^3 ax} = -\frac{1}{2a}\left(\frac{\cos ax}{\sin^2 ax} - \log_e \tan \frac{ax}{2}\right)$

256. $\displaystyle\int \frac{\cos^2 ax \, dx}{\sin^n ax} = -\frac{1}{n-1}\left(\frac{\cos ax}{a \sin^{n-1} ax} + \int \frac{dx}{\sin^{n-2} ax}\right)$

$(n \neq 1, \text{ see } 159)$

257. $\displaystyle\int \frac{\cos^3 ax \, dx}{\sin ax} = \frac{1}{a}\left(\frac{\cos^2 ax}{2} + \log_e \sin ax\right)$

258. $\displaystyle\int \frac{\cos^3 ax \, dx}{\sin^2 ax} = -\frac{1}{a}\left(\sin ax + \frac{1}{\sin ax}\right)$

259. $\displaystyle\int \frac{\cos^3 ax \, dx}{\sin^n ax} = \frac{1}{a}\left[\frac{1}{(n-3)\sin^{n-3} ax} - \frac{1}{(n-1)\sin^{n-1} ax}\right]$

$(n \neq 1, n \neq 3)$

260. $\displaystyle\int \frac{\cos^n ax}{\sin ax} \, dx = \frac{\cos^{n-1} ax}{a(n-1)} + \int \frac{\cos^{n-2} ax \, dx}{\sin ax}$ $\quad (n \neq 1)$

261. $\displaystyle\int \frac{\cos^n ax \, dx}{\sin^m ax} = -\frac{\cos^{n+1} ax}{a(m-1)\sin^{m-1} ax} - \frac{n-m+2}{m-1}\int \frac{\cos^n ax \, dx}{\sin^{m-2} ax} =$

$(m \neq 1)$

$\displaystyle \frac{\cos^{n-1} ax}{a(n-m)\sin^{m-1} ax} + \frac{n-1}{n-m}\int \frac{\cos^{n-2} ax \, dx}{\sin^m ax} =$ $\quad (m \neq n)$

$\displaystyle -\frac{\cos^{n-1} ax}{a(m-1)\sin^{m-1} ax} - \frac{n-1}{m-1}\int \frac{\cos^{n-2} ax \, dx}{\sin^{m-2} ax}$ $\quad (m \neq 1)$

262. $\displaystyle\int \frac{dx}{\sin ax\,(1 \pm \cos ax)} = \pm\frac{1}{2a(1 \pm \cos ax)} + \frac{1}{2a}\log_e \tan \frac{ax}{2}$

263. $\displaystyle\int \frac{dx}{\cos ax\,(1 \pm \sin ax)} = \mp\frac{1}{2a(1 \pm \sin ax)} + \frac{1}{2a}\log_e \tan \left(\frac{\pi}{4} + \frac{ax}{2}\right)$

264. $\displaystyle\int \frac{\sin ax \, dx}{\cos ax\,(1 \pm \cos ax)} = \frac{1}{a}\log_e \frac{1 \pm \cos ax}{\cos ax}$

265. $\displaystyle\int \frac{\cos ax\,dx}{\sin ax\,(1 \pm \sin ax)} = -\frac{1}{a}\log_e \frac{1 \pm \sin ax}{\sin ax}$

266. $\displaystyle\int \frac{\sin ax\,dx}{\cos ax\,(1 \pm \sin ax)} = \frac{1}{2a\,(1 \pm \sin ax)} \pm \frac{1}{2a}\log_e \tan\left(\frac{\pi}{4} + \frac{ax}{2}\right)$

267. $\displaystyle\int \frac{\cos ax\,dx}{\sin ax\,(1 \pm \cos ax)} = -\frac{1}{2a\,(1 \pm \cos ax)} \pm \frac{1}{2a}\log_e \tan\frac{ax}{2}$

268. $\displaystyle\int \frac{\sin ax\,dx}{\sin ax \pm \cos ax} = \frac{x}{2} \mp \frac{1}{2a}\log_e (\sin ax \pm \cos ax)$

269. $\displaystyle\int \frac{\cos ax\,dx}{\sin ax \pm \cos ax} = \pm\frac{x}{2} + \frac{1}{2a}\log_e (\sin ax \pm \cos ax)$

270. $\displaystyle\int \frac{dx}{\sin ax \pm \cos ax} = \frac{1}{a\sqrt{2}}\log_e \tan\left(\frac{ax}{2} \pm \frac{\pi}{8}\right)$

271. $\displaystyle\int \frac{dx}{1 + \cos ax \pm \sin ax} = \pm\frac{1}{a}\log_e \left(1 \pm \tan\frac{ax}{2}\right)$

272. $\displaystyle\int \frac{dx}{b \sin ax + c \cos ax} = \frac{1}{a\sqrt{b^2 + c^2}}\log_e \tan\frac{ax + \theta}{2}$

$$\left(\sin \theta = \frac{c}{\sqrt{b^2 + c^2}} \qquad \tan \theta = \frac{c}{b}\right)$$

273. $\displaystyle\int \frac{\sin ax\,dx}{b + c \cos ax} = -\frac{1}{ac}\log_e (b + c \cos ax)$

274. $\displaystyle\int \frac{\cos ax\,dx}{b + c \sin ax} = \frac{1}{ac}\log_e (b + c \sin ax)$

275. $\displaystyle\int \frac{\sin^2 ax\,dx}{b + c \cos^2 ax} = \frac{1}{ac}\sqrt{\frac{b + c}{b}}\arctan\left(\sqrt{\frac{b}{b + c}}\tan ax\right) - \frac{x}{c}$

276. $\displaystyle\int \frac{\sin ax \cos ax\,dx}{b \cos^2 ax + c \sin^2 ax} = \frac{1}{2a\,(c - b)}\log_e (b \cos^2 ax + c \sin^2 ax) \qquad (c \neq b)$

277. $\displaystyle\int \frac{dx}{b^2 \cos^2 ax + c^2 \sin^2 ax} = \frac{1}{abc}\arctan\left(\frac{c}{b}\tan ax\right)$

278. $\displaystyle\int \frac{dx}{b^2 \cos^2 ax - c^2 \sin^2 ax} = \frac{1}{2abc}\log_e \frac{c \tan ax + b}{c \tan ax - b}$

279. $\displaystyle\int \sin ax \cos bx\,dx = -\frac{\cos (a + b)x}{2(a + b)} - \frac{\cos (a - b)x}{2(a - b)}$

$(a^2 \neq b^2$; for $a = b$, see 224)

280. $\displaystyle\int \frac{dx}{b + c \cos ax + d \sin ax} =$

$$\begin{cases} \dfrac{-1}{a\sqrt{b^2 - c^2 - d^2}} \arcsin \dfrac{c^2 + d^2 + b(c \cos ax + d \sin ax)}{\sqrt{c^2 + d^2}\,(b + c \cos ax + d \sin ax)} \\ \qquad\qquad\qquad\qquad\qquad (b^2 > c^2 + d^2, \ |ax| < \pi) \\[4pt] \dfrac{1}{a\sqrt{c^2 + d^2 - b^2}} \\ \log_e \dfrac{c^2 + d^2 + b(c \cos ax + d \sin ax) + \sqrt{c^2 + d^2 - b^2}\,(c \sin ax - d \cos ax)}{\sqrt{c^2 + d^2}\,(b + c \cos ax + d \sin ax)} \\ \qquad\qquad\qquad\qquad\qquad (b^2 < c^2 + d^2, \ |ax| < \pi) \\[4pt] \dfrac{1}{ab}\left[\dfrac{b - (c + d)\cos ax + (c - d)\sin ax}{b + (c - d)\cos ax + (c + d)\sin ax} \right] \qquad (b^2 = c^2 + d^2) \end{cases}$$

INTEGRALS WITH TANGENT AND COTANGENT FUNCTIONS WHERE ($a \neq 0$)

281. $\displaystyle\int \tan ax \, dx = -\frac{1}{a} \log_e \cos ax$

282. $\displaystyle\int \tan^2 ax \, dx = \frac{1}{a} \tan ax - x$

283. $\displaystyle\int \tan^3 ax \, dx = \frac{1}{2a} \tan^2 ax + \frac{1}{a} \log_e \cos ax$

284. $\displaystyle\int \tan^n ax \, dx = \frac{1}{a(n-1)} \tan^{n-1} ax - \int \tan^{n-2} ax \, dx \qquad (n > 1)$

285. $\displaystyle\int \frac{dx}{b + c \tan ax} = \int \frac{\cot ax \, dx}{b \cot ax + c} =$

$$\frac{1}{b^2 + c^2}\left[bx + \frac{c}{a} \log_e (b \cos ax + c \sin ax) \right]$$

286. $\displaystyle\int \frac{dx}{\sqrt{b + c \tan^2 ax}} = \frac{1}{a\sqrt{b - c}} \arcsin\left(\sqrt{\frac{b - c}{b}} \sin ax \right)$

$$(b > 0, \ b^2 > c^2)$$

287. $\displaystyle\int \frac{\tan^n ax}{\cos^2 ax} dx = \frac{\tan^{n+1} ax}{a(n+1)} \qquad (n \neq -1)$

288. $\displaystyle\int \cot ax \, dx = \frac{1}{a} \log_e \sin ax$

289. $\displaystyle\int \cot^2 ax \, dx = \int \frac{dx}{\tan^2 ax} = -\frac{1}{a} \cot ax - x$

290. $\int \cot^3 ax\, dx = -\dfrac{1}{2a} \cot^2 ax - \dfrac{1}{a} \log_e \sin ax$

291. $\int \cot^n ax\, dx = \int \dfrac{dx}{\tan^n ax} = -\dfrac{1}{a(n-1)} \cot^{n-1} ax - \int \cot^{n-2} ax\, dx$

$$(n > 1)$$

292. $\int \dfrac{dx}{b + c \cot ax} = \int \dfrac{\tan ax\, dx}{b \tan ax + c} =$

$$\dfrac{1}{b^2 + c^2} \left[bx - \dfrac{c}{a} \log_e (c \cos ax + b \sin ax) \right]$$

293. $\int \dfrac{\cot^n ax}{\sin^2 ax}\, dx = \dfrac{-\cot^{n+1} ax}{a(n+1)} \qquad (n \neq -1)$

INTEGRALS WITH HYPERBOLIC FUNCTIONS WHERE $(a \neq 0)$

294. $\int \sinh x\, dx = \cosh x$

295. $\int \sinh^2 x\, dx = \dfrac{\sinh 2x}{4} - \dfrac{x}{2}$

296. $\int \dfrac{dx}{\sinh x} = \log_e \tanh \left(\dfrac{x}{2} \right)$

297. $\int \dfrac{dx}{\sinh^2 x} = -\coth x$

298. $\int \cosh x\, dx = \sinh x$

299. $\int \cosh^2 x\, dx = \dfrac{\sinh 2x}{4} + \dfrac{x}{2}$

300. $\int \dfrac{dx}{\cosh x} = 2 \arctan e^x = \arctan (\sinh x)$

301. $\int \dfrac{dx}{\cosh^2 x} = \tanh x$

302. $\int \dfrac{\sinh x}{\cosh^2 x}\, dx = -\dfrac{1}{\cosh x}$

303. $\int \dfrac{\cosh x}{\sinh^2 x}\, dx = -\dfrac{1}{\sinh x}$

304. $\int x \sinh x\, dx = x \cosh x - \sinh x$

305. $\int x \cosh x \, dx = x \sinh x - \cosh x$

306. $\int \tanh x \, dx = \log_e \cosh x$

307. $\int \tanh^2 x \, dx = x - \tanh x$

308. $\int \coth x \, dx = \log_e \sinh x$

309. $\int \coth^2 x \, dx = x - \coth x$

310. $\int \sinh^n ax \, dx$

$$= \begin{cases} \dfrac{1}{an} \sinh^{n-1} ax \cosh ax - \dfrac{n-1}{n} \displaystyle\int \sinh^{n-2} ax \, dx & (n > 0) \\[3mm] \dfrac{1}{a(n+1)} \sinh^{n+1} ax \cosh ax - \dfrac{n+2}{n+1} \displaystyle\int \sinh^{n+2} ax \, dx & (n < -1) \end{cases}$$

311. $\int \cosh^n ax \, dx$

$$= \begin{cases} \dfrac{1}{an} \sinh ax \cosh^{n-1} ax + \dfrac{n-1}{n} \displaystyle\int \cosh^{n-2} ax \, dx & (n > 0) \\[3mm] -\dfrac{1}{a(n+1)} \sinh ax \cosh^{n+1} ax + \dfrac{n+2}{n+1} \displaystyle\int \cosh^{n+2} ax \, dx & (n < -1) \end{cases}$$

312. $\int \sinh ax \sinh bx \, dx = \dfrac{\sinh (a+b)x}{2(a+b)} - \dfrac{\sinh (a-b)x}{2(a-b)}$

313. $\int \cosh ax \cosh bx \, dx = \dfrac{\sinh (a+b)x}{2(a+b)} + \dfrac{\sinh (a-b)x}{2(a-b)}$ $\left. \right\}$ $(a^2 \neq b^2)$

314. $\int \sinh ax \cosh bx \, dx = \dfrac{\cosh (a+b)x}{2(a+b)} + \dfrac{\cosh (a-b)x}{2(a-b)}$

315. $\int \sinh ax \sin ax \, dx = \dfrac{1}{2a} (\cosh ax \sin ax - \sinh ax \cos ax)$

316. $\int \cosh ax \cos ax \, dx = \dfrac{1}{2a} (\sinh ax \cos ax + \cosh ax \sin ax)$

317. $\int \sinh ax \cos ax \, dx = \dfrac{1}{2a} (\cosh ax \cos ax + \sinh ax \sin ax)$

318. $\int \cosh ax \sin ax \, dx = \dfrac{1}{2a} (\sinh ax \sin ax - \cosh ax \cos ax)$

INTEGRALS WITH EXPONENTIAL FUNCTIONS

319. $\int e^{ax}\, dx = \dfrac{1}{a} e^{ax}$

320. $\int xe^{ax}\, dx = \dfrac{e^{ax}}{a^2}(ax - 1)$

321. $\int x^2 e^{ax}\, dx = e^{ax}\left(\dfrac{x^2}{a} - \dfrac{2x}{a^2} + \dfrac{2}{a^3}\right)$

322. $\int x^n e^{ax}\, dx = \dfrac{1}{a} x^n e^{ax} - \dfrac{n}{a}\int x^{n-1} e^{ax}\, dx \qquad (n > 0)$

323. $\int \dfrac{e^{ax}}{x}\, dx = \log_e x + \dfrac{ax}{1 \cdot 1!} + \dfrac{(ax)^2}{2 \cdot 2!} + \dfrac{(ax)^3}{3 \cdot 3!} + \cdots$

324. $\int \dfrac{e^{ax}}{x^n}\, dx = \dfrac{1}{n-1}\left(-\dfrac{e^{ax}}{x^{n-1}} + a\int \dfrac{e^{ax}}{x^{n-1}}\, dx\right) \qquad (n > 1)$

325. $\int \dfrac{dx}{1 + e^{ax}} = \dfrac{1}{a}\log_e \dfrac{e^{ax}}{1 + e^{ax}}$

326. $\int \dfrac{dx}{b + ce^{ax}} = \dfrac{x}{b} - \dfrac{1}{ab}\log_e (b + ce^{ax})$

327. $\int \dfrac{e^{ax}\, dx}{b + ce^{ax}} = \dfrac{1}{ac}\log_e (b + ce^{ax})$

328. $\int \dfrac{dx}{be^{ax} + ce^{-ax}} = \dfrac{1}{a\sqrt{bc}} \arctan\left(e^{ax}\sqrt{\dfrac{b}{c}}\right) \qquad (bc > 0)$

$\qquad\qquad = \dfrac{1}{2a\sqrt{-bc}}\log_e \dfrac{c + e^{ax}\sqrt{-bc}}{c - e^{ax}\sqrt{-bc}} \qquad (bc < 0)$

329. $\int \dfrac{xe^{ax}\, dx}{(1 + ax)^2} = \dfrac{e^{ax}}{a^2(1 + ax)}$

330. $\int e^{ax}\log_e x\, dx = \dfrac{1}{a} e^{ax}\log_e x - \dfrac{1}{a}\int \dfrac{e^{ax}}{x}\, dx$

331. $\int e^{ax}\sin bx\, dx = \dfrac{e^{ax}}{a^2 + b^2}(a \sin bx - b \cos bx)$

332. $\int e^{ax}\cos bx\, dx = \dfrac{e^{ax}}{a^2 + b^2}(a \cos bx + b \sin bx)$

333. $\displaystyle\int xe^{ax}\sin bx\,dx = \frac{xe^{ax}}{a^2+b^2}(a\sin bx - b\cos bx) -$

$$\frac{e^{ax}}{(a^2+b^2)^2}\left[(a^2-b^2)\sin bx - 2\,ab\cos bx\right]$$

334. $\displaystyle\int xe^{ax}\cos bx\,dx = \frac{xe^{ax}}{a^2+b^2}(a\cos bx + b\sin bx) -$

$$\frac{e^{ax}}{(a^2+b^2)^2}\left[(a^2-b^2)\cos bx + 2\,ab\sin bx\right]$$

335. $\displaystyle\int e^{ax}\sin bx\sin cx\,dx = \frac{e^{ax}[(b-c)\sin(b-c)x + a\cos(b-c)x]}{2[a^2+(b-c)^2]} -$

$$\frac{e^{ax}[(b+c)\sin(b+c)x + a\cos(b+c)x]}{2[a^2+(b+c)^2]}$$

336. $\displaystyle\int e^{ax}\cos bx\cos cx\,dx = \frac{e^{ax}[(b-c)\sin(b-c)x + a\cos(b-c)x]}{2[a^2+(b-c)^2]} +$

$$\frac{e^{ax}[(b+c)\sin(b+c)x + a\cos(b+c)x]}{2[a^2+(b+c)^2]}$$

337. $\displaystyle\int e^{ax}\sin bx\cos cx\,dx = \frac{e^{ax}[a\sin(b-c)x - (b-c)\cos(b-c)x]}{2[a^2+(b-c)^2]} +$

$$\frac{e^{ax}[a\sin(b+c)x - (b+c)\cos(b+c)x]}{2[a^2+(b+c)^2]}$$

338. $\displaystyle\int e^{ax}\sin bx\sin(bx+c)\,dx = \frac{e^{ax}\cos c}{2a} -$

$$\frac{e^{ax}[a\cos(2bx+c) + 2b\sin(2bx+c)]}{2(a^2+4b^2)}$$

339. $\displaystyle\int e^{ax}\cos bx\cos(bx+c)\,dx = \frac{e^{ax}\cos c}{2a} +$

$$\frac{e^{ax}[a\cos(2bx+c) + 2b\sin(2bx+c)]}{2(a^2+4b^2)}$$

340. $\displaystyle\int e^{ax}\sin bx\cos(bx+c)\,dx = -\frac{e^{ax}\sin c}{2a} +$

$$\frac{e^{ax}[a\sin(2bx+c) - 2b\cos(2bx+c)]}{2(a^2+4b^2)}$$

341. $\displaystyle\int e^{ax}\cos bx\sin(bx+c)\,dx = \frac{e^{ax}\sin c}{2a} +$

$$\frac{e^{ax}[a\sin(2bx+c) - 2b\cos(2bx+c)]}{2(a^2+4b^2)}$$

342. $\displaystyle\int e^{ax} \sin^n bx \, dx = \frac{e^{ax} \sin^{n-1} bx \, (a \sin bx - nb \cos bx)}{a^2 + n^2 b^2} +$

$$\frac{n(n-1)b^2}{a^2 + n^2 b^2} \int e^{ax} \sin^{n-2} bx \, dx$$

343. $\displaystyle\int e^{ax} \cos^n bx \, dx = \frac{e^{ax} \cos^{n-1} bx \, (a \cos bx + nb \sin bx)}{a^2 + n^2 b^2} +$

$$\frac{n(n-1)b^2}{a^2 + n^2 b^2} \int e^{ax} \cos^{n-2} bx \, dx$$

INTEGRALS WITH LOGARITHMIC FUNCTIONS WHERE $(a \neq 0)$

344. $\displaystyle\int \log_e ax \, dx = x \log_e ax - x$

345. $\displaystyle\int (\log_e ax)^2 \, dx = x(\log_e ax)^2 - 2x \log_e ax + 2x$

346. $\displaystyle\int (\log_e ax)^n \, dx = x(\log_e ax)^n - n \int (\log_e ax)^{n-1} \, dx \qquad (n \neq -1)$

347. $\displaystyle\int \frac{dx}{\log_e ax} = \frac{1}{a} \left[\log_e (\log_e ax) + \log_e ax + \frac{(\log_e ax)^2}{2 \cdot 2!} + \frac{(\log_e ax)^3}{3 \cdot 3!} + \cdots \right]$

348. $\displaystyle\int x \log_e ax \, dx = \frac{x^2}{2} \log_e ax - \frac{x^2}{4}$

349. $\displaystyle\int x^2 \log_e ax \, dx = \frac{x^3}{3} \log_e ax - \frac{x^3}{9}$

350. $\displaystyle\int x^n \log_e ax \, dx = x^{n+1} \left[\frac{\log_e ax}{n+1} - \frac{1}{(n+1)^2} \right] \qquad (n \neq -1)$

351. $\displaystyle\int x^n (\log_e ax)^m \, dx = \frac{x^{n+1}}{n+1} (\log_e ax)^m - \frac{m}{n+1} \int x^n (\log_e ax)^{m-1} \, dx$

$$(m, n \neq -1)$$

352. $\displaystyle\int \frac{(\log_e ax)^n}{x} \, dx = \frac{(\log_e ax)^{n+1}}{n+1} \qquad (n \neq -1)$

353. $\displaystyle\int \frac{\log_e x}{x^n} \, dx = - \frac{\log_e x}{(n-1)x^{n-1}} - \frac{1}{(n-1)^2 x^{n-1}} \qquad (n \neq 1)$

354. $\displaystyle\int \frac{(\log_e x)^m}{x^n} \, dx = - \frac{(\log_e x)^m}{(n-1)x^{n-1}} + \frac{m}{n-1} \int \frac{(\log_e x)^{m-1}}{x^n} \, dx \qquad (n \neq 1)$

355. $\displaystyle\int \frac{x^n\,dx}{\log_e ax} = \frac{1}{a^{n+1}}\left[\log_e(\log_e ax) + (n+1)\log_e ax +\right.$

$$\left.\frac{(n+1)^2(\log_e ax)^2}{2\cdot 2!} + \frac{(n+1)^3(\log_e ax)^3}{3\cdot 3!} + \cdots\right] =$$

$$\frac{1}{a^{n+1}}\int \frac{e^y\,dy}{y} \qquad [y=(n+1)\log_e ax]$$

356. $\displaystyle\int \frac{x^n\,dx}{(\log_e ax)^m} = \frac{-x^{n+1}}{(m-1)(\log_e ax)^{m-1}} + \frac{n+1}{m-1}\int \frac{x^n\,dx}{(\log_e ax)^{m-1}} \qquad (m\neq 1)$

357. $\displaystyle\int \frac{dx}{x\log_e ax} = \log_e(\log_e ax)$

358. $\displaystyle\int \frac{dx}{x(\log_e ax)^n} = -\frac{1}{(n-1)(\log_e ax)^{n-1}}$

359. $\displaystyle\int \sin(\log_e ax)\,dx = \frac{x}{2}[\sin(\log_e ax) - \cos(\log_e ax)]$

360. $\displaystyle\int \cos(\log_e ax)\,dx = \frac{x}{2}[\sin(\log_e ax) + \cos(\log_e ax)]$

361. $\displaystyle\int e^{ax}\log_e bx\,dx = \frac{1}{a}e^{ax}\log_e bx - \frac{1}{a}\int \frac{e^{ax}}{x}\,dx$

INTEGRALS WITH INVERSE TRIGONOMETRIC AND HYPERBOLIC FUNCTIONS WHERE ($a>0$)

362. $\displaystyle\int \arcsin\frac{x}{a}\,dx = x\arcsin\frac{x}{a} + \sqrt{a^2-x^2}$

363. $\displaystyle\int x\arcsin\frac{x}{a}\,dx = \left(\frac{x^2}{2}-\frac{a^2}{4}\right)\arcsin\frac{x}{a} + \frac{x}{4}\sqrt{a^2-x^2}$

364. $\displaystyle\int x^2\arcsin\frac{x}{a}\,dx = \frac{x^3}{3}\arcsin\frac{x}{a} + \frac{1}{9}(x^2+2a^2)\sqrt{a^2-x^2}$

365. $\displaystyle\int x^n\arcsin\frac{x}{a}\,dx = \frac{x^{n+1}}{n+1}\arcsin\frac{x}{a} - \frac{1}{n+1}\int \frac{x^{n+1}}{\sqrt{a^2-x^2}}\,dx \qquad (n\neq -1)$

366. $$\int \frac{\arcsin \dfrac{x}{a}\, dx}{x} = \frac{x}{a} + \frac{1}{2 \cdot 3 \cdot 3}\frac{x^3}{a^3} + \frac{1 \cdot 3}{2 \cdot 4 \cdot 5 \cdot 5}\frac{x^5}{a^5} +$$
$$+ \frac{1 \cdot 3 \cdot 5}{2 \cdot 4 \cdot 6 \cdot 7 \cdot 7}\frac{x^7}{a^7} + \cdots \qquad (x^2 < a^2)$$

367. $$\int \frac{\arcsin \dfrac{x}{a}\, dx}{x^2} = -\frac{1}{x}\arcsin\frac{x}{a} - \frac{1}{a}\log_e \frac{a + \sqrt{a^2 - x^2}}{x}$$

368. $$\int \left(\arcsin \frac{x}{a}\right)^2 dx = x\left(\arcsin \frac{x}{a}\right)^2 + 2\left(\sqrt{a^2 - x^2}\,\arcsin \frac{x}{a} - x\right)$$

369. $$\int \arccos \frac{x}{a}\, dx = x \arccos \frac{x}{a} - \sqrt{a^2 - x^2}$$

370. $$\int x \arccos \frac{x}{a}\, dx = \left(\frac{x^2}{2} - \frac{a^2}{4}\right)\arccos \frac{x}{a} - \frac{x}{4}\sqrt{a^2 - x^2}$$

371. $$\int x^2 \arccos \frac{x}{a}\, dx = \frac{x^3}{3}\arccos \frac{x}{a} - \frac{1}{9}(x^2 + 2a^2)\sqrt{a^2 - x^2}$$

372. $$\int x^n \arccos \frac{x}{a}\, dx = \frac{x^{n+1}}{n+1}\arccos \frac{x}{a} + \frac{1}{n+1}\int \frac{x^{n+1}}{\sqrt{a^2 - x^2}}\, dx \qquad (n \neq -1)$$

373. $$\int \frac{\arccos \dfrac{x}{a}\, dx}{x} = \frac{\pi}{2}\log_e x - \frac{x}{a} - \frac{1}{2 \cdot 3 \cdot 3}\frac{x^3}{a^3} - \frac{1 \cdot 3}{2 \cdot 4 \cdot 5 \cdot 5}\frac{x^5}{a^5} -$$
$$- \frac{1 \cdot 3 \cdot 5}{2 \cdot 4 \cdot 6 \cdot 7 \cdot 7}\frac{x^7}{a^7} - \cdots \qquad (x^2 < a^2)$$

374. $$\int \frac{\arccos \dfrac{x}{a}\, dx}{x^2} = -\frac{1}{x}\arccos \frac{x}{a} + \frac{1}{a}\log_e \frac{a + \sqrt{a^2 - x^2}}{x}$$

375. $$\int \left(\arccos \frac{x}{a}\right)^2 dx = x\left(\arccos \frac{x}{a}\right)^2 - 2\left(\sqrt{a^2 - x^2}\,\arccos \frac{x}{a} + x\right)$$

376. $$\int \arctan \frac{x}{a}\, dx = x \arctan \frac{x}{a} - \frac{a}{2}\log_e (a^2 + x^2)$$

377. $$\int x \arctan \frac{x}{a}\, dx = \frac{1}{2}(x^2 + a^2)\arctan \frac{x}{a} - \frac{ax}{2}$$

378. $$\int x^2 \arctan \frac{x}{a}\, dx = \frac{x^3}{3}\arctan \frac{x}{a} - \frac{ax^2}{6} + \frac{a^3}{6}\log_e (a^2 + x^2)$$

379. $$\int x^n \arctan \frac{x}{a}\, dx = \frac{x^{n+1}}{n+1}\arctan \frac{x}{a} - \frac{a}{n+1}\int \frac{x^{n+1}\, dx}{a^2 + x^2} \qquad (n \neq -1)$$

380. $\displaystyle\int \frac{\arctan \dfrac{x}{a}\, dx}{x} = \frac{x}{a} - \frac{x^3}{3^2 a^3} + \frac{x^5}{5^2 a^5} - \frac{x^7}{7^2 a^7} + \cdots \quad (|x| < |a|)$

381. $\displaystyle\int \frac{\arctan \dfrac{x}{a}\, dx}{x^2} = -\frac{1}{x}\arctan\frac{x}{a} - \frac{1}{2a}\log_e \frac{a^2 + x^2}{x^2}$

382. $\displaystyle\int \frac{\arctan \dfrac{x}{a}\, dx}{x^n} = -\frac{1}{(n-1)x^{n-1}}\arctan\frac{x}{a} + \frac{a}{n-1}\int \frac{dx}{x^{n-1}(a^2 + x^2)}$

$$(n \neq 1)$$

383. $\displaystyle\int \operatorname{arccot}\frac{x}{a}\, dx = x \operatorname{arccot}\frac{x}{a} + \frac{a}{2}\log_e (a^2 + x^2)$

384. $\displaystyle\int x \operatorname{arccot}\frac{x}{a}\, dx = \frac{1}{2}(x^2 + a^2)\operatorname{arccot}\frac{x}{a} + \frac{ax}{2}$

385. $\displaystyle\int x^2 \operatorname{arccot}\frac{x}{a}\, dx = \frac{x^3}{3}\operatorname{arccot}\frac{x}{a} + \frac{ax^2}{6} - \frac{a^3}{6}\log_e (a^2 + x^2)$

386. $\displaystyle\int x^n \operatorname{arccot}\frac{x}{a}\, dx = \frac{x^{n+1}}{n+1}\operatorname{arccot}\frac{x}{a} + \frac{a}{n+1}\int \frac{x^{n+1}\, dx}{a^2 + x^2} \qquad (n \neq -1)$

387. $\displaystyle\int \frac{\operatorname{arccot}\dfrac{x}{a}\, dx}{x} = \frac{\pi}{2}\log_e x - \frac{x}{a} + \frac{x^3}{3^2 a^3} - \frac{x^5}{5^2 a^5} + \frac{x^7}{7^2 a^7} - \cdots$

388. $\displaystyle\int \frac{\operatorname{arccot}\dfrac{x}{a}\, dx}{x^2} = -\frac{1}{x}\operatorname{arccot}\frac{x}{a} + \frac{1}{2a}\log_e \frac{a^2 + x^2}{x^2}$

389. $\displaystyle\int \frac{\operatorname{arccot}\dfrac{x}{a}\, dx}{x^n} = -\frac{1}{(n-1)x^{n-1}}\operatorname{arccot}\frac{x}{a} - \frac{a}{n-1}\int \frac{dx}{x^{n-1}(a^2 + x^2)}$

$$(n \neq 1)$$

390. $\displaystyle\int \sinh^{-1}\frac{x}{a}\, dx = x \sinh^{-1}\frac{x}{a} - \sqrt{x^2 + a^2}$

391. $\displaystyle\int x \sinh^{-1}\frac{x}{a}\, dx = \frac{1}{2}\left(x^2 + \frac{a^2}{2}\right)\sinh^{-1}\frac{x}{a} - \frac{x}{4}\sqrt{x^2 + a^2}$

392. $\displaystyle\int \cosh^{-1}\frac{x}{a}\, dx = x \cosh^{-1}\frac{x}{a} \mp \sqrt{x^2 - a^2} \left(\text{upper sign for } \cosh^{-1}\frac{x}{a} > 0\right)$

393. $\displaystyle\int \tanh^{-1}\frac{x}{a}\, dx = x \tanh^{-1}\frac{x}{a} + \frac{a}{2}\log_e (a^2 - x^2)$

394. $\displaystyle\int x \tanh^{-1}\frac{x}{a}\,dx = \frac{x^2 - a^2}{2}\tanh^{-1}\frac{x}{a} + \frac{ax}{2}$

395. $\displaystyle\int \coth^{-1}\frac{x}{a}\,dx = x\coth^{-1}\frac{x}{a} + \frac{a}{2}\log_e(x^2 - a^2)$

DEFINITE INTEGRALS*

INTEGRALS WITH ALGEBRAIC FUNCTIONS

396. $\displaystyle\int_1^\infty \frac{dx}{x^n} = \frac{1}{n-1} \qquad (n > 1)$

397. $\displaystyle\int_0^\infty \frac{a\,dx}{a^2 + x^2} = \begin{cases} \dfrac{\pi}{2} & (a > 0) \\[2mm] 0 & (a = 0) \\[2mm] -\dfrac{\pi}{2} & (a < 0) \end{cases}$

398. $\displaystyle\int_0^1 x^\alpha (1-x)^\beta\,dx = 2\int_0^1 x^{2\alpha+1}(1-x^2)^\beta\,dx$

$$= \int_0^\infty \frac{x^\alpha}{(1+x)^{\alpha+\beta+2}}\,dx$$

$$= \frac{\Gamma(\alpha+1)\Gamma(\beta+1)}{\Gamma(\alpha+\beta+2)} = B(\alpha+1,\beta+1)$$

399. $\displaystyle\int_0^\infty \frac{dx}{(1+x)x^a} = \frac{\pi}{\sin a\pi} \qquad (a < 1)$

400. $\displaystyle\int_0^\infty \frac{x^{a-1}\,dx}{1+x} = \frac{\pi}{\sin a\pi} \qquad (0 < a < 1)$

401. $\displaystyle\int_0^\infty \frac{dx}{(1-x)x^a} = -\pi\cot a\pi \qquad (a < 1)$

402. $\displaystyle\int_0^\infty \frac{x^{a-1}}{1+x^b}\,dx = \frac{\pi}{b\sin(a\pi/b)} \qquad (0 < a < b)$

403. $\displaystyle\int_0^1 \frac{dx}{\sqrt{1-x^a}} = \frac{\sqrt{\pi}\,\Gamma(1/a)}{a\Gamma\left(\dfrac{2+a}{2a}\right)}$

*Note: m and n are integers.

INTEGRALS WITH TRIGONOMETRIC FUNCTIONS

404. $\displaystyle\int_0^\pi \sin mx \cos nx \, dx = \begin{cases} 0 & (m - n \text{ even}) \\[2mm] \dfrac{2m}{m^2 - n^2} & (m - n \text{ odd}) \end{cases}$

405. $\displaystyle\int_0^\pi \sin mx \sin (nx + \theta) \, dx = \int_0^\pi \cos mx \cos (nx + \theta) \, dx$

$$= \begin{cases} 0 & (m \neq n) \\[2mm] \dfrac{\pi}{2} \cos \theta & (m = n) \end{cases}$$

406. $\displaystyle\int_0^{\pi/2} \sin^a x \, dx = \int_0^{\pi/2} \cos^a x \, dx = \frac{1}{2} \sqrt{\pi} \, \frac{\Gamma\left(\dfrac{a+1}{2}\right)}{\Gamma\left(\dfrac{a}{2}+1\right)} \qquad (a > -1)$

$$= \begin{cases} \dfrac{1 \cdot 3 \cdot 5 \cdots (a-1)}{2 \cdot 4 \cdot 6 \cdots a} \cdot \dfrac{\pi}{2} & (a = 2, 4, \ldots) \\[4mm] \dfrac{2 \cdot 4 \cdot 6 \cdots (a-1)}{1 \cdot 3 \cdot 5 \cdot 7 \cdots a} & (a = 3, 5, \ldots) \end{cases}$$

407. $\displaystyle\int_0^{\pi/2} \sin^{2\alpha+1} x \cos^{2\beta+1} x \, dx = \frac{\Gamma(\alpha+1)\Gamma(\beta+1)}{2\Gamma(\alpha+\beta+2)}$

$$= \frac{1}{2} B(\alpha+1, \beta+1) \qquad (\alpha, \beta \neq -1)$$

$$= \frac{\alpha! \beta!}{2(\alpha+\beta+1)!} \qquad (\alpha, \beta \text{ integers} > 0)$$

Use formula (407) to obtain:

$$\int_0^{\pi/2} \sqrt{\sin x} \, dx \qquad \int_0^{\pi/2} \sqrt[3]{\sin x} \, dx \qquad \int_0^{\pi/2} \frac{dx}{\sqrt[3]{\cos x}}$$

408. $\displaystyle\int_0^\infty \frac{\sin ax}{x} \, dx = \begin{cases} \dfrac{\pi}{2} & (a > 0) \\[3mm] -\dfrac{\pi}{2} & (a < 0) \end{cases}$

409. $\displaystyle\int_0^\alpha \frac{\cos ax \, dx}{x} = \infty \qquad (\alpha \neq 0)$

410. $\displaystyle\int_0^\infty \frac{\tan ax \, dx}{x} = \begin{cases} \dfrac{\pi}{2} & (a > 0) \\[3mm] -\dfrac{\pi}{2} & (a < 0) \end{cases}$

411. $\displaystyle\int_0^\infty \frac{\cos ax - \cos bx}{x}\, dx = \log_e \frac{b}{a} \qquad (a, b \neq 0)$

412. $\displaystyle\int_0^\infty \frac{\sin x \cos ax}{x}\, dx = \begin{cases} \dfrac{\pi}{2} & (|a| < 1) \\[2mm] \dfrac{\pi}{4} & (|a| = 1) \\[2mm] 0 & (|a| > 1) \end{cases}$

413. $\displaystyle\int_0^\infty \frac{\sin x\, dx}{\sqrt{x}} = \int_0^\infty \frac{\cos x\, dx}{\sqrt{x}} = \sqrt{\dfrac{\pi}{2}}$

414. $\displaystyle\int_0^\infty \frac{x \sin bx}{a^2 + x^2}\, dx = \frac{\pi}{2} e^{-|ab|} \qquad (b > 0)$

415. $\displaystyle\int_0^\infty \frac{\cos ax}{1 + x^2}\, dx = \frac{\pi}{2} e^{-|a|}$

416. $\displaystyle\int_0^\infty \frac{\sin^2 ax}{x^2}\, dx = \frac{\pi}{2} |a|$

417. $\displaystyle\int_0^\infty \frac{\sin ax \sin bx}{x^2}\, dx = \frac{\pi a}{2} \qquad (a < b)$

418. $\displaystyle\int_0^\infty \cos (x^2)\, dx = \int_0^\infty \sin (x^2)\, dx = \frac{1}{2} \sqrt{\dfrac{\pi}{2}}$

419. $\displaystyle\int_0^\pi \sin^2 mx\, dx = \int_0^\pi \cos^2 mx\, dx = \frac{\pi}{2}$

420. $\displaystyle\int_0^\pi \frac{dx}{a + b \cos x} = \frac{\pi}{\sqrt{a^2 - b^2}} \qquad (a > b > 0)$

421. $\displaystyle\int_0^{\pi/2} \frac{dx}{a + b \cos x} = \frac{\arccos (b/a)}{\sqrt{a^2 - b^2}} \qquad (a > b)$

422. $\displaystyle\int_0^{\pi/2} \frac{dx}{a^2 \cos^2 x + b^2 \sin^2 x} = \frac{\pi}{2ab} \qquad (ab \neq 0)$

423. $\displaystyle\int_0^{\pi/2} \frac{dx}{(a^2 \cos^2 x + b^2 \sin^2 x)^2} = \frac{\pi (a^2 + b^2)}{4a^3 b^3}$

424. $\displaystyle\int_0^\pi \frac{(a - b \cos x)\, dx}{a^2 - 2ab \cos x + b^2} = \begin{cases} 0 & (a^2 < b^2) \\[2mm] \dfrac{\pi}{2a} & (a = b) \\[2mm] \dfrac{\pi}{a} & (a^2 > b^2) \end{cases}$

425. $\displaystyle\int_0^\pi \frac{\cos nx\, dx}{1 - 2b\cos x + b^2} = \frac{\pi b^n}{1 - b^2}$ $\qquad (n \geq 0, |b| < 1)$

426. $\displaystyle\int_0^1 \frac{dx}{1 + 2x\cos a + x^2} = \frac{a}{2\sin a}$ $\qquad \left(0 < a < \dfrac{\pi}{2}\right)$

427. $\displaystyle\int_0^\infty \frac{dx}{1 + 2x\cos a + x^2} = \frac{a}{\sin x}$ $\qquad \left(0 < a < \dfrac{\pi}{2}\right)$

428. $\displaystyle\int_0^{\pi/2} \frac{\sin x\, dx}{\sqrt{1 - k^2\sin^2 x}} = \frac{1}{2k}\log_e\frac{1 + k}{1 - k}$

429. $\displaystyle\int_0^{\pi/2} \frac{\cos x\, dx}{\sqrt{1 - k^2\sin^2 x}} = \frac{1}{k}\arcsin k$

430. $\displaystyle\int_0^{\pi/2} \frac{\sin^2 x\, dx}{\sqrt{1 - k^2\sin^2 x}} = \frac{1}{k^2}(K - E)$

431. $\displaystyle\int_0^{\pi/2} \frac{\cos^2 x\, dx}{\sqrt{1 - k^2\sin^2 x}} = \frac{1}{k^2}[E - (1 - k^2)K]$

$\qquad\qquad (|k| < 1)$

INTEGRALS WITH EXPONENTIAL AND HYPERBOLIC FUNCTIONS WHERE ($a > 0$)

432. $\displaystyle\int_0^\infty e^{-ax}\, dx = \frac{1}{a}$

433. $\displaystyle\int_0^\infty x^b e^{-ax}\, dx = \frac{\Gamma(b + 1)}{a^{b+1}}$ $\qquad (a > 0, b > -1)$

$\qquad\qquad = \dfrac{b!}{a^{b+1}}$ $\qquad (a > 0, b = 0, 1, 2, \ldots)$

434. $\displaystyle\int_0^\infty x^b e^{-ax^2}\, dx = \frac{\Gamma\left(\dfrac{b + 1}{2}\right)}{2a^{(b+1)/2}}$ $\qquad (a > 0, b > -1)$

$\qquad\qquad = \begin{cases} \dfrac{1 \cdot 3\, \cdots\, (b - 1)\sqrt{\pi}}{2^{(b/2)+1}a^{(b+1)/2}} & (a > 0, b = 0, 2, 4, \ldots) \\[3mm] \dfrac{\left(\dfrac{b - 1}{2}\right)!}{2a^{(b+1)/2}} & (a > 0, b = 1, 3, 5, \ldots) \end{cases}$

435. $\displaystyle\int_0^\infty e^{-a^2 x^2}\, dx = \frac{\sqrt{\pi}}{2a}$

436. $\displaystyle\int_0^\infty x e^{-x^2}\, dx = \frac{1}{2}$

437. $\displaystyle\int_0^\infty x^2 e^{-x^2}\,dx = \frac{\sqrt{\pi}}{4}$

438. $\displaystyle\int_0^\infty \sqrt{x}\,e^{-ax}\,dx = \frac{1}{2a}\sqrt{\frac{\pi}{a}}$

439. $\displaystyle\int_0^\infty \frac{e^{-ax}}{\sqrt{x}}\,dx = \sqrt{\frac{\pi}{a}}$

440. $\displaystyle\int_0^\infty e^{(-x^2-a^2/x^2)}\,dx = \frac{1}{2}\,e^{-2a}\sqrt{\pi}$

441. $\displaystyle\int_0^\infty \frac{e^{-ax}-e^{-bx}}{x}\,dx = \log_e \frac{b}{a} \qquad (a,\,b>0)$

442. $\displaystyle\int_0^\infty \frac{x\,dx}{e^x-1} = \frac{\pi^2}{6}$

443. $\displaystyle\int_0^\infty \frac{x\,dx}{e^x+1} = \frac{\pi^2}{12}$

444. $\displaystyle\int_0^\infty e^{-ax}\cos bx\,dx = \frac{a}{a^2+b^2}$

445. $\displaystyle\int_0^\infty e^{-ax}\sin bx\,dx = \frac{b}{a^2+b^2}$

446. $\displaystyle\int_0^\infty e^{-ax}\cosh bx\,dx = \frac{a}{a^2-b^2} \qquad (a>b\geq 0)$

447. $\displaystyle\int_0^\infty e^{-ax}\sinh bx\,dx = \frac{b}{a^2-b^2} \qquad (a>b\geq 0)$

448. $\displaystyle\int_0^\infty x e^{-ax}\sin bx\,dx = \frac{2ab}{(a^2+b^2)^2}$

449. $\displaystyle\int_0^\infty x e^{-ax}\cos bx\,dx = \frac{a^2-b^2}{(a^2+b^2)^2}$

450. $\displaystyle\int_0^\infty e^{-a^2x^2}\cos bx\,dx = \frac{\sqrt{\pi}\cdot e^{-b^2/4a^2}}{2a}$

451. $\displaystyle\int_0^\infty x^2 e^{-ax}\sin bx\,dx = \frac{2b(3a^2-b^2)}{(a^2+b^2)^3}$

452. $\displaystyle\int_0^\infty x^2 e^{-ax}\cos bx\,dx = \frac{2a(a^2-3b^2)}{(a^2+b^2)^3}$

453. $\displaystyle\int_0^\infty \frac{e^{-ax}\sin x}{x}\,dx = \arctan\frac{1}{a}$

454. $\displaystyle\int_0^\infty \frac{dx}{\cosh ax} = \frac{\pi}{2a}$

455. $\displaystyle\int_0^\infty \frac{x\,dx}{\sinh ax} = \frac{\pi^2}{4a^2}$

INTEGRALS WITH LOGARITHMIC FUNCTIONS

456. $\displaystyle\int_0^1 \log_e |\log_e x|\,dx = \int_0^\infty e^{-x}\log_e x\,dx = -C = -0.577\ 2157\cdots$

457. $\displaystyle\int_0^1 \frac{\log_e x}{1-x}\,dx = -\frac{\pi^2}{6}$

458. $\displaystyle\int_0^1 \frac{\log_e x}{1+x}\,dx = -\frac{\pi^2}{12}$

459. $\displaystyle\int_0^1 \frac{\log_e x}{1-x^2}\,dx = -\frac{\pi^2}{8}$

460. $\displaystyle\int_0^1 \log_e\left(\frac{1+x}{1-x}\right)\cdot\frac{dx}{x} = \int_0^\infty \log_e\left(\frac{e^x+1}{e^x-1}\right)dx = \frac{\pi^2}{4}$

461. $\displaystyle\int_0^1 \frac{\log_e x}{\sqrt{1-x^2}}\,dx = -\frac{\pi}{2}\log_e 2$

462. $\displaystyle\int_0^1 x\log_e(1-x)\,dx = -\frac{3}{4}$

463. $\displaystyle\int_0^1 x\log_e(1+x)\,dx = \frac{1}{4}$

464. $\displaystyle\int_0^1 \frac{\log_e(1+x)}{x}\,dx = \frac{\pi^2}{12}$

465. $\displaystyle\int_0^1 \frac{\log_e(1+x)}{x^2+1}\,dx = \frac{\pi}{8}\log_e 2$

466. $\displaystyle\int_0^1 \frac{x^b-x^a}{\log_e x}\,dx = \log_e\frac{1+b}{1+a} \qquad (a, b > -1)$

467. $\displaystyle\int_0^1 \left(\log_e\frac{1}{x}\right)^{1/2}dx = \frac{\sqrt{\pi}}{2}$

468. $\displaystyle\int_0^1 \left(\log_e\frac{1}{x}\right)^{-1/2}dx = \sqrt{\pi}$

469. $\displaystyle\int_0^1 \left(\log_e\frac{1}{x}\right)^a dx = \Gamma(a+1) \qquad (a > -1)$

470. $\displaystyle\int_0^1 (\log_e x)^n\,dx = (-1)^n\cdot n! \qquad (n = 1, 2, \ldots)$

471. $\displaystyle\int_0^1 x^n \left(\log_e \frac{1}{x}\right)^a dx = \frac{\Gamma(a+1)}{(n+1)^{a+1}}$ $(a, n > -1)$

472. $\displaystyle\int_0^{\pi/2} \log_e \sin x \, dx = \int_0^{\pi/2} \log_e \cos x \, dx = -\frac{\pi}{2} \log_e 2$

473. $\displaystyle\int_0^{\pi} x \log_e \sin x \, dx = -\frac{\pi^2}{2} \log_e 2$

474. $\displaystyle\int_0^{\pi} \log_e (a \pm b \cos x) \, dx = \pi \log_e \left(\frac{a + \sqrt{a^2 - b^2}}{2}\right)$ $(a \geq b)$

475. $\displaystyle\int_0^{\pi} \frac{\log_e (1 + \sin a \cos x)}{\cos x} dx = \pi a$

476. $\displaystyle\int_0^{\pi/2} \sin x \log_e \sin x \, dx = \log_e 2 - 1$

477. $\displaystyle\int_0^{\pi/2} \log_e \tan x \, dx = 0$

478. $\displaystyle\int_0^{\pi} \log_e (a^2 - 2ab \cos x + b^2) \, dx = \begin{cases} 2\pi \log_e a & (a \geq b > 0) \\ 2\pi \log_e b & (b \geq a > 0) \end{cases}$

479. $\displaystyle\int_0^{\pi/4} \log_e (1 + \tan x) \, dx = \frac{\pi}{8} \log_e 2$

10
Differential Equations

ORDINARY DIFFERENTIAL EQUATIONS

An equation involving derivatives or differentials is a differential equation. A differential equation is of order n if the equation involves a derivative of order n and contains no higher order derivative.

If the equation has derivatives with respect to one variable only, it is an ordinary differential equation, otherwise it is a partial differential equation. For example, the equations:

$$\frac{d^2y}{dx^2} + k^2 y = 0 \tag{Eq 1}$$

$$\frac{d^2y}{dx^2} = \sqrt{1 + y^2 + \frac{dy}{dx}} \tag{Eq 2}$$

$$y - x\frac{dy}{dx} + 3\frac{dx}{dy} = 0 \tag{Eq 3}$$

are ordinary differential equations. The equation:

$$y\frac{\partial^2 z}{\partial x^2} + zx\frac{\partial^2 z}{\partial x \partial y} - \frac{\partial z}{\partial y} = xyz \tag{Eq 4}$$

is a partial differential equation. The degree of a differential equation refers to the greatest power to which the highest-order derivative occurs in an equation that has been made rational and integral in its derivatives. For the ordinary differential equation of order n:

$$F(x, y, y', y'', \ldots, y^{(n)}) = 0 \tag{Eq 5}$$

a solution, or integral, is a function $y = \phi(x)$ for which F is transformed into a function identically zero for all values of x, when $\phi(x)$, $\phi'(x)$, $\ldots$, $\phi^{(n)}(x)$ are substituted for y, y', $\ldots$, $y^{(n)}$, respectively. The general solution of Eq 5 has the form:

$$y = \Phi(x, c_1, c_2, \ldots, c_n) \tag{Eq 6}$$

where c_1, c_2, $\ldots$, c_n arbitrary constants. If Eq 6 is differentiated n times with respect to x and if the n constants c_i which appear in the resulting n equations and Eq 6 are eliminated, the resulting differential equation is Eq 5. Equation 6 is the primitive of Eq 5.

A particular solution is a solution obtained by giving specific values to the constants in Eq 6. Singular solutions to Eq 5 are solutions which may exist but cannot be obtained by giving the constants c_i special values.

A differential equation is considered solved when the solution has been reduced to quadratures or if y has been obtained merely as an implicit function of x by $\psi(x, y, c_1, \ldots, c_n) = 0$.

FIRST-ORDER EQUATIONS

A first-order differential equation in the form:

$$\frac{dy}{dx} = f(x, y) \tag{Eq 7}$$

has a solution $y = y(x)$ through every point $(x = x_0, y = y_0)$ having a neighborhood in which $f(x, y)$ is continuous. For example, if D is a region of points (x, y), (x, η) where $f(x, y)$ is single-valued, bounded, and continuous, and the condition $|f(x, y) - f(x, \eta)| \leq M|y - \eta|$ holds for some real M independent of y and η, then Eq 7 has a unique solution $y = y(x)$ through every point $(x = x_0, y = y_0)$ of D. The solution $y(x)$ is a continuous function of the given value $y_0 = y(x_0)$. Each solution extends to the boundary of D.

Methods of Solution. The following special types of first-order equations can be solved with relative ease:

- **Equations with variables that are separable:** $y' = f_1(x)/f_2(y)$. The solution can be obtained from $\int f_2(y)\, dy = \int f_1(x)\, dx + C$
- **Homogeneous first-order equations:** $y' = f(y/x)$. Introduce $\overline{y} = y/x$ to reduce the equation to one in which variables can be separated

Separation of Variables. For the differential equation:

$$M\, dx + N\, dy = 0 \tag{Eq 8}$$

where $M(x, y)$ and $N(x, y)$ are functions of x and y. If M and N are products of factors, each being a function either of x alone or of y alone, then Eq 8 takes the form:

$$A(x)P(y)\, dx + B(x)Q(y)\, dy = 0 \tag{Eq 9}$$

where A and B are functions of x alone, and P and Q are functions of y alone. The general solution of Eq 9 is:

$$\int \frac{A(x)}{B(x)}\, dx + \int \frac{Q(y)}{P(y)}\, dy = c \tag{Eq 10}$$

with c a constant.

The expression $\dfrac{dy}{dx} = -\dfrac{x}{y}$ can be written as $x\,dx + y\,dy = 0$. It has the so-

lution $\int x\,dx + \int y\,dy = \dfrac{x^2}{2} + \dfrac{y^2}{2} = c$. If $c = \dfrac{r^2}{2}$, then $x^2 + y^2 = r^2$, is a set of con-

centric circles. An infinite number of solutions exists, depending on the value of r, and through each point in the plane there passes only one circle.

Homogeneous Equations. If $f(kx, ky) = k^n f(x, y)$, a function $f(x, y)$ is homogeneous of the nth degree in x and y. An equation:

$$P(x, y)\,dx + Q(x, y)\,dy = 0 \qquad\qquad \text{(Eq 11)}$$

is homogeneous when functions $P(x, y)$ and $Q(x, y)$ are homogeneous in x and y. The variables can be separated by substituting $y = vx$.

For example, to solve $(x^2 + y^2)\,dx - 2\,xy\,dy = 0$, which is of the form $P(x, y)\,dx + Q(x, y)\,dy = 0$, where P and Q are homogeneous functions of the second degree, substitute $y = vx$. The equation becomes $(1 + v^2)\,dx - 2v(x\,dv + v\,dx) = 0$. Separating variables produces:

$$\frac{dx}{x} - \frac{2v}{1 - v^2}\,dv = 0$$

By integrating, $\log_e x(1 - v^2) = \log_e c$; by replacing $v = \dfrac{y}{x}$, $\log\left(1 - \dfrac{y^2}{x^2}\right)x = \log_e c$; and by taking exponentials, $x^2 - y^2 = cx$.

Exact Differential Equation. The equation:

$$P(x, y)\,dx + Q(x, y)\,dy = 0 \qquad\qquad \text{(Eq 12)}$$

is an exact differential equation when the expression on the left side is an exact differential, $d\phi\left(\dfrac{\partial P}{\partial y} = \dfrac{\partial Q}{\partial x}\right)$. The solution is obtained from:

$$\phi(x, y) = \int P(x, y)\,dx + \int\left[Q(x, y) - \frac{\partial}{\partial y}\int P(x, y)\,dy\right]dy = C \qquad \text{(Eq 13)}$$

If the expression on the left of Eq 12 is not an exact differential $\left(\dfrac{\partial P}{\partial y} \neq \dfrac{\partial Q}{\partial x}\right)$, an integrating factor $\mu = \mu(x, y)$ may be found to permit multiplication of Eq 12 by $\mu(x, y)$ to yield an exact differential equation. The partial differential equation:

$$\mu\left(\frac{\partial P}{\partial y} - \frac{\partial Q}{\partial x}\right) = Q\frac{\partial \mu}{\partial x} - P\frac{\partial \mu}{\partial y} \qquad\qquad \text{(Eq 14)}$$

is satisfied by the integrating factor $\mu(x, y)$.

Linear Differential Equation. The linear first-order equation $y' + a(x)y = f(x)$ can be modified by the integrating factor $\mu = \mu(x) = \exp\int a(x)\,dx$. The complete primitive becomes:

$$y = \frac{1}{\mu(x)} \left[\int f(x)\mu(x)\,dx + C \right] \qquad \text{(Eq 15)}$$

Many first-order equations can be reduced by transformation of variables. In particular:

- $y' = f(\alpha x + \alpha y)$ is reduced to an equation with variables that are separable by introducing $\bar{y} = \alpha x + \beta y$

- $y' = \dfrac{\alpha_1 x + \beta_1 y + \gamma_1}{\alpha_2 x + \beta_2 y + \gamma_2}$ is reduced to a homogeneous first-order equation by a coordinate translation if $\alpha_1\beta_2 - \alpha_2\beta_1 \neq 0$; or by introducing $\bar{y} = \alpha_2 x + \beta_2 y + \gamma_2$ to separate the variables

Bernoulli's Differential Equation. The Bernoulli Equation is:

$$\frac{dy}{dx} + P(x)y = Q(x)y^n \qquad \text{(Eq 16)}$$

in which $n \neq 1$, is reduced to a linear equation by substituting $z = y^{1-n}$. The general solution is:

$$y = e^{-\int P(x)\,dx} \left[(1 - n) \int e^{(1-n)\int P(x)\,dx} Q(x)\,dx + c \right]^{\frac{1}{1-n}} \qquad \text{(Eq 17)}$$

For example, the equation $\dfrac{dy}{dx} - xy = xy^2$ can be solved by substituting $z = y^{-1}$ to obtain $\dfrac{dy}{dx} + xz = -x$. The general integral is:

$$z = ce^{-x^2/2} - 1 \quad \text{or} \quad y = \frac{1}{ce^{-x^2/2} - 1}$$

Riccati Equations. The general Riccati differential equation:

$$y' = a(x)y^2 + b(x)y + c(x) \qquad \text{(Eq 18)}$$

can be simplified by the transformation $y = 1/\bar{y}$. The transformations:

$$x = \bar{x} \quad y = \frac{-\bar{y}'}{a(x)\bar{y}}$$

lead to a homogeneous second-order equation for $\bar{y} = \bar{y}(x)$:

$$\bar{y}'' - \left[\frac{a'(x)}{a(x)} + b(x) \right]\bar{y}' + a(x)c(x)\bar{y} = 0 \qquad \text{(Eq 19)}$$

If a particular integral $y_1(x)$ of Eq 18 is known, the transformation:

$$y = y_1(x) + \frac{1}{\bar{y}}$$

produces a linear differential equation. If two particular integrals y_1, y_2 or three particular integrals y_1, y_2, y_3 are known, then:

$$y = y_1 + \frac{y_2 - y_1}{1 + C \exp \int a(x)(y_2 - y_1)\,dx}$$

$$y = \frac{y_1(y_2 - y_3) + Cy_2(y_1 - y_3)}{y_2 - y_3 + C(y_1 - y_3)} \qquad \text{(Eq 20)}$$

SECOND-ORDER EQUATIONS

The equation:

$$F\left(x, y, \frac{dy}{dx}, \frac{d^2y}{dx^2}\right) = 0 \qquad \text{(Eq 21)}$$

is a second order differential equation. The method of solution is straightforward if some of these variables are missing. With y and $\frac{dy}{dx}$ missing, for example, the equation:

$$\frac{d^2y}{dx^2} = f(x) \qquad \text{(Eq 22)}$$

has the solution $y = \int dx \int f(x)\,dx + cx + c_1$.

For the equation:

$$\frac{d^2y}{dx^2} = f(y) \qquad \text{(Eq 23)}$$

with x and $\frac{dy}{dx}$ missing, both sides can be multiplied by $2\frac{dy}{dx}$ to obtain:

$$x = \int \frac{dy}{\sqrt{c + 2\int f(y)\,dy}} + c_1 \qquad \text{(Eq 24)}$$

In the equation:

$$\frac{d^2y}{dx^2} = f\left(\frac{dy}{dx}\right) \qquad \text{(Eq 25)}$$

with x and y missing, using the transformations:

$$\frac{dy}{dx} = p \qquad \frac{d^2y}{dx^2} = \frac{dp}{dx} \qquad \text{(Eq 26)}$$

produces

$$x = \int \frac{dp}{f(p)} + c$$

This equation can be solved for p; p can be replaced by $\frac{dy}{dx}$; the resulting first order equation can then be solved.

Homogeneous linear second-order equations in the form:

$$Lw \equiv \frac{d^2 w}{dz^2} + a_1(z)\frac{dw}{dz} + a_2(z)w = 0 \qquad \text{(Eq 27)}$$

are equivalent to

$$\frac{d}{dz}\left[p(z)\frac{dw}{dz}\right] + q(z)w = 0 \qquad \text{(Eq 28)}$$

with

$$p(z) = \exp \int a_1(z)\,dz \qquad q(z) = a_2(z)p(z)$$

When a solution $w_1(z)$ of Eq 27 or 28 is known, the complete primitive is:

$$w(z) = w_1(z)\left[C_1 + C_2 \int \frac{dz}{w_1^2(z)p(z)}\right] \qquad \text{(Eq 29)}$$

Homogeneous Differential Equation with Constant Coefficients. A solution of the equation:

$$\frac{d^n y}{dx^n} + a_1\frac{d^{n-1}y}{dx^{n-1}} + \cdots + a_{n-1}\frac{dy}{dx} + a_n y = 0 \qquad \text{(Eq 30)}$$

becomes

$$y_k = ce^{r_k x} \qquad \text{(Eq 31)}$$

if r_k is a root of the algebraic equation:

$$r^n + a_1 r^{n-1} + \cdots + a_{n-1}r + a_n = 0 \qquad \text{(Eq 32)}$$

If n roots $r_1, r_2, \ldots, r_n$ of Eq 32 differ, then:

$$y = c_1 e^{r_1 x} + c_2 e^{r_2 x} + \cdots + c_n e^{r_n x} \qquad \text{(Eq 33)}$$

becomes a general solution of Eq 30. If k roots are equal, $r_1 = r_2 = \cdots = r_k$ while $r_{k+1}, \ldots, r_n$ differ, then:

$$y = (c_1 + c_2 x + \cdots + c_k x^{k-1})e^{r_1 x} + c_{k+1}e^{r_{k+1}x} + \cdots + c_n e^{r_n x} \qquad \text{(Eq 34)}$$

becomes a general solution. If $r_1 = p + iq$, $r_2 = p - iq$ are conjugate complex roots of Eq 32, then:

$$c_1 e^{r_1 x} + c_2 e^{r_2 x} = e^{px}(C_1 \cos qx + C_2 \sin qx) \qquad \text{(Eq 35)}$$

Nonhomogeneous Differential Equations with Constant Coefficients. The general solution of nonhomogeneous differential equations with constant coefficients is:

$$Ly \equiv a_0\frac{d^r y}{dt^r} + a_1\frac{d^{r-1}}{dt^{r-1}} + \cdots + a_r y = f(t) \qquad \text{(Eq 36)}$$

If $f(t) = 0$ for $t \leq 0$, the particular integral $y = y_N(t)$ of Eq 36 with $y_N = y'_N = y''_N = \cdots = y_N^{(r-1)} = 0$ for $t \leq 0$ is the normal response to the given forcing function $f(t)$.

Each function $y_k = y_k(t)$ of a system of linear differential equations with constant coefficients:

$$\phi_{j1}\left(\frac{d}{dt}\right)y_1 + \phi_{j2}\left(\frac{d}{dt}\right)y_2 + \cdots + \phi_{jn}\left(\frac{d}{dt}\right)y_n = f_j(t) \qquad \text{(Eq 37)}$$

$$(j = 1, 2, \ldots, n)$$

is the sum of the corresponding solution function of a complementary homogeneous system and a particular solution function.

Euler's Homogeneous Equation. For the equation:

$$x^n\frac{d^n y}{dx^n} + ax^{n-1}\frac{d^{n-1}y}{dx^{n-1}} + \cdots + a_{n-1}x\frac{dy}{dx} + a_n y = 0 \qquad \text{(Eq 38)}$$

place $x = e^t$ because:

$$x\frac{dy}{dx} = \frac{dy}{dt} \qquad x^2\frac{d^2 y}{dx^2} = \left[\frac{d}{dt}\left(\frac{d}{dt} - 1\right)\right]y$$

$$x^3\frac{d^3 y}{dx^3} = \left[\frac{d}{dt}\left(\frac{d}{dt} - 1\right)\left(\frac{d}{dt} - 2\right)\right]y, \ldots \qquad \text{(Eq 39)}$$

then Eq 38 becomes a linear homogeneous differential equation with constant coefficients.

Depression of Order. When for a linear homogeneous differential equation a particular integral is known, the order of the equation can be lowered. If y_1 is a particular integral of:

$$\frac{d^n y}{dx^n} + P_1(x)\frac{d^{n-1}y}{dx^{n-1}} + \cdots + P_{n-1}(x)\frac{dy}{dx} + P_n(x) = 0 \qquad \text{(Eq 40)}$$

$y = y_1 z$ can be substituted. The coefficient of z is zero. Placing $\frac{dz}{dx} = u$ reduces the equation to the $(n-1)$ st order. For example, for the equation:

$$\frac{d^2 y}{dx^2} + p(x)\frac{dy}{dx} + q(x)y = 0$$

let $y = y_1 z$. Then:

$$\frac{dy}{dx} = y_1\frac{dz}{dx} + z\frac{dy_1}{dx}$$

$$\frac{d^2 y}{dx^2} = y_1\frac{d^2 z}{dx^2} + 2\frac{dy_1}{dx}\frac{dz}{dx} + z\frac{d^2 y_1}{dx^2}$$

Substituting in the original equation produces:

$$y_1\frac{d^2 z}{dx^2} + 2\frac{dy_1}{dx}\frac{dz}{dx} + z\frac{d^2 y_1}{dx^2} + p\left[y_1\frac{dz}{dx} + z\frac{dy_1}{dx}\right] + qy_1 z = 0$$

Because the coefficient of z is zero, this expression reduces to:

$$y_1 \frac{d^2 z}{dx^2} + \left(2\frac{dy_1}{dx} + py_1\right)\frac{dz}{dx} = 0$$

By writing $\frac{dz}{dx} = u$, $\frac{du}{u} + \left(2\frac{dy_1}{dx} + py_1\right)\frac{dx}{y_1} = 0$

Integrating produces:

$$\log_e u + \int p\,dx + \log_e y_1^2 = \log_e c \qquad \text{or} \qquad u = \frac{c}{|y_1^2}e^{-\int p\,dx}$$

Integrating again gives z, and:

$$y = y_1 \int \frac{c}{y_1^2} e^{-\int p\,dx}\,dx + c_1$$

PFAFFIAN DIFFERENTIAL EQUATIONS

A Pfaffian differential equation, or first-order linear total differential equation:

$$P(x, y, z)\,dx + Q(x, y, z)\,dy + R(x, y, z)\,dx = 0 \qquad \text{(Eq 41)}$$

with continuously differentiable coefficients P, Q, R, can be interpreted geometrically as a condition $\mathbf{P} \cdot d\mathbf{r} = 0$ on the tangent vector $d\mathbf{r} \equiv (dx, dy, dz)$ of an integral curve. The curve is described by two equations $f(x, y, z) = 0$, $g(x, y, z, C) = 0$, with C a constant of integration. To determine the integral curves on an arbitrary regular surface:

$$f(x, y, z) = 0 \qquad \text{(Eq 42)}$$

solve the ordinary differential equation obtained by eliminating z and dz from Eq 41 and solve the equation $df(x, y, z) = 0$.

Eq 41 is integrable if there exists an integrating factor $\mu = \mu(x, y, z)$ for which $\mu(P\,dx + Q\,dy + R\,dz)$ is an exact differential $d\phi(x, y, z)$; that is, if:

$$P\left(\frac{\partial Q}{\partial z} - \frac{\partial R}{\partial y}\right) + Q\left(\frac{\partial R}{\partial x} - \frac{\partial P}{\partial z}\right) + R\left(\frac{\partial P}{\partial y} - \frac{\partial Q}{\partial x}\right) = 0 \qquad \text{(Eq 43)}$$

In such a case, each curve on an integral surface, $\phi(x, y, z) = C$, orthogonal to a series of curves described by $\frac{dx}{P} = \frac{dy}{Q} = \frac{dz}{R}$ is a solution.

SYSTEMS OF LINEAR DIFFERENTIAL EQUATIONS WITH CONSTANT COEFFICIENTS

For n linear equations with constant coefficients and n dependent variables and one independent variable t, a solution may be reached with the symbolic algebraic method. If $n = 2$:

$$\left.\begin{array}{l}(D^n + a_1 D^{n-1} + \cdots + a_n)x + (D^m + b_1 D^{m-1} + \cdots + b_m)y = R(t)\\(D^p + c_1 D^{p-1} + \cdots + c_p)x + (D^q + d_1 D^{q-1} + \cdots + d_q)y = S(t)\end{array}\right\} \qquad \text{(Eq 44)}$$

where $D = \dfrac{d}{dt}$. The equations may be expressed as:

$$P_1(D)x + Q_1(D)y = R \qquad P_2(D)x + q_2(D)y = S$$

Either x or y can be eliminated to solve the equation obtained by treating these as algebraic equations. For example, the system of equations:

$$\frac{dx}{dt} + \frac{dy}{dt} + 2x + y = 0 \qquad \text{(Eq 45a)}$$

$$\frac{dy}{dt} + 5x + 3y = 0 \qquad \text{(Eq 45b)}$$

can be written

$$(D + 2)x + (D + 1)y = 0 \qquad 5x + (D + 3)y = 0$$

by using the symbol D. Eliminating x, $(D^2 + 1)y = 0$. Using Eq 35, Eq 45(a) has the solution $y = c_1 \cot t + c_2 \sin t$. Substituting this result in Eq 45(b), $x = -\dfrac{3c_1 + c_2}{5} \cos t + \dfrac{c_1 - 3c_2}{5} \sin t$.

SIMULTANEOUS TOTAL DIFFERENTIAL EQUATIONS

The system:

$$\begin{cases} P_1 dx + Q_1 dy + R_1 dz = 0 \\ P_2 dx + Q_2 dy + R_2 dz = 0 \end{cases} \qquad \text{(Eq 46)}$$

where P_1, Q_1, R_1, P_1, are functions of x, y, and z, may be written:

$$\frac{dx}{P} = \frac{dy}{Q} = \frac{dz}{R} \qquad \text{(Eq 47)}$$

where

$$P = \begin{vmatrix} Q_1 & R_1 \\ Q_2 & R_2 \end{vmatrix} \qquad Q = \begin{vmatrix} R_1 & P_1 \\ R_2 & P_2 \end{vmatrix} \qquad R = \begin{vmatrix} P_1 & Q_1 \\ P_2 & Q_2 \end{vmatrix} \qquad \text{(Eq 48)}$$

The general solution of Eq 46 consists of relationships involving two arbitrary constants:

$$\phi_1(x, y, z, c_1) = 0 \qquad \phi_2(x, y, z, c_2) = 0 \qquad \text{(Eq 49)}$$

PARTIAL DIFFERENTIAL EQUATIONS

Partial differential equations involve partial derivatives. Explicit solutions can be reached in only a relatively few cases and usually involve arbitrary functions, in a manner similar to the solutions of ordinary differential equations, which involve arbitrary constants. In practice, a problem usually involves determining a function that satisfies the differential equation and meets specific initial or boundary conditions.

PARTIAL DIFFERENTIAL EQUATIONS OF THE FIRST ORDER

Interpreted geometrically for a first-order partial differential equation:

$$F(x, y, z, p, q) = 0 \qquad \left(p \equiv \frac{\partial z}{\partial x},\, q \equiv \frac{\partial z}{\partial y};\, F_{p^2} + F_{q^2} = 0\right) \tag{Eq 50}$$

with an unknown function $z = z(x, y)$, assume the given function F is single-valued and twice continuously differentiable and x, y, z as rectangular cartesian coordinates. Every solution $z = z(x, y)$ of Eq 50 represents a surface with a normal having the direction numbers p, q, -1 at every surface point (x, y, z). The solution surface is defined by:

$$dx : dy : dz = F_p : F_q : (pF_p + qF_q)$$

at every point (x, y, z). A set of values (x, y, z, p, q) describes a planar element associating the direction numbers p, q, -1 with a point (x, y, z).

Characteristic Equations. A set of differentiable functions:

$$x = x(t) \qquad y = y(t) \qquad z = z(t) \qquad p = p(t) \qquad q = q(t) \tag{Eq 51}$$

represents the points and tangent planes along a strip of a regular surface if the functions (Eq 51) satisfy the strip condition:

$$\frac{dz}{dt} = p\frac{dx}{dt} = q\frac{dy}{dt}$$

Every set of functions (Eq 51) that satisfies the characteristic ordinary differential equations associated with Eq 50, that is:

$$\left. \begin{array}{ll} \dfrac{dz}{dt} = p\dfrac{dx}{dt} + q\dfrac{dy}{dt} & \dfrac{dx}{dt} = F_p \qquad \dfrac{dy}{dt} = F_q \\[2ex] \dfrac{dp}{dt} = -(pF_z + F_x) & \dfrac{dq}{dt} = -(qF_z + F_y) \end{array} \right\} \tag{Eq 52}$$

together with Eq 50 describe a characteristic strip.

Linear First-Order Partial Equation. The equation:

$$Ap + Bq = C \tag{Eq 53}$$

for which A, B, and C are functions of x, y, and z and:

$$p = \frac{\partial z}{\partial x} = z_x \qquad q = \frac{\partial z}{\partial y} = z_y$$

has the general solution $\Phi(u, v) = 0$. In this general solution, Φ is an arbitrary function, $u(x, y, z) = c_1$ and $v(x, y, z) = c_2$. These elements form the general solution of the differential equations:

$$\frac{dx}{A} = \frac{dy}{B} = \frac{dz}{C} \tag{Eq 54}$$

The normal to the surface $\Phi(u, v) = 0$ is perpendicular to the curves of Eq 54. The characteristic curves of Eq 53 are $u = c_1$ and $v = c_2$.

General Solution. For the partial differential equation $F(x, y, z, p, q) = 0$, since z is a function of x and y, then $dz = p\, dx + q\, dy$. If another relationship can be found among x, y, z, p, q, so as to produce $f(x, y, z, p, q) = 0$, then p and q can be eliminated. The solution of the resulting ordinary differential equation, involving x, y, z satisfies the given equation, $F(x, y, z, p, q) = 0$. The following linear partial differential equation must be satisfied by the unknown function f:

$$\frac{\partial F}{\partial p}\frac{\partial f}{\partial x} + \frac{\partial F}{\partial q}\frac{df}{\partial y} + \left(p\frac{\partial F}{\partial p} + q\frac{\partial F}{\partial q}\right)\frac{\partial f}{\partial z} - \left(\frac{\partial F}{\partial x} + p\frac{\partial F}{\partial z}\right)\frac{\partial f}{\partial p} -$$

$$\left(\frac{\partial F}{\partial y} + q\frac{\partial F}{\partial z}\right)\frac{\partial f}{\partial q} = 0 \quad \text{(Eq 55)}$$

This equation is satisfied by any of the solutions of the system:

$$\frac{\partial x}{\frac{\partial F}{\partial p}} = \frac{\partial y}{\frac{\partial F}{\partial q}} = \frac{dz}{p\frac{\partial F}{\partial p} + q\frac{\partial F}{\partial q}} = \frac{-dp}{\frac{\partial F}{\partial x} + p\frac{\partial F}{\partial z}} = \frac{-dq}{\frac{\partial F}{\partial y} + q\frac{\partial F}{\partial z}} \quad \text{(Eq 56)}$$

PARTIAL DIFFERENTIAL EQUATIONS OF THE SECOND ORDER

A linear second-order partial differential equation with two independent variables has the form:

$$L = Ar + 2Bs + Ct + Dp + Eq + Fz = f(x, y) \quad \text{(Eq 57)}$$

for which

$$r = \frac{\partial^2 z}{\partial x^2} \qquad s = \frac{\partial^2 z}{\partial x\, \partial y} \qquad t = \frac{\partial^2 z}{\partial y^2} \qquad p = \frac{\partial z}{\partial x} \qquad q = \frac{\partial z}{\partial y}$$

Coefficients $A, \ldots, F$ are real continuous functions of the real variables x and y. For the following homogeneous partial differential equation of the first order:

$$Ap^2 + 2Bpq + Cq^2 = 0 \quad \text{(Eq 58)}$$

assume that two solutions are $\xi = \xi(x, y)$, $\eta = \eta(x, y)$.

The homogeneous form of Eq 57, $L = 0$, is the parabolic type, if $B^2 - AC = 0$, and has the normal form:

$$\frac{\partial^2 z}{\partial \xi^2} + a\frac{\partial z}{\partial \xi} + b\frac{\partial z}{\partial \eta} + cz = 0 \quad \text{(Eq 59)}$$

where a, b, c are functions of ξ and η.

If $B^2 - AC > 0$ in Eq 58, the homogeneous form of Eq 57 is hyperbolic, which has two normal forms:

$$\frac{\partial^2 z}{\partial \xi \partial \eta} + a \frac{\partial z}{\partial \xi} + b \frac{\partial z}{\partial \eta} + cz = 0 \qquad \text{(Eq 60)}$$

$$\frac{\partial^2 z}{\partial \xi^2} - \frac{\partial^2 z}{\partial \eta^2} + a \frac{\partial z}{\partial \xi} + b \frac{\partial z}{\partial \eta} + cz = 0 \qquad \text{(Eq 61)}$$

The equation is an elliptic type which has the normal form:

$$\frac{\partial^2 z}{\partial \xi^2} + \frac{\partial^2 z}{\partial z^2} + a \frac{\partial z}{\partial \xi} + b \frac{\partial z}{\partial \eta} + cz = 0 \qquad \text{(Eq 62)}$$

when $B^2 - AC < 0$.

Laplace's Equation. The general solution of the equation:

$$\frac{\partial^2 \phi}{\partial x^2} + \frac{\partial^2 \phi}{\partial y^2} = 0 \qquad \text{(Eq 63)}$$

is of the form

$$\phi = f_1(x + iy) + f_2(x - iy) \qquad i^2 = -1 \qquad \text{(Eq 64)}$$

with f_1 and f_2 being arbitrary functions. In practice this solution is too general, because determining this function so as to satisfy given boundary conditions is difficult. A function which satisfies Eq 63 is a harmonic function.

A useful method depends upon the assumption that a particular solution is a product of functions each containing only one of the variables. Combining a number of such solutions often results in a sufficiently general solution. For example, assuming:

$$\phi = X(x) \cdot Y(y) \qquad \text{(Eq 65)}$$

is a solution of Eq 63, then $(X''/X) + (Y''/Y) = 0$. From this:

$$\frac{1}{X}\frac{d^2 X}{dx^2} = -\omega^2 \qquad \frac{1}{Y}\frac{d^2 Y}{dy^2} = \omega^2 \qquad \text{(Eq 66)}$$

where ω is a constant. Solutions to Eq 66 are:

$$X = c_1 \cos \omega x + c_2 \sin \omega x \qquad Y = c_3 e^{\omega y} + c_4 e^{-\omega y}$$

in which c_1, c_2, c_3, c_4 are arbitrary constants. Equation 65 becomes:

$$\phi \equiv \phi(\omega) = e^{\omega y}(A_\omega \cos \omega x + B_\omega \sin \omega x) + e^{-\omega y}(C_\omega \cos \omega x + D_\omega \sin \omega x)$$

in which $A_\omega, B_\omega, C_\omega, D_\omega$ are arbitrary constants. Generally:

$$\phi = \sum_{\omega=0}^{\infty} \phi(\omega) \qquad \text{(Eq 67)}$$

may be assumed to be a solution to Eq 63, with the constants determined so that Eq 67 will satisfy initial or boundary conditions of a particular problem.

Equations Linear in the Second Derivatives. The general second-order equation linear in the second derivative may be expressed as:

$$Ar + Bs + Ct = V \tag{Eq 68}$$

for which A, B, C, V are functions of x, y, z, p, q. From the equations:

$$A\,dy^2 - B\,dx\,dy + C\,dx^2 = 0 \tag{Eq 69}$$

$$A\,dp\,dy + C\,dq\,dx - V\,dx\,dy = 0 \tag{Eq 70}$$

$$p\,dx + q\,dy = dz \tag{Eq 71}$$

one or two relationships may be derived between x, y, z, p, q. These are intermediary integrals. From these, the solution of Eq 68 may be deduced. To obtain an intermediary integral, resolve Eq 69, assuming that the left member is not a perfect square, into the equations $dy - n_1 dx = 0$ and $dy - n_2 dx = 0$. From the first and from Eq 70, combined with Eq 71, if necessary, obtain the two integrals $u_1(x, y, z, p, q) = a$ and $v_1(x, y, z, p, q) = b$. Then $u_1 = f_1(v_1)$, with f_1 an arbitrary function, becomes an intermediary integral. In the same way, from $dy - n_2 dx = 0$, another pair of integrals $u_2 = a_1, v_2 = b_1$ is obtained. Then $u_2 = f_2(v_2)$ is an intermediary integral. If $n_1 = n_2$, the intermediary integral may be integrated to determine the final integral. If $n_1 \neq n_2$, the two intermediary integrals are solved for p and q and substituted in $p\,dx + q\,dy = dz$. The result is integrated.

Homogeneous Equation with Constant Coefficients. The equation:

$$\frac{\partial^2 z}{\partial x^2} + A_1 \frac{\partial^2 z}{\partial x \partial y} + A_2 \frac{\partial^2 z}{\partial y^2} = 0 \tag{Eq 72}$$

is equivalent to

$$\left(\frac{\partial}{\partial x} - m_1 \frac{\partial}{\partial y}\right)\left(\frac{\partial}{\partial x} - m_2 \frac{\partial}{\partial y}\right) z = 0 \tag{Eq 73}$$

where m_1 and m_2 are roots of the auxiliary equation $X^2 + A_1 X + A_2 = 0$. The general solution of Eq 73 is:

$$z = f_1(y + m_1 z) + f_2(y + m_2 x) \tag{Eq 74}$$

Euler's Equation. The general Euler's equation:

$$a \frac{\partial^2 z}{\partial x^2} + 2b \frac{\partial^2 z}{\partial x \partial y} + c \frac{\partial^2 z}{\partial y^2} = 0 \tag{Eq 75}$$

for which a, b, and c are constants, has the general solutions:

$$z = \phi(x + \lambda_1 y) + \psi(x + \lambda_2 y) \quad \text{if } b^2 \neq ac \tag{Eq 76}$$

$$z = \phi(x + \lambda_1 y) + (\gamma x + \delta y)\psi(x + \lambda_1 y) \quad \text{if } b^2 = ac \tag{Eq 77}$$

where λ_1 and λ_2 are the roots of $a + 2b\lambda + c\lambda^2 = 0$. ϕ and ψ are arbitrary functions, and γ and δ are arbitrary constants. The general solution of $\partial^2 x/\partial x \partial y = 0$ is $z = \phi(x) + \psi(y)$; ϕ and ψ are arbitrary functions. The general solution of $\partial^2 u/\partial t^2 = a^2 \partial^2 u/\partial x^2$ is $u = \phi(x + at) + \psi(x - at)$; ϕ and ψ are arbitrary functions.

LINEAR PARTIAL DIFFERENTIAL EQUATIONS

Physical background	One-dimensional	Multidimensional
Parabolic(a) Heat conduction, diffusion	$\dfrac{\partial^2 \Phi}{\partial x^2} - \dfrac{1}{\gamma^2}\dfrac{\partial \Phi}{\partial t} = f(x, t)$	$\nabla^2 \Phi - \dfrac{1}{\gamma^2}\dfrac{\partial \Phi}{\partial t} = f(\mathbf{r}, t)$
Hyperbolic(b) Waves (strings, membranes, fluids, electromagnetic)	$\dfrac{\partial^2 \Phi}{\partial x^2} - \dfrac{1}{c^2}\dfrac{\partial^2 \Phi}{\partial t^2} = f(x, t)$	$\nabla^2 \Phi - \dfrac{1}{c^2}\dfrac{\partial^2 \Phi}{\partial t^2} = f(\mathbf{r}, t)$
Damped waves, transmission lines	$\dfrac{\partial^2 \Phi}{\partial x^2} - a_0\dfrac{\partial^2 \Phi}{\partial t^2} - a_1\dfrac{\partial \Phi}{\partial t} -$ $a_2 \Phi = f(x, t)$	$\nabla^2 \Phi - a_0\dfrac{\partial^2 \Phi}{\partial t} - a_1\dfrac{\partial \Phi}{\partial t} -$ $a_2 \Phi = f(\mathbf{r}, t)$
Elliptic(c) Static case	$\dfrac{\partial^2 \Phi}{\partial x^2} = f(x)$	$\nabla^2 \Phi = f(\mathbf{r})$
4th order(b) Elastic vibrations	$\dfrac{\partial^4 \Phi}{\partial x^4} + \dfrac{1}{c^2}\dfrac{\partial^2 \Phi}{\partial t^2} = f(x, t)$	$\nabla^2\nabla^2 \Phi + \dfrac{1}{c^2}\dfrac{\partial^2 \Phi}{\partial t^2} =$ $f(\mathbf{r}, t)$
4th order(c) Static case	$\dfrac{\partial^4 \Phi}{\partial x^4} = f(x)$	$\nabla^2\nabla^2 \Phi = f(\mathbf{r})$

(a) Boundary conditions; initial conditions on Φ. (b) Boundary conditions; initial conditions on Φ and $\partial\Phi/\partial t$. (c) Boundary conditions only

SEPARATION OF VARIABLES

In many important applications, a solution of the form:

$$\Phi = \Phi(x_1, x_2, \ldots, x_n) = \phi_1(x_1)\phi_0(x_2, x_3, \ldots, x_n) \qquad \text{(Eq 78)}$$

can be reached by rewriting a partial differential equation in the separated form:

$$F_1\left(x_1, \phi_1, \frac{d\phi_1}{dx_1}, \frac{d^2\phi_1}{dx_1^2}, \ldots\right) = F_0\left(x_2, x_3, \ldots, x_n; \phi_0; \frac{\partial\phi_0}{\partial x_2}, \frac{\partial\phi_0}{\partial x_3}, \ldots\right)$$

The unknown functions $\phi_1(x_1)$ and $\phi_0(x_2, x_3, \ldots, x_n)$ must satisfy the differential equations:

$$F_1\left(x_1, \phi_1, \frac{d\phi_1}{dx_1}, \frac{d^2\phi_1}{dx_1^2}, \ldots\right) = C \qquad\qquad \text{(Eq 79)}$$

$$F_2\left(x_2, x_3, \ldots, x_n; \phi_0; \frac{\partial\phi_0}{\partial x_2}, \frac{\partial\phi_0}{\partial x_3}, \ldots\right) = C \qquad\qquad \text{(Eq 80)}$$

where C is a constant of integration, or separation constant, to be determined according to boundary or other conditions. Equation 79 is an ordinary differential equation for the unknown function $\phi_1(x_1)$. With Eq 80, the separation process may be repeated.

11
Laplace Transformation

FUNDAMENTAL TRANSFORMATION RULES

The methods of Laplace and Fourier transformation and the Heaviside operational calculus are essentially aspects of the same method. This method simplifies solutions of such problems as ordinary differential equations with constant coefficients, linear differential equations with variable coefficients, integral equations of the convolution, or Faltung, type, and partial differential equations.

Direct Laplace Transformation. The Laplace transform $\mathcal{L}(F)$ of a function $F(t)$ may be expressed as:

$$\mathcal{L}(F) = f(s) = \int_0^\infty e^{-st} F(t)\, dt \tag{Eq 1}$$

with t a real variable, s a complex variable, $F(t)$ a real function of t which equals zero for $t < 0$, $f(s)$ a function of s, and e the base of the natural logarithms. If the function $F(t)$ is known and the integral:

$$f(s) = \int_0^\infty e^{-st} F(t)\, dt \tag{Eq 2}$$

can be computed, the function $f(s)$ may be determined and the direct Laplace transform:

$$f(s) = \mathcal{L}F(t) \tag{Eq 3}$$

obtained. If the function $f(s)$ is known, the integral:

$$F(t) = \frac{1}{2\pi j} \int_{c-j\infty}^{c+j\infty} e^{st} f(s)\, ds \tag{Eq 4}$$

must be used to determine the function $F(t)$. If this integral can be evaluated, the inverse transform:

$$F(t) = \mathcal{L}^{-1} f(s) \tag{Eq 5}$$

may be obtained. The computation of several direct transforms may be evaluated by the integration of Eq 2.

Inverse Transformation. The inverse transform of a function $f(s)$ is computed by the use of the equation:

$$F(t) = \frac{1}{2\pi j} \int_{c-j\infty}^{c+j\infty} f(s)e^{st}\,ds \tag{Eq 6}$$

The line integral for $F(t)$ can be evaluated by transforming it into a closed contour (Fig. 1). Defining the closed contour Γ as the straight line parallel to the axis of imaginaries at a distance c to the right of the axis and the large semicircle s_0 with center at $(c, 0)$, then:

$$\oint_\Gamma e^{st}f(s)\,ds = \int_{c+jR}^{c-jR} e^{st}f(s)\,ds + \int_{s_0} e^{st}f(s)\,ds \tag{Eq 7}$$

The evaluation of the contour integral along Γ is simplified by designating $\phi(s)$ as an integrable function of the complex variable s:

$$\lim_{|s|\to\infty} |\phi(s)| = 0 \tag{Eq 8}$$

Then:

$$\lim_{R\to\infty} \left| \int_{s_0} e^{st}\phi(s)\,ds \right| = 0 \qquad t > 0 \qquad \mathrm{Re}\ s \le 0 \tag{Eq 9}$$

The function $\phi(s) = f(s)$ frequently has such properties that the integral around the large semicircle defined by Eq 7 vanishes as $R \to \infty$. Thus:

$$F(t) = \frac{1}{2\pi j} \int_{c-j\infty}^{c+j\infty} f(s)e^{st}\,ds = \lim_{R\to\infty} \frac{1}{2\pi j} \oint_s e^{st}f(s)\,ds \tag{Eq 10}$$

and

$$\oint_\Gamma e^{st}f(s)\,ds = 2\pi j \sum \mathrm{Res}\ e^{st}f(s) \text{ inside } \Gamma \tag{Eq 11}$$

Hence, from Eq 10:

$$F(t) = \sum \mathrm{Res}\ e^{st}f(s) \text{ inside } \Gamma \tag{Eq 12}$$

if R is sufficiently large to include all singularities.

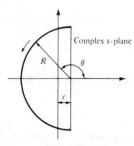

Figure 1

Transformation of nth Derivative. If $\mathcal{L}[F(t)] = f(s)$, then:

$$\mathcal{L}\left[\frac{d^n F(t)}{dt^n}\right] = s^n f(s) - \sum_{k=0}^{n-1} F^{(k)}(0+) \cdot s^{n-1-k} \qquad \text{(Eq 13)}$$

where $F^{(2)}(0+)$ means $\dfrac{d^2 F(t)}{dt^2}$ evaluated for $t \to 0$, and $F^{(0)}(0+)$ means $F(0+)$, and $n = 1, 2, 3, \cdots n$.

Transformation of nth Integral. If $\mathcal{L}[F(t)] = f(s)$, then:

$$\mathcal{L}\left[\int\int \cdots \int F(t)dt\right] = s^{-n} f(s) + \sum_{k=-1}^{-n} F^{(k)}(0+) \cdot s^{-n-1-k} \qquad \text{(Eq 14)}$$

where $F^{(-2)}(0+)$ means $\int\int F(t)\, dt\, dt$ evaluated for $t \to 0$, and $n = 1, 2, 3, \cdots n$.

Inverse Transformation of Product. If:

$$\mathcal{L}^{-1}[f_1(s)] = F_1(t) \qquad \mathcal{L}^{-1}[f_2(s)] = F_2(t) \qquad \text{(Eq 15)}$$

then

$$\mathcal{L}^{-1}[f_1(s) \cdot f_2(s)] = \int_0^t F_1(t-\lambda) \cdot F_2(\lambda)\, d\lambda \qquad \text{(Eq 16)}$$

Linear Transformations $\mathcal{L}$ and $\mathcal{L}^{-1}$. Designating k_1, k_2 as real constants, then:

$$\mathcal{L}[k_1 F_1(t) + k_2 F_2(t)] = k_1 \mathcal{L}[F_1(t)] + k_2 \mathcal{L}[F_2(t)] \qquad \text{(Eq 17)}$$

and

$$\mathcal{L}^{-1}[k_1 f_1(s) + k_2 f_2(s)] = k_1 \mathcal{L}^{-1}[f_1(s)] + k_2 \mathcal{L}^{-1}[f_2(s)] \qquad \text{(Eq 18)}$$

THEOREMS

Some general theorems concerning operations on transforms are given below.

Theorem 1. The Laplace transform of a constant k is that constant divided by s:

$$\mathcal{L}(k) = \frac{k}{s} \qquad \text{(Eq 19)}$$

From the fundamental definition of the direct Laplace transform:

$$\mathcal{L}(k) = \int_0^\infty e^{-st} k\, dt = k\left[-\frac{e^{-st}}{s}\right]_0^\infty = \frac{k}{s} \qquad \text{(Eq 20)}$$

and the integral vanishes at the upper limit.

Theorem 2. The equation:

$$\mathscr{L}\, k\phi(t) = k\, \mathscr{L}\, \phi(t) \qquad\qquad \text{(Eq 21)}$$

where k is a constant, may be proved in the following manner:

$$\mathscr{L}\, k\phi(t) = \int_0^\infty e^{-st} k\phi(t)\, dt = k \int_0^\infty e^{-st} \phi(t)\, dt = k\, \mathscr{L}\, \phi(t) \qquad\qquad \text{(Eq 22)}$$

Theorem 3. If F is a continuous differentiable function and if F and dF/dt can be transformed, then:

$$\mathscr{L}\, \frac{dF}{dt} = s\, \mathscr{L}\, F(t) - F(0) \qquad\qquad \text{(Eq 23)}$$

which is a useful equation for solving differential equations with constant coefficients. The equation is developed by:

$$\mathscr{L}\, \frac{dF}{dt} = \int_0^\infty e^{-st}\, \frac{dF}{dt}\, dt = Fe^{-st}\Big|_0^\infty + s \int_0^\infty e^{-st} F\, dt = s\, \mathscr{L}\, F - F(0) \qquad \text{(Eq 24)}$$

with integration performed by parts.

Theorem 4. If F is continuous with derivatives of orders $1, 2, \cdots, n$ which can be transformed, then:

$$\mathscr{L}\, \frac{d^n F}{dt^n} = s^n\, \mathscr{L}\, F - \sum_{k=0}^{n-1} F^{(k)}(0)\, s^{n-k-1} \qquad\qquad \text{(Eq 25)}$$

where

$$F^{(k)}(0) = \frac{d^k F}{dt^k}$$

is evaluated at $t = 0$. As an extension of Theorem 3:

$$\mathscr{L}\, \frac{d^n F}{dt^n} = s\, \mathscr{L}\, \frac{d^{n-1} F}{dt^{n-1}} - \left(\frac{d^{n-1} F}{dt^{n-1}}\right)_{t=0} \qquad\qquad \text{(Eq 26)}$$

By repeated applications, Eq 25 is obtained. Further, if:

$$F_r = \frac{d^r F}{dt^r} \qquad\qquad \text{(Eq 27)}$$

is evaluated at $t = 0$, the transforms of the first four derivatives are:

$$\mathscr{L}\, \frac{dF}{dt} = s\, \mathscr{L}\, F - F_0 \qquad\qquad \text{(Eq 28)}$$

$$\mathscr{L}\, \frac{d^2 F}{dt^2} = s^2\, \mathscr{L}\, F - sF_0 - F_1 \qquad\qquad \text{(Eq 29)}$$

$$\mathscr{L}\, \frac{d^3 F}{dt^3} = s^3\, \mathscr{L}\, F - s^2 F_0 - sF_1 - F_2 \qquad\qquad \text{(Eq 30)}$$

$$\mathcal{L}\,\frac{d^4 F}{dt^4} = s^4\,\mathcal{L}F - s^3 F_0 - s^2 F_1 - sF_2 - F_3 \qquad\text{(Eq 31)}$$

which are useful in transforming differential equations.

Theorem 5. The Faltung or convolution theorem is developed below. It is sometimes called the superposition theorem. Let:

$$\mathcal{L}\,F_1(t) = f_1(s) \qquad\text{(Eq 32)}$$

and

$$\mathcal{L}\,F_2(t) = f_2(s) \qquad\text{(Eq 33)}$$

Then, according to the theorem:

$$\mathcal{L}\int_0^t F_1(y)F_2(t-y)\,dy = \mathcal{L}\int_0^t F_2(y)F_1(t-y)\,dy = f_1 f_2 \qquad\text{(Eq 34)}$$

In developing this theorem, let:

$$\mathcal{L}\,F_3(t) = f_1(s)f_2(s) \qquad\text{(Eq 35)}$$

then

$$F_3(t) = \frac{1}{2\pi j}\int_{c-j\infty}^{c+j\infty} f_1(s)f_2(s)e^{st}\,ds \qquad\text{(Eq 36)}$$

However:

$$f_2(s) = \int_0^\infty e^{-sy}F_2(y)\,dy \qquad\text{(Eq 37)}$$

therefore

$$F_3(t) = \frac{1}{2\pi j}\int_0^\infty F_2(y)\,dy\int_{c-j\infty}^{c+j\infty} f_1(s)e^{s(t-y)}\,ds \qquad\text{(Eq 38)}$$

if the order of integration is reversed. However:

$$\frac{1}{2\pi j}\int_{c-j\infty}^{c+j\infty} f_1(s)e^{s(t-y)}\,ds = F_1(t-y) \qquad\text{(Eq 39)}$$

hence

$$F_3(t) = \int_0^\infty F_2(y)F_1(t-y)\,dy \qquad\text{(Eq 40)}$$

Now, $F_1(t) = 0$, if t is less than 0, and:

$$F_1(t-y) = 0, \qquad \text{for } y > t \qquad\text{(Eq 41)}$$

Because the infinite limit of integration may be replaced by the limit t, Eq 40 may be written as:

$$F_3(t) = \int_0^t F_2(y)F_1(t-y)\,dy \qquad\text{(Eq 42)}$$

or

$$F_3(t) = \int_0^t F_1(y)F_2(t-y)\,dy \tag{Eq 43}$$

APPLICATIONS OF LAPLACE TRANSFORMS

Real Indefinite Integration. If $\mathscr{L}F(t) = f(s)$ and $\int F(t)\,dt$ can be transformed, then:

$$\mathscr{L}\int F(t)\,dt = \frac{1}{s}f(s) + \frac{1}{s}\int^0 F(t)\,dt \tag{Eq 44}$$

By the definition of the Laplace transform:

$$\mathscr{L}\int F(t)\,dt = \int_0^\infty e^{-st}\left[\int F(t)\,dt\right]dt \tag{Eq 45}$$

Integrating by parts produces:

$$\mathscr{L}\int F(t)\,dt = -\frac{1}{s}e^{-st}\int F(t)\,dt\Big|_0^\infty + \frac{1}{s}\int_0^\infty e^{-st}F(t)\,dt \tag{Eq 46}$$

Evaluating the limits and using $\mathscr{L}F(t) = f(s)$ gives:

$$\mathscr{L}\int F(t)\,dt = \frac{1}{s}f(s) + \frac{1}{s}\int^0 F(t)\,dt \tag{Eq 47}$$

for which $\int^0 F(t)\,dt$ indicates the initial value of the integral.

Real Definite Integration. If $\mathscr{L}F(t) = f(s)$ and the expression $\int_0^t F(t')\,dt'$ can be transformed, then:

$$\mathscr{L}\int_0^t F(t')\,dt' = \frac{1}{s}f(s) \tag{Eq 48}$$

Integrating by parts yields:

$$\mathscr{L}\int_0^t F(t')\,dt' = -\frac{1}{s}e^{-st}\int_0^t F(t')\,dt'\Big|_0^\infty + \frac{1}{s}f(s) \tag{Eq 49}$$

The first term vanishes at the upper limit because it contains an exponential function and at the lower limit because of the definite integral. Hence only the second term remains, as expressed in Eq 48. Following the same steps produces:

$$\mathscr{L}\int_0^t \int_0^{t'} F(t'')\,dt''\,dt' = \frac{1}{s^2}f(s) \tag{Eq 50}$$

where $\mathscr{L}F(t) = f(s)$.

Complex Differentiation. If $\mathscr{L}F(t) = f(s)$, then

$$\mathscr{L}\,tF(t) = -\frac{df(s)}{ds} \tag{Eq 51}$$

According to the definition of $f(s)$ as indicated by $\mathcal{L} F(t) = f(s)$:

$$f(s) = \int_0^t e^{-st} F(t) \, dt \qquad \text{(Eq 52)}$$

By differentiating both sides of Eq 52 with respect to s:

$$\frac{df(s)}{ds} = \frac{d}{ds} \int_0^t e^{-st} F(t) \, dt \qquad \text{(Eq 53)}$$

Because the integration involves t only, the order of integration and differentiation may be interchanged for Eq 53. Thus:

$$\frac{df(s)}{ds} = -\int_0^t e^{-st} t F(t) \, dt = -\mathcal{L} \, t F(t) \qquad \text{(Eq 54)}$$

Differentiation with a Second Independent Variable. For a function of two independent variables $F = F(x, t)$ if $\mathcal{L} F(x, t) = f(x, s)$, then:

$$\mathcal{L} \frac{\partial F(x, t)}{\partial x} = \frac{\partial f(x, s)}{\partial x} \qquad \text{(Eq 55)}$$

From the definition of Laplace transformation:

$$\mathcal{L} \frac{\partial F(x, t)}{\partial x} = \int_0^\infty e^{-st} \frac{\partial F(x, t)}{\partial x} \, dt \qquad \text{(Eq 56)}$$

Because x is not a variable of integration, the order of differentiation and integration may be interchanged. Thus:

$$\mathcal{L} \frac{\partial F(x, t)}{\partial x} = \frac{\partial}{\partial x} \int_0^t e^{-st} F(x, t) \, dt$$
$$= \frac{\partial f(x, s)}{\partial x} \qquad \text{(Eq 57)}$$

Integration with a Second Independent Variable. For a function of two independent variables $F = F(x, t)$ if $\mathcal{L} F(x, t) = f(x, s)$, then:

$$\mathcal{L} \int_{x_1}^{x_2} F(x', t) \, dx' = \int_{x_1}^{x_2} f(x', s) \, dx' \qquad \text{(Eq 58)}$$

The method for developing Eq 58 is identical to the development of Eq 55 by using Eq 56 and 57.

Periodic Functions. If $F(t)$ is a periodic function with fundamental period T, $F(t + T) = F(t)$ where $t > 0$, and if $F(t)$ is sectionally continuous over a period $0 < t < T$, then its direct transformation is expressed as:

$$\mathcal{L} F(t) = \int_0^\infty e^{-st} F(t) \, dt$$
$$= \sum_{n=0}^\infty \int_{nT}^{(n+1)T} e^{-st} F(t) \, dt \qquad \text{(Eq 59)}$$

Further, if

$$u = t - nT \qquad \text{(Eq 60)}$$

and, as a result of the periodicity of the function $F(t)$:

$$F(u + nT) = F(u) \qquad \text{(Eq 61)}$$

then Eq 59 may be written:

$$\mathscr{L}\, F(t) = \sum_{n=0}^{\infty} e^{-nTs} \int_0^T e^{-su} F(u)\, du \qquad \text{(Eq 62)}$$

Additionally, using:

$$\sum_{n=0}^{n=\infty} e^{-nTs} = \frac{1}{1 - e^{-Ts}} \qquad \text{(Eq 63)}$$

Eq 62 may be written in the form:

$$\mathscr{L}\, F(t) = \frac{1}{1 - e^{-Ts}} \int_0^T e^{-st} F(t)\, dt \qquad \text{(Eq 64)}$$

This equation can be used to obtain the transform of the function represented in Fig. 2. Substituting the expression:

$$\int_0^T F(t) e^{-st}\, dt = \int_0^a e^{-st}\, dt - \int_a^{2a} e^{-st}\, dt$$

$$= \frac{1 - e^{-sa} - e^{-sa} + e^{-2sa}}{s} \qquad \text{(Eq 65)}$$

$$= \frac{1 - 2e^{-sa} + e^{-2sa}}{s} = \frac{(1 - e^{-sa})^2}{s}$$

into Eq 64 yields

$$\mathscr{L}\, F(t) = \frac{(1 - e^{-sa})^2}{s(1 - e^{-2sa})} = \frac{1 - e^{-sa}}{s(1 + e^{-sa})} \qquad \text{(Eq 66)}$$

$$= \frac{e^{sa/2} - e^{-sa/2}}{s(e^{sa/2} + e^{-sa/2})} = \frac{\sinh(sa/2)}{s \cosh(sa/2)} = \frac{\tanh(as/2)}{s}$$

Operational Method. The operational method for solving differential equations is essentially the same as that known as Heaviside's operational calculus. The relationship between a function $f(s)$ and another function $h(t)$ may be expressed in the form:

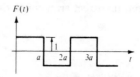

Figure 2

$$f(s) = \int_0^\infty e^{-st} h(t)\, dt \qquad \text{Re } s > 0 \tag{Eq 67}$$

where s is a complex number with its real part greater than zero and $h(t)$ is a function for which the infinite integral of Eq 67 converges and is a function that satisfies the condition $h(t) = 0$ for $t < 0$. The functional relationship between $f(s)$ and $h(t)$ is written as:

$$f(s) = \mathscr{L}\, h(t) \tag{Eq 68}$$

with the symbol $\mathscr{L}$ denoting the "Laplace transform of." The relationship is also written in the form:

$$h(t) = \mathscr{L}^{-1} f(s) \tag{Eq 69}$$

with $h(t)$ the inverse Laplace transform of $f(s)$. For example, the functional relationship:

$$y(s) = \int_0^\infty e^{-st} x(t)\, dt \tag{Eq 70}$$

is written symbolically as:

$$y(s) = \mathscr{L}\, x(t) \tag{Eq 71}$$

To determine $\mathscr{L}(dx/dt)$ in terms of $y(s)$, integrate:

$$\mathscr{L}\left(\frac{dx}{dt}\right) = \int_0^\infty e^{-st}\left(\frac{dx}{dt}\right) dt \tag{Eq 72}$$

by parts to obtain:

$$\int_0^\infty e^{-st}\left(\frac{dx}{dt}\right) dt = \left. e^{-st} x \right|_0^\infty + s \int_0^\infty e^{-st} x\, dt \tag{Eq 73}$$

Using the assumptions that:

$$\lim_{t\to\infty} (e^{-st} x) = 0 \text{ and } \int_0^\infty e^{-st} x\, dt$$

exists for s greater than some fixed positive number, then Eq 73 becomes:

$$\mathscr{L}\left(\frac{dx}{dt}\right) = -x_0 + sy \tag{Eq 74}$$

where $x_0 = x(0)$. To compute the Laplace transform of d^2x/dt^2, let:

$$u = \frac{dx}{dt} \tag{Eq 75}$$

From Eq 74:

$$\mathscr{L}\left(\frac{d^2x}{dt^2}\right) = \mathscr{L}\left(\frac{du}{dt}\right) = -u_0 + s\,\mathscr{L}\left(\frac{dx}{dt}\right) = -x_1 - sx_0 + s^2 y \tag{Eq 76}$$

where x_1 is the value of dx/dt at $t = 0$. Continuing the process produces:

$$\mathcal{L}\frac{d^3x}{dt^3} = s^3y - s^2x_0 - sx_1 - x_2 \qquad \text{(Eq 77)}$$

$$\mathcal{L}\frac{d^4x}{dt^4} = s^4y - s^3x_0 - s^2x_1 - sx_2 - x_3 \qquad \text{(Eq 78)}$$

and

$$\mathcal{L}\frac{d^nx}{dt^n} = s^ny - (s^{n-1}x_0 + s^{n-2}x_1 + s^{n-3}x_2 + \cdots + x_{n-1}) \qquad \text{(Eq 79)}$$

where

$$x_n = \frac{d^nx}{dt^n} \qquad \text{(Eq 80)}$$

is evaluated at $x = 0$.

TABLE OF LAPLACE TRANSFORMS

Entries $f(s)$ give values of the Laplace transform $\mathcal{L}[F(t)] \equiv f(s)$ of the function $F(t)$. The entries in column $F(t)$ define $F(t)$ for $t \geqq 0$; a, b, c, k are constants; $f(s) = \int_0^\infty e^{-st}F(t)\,dt$

$f(s) \equiv \mathcal{L}[F(t)]$		$F(t)$
$1/s$		1
$1/s^2$		t
$1/s^n$	$n = 1, 2, \ldots$	$t^{n-1}/(n-1)!$
$1/(s-a)$		e^{at}
$1/(s-a)^2$		te^{at}
$1/(s-a)^n$	$n = 1, 2, \ldots$	$t^{n-1}e^{at}/(n-1)!$
$a/(s^2+a^2)$		$\sin at$
$s/(s^2+a^2)$		$\cos at$
$a/(s^2-a^2)$		$\sinh at$
$s/(s^2-a^2)$		$\cosh at$
$(s\sin b + a\cos b)/(s^2+a^2)$		$\sin(at+b)$
$(s\cos b - a\sin b)/(s^2+a^2)$		$\cos(at+b)$
$2as/(s^2+a^2)^2$		$t\sin at$
$(s^2-a^2)/(s^2+a^2)^2$		$t\cos at$
$1/\sqrt{s}$		$1/\sqrt{\pi t}$

$f(s) \equiv \mathscr{L}[F(t)]$		$F(t)$
$s^{-3/2}$		$2\sqrt{t/\pi}$
$s^{-[n+(1/2)]}$	$n = 1, 2, \ldots$	$2^n t^{n-(1/2)}/[1 \cdot 3 \cdot 5 \ldots (2n-1)\sqrt{\pi}]$
$\Gamma(k)/s^k$	$k > 0$	t^{k-1}
$\Gamma(k)/(s-a)^k$	$k > 0$	$t^{k-1}e^{at}$
$1/[(s-a)(s-b)]$*		$(e^{at} - e^{bt})/(a-b)$
$s/[(s-a)(s-b)]$*		$(ae^{at} - be^{bt})/(a-b)$
$1/[(s-a)(a-b)(s-c)]$*		$\begin{cases}[(b-c)e^{at} + (c-a)e^{bt} + (a-b)e^{ct}]/A \\ \quad \text{where } A = -(a-b)(b-c)(c-a)\end{cases}$
$1/[s(s^2+a^2)]$		$(1 - \cos at)/a^2$
$1/[s^2(s^2+a^2)]$		$(at - \sin at)/a^3$
$1/(s^2+a^2)^2$		$(\sin at - at \cos at)/[2a^3]$
$s/(s^2+a^2)^2$		$(t \sin at)/[2a]$
$s^2/(s^2+a^2)^2$		$(\sin at + at \cos at)/[2a]$
$s/[(s^2+a^2)(s^2+b^2)]$	$a^2 \neq b^2$	$(\cos at - \cos bt)/(b^2 - a^2)$
$1/[(s-a)^2+b^2]$		$(e^{at} \sin bt)/b$
$(s-a)/[(s-a)^2+b^2]$		$e^{at} \cos bt$
$3a^2/(s^3+a^3)$		$\begin{cases}e^{-at} - e^{at/2} \cdot A \\ \quad \text{where } A = \cos(\sqrt{3}\,at/2) - \\ \qquad \sqrt{3} \sin(\sqrt{3}\,at/2)\end{cases}$
$3as/(s^3+a^3)$		$\begin{cases}e^{-at} + e^{at/2} \cdot A \\ \quad \text{where } A = \cos(\sqrt{3}\,at/2) + \\ \qquad \sqrt{3} \sin(\sqrt{3}\,at/2)\end{cases}$
$4a^3/(s^4+4a^4)$		$\sin at \cosh at - \cos at \sinh at$
$s/(s^4+4a^4)$		$[1/(2a^2)] \sin at \sinh at$
$1/(s^4-a^4)$		$(\sinh at - \sin at)/[2a^3]$
$s/(s^4-a^4)$		$(\cosh at - \cos at)/[2a^2]$
$8a^3s^2/(s^2+a^2)^3$		$(1 + a^2t^2) \sin at - at \cos at$
$(1/s)[(s-1)/s]^n$ **		$L_n(t) = (e^t/n!)[d^n(t^n e^{-t})/dt^n]$
$\sqrt{s-a} - \sqrt{s-b}$		$(e^{bt} - e^{at})/(2\sqrt{\pi t^3})$

(continued)

*a, b, and c are distinct constants.

**$L_n(t)$ is the Laguerre polynomial of degree n.

$f(s) \equiv \mathcal{L}[F(t)]$	$F(t)$
$s/(s-a)^{3/2}$	$e^{at}(1+2at)/\sqrt{\pi t}$
$1/(\sqrt{s}+a)$***	$(1/\sqrt{\pi t})-ae^{a^2 t}\,\mathrm{erfc}\,(a\sqrt{t})$
$\sqrt{s}/(s+a^2)$	$(1/\sqrt{\pi t})-(2ae^{-a^2 t}/\sqrt{\pi})\displaystyle\int_0^{a\sqrt{t}} e^{\lambda^2}\,d\lambda$
$\sqrt{s}/(s-a^2)$***	$(1/\sqrt{\pi t})+ae^{a^2 t}\mathrm{erf}\,(a\sqrt{t})$
$1/[\sqrt{s}(s+a^2)]$	$[2/(a\sqrt{\pi})]e^{-a^2 t}\displaystyle\int_0^{a\sqrt{t}} e^{\lambda^2}\,d\lambda$
$1/[\sqrt{s}(s-a^2)]$	$(e^{a^2 t}/a)\,\mathrm{erf}\,(a\sqrt{t})$
$1/[\sqrt{s}(\sqrt{s}+a)]$	$e^{a^2 t}\mathrm{erfc}\,(a\sqrt{t})$
$(b^2-a^2)/[(s-a^2)(\sqrt{s}+b)]$	$e^{a^2 t}[b-a\,\mathrm{erf}\,(a\sqrt{t})]-be^{b^2 t}\mathrm{erfc}(b\sqrt{t})$
$(b^2-a^2)/[\sqrt{s}(s-a^2)(\sqrt{s}+b)]$	$e^{a^2 t}[(b/a)\,\mathrm{erf}\,(a\sqrt{t})-1]+e^{b^2 t}\mathrm{erfc}(b\sqrt{t})$
$1/[(s+a)\sqrt{s+b}]$	$(1/\sqrt{b-a})\,c^{-at}\,\mathrm{erf}\,(\sqrt{b-a}\,\sqrt{t})$
$1/[\sqrt{s+a}\,\sqrt{s+b}]$†	$e^{-(a+b)t/2}\,I_0\,[(a-b)t/2]$
$1/[(s+a)^{1/2}(s+b)^{3/2}]$	$\begin{cases} te^{-(a+b)t/2}\cdot B \\ \quad \text{where } B\equiv I_0[(a-b)t/2]+ \\ \quad I_1[(a-b)t/2] \end{cases}$
$\Gamma(k)/[(s+a)^k(s+b)^k]\qquad k>0$	$\begin{cases} \sqrt{\pi}C[t/(a-b)]^{k-(1/2)}e^{-(a+b)t/2} \\ \quad \text{where } C\equiv I_{k-1/2}\,[(a-b)t/2] \end{cases}$
$(\sqrt{s+2a}-\sqrt{s})/(\sqrt{s+2a}+\sqrt{s})$	$(1/t)\,e^{-at}\,I_1\,(at)$
$(1-s)^n/s^{[n+(1/2)]}$‡	$n!H_{2n}(\sqrt{t})/[(2n)!\sqrt{\pi t}]$
$(1-s)^n/s^{[n+(3/2)]}$	$-n!H_{2n+1}(\sqrt{t})/[\sqrt{\pi}(2n+1)!]$
$(\sqrt{s+2a}/\sqrt{s})-1$	$ae^{-at}[I_1(at)+I_0(at)]$
$(\sqrt{s+a}+\sqrt{s})^{-2v}/(\sqrt{s}\sqrt{s+a})$ $v>-1$	$(1/a^v)\,e^{-at/2}I_v(at/2)$
$(a-b)^k/(\sqrt{s+a}+\sqrt{s+b})^{2k}$ $k>0$	$(k/t)\,e^{-(a+b)t/2}I_k[(a-b)t/2]$

(continued)

*** $\mathrm{erf}\,y=\dfrac{2}{\sqrt{\pi}}\displaystyle\int_0^y e^{-u^2}\,du$

$\mathrm{erfc}\,y=1-\mathrm{erf}\,y$

† $I_n(x)\equiv i^{-n}J_n(ix)$, where J_n is Bessel's function of the first kind.

‡ $H_n(x)\equiv e^{x^2}[d^n(e^{-x^2})/dx^n]$ is the Hermite polynomial.

$f(s) \equiv \mathcal{L}[F(t)]$		$F(t)$
$(s^2 + a^2)^{-1/2}$		$J_0(at)$
$(s^2 + a^2)^{-k}$	$k > 0$	$[\sqrt{\pi}/\Gamma(k)][t/2a]^{k-(1/2)}J_{k-1/2}(at)$
$(s^2 - a^2)^{-k}$	$k > 0$	$[\sqrt{\pi}/\Gamma(k)][t/2a]^{k-(1/2)}I_{k-1/2}(at)$
$(\sqrt{s^2 + a^2} - s)^v/\sqrt{s^2 + a^2}$		$a^v J_v(at)$
	$v > -1$	
$(\sqrt{s^2 + a^2} - s)^k$	$k > 0$	$(ka^k/t)J_k(at)$
$(s - \sqrt{s^2 - a^2})^v/\sqrt{s^2 - a^2}$		$a^v I_v(at)$
	$v > -1$	
$s^{-1}e^{-k/s}$		$J_0(2\sqrt{kt})$
$s^{-1/2}e^{-k/s}$		$(1/\sqrt{\pi t}) \cos(2\sqrt{kt})$
$s^{-1/2}e^{k/s}$		$(1/\sqrt{\pi t}) \cosh(2\sqrt{kt})$
$s^{-3/2}e^{-k/s}$		$(1/\sqrt{\pi k}) \sin(2\sqrt{kt})$
$s^{-3/2}e^{k/s}$		$(1/\sqrt{\pi k}) \sinh(2\sqrt{kt})$
$s^{-\mu}e^{-k/s}$	$\mu > 0$	$(t/k)^{(\mu-1)/2}J_{\mu-1}(2\sqrt{kt})$
$s^{-\mu}e^{k/s}$	$\mu > 0$	$(t/k)^{(\mu-1)/2}I_{\mu-1}(2\sqrt{kt})$
$e^{-k\sqrt{s}}$	$k > 0$	$[k/(2\sqrt{\pi t^3})] \exp[-k^2/(4t)]$
$(1/\sqrt{s})e^{-k\sqrt{s}}$	$k \geqq 0$	$(1/\sqrt{\pi t}) \exp[-k^2/(4t)]$
$s^{-1}e^{-k\sqrt{s}}$	$k \geqq 0$	$\text{erfc}[k/(2\sqrt{t})]$
$s^{-3/2}e^{-k\sqrt{s}}$	$k \geqq 0$	$\begin{cases} 2\sqrt{t/\pi} \exp[-k^2/(4t)] - \\ \quad k\,\text{erfc}[k/(2\sqrt{t})] \end{cases}$
$ae^{-k\sqrt{s}}/[s(a + \sqrt{s})]$	$k \geqq 0$	$\begin{cases} -e^{ak}e^{a^2t}\,\text{erfc}\,A + \text{erfc}[k/(2\sqrt{t})] \\ \quad \text{where } A = a\sqrt{t} + k/(2\sqrt{t}) \end{cases}$
$e^{-k\sqrt{s}}/[\sqrt{s}(a + \sqrt{s})]$	$k \geqq 0$	$e^{ak}e^{a^2t}\,\text{erfc}\,A$
$e^{-k\sqrt{s(s+a)}}/\sqrt{s(s+a)}$		$\begin{cases} 0 & \text{when } 0 < t < k \\ e^{-at/2}I_0\left(\frac{1}{2}a\sqrt{t^2 - k^2}\right) & \text{when } t > k \end{cases}$
$e^{-k\sqrt{s^2+a^2}}/\sqrt{s^2 + a^2}$		$\begin{cases} 0 & \text{when } 0 < t < k \\ J_0(a\sqrt{t^2 - k^2}) & \text{when } t > k \end{cases}$
$e^{-k\sqrt{s^2-a^2}}/\sqrt{s^2 - a^2}$		$\begin{cases} 0 & \text{when } 0 < t < k \\ I_0(a\sqrt{t^2 - k^2}) & \text{when } t > k \end{cases}$
$e^{-k(\sqrt{s^2+a^2}-s)}/\sqrt{s^2 + a^2}$	$k \geqq 0$	$J_0(a\sqrt{t^2 + 2kt})$

(continued)

$f(s) \equiv \mathscr{L}[F(t)]$	$F(t)$
$e^{-ks} - e^{-k\sqrt{s^2+a^2}}$	$\begin{cases} 0 \qquad\qquad \text{when } 0 < t < k \\ (ak/\sqrt{t^2-k^2})\,J_1(a\sqrt{t^2-k^2}) \\ \qquad\qquad \text{when } t > k \end{cases}$
$e^{-k\sqrt{s^2-a^2}} - e^{-ks}$	$\begin{cases} 0 \qquad\qquad \text{when } 0 < t < k \\ (ak/\sqrt{t^2-k^2})/I_1(a\sqrt{t^2-k^2}) \\ \qquad\qquad \text{when } t > k \end{cases}$
$[a^v \exp(-k\sqrt{s^2+a^2})]/$ $[\sqrt{s^2+a^2}(\sqrt{s^2+a^2}+s)^v]\; v > -1$	$\begin{cases} 0 \qquad\qquad \text{when } 0 < t < k \\ [(t-k)/t+k)]^{v/2}J_v(a\sqrt{t^2-k^2}) \\ \qquad\qquad t > k \end{cases}$
$(1/s)\log s\ddagger$	$\Gamma'(1) - \log t,\ \Gamma'(1) = -0.5772157$
$s^{-k}\log s\ddagger \qquad\qquad k > 0$	$t^{k-1}[\Gamma'(k) - \Gamma(k)\log t][\Gamma(k)]^{-2}$
$(s-a)^{-1}\log s\ddagger \qquad a > 0$	$e^{at}[\log a - \text{Ei}(-at)]$
$(s^2+1)^{-1}\log s\ddagger$	$\cos t\ \text{Si}\ t - \sin t\ \text{Ci}\ t \equiv H(t)$
$s(s^2+1)^{-1}\log s\ddagger$	$-\sin t\ \text{Si}\ t - \cos t\ \text{Ci}\ t$
$s^{-1}\log(1+ks)\ddagger \qquad k > 0$	$-\text{Ei}(-t/k)$
$\log[(s-a)/(s-b)]$	$t^{-1}(e^{bt} - e^{at})$
$\log[(s+a)/(s-a)]$	$2t^{-1}\sinh at \qquad\qquad \text{Re } s > \text{Re } a$
$s^{-1}\log(1+k^2s^2)$	$-2\ \text{Ci}\ (t/k)$
$s^{-1}\log(s^2+a^2) \qquad a > 0$	$2\log a - 2\ \text{Ci}\ (at)$
$s^{-2}\log(s^2+a^2) \qquad a > 0$	$2a^{-1}[at\log a + \sin at - at\ \text{Ci}\ at]$

(continued)

$\ddagger \log s \equiv \log_e s \equiv \ln s.$

$\text{Ei}\ t = \displaystyle\int_{-\infty}^{t} r^{-1}e^r dr \qquad t < 0 \qquad \text{(the exponential-integral function)}$

$-\text{Ei}(-t) = \displaystyle\int_{1}^{\infty} x^{-1}e^{-tx}dx \qquad t > 0$

$\text{Ci}\ t = -\displaystyle\int_{t}^{\infty} r^{-1}\cos r dr = -\int_{1}^{\infty} x^{-1}\cos tx\ dx \qquad t > 0$

$\qquad\qquad\qquad\qquad\qquad \text{(the cosine-integral function)}$

$\text{Si}\ t = \displaystyle\int_{0}^{t} r^{-1}\sin r dr \qquad t > 0 \qquad \text{(the sine-integral function)}$

$H(t) = \cos t\ \text{Si}\ t - \sin t\ \text{Ci}\ t \qquad t > 0$

$f(s) \equiv \mathcal{L}[F(t)]$		$F(t)$
$\log[(s^2 + a^2)s^2]$		$2t^{-1}(1 - \cos at)$
$\log[(s^2 - a^2)/s^2]$		$2t^{-1}(1 - \cosh at)$
$\cot^{-1}[(s - b)/a]$		$t^{-1}e^{bt}\sin at$
$\cot^{-1}(s/k)$		$t^{-1}\sin kt$
$(1/s)\cot^{-1}(s/k)$		$\operatorname{Si} kt$
$e^{k^2 s^2}\operatorname{erfc}(ks)$	$k > 0$	$[1/(k\sqrt{\pi})]\exp[-t^2/(4k^2)]$
$s^{-1}e^{k^2 s^2}\operatorname{erfc}(ks)$	$k > 0$	$\operatorname{erf}[t/(2k)]$
$e^{ks}\operatorname{erfc}\sqrt{ks}$	$k > 0$	$\sqrt{k}/[\pi\sqrt{t}(t + k)]$
$s^{-1/2}\operatorname{erfc}\sqrt{ks}$		$\begin{cases} 0 & \text{when } 0 < t < k \\ (\pi t)^{-1/2} & \text{when } t > k \end{cases}$
$s^{-1/2}e^{ks}\operatorname{erfc}\sqrt{ks}$	$k > 0$	$1/\sqrt{\pi(t + k)}$
$s^{-1/2}e^{k^2/s}\operatorname{erfc}(k/\sqrt{s})$		$(1/\sqrt{\pi t})e^{-2k\sqrt{t}}$
$\operatorname{erf}(k/\sqrt{s})$		$[1/(\pi t)]\sin(2k\sqrt{t})$
$K_0(ks)$††		$\begin{cases} 0 & \text{when } 0 < t < k \\ (t^2 - k^2)^{-1/2} & \text{when } t > k \end{cases}$
$K_0(k\sqrt{s})$		$[1/(2t)]\exp[-k^2/(4t)]$
$s^{-1}e^{ks}K_1(ks)$		$(1/k)\sqrt{t(t + 2k)}$
$s^{-1/2}K_1(k\sqrt{s})$		$(1/k)\exp[-k^2/(4t)]$
$s^{-1/2}e^{k/s}K_0(k/s)$		$(2/\sqrt{\pi t})K_0(2\sqrt{2\,kt})$
$\pi e^{-ks}I_0(ks)$		$\begin{cases} [t(2k - t)]^{-1/2} & \text{when } 0 < t < 2k \\ 0 & \text{when } t > 2k \end{cases}$
$e^{-ks}I_1(ks)$		$\begin{cases} (k - t)/[\pi k\sqrt{t(2k - t)}] & \text{when } 0 < t < 2k \\ 0 & \text{when } t > 2k \end{cases}$
$-e^{as}\operatorname{Ei}(-as)$		$(t + a)^{-1}$ $a > 0$
$a^{-1} + se^{as}\operatorname{Ei}(-as)$		$(t + a)^{-2}$ $a > 0$
$[(\pi/2) - \operatorname{Si} s]\cos s$		$(t^2 + 1)^{-1}$
$+ \operatorname{Ci} s \sin s$	$s > 0$	

(continued)

†† $K_n(x)$ is Bessel's function of the second kind for the imaginary argument.

$f(s) \equiv \mathscr{L}[F(t)]$		$F(t)$
		Step functions
s^{-1}		$U(t) = \begin{cases} 0 & \text{when } t < 0 \\ 1 & \text{when } t \geqq 0 \end{cases}$
		Heaviside unit function
$s^{-1}e^{-ks}$		$U(t - k) = \begin{cases} 0 & \text{when } t < k \\ 1 & \text{when } t \geqq k \end{cases}$
e^{-as}	$a \geqq 0$	$\delta(t - a)$
$s^k e^{-as}$	$a \geqq 0$	$\delta^{(k)}(t - a)$ $\qquad k = 1, 2, \dots$
$s^{-2}e^{-ks}$		$S_k(t) = \begin{cases} 0 & \text{when } t < k \\ t - k & \text{when } t \geqq k \end{cases}$
$2s^{-3}e^{-ks}$		$\begin{cases} 0 & \text{when } t < k \\ (t - k)^2 & \text{when } t \geqq k \end{cases}$
$\Gamma(\mu) \cdot s^{-\mu}e^{-ks}$	$\mu > 0$	$\begin{cases} 0 & \text{when } t < k \\ (t - k)^{\mu - 1} & \text{when } t \geqq k \end{cases}$
$s^{-1}(1 - e^{-ks})$		$\begin{cases} 1 & \text{when } 0 < t < k \\ 0 & \text{when } t > k \end{cases}$
$s^{-1}(1 - e^{-ks})^{-1} =$ $\quad (2s)^{-1}\left(1 + \coth\dfrac{1}{2}ks\right)$‡‡		$\begin{cases} 1 + [t/k] = n \\ \quad \text{when } (n - 1)k < t < nk, \\ \qquad\qquad\qquad n = 1, 2, \dots \end{cases}$
$s^{-1}\tanh ks$		$\begin{cases} M(2k, t) = (-1)^{n-1} \\ \quad \text{when } 2k(n - 1) < t < 2kn, \\ \qquad\qquad\qquad n = 1, 2, \dots \end{cases}$
		Square-wave function
$s^{-1}(1 + e^{-ks})^{-1}$		$\begin{cases} [M(k, t) + 1]/2 = [1 - (-1)^n]/2 \\ \quad \text{when } (n - 1)k < t < nk, \\ \quad n = 1, 2, \dots \qquad\qquad t > 0 \end{cases}$
$(s \sinh ks)^{-1}$		$\begin{cases} F(t) = 2(n - 1) \\ \quad \text{when } (2n - 3)k < t < (2n - 1)k \\ \qquad\qquad n = 1, 2, \dots \ t > 0 \end{cases}$

(continued)

‡‡ When $t > 0$, $[t]$ denotes the greatest integer $(0, 1, 2, \dots)$ that does not exceed the number t.

$f(s) \equiv \mathcal{L}[F(t)]$	$F(t)$
$s^{-1}\coth ks$	$\begin{cases} F(t) = 2n - 1 \\ \quad \text{when } 2k(n-1) < t < 2kn, \\ \qquad n = 1, 2, \ldots \end{cases}$
$(s\cosh ks)^{-1}$	$\begin{cases} M(2k, t+3k) + 1 = 1 + (-1)^n \\ \quad \text{when } (2n-3)k < t < (2n-1)k, \\ \quad n = 1, 2, \ldots \qquad t > 0 \end{cases}$
$s^{-1}(e^{-as} - e^{-bs})$	$F(t) = \begin{cases} 0 & \text{for } 0 < t < a \\ 1 & \text{for } a < t < b \\ 0 & \text{for } t > b \end{cases}$
$(m/s^2) - (ma/2s)[\coth(as/2) - 1]$	$\begin{cases} F(t) = m(t - na) \\ \quad \text{when } na < t < (n+1)a, \\ \qquad n = 0, 1, 2, \ldots \end{cases}$
$s^{-2}\tanh(cs/2)$	$\begin{cases} H(c, t) = \begin{cases} t & \text{when } 0 < t < c \\ 2c - t & \text{when } c < t < 2c \end{cases} \\ H(c, t + 2nc) = H(c, t) \\ \qquad\qquad n = 1, 2, \ldots \end{cases}$ **Triangular wave**
$k(s^2 + k^2)^{-1}\coth[\pi s/(2k)]$	$\lvert\sin kt\rvert$ **Full-wave rectification of sin kt**
$[(s^2 + 1)(1 - e^{-\pi s})]^{-1}$	$\begin{cases} \sin t \text{ when } (2n-2)\pi < t < (2n-1)\pi \\ 0 \quad \text{when } (2n-1)\pi < t < 2n\pi \\ \qquad\qquad n = 1, 2, \ldots \end{cases}$ **Half-wave rectification of sin t**
$[(E/s) + (m/s^2)]e^{-as}$	$F(t) = \begin{cases} 0 & \text{for } 0 < t < a \\ E + m(t - a) & \text{for } t > a \end{cases}$
$(m/s^2)(1 - e^{-as})$	$F(t) = \begin{cases} mt & \text{for } 0 < t < a \\ ma & \text{for } t > a \end{cases}$
$(m/s^2)(1 - 2e^{-as} + e^{-2as})$ $= (m/s^2)(1 - e^{-as})^2$	$F(t) = \begin{cases} mt & \text{for } 0 < t < a \\ -m(t - 2a) & \text{for } a < t < 2a \\ 0 & \text{for } t > 2a \end{cases}$
$(m/s^2)[1 - (1 + as)e^{-as}]$	$F(t) = \begin{cases} mt & \text{for } 0 < t < a \\ 0 & \text{for } t > a \end{cases}$

12
Vector Analysis

A scalar is defined by magnitude only and is designated by ordinary letters such as a, b, c, r; A, B, C, R; or α, β, γ. Examples are length, time, temperature, and mass.

A vector is defined by magnitude, direction, and sense and is designated by boldface letters such as $\mathbf{a}, \mathbf{b}, \mathbf{c}, \mathbf{r}$; or $\mathbf{A}, \mathbf{B}, \mathbf{C}, \mathbf{R}$. Examples are force, moment, displacement, velocity, and acceleration. A vector $\mathbf{r}$ is graphically represented by a directed segment described by the vector origin, O, and its end point T. The magnitude r of the vector $\mathbf{r}$ is the length of this segment:

$$r = |\mathbf{r}| = \overline{OT}$$

A vector of unit magnitude is represented by unit vector $\mathbf{e}$. Any vector $\mathbf{r}$ can be represented analytically as:

$$\mathbf{r} = r\mathbf{e} \quad \text{or} \quad \mathbf{e} = \frac{\mathbf{r}}{r}$$

A vector $\mathbf{V}$ is represented in three-dimensional space as the vector sum of its three mutually perpendicular components:

$$\mathbf{V} = \mathbf{i}V_x + \mathbf{j}V_y + \mathbf{k}V_z$$

where $\mathbf{i}, \mathbf{j}, \mathbf{k}$ are the unit vectors in the x, y, and z directions (Fig. 1). The direction of vector quantity $\mathbf{i}V_x$ is specified by the unit vector $\mathbf{i}$ in the x-direction and a magnitude equal to V_x, the x-component of the vector $\mathbf{V}$. The scalar magnitude of $\mathbf{V}$ is:

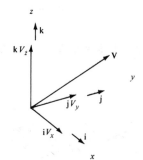

Figure 1

$$|\mathbf{V}| = V = \sqrt{V_x^2 + V_y^2 + V_z^2}$$

Any vector $\mathbf{V}$ may be multiplied by a scalar a to give the vector $\mathbf{V}a$ or $a\mathbf{V}$. The product has magnitude aV and direction $\mathbf{V}$.

VECTOR ADDITION

Vectors $\mathbf{P}$ and $\mathbf{Q}$ may be added to obtain sum $\mathbf{P} + \mathbf{Q}$, as shown in Fig. 2(a) where the two vectors are two legs of the parallelogram. The sum may be written:

$$\mathbf{P} + \mathbf{Q} = (\mathbf{i}P_x + \mathbf{j}P_y + \mathbf{k}P_z) + (\mathbf{i}Q_x + \mathbf{j}Q_y + \mathbf{k}Q_z)$$
$$= \mathbf{i}(P_x + Q_x) + \mathbf{j}(P_y + Q_y) + \mathbf{k}(P_z + Q_z)$$

The sum may be obtained by combining the vectors head-to-tail in either order (Fig. 2b). Thus, $\mathbf{P} + \mathbf{Q} = \mathbf{Q} + \mathbf{P}$, vector addition is commutative.

Vector addition is also associative. The sum of the three vectors $\mathbf{P}$, $\mathbf{Q}$, $\mathbf{R}$ may be formed by adding $\mathbf{P}$ to the sum of $\mathbf{Q}$ and $\mathbf{R}$ or by adding the sum of $\mathbf{P}$ and $\mathbf{Q}$ to $\mathbf{R}$ (Fig. 3). Thus, $\mathbf{P} + (\mathbf{Q} + \mathbf{R}) = (\mathbf{P} + \mathbf{Q}) + \mathbf{R}$.

The subtraction of a vector is equivalent to adding a negative vector. The vector difference between $\mathbf{P}$ and $\mathbf{Q}$ of Fig. 4 is $\mathbf{P} - \mathbf{Q} = \mathbf{P} + (-\mathbf{Q})$.

DOT OR SCALAR PRODUCT

The dot or scalar product of two vectors $\mathbf{P}$ and $\mathbf{Q}$ in Fig. 5a, is defined as $\mathbf{P} \cdot \mathbf{Q} = PQ \cos \theta$ where θ is the angle between the vectors. This product is the magnitude of $\mathbf{P}$ multiplied by the component $Q \cos \theta$ of $\mathbf{Q}$ in the direction of $\mathbf{P}$, as shown in Fig. 5b. The product may be viewed as the magnitude of $\mathbf{Q}$ multiplied by the component $P \cos \theta$ of $\mathbf{P}$ in the direction of $\mathbf{Q}$, Fig. 5c. Because the scalar terms in the scalar multiplication may be interchanged, the commutative law, $\mathbf{P} \cdot \mathbf{Q} = \mathbf{Q} \cdot \mathbf{P}$, holds for the dot product. According to the definition of the dot product:

$$\mathbf{i} \cdot \mathbf{i} = \mathbf{j} \cdot \mathbf{j} = \mathbf{k} \cdot \mathbf{k} = 1$$

and

$$\mathbf{i} \cdot \mathbf{j} = \mathbf{j} \cdot \mathbf{i} = \mathbf{i} \cdot \mathbf{k} = \mathbf{k} \cdot \mathbf{i} = \mathbf{j} \cdot \mathbf{k} = \mathbf{k} \cdot \mathbf{j} = 0$$

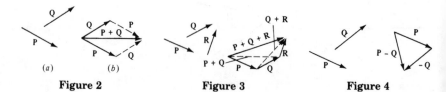

(a)	(b)	
Figure 2	Figure 3	Figure 4

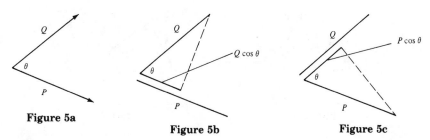

Figure 5a

Figure 5b

Figure 5c

Thus:

$$\mathbf{P} \cdot \mathbf{Q} = (\mathbf{i}P_x + \mathbf{j}P_y + \mathbf{k}P_z) \cdot (\mathbf{i}Q_x + \mathbf{j}Q_y + \mathbf{k}Q_z)$$
$$= P_x Q_x + P_y Q_y + P_z Q_z$$

and

$$\mathbf{P} \cdot \mathbf{P} = P_x{}^2 + P_y{}^2 + P_z{}^2$$

Two vectors $\mathbf{P}$ and $\mathbf{Q}$ are perpendicular when their dot product vanishes, that is, $\mathbf{P} \cdot \mathbf{Q} = 0$. The angle θ between two vectors $\mathbf{P}_1$ and $\mathbf{P}_2$ may be found from their dot product expression $\mathbf{P}_1 \cdot \mathbf{P}_2 = P_1 P_2 \cos \theta$, that is:

$$\cos \theta = \frac{\mathbf{P}_1 \cdot \mathbf{P}_2}{P_1 P_2} = \frac{P_{1x}P_{2x} + P_{1y}P_{2y} + P_{1z}P_{2z}}{P_1 P_2} = l_1 l_2 + m_1 m_2 + n_1 n_2$$

where l, m, n represent direction cosines of the vectors. Two vectors are perpendicular when their direction cosines conform to the relationship $l_1 l_2 + m_1 m_2 + n_1 n_2 = 0$. The following expansion shows that the distributive law holds for the dot product:

$$\mathbf{P} \cdot (\mathbf{Q} + \mathbf{R}) = (\mathbf{i}P_x + \mathbf{j}P_y + \mathbf{k}P_z) \cdot (\mathbf{i}[Q_x + R_x] + \mathbf{j}[Q_y + R_y] + \mathbf{k}[Q_z + R_z])$$
$$= P_x(Q_x + R_x) + P_y(Q_y + R_y) + P_z(Q_z + R_z)$$
$$= (P_x Q_x + P_y Q_y + P_z Q_z) + (P_x R_x + P_y R_y + P_z R_z)$$

so that
$$\mathbf{P} \cdot (\mathbf{Q} + \mathbf{R}) = \mathbf{P} \cdot \mathbf{Q} + \mathbf{P} \cdot \mathbf{R}.$$

CROSS OR VECTOR PRODUCT

The cross or vector product for the vectors $\mathbf{P}$ and $\mathbf{Q}$ of Fig. 6 is written as $\mathbf{P} \times \mathbf{Q}$. This product is a vector with magnitude equal to the product of the magnitudes of $\mathbf{P}$ and $\mathbf{Q}$ multiplied by the sine of the angle θ (less than $180°$) between them. If $\mathbf{n}$ is a unit vector with the direction and sense of $\mathbf{P} \times \mathbf{Q}$, the cross product may be written $\mathbf{P} \times \mathbf{Q} = \mathbf{n}PQ \sin \theta$.

From Fig. 6, $\mathbf{P} \times \mathbf{Q} = -\mathbf{Q} \times \mathbf{P}$; this is derived by using the right hand rule and reversing the order of vector multiplication. Thus, the commutative law does not hold for the cross product.

Distributive Law of Vector Multiplication. The distributive law of multiplication holds for the cross or vector product. The edges of the prism in Fig. 7 are the vectors $\mathbf{P}$, $\mathbf{Q}$, $\mathbf{P} + \mathbf{Q}$, and $\mathbf{R}$. The vectors representing the faces are:

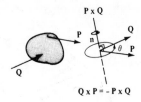

Figure 6

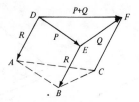

Figure 7

$$\overline{ABED} = \mathbf{R} \times \mathbf{P}$$
$$\overline{BCFE} = \mathbf{R} \times \mathbf{Q}$$
$$\overline{ACFD} = (\mathbf{P} + \mathbf{Q}) \times \mathbf{R}$$
$$\overline{ABC} = \tfrac{1}{2}(\mathbf{Q} \times \mathbf{P})$$
$$\overline{DEF} = \tfrac{1}{2}(\mathbf{P} \times \mathbf{Q})$$

Therefore, the representative vector for the entire surface is:

$$\mathbf{R} \times \mathbf{P} + \mathbf{R} \times \mathbf{Q} + (\mathbf{P} + \mathbf{Q}) \times \mathbf{R} + \tfrac{1}{2}(\mathbf{Q} \times \mathbf{P}) + \tfrac{1}{2}(\mathbf{P} \times \mathbf{Q}) = 0$$

or

$$(\mathbf{P} + \mathbf{Q}) \times \mathbf{R} = \mathbf{P} \times \mathbf{R} + \mathbf{Q} \times \mathbf{R}$$

By definition of the vector product, the following relationships hold for the unit vectors:

$$\mathbf{i} \times \mathbf{j} = \mathbf{k} \quad \mathbf{j} \times \mathbf{k} = \mathbf{i} \quad \mathbf{k} \times \mathbf{i} = \mathbf{j}$$
$$\mathbf{i} \times \mathbf{i} = \mathbf{j} \times \mathbf{j} = \mathbf{k} \times \mathbf{k} = 0$$

If vectors $\mathbf{P}$ and $\mathbf{Q}$ are written in terms of their rectangular components:

$$\mathbf{P} = \mathbf{i}P_x + \mathbf{j}P_y + \mathbf{k}P_z$$

and

$$\mathbf{Q} = \mathbf{i}Q_x + \mathbf{j}Q_y + \mathbf{k}Q_z$$

the result is:

$$\mathbf{P} \times \mathbf{Q} = (\mathbf{i}P_x + \mathbf{j}P_y + \mathbf{k}P_z) \times (\mathbf{i}Q_x + \mathbf{j}Q_y + \mathbf{k}Q_z)$$
$$= \mathbf{i}(P_yQ_z - P_zQ_y) + \mathbf{j}(P_zQ_x - P_xQ_z) + \mathbf{k}(P_xQ_y - P_yQ_x)$$

This expression can be represented by the determinant:

$$\mathbf{P} \times \mathbf{Q} \begin{vmatrix} \mathbf{i} & \mathbf{j} & \mathbf{k} \\ P_x & P_y & P_z \\ Q_x & Q_y & Q_z \end{vmatrix}$$

The triple scalar product is the dot product of two vectors with one vector a cross product of two additional vectors. This product is a scalar and is given by:

$$(\mathbf{P} \times \mathbf{Q}) \cdot \mathbf{R} = \mathbf{R} \cdot (\mathbf{P} \times \mathbf{Q}) = -\mathbf{R} \cdot (\mathbf{Q} \times \mathbf{P})$$

or

$$\mathbf{P} \times \mathbf{Q} \cdot \mathbf{R} = \mathbf{P} \cdot \mathbf{Q} \times \mathbf{R}$$

The dot and the cross may be interchanged without changing the value of the triple scalar product. In addition, expansion shows that:

$$\mathbf{P} \times \mathbf{Q} \cdot \mathbf{R} = \begin{vmatrix} P_x & P_y & P_z \\ Q_x & Q_y & Q_z \\ R_x & R_y & R_z \end{vmatrix}$$

The triple vector product is the cross product of two vectors for which one of the vectors is a cross product of two additional vectors. This product, a vector, is given by:

$$(\mathbf{P} \times \mathbf{Q}) \times \mathbf{R} = -\mathbf{R} \times (\mathbf{P} \times \mathbf{Q}) = \mathbf{R} \times (\mathbf{Q} \times \mathbf{P})$$

The triple vector product is equivalent to:

$$(\mathbf{P} \times \mathbf{Q}) \times \mathbf{R} = (\mathbf{R} \cdot \mathbf{P})\mathbf{Q} - (\mathbf{R} \cdot \mathbf{Q})\mathbf{P}$$

or

$$\mathbf{P} \times (\mathbf{Q} \times \mathbf{R}) = (\mathbf{P} \cdot \mathbf{R})\mathbf{Q} - (\mathbf{P} \cdot \mathbf{Q})\mathbf{R}$$

DERIVATIVES OF VECTORS

The derivative of a vector $\mathbf{P}$ with respect to a scalar, such as the time t, is expressed as the limit of the ratio of the change $\Delta \mathbf{P}$ in $\mathbf{P}$ to the corresponding change Δt in t, as Δt approaches zero. Thus:

$$\frac{d\mathbf{P}}{dt} = \lim_{\Delta t \to 0} \frac{\Delta \mathbf{P}}{\Delta t}$$

$$= \lim_{\Delta t \to 0} \left(\mathbf{i} \frac{\Delta P_x}{\Delta t} + \mathbf{j} \frac{\Delta P_y}{\Delta t} + \mathbf{k} \frac{\Delta P_z}{\Delta t} \right)$$

where $\Delta \mathbf{P}$ is expressed in terms of its components. Thus:

$$\frac{d\mathbf{P}}{dt} = \mathbf{i} \frac{dP_x}{dt} + \mathbf{j} \frac{dP_y}{dt} + \mathbf{k} \frac{dP_z}{dt}$$

and

$$\frac{d^n\mathbf{P}}{dt^n} = \mathbf{i} \frac{d^n P_x}{dt^n} + \mathbf{j} \frac{d^n P_y}{dt^n} + \mathbf{k} \frac{d^n P_z}{dt^n}$$

The derivative of the sum of two vectors is:

$$\frac{d(\mathbf{P} + \mathbf{Q})}{dt} = \lim_{\Delta t \to 0} \frac{\Delta(\mathbf{P} + \mathbf{Q})}{\Delta t} = \lim_{\Delta t \to 0} \left(\frac{\Delta \mathbf{P}}{\Delta t} + \frac{\Delta \mathbf{Q}}{\Delta t} \right)$$

$$= \frac{d\mathbf{P}}{dt} + \frac{d\mathbf{Q}}{dt}$$

The same rule applies to the derivative of the product of a vector $\mathbf{P}$ and a scalar u as for the product of two scalar quantities; hence:

$$\frac{d(\mathbf{P}u)}{dt} = \lim_{\Delta t \to 0} \frac{(\mathbf{P} + \Delta \mathbf{P})(u + \Delta u) - \mathbf{P}u}{\Delta t}$$

$$= \lim_{\Delta t \to 0} \frac{\mathbf{P}\Delta u + u\Delta \mathbf{P}}{\Delta t} = \lim_{\Delta t \to 0} \left(\mathbf{P}\frac{\Delta u}{\Delta t} + u\frac{\Delta \mathbf{P}}{\Delta t} \right)$$

$$= \mathbf{P}\frac{du}{dt} + u\frac{d\mathbf{P}}{dt}$$

The rules for the product of two scalar quantities apply to the derivatives of the scalar (dot) product and the vector (cross) product of two vectors. Thus for the dot product:

$$\frac{d(\mathbf{P} \cdot \mathbf{Q})}{dt} = \lim_{\Delta t \to 0} \frac{(\mathbf{P} + \Delta \mathbf{P}) \cdot (\mathbf{Q} + \Delta \mathbf{Q}) - \mathbf{P} \cdot \mathbf{Q}}{\Delta t}$$

$$= \lim_{\Delta t \to 0} \frac{\mathbf{P} \cdot \Delta \mathbf{Q} + \mathbf{Q} \cdot \Delta \mathbf{P} + \Delta \mathbf{P} \cdot \Delta \mathbf{Q}}{\Delta t}$$

$$= \lim_{\Delta t \to 0} \left(\mathbf{P} \cdot \frac{\Delta \mathbf{Q}}{\Delta t} + \frac{\Delta \mathbf{P}}{\Delta t} \cdot \mathbf{Q} + \frac{\Delta \mathbf{P} \cdot \Delta \mathbf{Q}}{\Delta t} \right)$$

$$= \mathbf{P} \cdot \frac{d\mathbf{Q}}{dt} + \frac{d\mathbf{P}}{dt} \cdot \mathbf{Q}$$

Because the third term is of a higher order than the terms that remain, it drops out in the limit. For the cross product, the derivative is:

$$\frac{d(\mathbf{P} \times \mathbf{Q})}{dt} = \lim_{\Delta t \to 0} \frac{(\mathbf{P} + \Delta \mathbf{P}) \times (\mathbf{Q} + \Delta \mathbf{Q}) - \mathbf{P} \times \mathbf{Q}}{\Delta t}$$

$$= \lim_{\Delta t \to 0} \frac{\mathbf{P} \times \Delta \mathbf{Q} + \Delta \mathbf{P} \times \mathbf{Q} + \Delta \mathbf{P} \times \Delta \mathbf{Q}}{\Delta t}$$

$$= \lim_{\Delta t \to 0} \left(\mathbf{P} \times \frac{\Delta \mathbf{Q}}{\Delta t} + \frac{\Delta \mathbf{P}}{\Delta t} \times \mathbf{Q} + \frac{\Delta \mathbf{P} \times \Delta \mathbf{Q}}{\Delta t} \right)$$

$$= \mathbf{P} \times \frac{d\mathbf{Q}}{dt} + \frac{d\mathbf{P}}{dt} \times \mathbf{Q}$$

The third term disappears in the limit, again, because it is of a higher order than those that remain.

GRADIENT

With $\phi(x, y, z)$ a scalar function of position in space, that is, of the coordinates x, y, z, increasing the coordinates x, y, z by dx, dy, dz, respectively, produces:

$$d\phi = \frac{\partial \phi}{\partial x} dx + \frac{\partial \phi}{\partial y} dy + \frac{\partial \phi}{\partial z} dz \qquad \text{(Eq 1)}$$

If the vector representing the displacement specified by dx, dy, dz is denoted by $d\mathbf{r}$, then:

$$dr = idx + jdy + kdz \qquad \text{(Eq 2)}$$

A vector differential operator ∇ is defined by:

$$\nabla = i\frac{\partial}{\partial x} + j\frac{\partial}{\partial y} + k\frac{\partial}{\partial z} \qquad \text{(Eq 3)}$$

and the gradient of a scalar function $\phi(x, y, z)$ is defined by:

$$\text{grad } \phi = i\frac{\partial \phi}{\partial x} + j\frac{\partial \phi}{\partial y} + k\frac{\partial \phi}{\partial z} \qquad \text{(Eq 4)}$$

Operating with ∇ on the scalar function $\phi(x, y, z)$ produces:

$$\nabla \phi = i\frac{\partial \phi}{\partial x} + j\frac{\partial \phi}{\partial y} + k\frac{\partial \phi}{\partial z} = \text{a vector} \qquad \text{(Eq 5)}$$

which is Eq 4 defined as the gradient of ϕ. From Eq 1 and 2:

$$d\phi = \left(i\frac{\partial \phi}{\partial x} + j\frac{\partial \phi}{\partial y} + k\frac{\partial \phi}{\partial z} \right) \cdot (idx + jdy + kdz)$$

$$= (\nabla \phi) \cdot dr \qquad \text{(Eq 6)}$$

The equation, $\phi(x, y, z) = \text{const}$, represents a surface; as the value of the constant is changed, a family of surfaces is obtained. For example, for the surfaces of Fig. 8, if dn denotes the distance along the normal from the point P to the surface S_2, the expression may be written $dn = n \cdot dr$ where n is the unit normal to the surface S_1 at P. The result is:

$$d\phi = \frac{\partial \phi}{\partial n} dn = \frac{\partial \phi}{\partial n} n \cdot dr = (\nabla \phi \cdot dr \qquad \text{(Eq 7)}$$

and, in particular, if dr lies in the surface S_1, $d\phi = (\nabla \phi) \cdot dr = 0$, which indicates that the vector $\nabla \phi$ is normal to the surface $\phi = \text{const}$. Because the vector dr is arbitrary, the expression from Eq 7 becomes:

$$\nabla \phi = \left(\frac{\partial \phi}{\partial n} \right) n \qquad \text{(Eq 8)}$$

Hence, $\nabla \phi$ is a vector with a magnitude equal to the maximum rate of change of ϕ with respect to the space variables and with a direction of that change.

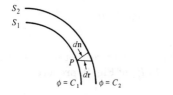

Figure 8

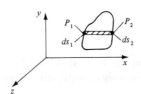

Figure 9

INTEGRATION OF VECTORS

If $\mathbf{V}$ is a function of x, y, and z and if an element of volume is $d\tau = dx\,dy\,dz$, the integral of $\mathbf{V}$ over the volume can be expressed as the vector sum of the three integrals of its components:

$$\int \mathbf{V}\,d\tau = \mathbf{i} \int V_x\,d\tau + \mathbf{j} \int V_y\,d\tau + \mathbf{k} \int V_z\,d\tau$$

DIVERGENCE

The scalar product of the vector operator ∇ and a vector $\mathbf{A}$ produces a scalar called the divergence of $\mathbf{A}$; that is:

$$\nabla \cdot \mathbf{A} = \frac{\partial A_x}{\partial x} + \frac{\partial A_y}{\partial y} + \frac{\partial A_z}{\partial z} = \operatorname{div} \mathbf{A}$$

a quantity that has important applications in hydrodynamics. For example, for a fluid of density $\rho(x, y, z, t)$ and velocity $\mathbf{v} = \mathbf{v}(x, y, z, t)$, if $\mathbf{V} = \mathbf{v}\rho$ and $\mathbf{S}$ is the representative vector of a plane surface area, then $\mathbf{V} \cdot \mathbf{S}$ is the mass of fluid flowing through the surface $\mathbf{S}$ in a unit time.

GAUSS' THEOREM

According to Gauss' theorem, the volume integral of the divergence of a vector field $\mathbf{A}$ for volume V is equal to the surface integral of $\mathbf{A}$ for the closed surface surrounding the volume V:

$$\iiint_v (\nabla \cdot \mathbf{A})\,dv = \iint_s \mathbf{A} \cdot d\mathbf{s} \qquad \text{(Eq 9)}$$

Expanding the left-hand side of Eq 9 produces:

$$\iiint_v (\nabla \cdot \mathbf{A})\,dv = \iiint_v \left(\frac{\partial A_x}{\partial x} + \frac{\partial A_y}{\partial y} + \frac{\partial A_z}{\partial z} \right) dx\,dy\,dz$$

$$= \iiint_v \frac{\partial A_x}{\partial x}\,dx\,dy\,dz + \iiint_v \frac{\partial A_y}{\partial y}\,dx\,dy\,dz +$$

$$\iiint_v \frac{\partial A_z}{\partial z}\,dx\,dy\,dz$$

Integrating the first integral on the right with respect to x, along a strip of cross section $dy\,dz$ extending from P_1 to P_2 of Fig. 9, produces:

$$\iiint_v \frac{\partial A_x}{\partial x}\,dx\,dy\,dz = \iint [A_x(x_2, y, z) - A_x(x_1, y, z)]\,dy\,dz$$

The coordinates of P_1 are x_1, y, z, and (x_2, y, z) are the coordinates of P_2. At P_1, $dy\,dz = -ds_x$. At P_2, $dy\,dz = ds_x$. Thus:

$$\iiint_v \frac{\partial A_x}{\partial x}\,dx\,dy\,dz = \iint_s A_x ds_x \qquad \text{(Eq 10)}$$

where the surface integral on the right is evaluated over the entire surface. In the same manner:

$$\iiint_v \frac{\partial A_y}{\partial x}\,dx\,dy\,dz = \iint_s A_y ds_y \qquad \text{(Eq 11)}$$

and

$$\iiint_v \frac{\partial A_z}{\partial z}\,dx\,dy\,dz = \iint_s A_z ds_z \qquad \text{(Eq 12)}$$

Gauss' theorem is obtained by adding Eq 10, 11, and 12:

$$\iiint_v (\nabla \cdot \mathbf{A})\,dv = \iint_s (A_x ds_x + A_y ds_y + A_z ds_z) = \iint_s \mathbf{A} \cdot d\mathbf{s}$$
$$\text{(Eq 13)}$$

GREEN'S THEOREM

By using Gauss' theorem, important transformations can be made. For example, in the expression $\mathbf{A} = u\nabla w$ consider the vector field $\mathbf{A}$ to be the product of a scalar function u and the gradient of another scalar function w. If the following value of $\nabla \cdot \mathbf{A}$:

$$\nabla \cdot \mathbf{A} = \frac{\partial A_x}{\partial x} + \frac{\partial A_y}{\partial y} + \frac{\partial A_z}{\partial z} = \frac{\partial}{\partial x}\left(u\frac{\partial w}{\partial x}\right) + \frac{\partial}{\partial y}\left(u\frac{\partial w}{\partial y}\right) + \frac{\partial}{\partial z}\left(u\frac{\partial w}{\partial z}\right)$$

$$= u\left(\frac{\partial^2 w}{\partial x^2} + \frac{\partial^2 w}{\partial y^2} + \frac{\partial^2 w}{\partial z^2}\right) + \frac{\partial u}{\partial x}\frac{\partial w}{\partial x} + \frac{\partial u}{\partial y}\frac{\partial w}{\partial y} + \frac{\partial u}{\partial z}\frac{\partial w}{\partial z}$$

$$= u\nabla^2 w + \nabla u \cdot \nabla w \qquad \text{(Eq 14)}$$

is substituted in the left-hand side of Gauss' theorem in Eq 13, the expression:

$$\iiint_v (u\nabla^2 w + \nabla u \cdot \nabla w)\,dv = \iint_s (u\nabla w) \cdot d\mathbf{s} \qquad \text{(Eq 15)}$$

is obtained. This transformation is the first form of Green's theorem. If the functions u and w of Eq 15 are interchanged, then:

$$\iiint_v (w\nabla^2 u + \nabla u \cdot \nabla w)\,dv = \iint_s (w\nabla u) \cdot d\mathbf{s} \qquad \text{(Eq 16)}$$

Subtracting Eq 16 from Eq 15, produces:

$$\iiint_v (u \nabla^2 w - w \nabla^2 u)\, dv = \iint_s (u \nabla w - w \nabla u) \cdot d\mathbf{s} \qquad \text{(Eq 17)}$$

the second form of Green's theorem.

THE CURL OF A VECTOR FIELD

The curl, or rotation, of a vector field $\mathbf{A}$ is defined as the vector function of space obtained by taking the vector product of the operator ∇ and $\mathbf{A}$. That is:

$$\text{curl } \mathbf{A} = \nabla \times \mathbf{A}$$

$$= \mathbf{i}\left(\frac{\partial A_z}{\partial y} - \frac{\partial A_y}{\partial z}\right) + \mathbf{j}\left(\frac{\partial A_x}{\partial z} - \frac{\partial A_z}{\partial x}\right) + \mathbf{k}\left(\frac{\partial A_y}{\partial x} - \frac{\partial A_x}{\partial y}\right)$$

In determinant form:

$$\nabla \times \mathbf{A} = \begin{vmatrix} \mathbf{i} & \mathbf{j} & \mathbf{k} \\ \dfrac{\partial}{\partial x} & \dfrac{\partial}{\partial y} & \dfrac{\partial}{\partial z} \\ A_x & A_y & A_z \end{vmatrix}$$

If $\mathbf{A} = \nabla \phi$:

$$\nabla \times \mathbf{A} = \nabla \times (\nabla \phi) = \mathbf{i}\left(\frac{\partial^2 \phi}{\partial y \partial z} - \frac{\partial^2 \phi}{\partial z \partial y}\right) +$$

$$\mathbf{j}\left(\frac{\partial^2 \phi}{\partial z \partial x} - \frac{\partial^2 \phi}{\partial x \partial z}\right) + \mathbf{k}\left(\frac{\partial^2 \phi}{\partial x \partial y} - \frac{\partial^2 \phi}{\partial y \partial x}\right) = 0$$

If $\mathbf{A}$ is the gradient of a scalar, the curl of $\mathbf{A}$ vanishes.

STOKES' THEOREM

A circulation of a vector function $\mathbf{F}$ about a closed path C equals a vector flow of the same vector function over an arbitrary surface bounded by C, as in:

$$\oint_C \mathbf{F} \cdot d\mathbf{r} = \int_S (\nabla \times \mathbf{F}) \cdot d\mathbf{S}$$

In Cartesian coordinates:

$$\oint_C \mathbf{F} \cdot d\mathbf{r} = \int_C (F_x\, dx + F_y\, dy + F_z\, dz)$$

$$= \iint_{\Sigma yz}\left(\frac{\partial F_z}{\partial y} - \frac{\partial F_y}{\partial z}\right) dy\, dz + \iint_{\Sigma zx}\left(\frac{\partial F_x}{\partial z} - \frac{\partial F_z}{\partial x}\right) dz\, dx +$$

$$\iint_{\Sigma xy}\left(\frac{\partial F_y}{\partial x} - \frac{\partial F_x}{\partial y}\right) dx\, dy$$

Thus, a surface integral can be reduced to a line integral.

13
Fourier Series and Transforms

BASIC CASE

Any single-valued function $F(t)$ that is continuous except for a finite number of finite discontinuities in an interval:

$$-\frac{T}{2} \le t \le \frac{T}{2}$$

and has a finite number of maxima and minima in this interval may be represented by a convergent Fourier series:

$$F(t) = \frac{A_0}{2} + \sum_{n=1}^{\infty} (A_n \cos nwt + B_n \sin nwt) \tag{Eq 1}$$

At all points of continuity of $F(t)$, the series converges to $F(t)$. Under these conditions, known as Dirichlet conditions, the function $F(t)$ may be represented over a complete period and hence from $t = -\infty$ to $t = +\infty$, except at discontinuities, by a series of harmonic functions. The frequencies of these functions are integral multiples of the fundamental frequency. For $n = 0$, $1, 2, \ldots$

$$A_n = \frac{2}{T} \int_{-T/2}^{T/2} F(t) \cos nwt \, dt \tag{Eq 2}$$

$$B_n = \frac{2}{T} \int_{-T/2}^{T/2} F(t) \sin nwt \, dt \tag{Eq 3}$$

The relationships in Eq 2 and Eq 3 are called Euler's formulas. The series in Eq 1 may not converge or may converge for only some values of t. Although the series in Eq 1 may converge for some value t_1, the sum of the series may not necessarily equal $F(t_1)$. The period T equals $2\pi/w$, t is time (in seconds), and w is the fundamental frequency (in radians per second).

If the series represented in Eq 1 converges in some interval $\xi \le t < (\xi + T)$, then Eq 1 represents a function of period T defined for all values of t.

If Eq 1 converges uniformly to $F(t)$ in $-T/2 \leqq t \leqq T/2$, A_n and B_n are given by Eq 2 and 3.

The Fourier series of $F(t)$ converges uniformly to $F(t)$ in an interval that is interior to an interval for which $F(t)$ is continuous and is the difference of two bounded increasing functions. A function $F(t)$ is bounded in (a, b) if two constants h and K exist for which $h \leqq F(t) \leqq K$ for all t satisfying $a \leqq t \leqq b$.

Complex Representation. If the sum of Eq 1 is $F(t)$, the relationship can be described by the complex representation:

$$F(t) = a_0 + a_1 r^{jwt} + a_2 e^{2jwt} + \cdots + a_n e^{jnwt} + \cdots +$$
$$a_{-1} e^{-jwt} + a_{-2} e^{-2jwt} + \cdots + a_{-n} e^{-jnwt} + \cdots$$

$$= \sum_{n=-\infty}^{n=+\infty} a_n e^{jnwt} \qquad \text{(Eq 4)}$$

where

$$w = \frac{2\pi}{T} \qquad \text{(Eq 5)}$$

Since $F(t)$ is real, the coefficients of the series in Eq 4 must produce no imaginary terms. To determine a_0, both sides are integrated over a complete period, from 0 to $T = 2\pi/w$. Thus:

$$\int_0^{2\pi/w} F(t)\,dt = \int_0^{2\pi/w} \left(\sum_{n=-\infty}^{n=+\infty} a_n e^{jnwt} \right) dt$$

$$= \sum_{n=-\infty}^{n=+\infty} a_n \int_0^{2\pi/w} e^{jnwt} dt \qquad \text{(Eq 6)}$$

where term-by-term integration is assumed valid. The integral of the general term is:

$$\int_0^{2\pi/w} e^{jnwt}\,dt = \frac{1}{jnw} e^{jnwt} \Big|_0^{2\pi/w} = \frac{1}{jnw}(e^{j2n\pi} - 1) = 0 \qquad \text{(Eq 7)}$$

for $n \neq 0$. If $n = 0$:

$$\int_0^{2\pi/w} dt = \frac{2\pi}{w} = T \qquad \text{(Eq 8)}$$

Hence, Eq 6 becomes:

$$\int_0^T F(t)\,dt = a_0 T \qquad \text{(Eq 9)}$$

or

$$a_0 = \frac{1}{T} \int_0^T F(t)\,dt = \overline{F(t)} \qquad \text{(Eq 10)}$$

where $\overline{F(t)}$ is the mean value of $F(t)$.

To determine other coefficients, both sides of Eq 4 are multiplied by e^{-jnwt} and the result integrated from $t = 0$ to $t = T = 2\pi/w$:

$$\int_0^T F(t)e^{-jnwt}\,dt = a_n T \qquad\qquad\text{(Eq 11)}$$

or

$$a_n = \frac{1}{T}\int_0^T F(t)e^{-jnwt}\,dt \qquad\qquad\text{(Eq 12)}$$

which gives the coefficient of the general term in Eq 4. From Eq 12 also is derived the relationship:

$$a_{-n} = \frac{1}{T}\int_0^T F(t)e^{jnwt}\,dt \qquad\qquad\text{(Eq 13)}$$

Thus, a_n and a_{-n} are conjugate imaginaries, and:

$$a_{-n} = \bar{a}_n \qquad\qquad\text{(Eq 14)}$$

Equation 4 also may be written in the form:

$$
\begin{aligned}
F(t) &= \sum_{n=-\infty}^{n=-1} a_n e^{jnwt} + a_0 + \sum_{n=1}^{n=\infty} a_n e^{jnwt} \\
&= \sum_{n=\infty}^{n=1} a_{-n} e^{-jnwt} + a_0 + \sum_{n=1}^{n=\infty} a_n e^{jnwt} \\
&= a_0 + \sum_{n=1}^{n=\infty} (a_n e^{jnwt} + a_{-n} e^{-jnwt}) \qquad\qquad\text{(Eq 15)}
\end{aligned}
$$

From Euler's equations, this expression may be written as:

$$F(t) = a_0 + \sum_{n=1}^{n=\infty} (a_n + a_{-n})\cos nwt + \sum_{n=1}^{n=\infty} j(a_n - a_{-n})\sin nwt \qquad\text{(Eq 16)}$$

If:

$$A_n = a_n + a_{-n} \qquad B_n = j(a_n - a_{-n}) \qquad \frac{A_0}{2} = a_0 \qquad\text{(Eq 17)}$$

the result is Eq 1, the usual real form of the Fourier series. In complex or real form of Fourier series, the constant term always equals the mean value of the function.

A third form of the Fourier series involving phase angles may be obtained from Eq 1 by letting:

$$
\begin{aligned}
A_n \cos nwt + B_n \sin nwt &= C_n \cos(nwt - \phi_n) \\
&= C_n \cos nwt \cos\phi_n + C_n \sin nwt \sin\phi_n \qquad\text{(Eq 18)}
\end{aligned}
$$

Equating the coefficients of like cosine and sine terms:

$$A_n = C_n \cos\phi_n \qquad B_n = C_n \sin\phi_n \qquad\qquad\text{(Eq 19)}$$

Hence:

$$C_n = \sqrt{A_n^2 + B_n^2} \qquad \phi_n = \tan^{-1}\frac{B_n}{A_n} \tag{Eq 20}$$

The series then takes the form:

$$F(t) = \frac{A_0}{2} + \sum_{n=1}^{n=\infty} C_n \cos(nwt - \phi_n) \tag{Eq 21}$$

or

$$F(t) = \frac{A_0}{2} + \sum_{n=1}^{n=\infty} C_n \sin\left(nwt + \frac{\pi}{2} - \phi_n\right) \tag{Eq 22}$$

In Eq 4, $F(t)$ is the Fourier transform of a_n, where:

$$a_n = \frac{1}{T}\int_{-T/2}^{T/2} F(t) e^{-jnwt} dt$$

Thus:

$$a_n = \frac{1}{2}\sqrt{A_n^2 + B_n^2}\exp\left[j\tan^{-1}\left(\frac{-B_n}{A_n}\right)\right]$$

The amplitude spectrum of $F(t)$ is:

$$|a_n| = \frac{1}{2}\sqrt{A_n^2 + B_n^2}$$

The phase spectrum of $F(t)$ is:

$$\theta_n = \tan^{-1}\left(\frac{-B_n}{A_n}\right)$$

and

$$F(t) = \sum_{n=-\infty}^{n=\infty} |A_n| e^{j(nwt + \theta_n)}$$

The auto-correlation function of $F_1(t)$ is:

$$\phi_{11}(\tau) = \frac{1}{T}\int_{-T/2}^{T/2} F_1(t) F_1(t + \tau)\, dt = \sum_{n=-\infty}^{n=\infty} \Phi_{11}(n) e^{jnw\tau}$$

where

$$\Phi_{11}(n) = |a_n^1|^2$$

is the power spectrum, and

$$\Phi_{11}(n) = \frac{1}{T}\int_{-T/2}^{T/2} \phi_{11}(\tau) e^{-jnw\tau}\, d\tau$$

Also:

$$\frac{1}{T} \int_{-T/2}^{T/2} [F_1(t)]^2 \, dt = \sum_{n=-\infty}^{n=\infty} |a_n^1|^2$$

which is known as Parseval's formula. The cross-correlation function of two periodic functions $F_1(t)$ and $F_2(t)$ of the same fundamental frequency is:

$$\phi_{12}(\tau) = \frac{1}{T} \int_{-T/2}^{T/2} F_1(t) F_2(t + \tau) \, dt$$

where τ is a displacement in t. The convolution of $F_1(t)$ and $F_2(t)$ is:

$$\frac{1}{T} \int_{-T/2}^{T/2} F_1(t) F_2(t - \tau) \, dt$$

Table 1 gives values of the finite sine transform $F_s(n)$ of the function $f(x)$ for:

$$F_s(n) = \int_0^\pi f(x) \sin nx \, dx \qquad n = 1, 2, \ldots$$

Table 2 gives values of the finite cosine transform $F_c(n)$ of the function $f(x)$ for:

$$F_c(n) = \int_0^\pi f(x) \cos nx \, dx \qquad n = 0, 1, 2, \ldots$$

Table 1 Finite sine transforms(a)

$F_s(n)$	$f(x)$
$(-1)^{n+1}F_s(n)$	$f(\pi - x)$
$[1 - (-1)^n]/n$	1
$1/n$	$(\pi - x)/\pi$
$(-1)^{n+1}/n$	x/π
$\dfrac{2}{n^2}\sin\dfrac{n\pi}{2}$	$\begin{cases} x & \text{for } 0 < x < \pi/2 \\ \pi - x & \text{for } \pi/2 < x < \pi \end{cases}$
$[1 - (-1)^n]/n^3$	$x(\pi - x)/2$
$(-1)^{n+1}/n^3$	$x(\pi^2 - x^2)/(6\pi)$
$[\pi^2(-1)^{n-1}/n] - 2[1 - (-1)^n]/n^3$	x^2
$\pi(-1)^n[(6/n^3) - (\pi^2/n)]$	x^3
$(\pi/n^2)\sin nc \qquad 0 < c < \pi$	$\begin{cases} (\pi - c)x & \text{for } x \le c \\ c(\pi - x) & \text{for } x \ge c \end{cases}$
$(\pi/n)\cos nc \qquad 0 \le c \le \pi$	$\begin{cases} -x & \text{for } x < c \\ \pi - x & \text{for } x > c \end{cases}$
$n[1 - (-1)^n e^{c\pi}]/(n^2 + c^2)$	e^{cx}
$n/(n^2 + c^2)$	$\sinh c(\pi - x)/\sinh c\pi$
$n/(n^2 - k^2) \qquad |k| \neq 0, 1, 2, \ldots$	$\sin k(\pi - x)/\sin k\pi$
0 if $n \neq m \qquad \pi/2$ if $n = m$	$\sin mx \qquad\qquad m = 1, 2, \ldots$
$n[1 - (-1)^n \cos k\pi]/(n^2 - k^2)$	$\cos kx \qquad\qquad |k| \neq 1, 2, \ldots$
$\begin{cases} n[1 - (-1)^{n+m}]/(n^2 - m^2) \\ \qquad\qquad \text{if } n \neq m \\ 0 \qquad\qquad\quad \text{if } n = m \end{cases}$	$\cos mx \qquad\qquad m = 1, 2, \ldots$
$n/(n^2 - k^2)^2 \qquad |k| \neq 0, 1, 2, \ldots$	$\dfrac{\pi \sin kx}{2k \sin^2 k\pi} - \dfrac{x \cos k(\pi - x)}{2k \sin k\pi}$
$b^n/n \qquad\qquad\qquad |b| \le 1$	$\dfrac{2}{\pi}\tan^{-1}\left[\dfrac{b \sin x}{(1 - b \cos x)}\right]$
$[1 - (-1)^n]b^n/n \qquad |b| \le 1$	$\dfrac{2}{\pi}\tan^{-1}\left[\dfrac{2b \sin x}{(1 - b^2)}\right]$

(a) $f(x)$ is defined on the interval $0 < x < \pi$; c, k, and b are constants

Table 2   Finite cosine transforms(a)

$F_c(n)$		$f(x)$	
$(-1)^n F_c(n)$		$f(\pi - x)$	
$\begin{cases} 0 & \text{if } n = 1, 2, \ldots \\ \pi & \text{if } n = 0 \end{cases}$		1	
$\begin{cases} (2/n)\sin(n\pi/2) & \text{if } n = 1, 2, \ldots \\ 0 & \text{if } n = 0 \end{cases}$		1 -1	for $0 < x < \pi/2$ for $\pi/2 < x < \pi$
$\begin{cases} (2/n)\sin nc & \text{if } n = 1, 2, \ldots \\ 2c - \pi & \text{if } n = 0 \end{cases}$		1 -1	for $0 < x < c$ for $c < x < \pi$
$\begin{cases} [(-1)^n - 1]/n^2 & \text{if } n \neq 0 \\ \pi^2/2 & \text{if } n = 0 \end{cases}$		x	
$\begin{cases} (-1)^n/n^2 & \text{if } n \neq 0 \\ \pi^2/6 & \text{if } n = 0 \end{cases}$		$x^2/(2\pi)$	
$\begin{cases} 1/n^2 & \text{if } n \neq 0 \\ 0 & \text{if } n = 0 \end{cases}$		$|(\pi - x)^2/(2\pi)| - \pi/6$	
$\begin{cases} \dfrac{3\pi^2(-1)^n}{n^2} + \dfrac{6[1 - (-1)^n]}{n^4} & \text{if } n \neq 0 \\ \pi^4/4 & \text{if } n = 0 \end{cases}$		x^3	
$[(-1)^n e^{c\pi} - 1]/(n^2 + c^2)$		e^{cx}/c	
$\dfrac{(-1)^n \cos k\pi - 1}{n^2 - k^2}$ if $|k| \neq 0, 1, 2, \ldots$		$(\sin kx)/k$	
$\begin{cases} \dfrac{(-1)^{n+m} - 1}{n^2 - m^2} & \text{if } n \neq m \\ 0 & \text{if } n = m = 1, 2, \ldots \end{cases}$		$(\sin mx)/m$	
$1/(n^2 - k^2)$ if $|k| \neq 0, 1, 2, \ldots$		$-\cos k(\pi - x)/(k\sin k\pi)$	
$\begin{cases} 0 & \text{if } n \neq m \\ \pi/2 & \text{if } n = m = 1, 2, \ldots \end{cases}$		$\cos mx$	
$1/(n^2 + c^2)$		$\cosh c(\pi - x)/(c\sinh c\pi)$	
$\begin{cases} b^n & \text{if } n \neq 0 \\ 0 & \text{if } n = 0, |b| < 1 \end{cases}$		$\dfrac{2b(\cos x - b)}{\pi(1 - 2b\cos x + b^2)}$	

(a) $f(x)$ is defined over the interval $0 < x < \pi$; c, k, and b are constants

14
Statistics and Probability

In engineering and physics, some processes cannot be determined exactly. In evaluating such phenomena, the methods of statistics and the theory of probability are used.

STATISTICAL DISTRIBUTIONS

A variate is a single quantity measured for each member of a set of objects, or population, which may be a group of people, objects, or perhaps a set of results of a physical or chemical experiment. Variates usually are denoted by such symbols as x or y. The values of a variate x are denoted by a finite set of numbers $x_1, x_2, x_3, \ldots, x_n$.

FREQUENCY

For any given population, the frequency f_r is the number of times a value x_r of a variate is observed. For example, a merchant may have three price levels for a similar product, three priced at \$3,500, four at \$4,000, and two at \$2,000. Restated, $x_1 = \$3,500$ and $f_1 = 3$; $x_2 = \$4,000$ and $f_2 = 4$; and $x_3 = \$2,000$ and $f_3 = 2$. The total in the population is N, where:

$$N = f_1 + f_2 + f_3 = 3 + 4 + 2 = 9 \qquad \text{(Eq 1)}$$

The total value of the products S is:

$$S = f_1 x_1 + f_2 x_2 + f_3 x_3 = 3(3{,}500) + 4(4{,}000) + 2(2{,}000) = 30{,}500 \qquad \text{(Eq 2)}$$

The average or mean price $\bar{x}$ is expressed as:

$$\bar{x} = \frac{1}{N}(f_1 x_1 + f_2 x_2 + f_3 x_3) = \$3{,}388 = \frac{1}{N}\sum_{r=1}^{3} f_r x_r \qquad \text{(Eq 3)}$$

MEAN OF A DISTRIBUTION

Arithmetic Mean. The arithmetic mean $\bar{x}$ of the variate x is the sum of the values of x for each member of the set divided by N:

$$\bar{x} = \frac{1}{N} \sum_{r=1}^{k} f_r x_r \qquad k = \text{number of frequencies} \tag{Eq 4}$$

For a typical value a of the variate x:

$$d_r = x_r - a \qquad r = 1, 2, 3, \ldots, N \tag{Eq 5}$$

Thus, d_r is the deviation of x_r from the typical value a. For variate d with a distribution f_r over the values d_r, the mean $\bar{d}$ is:

$$\bar{d} = \frac{1}{N} \sum_{r=1}^{k} f_r d_r \tag{Eq 6}$$

The relationship of $\bar{d}$ to $\bar{x}$ can be written in the form:

$$\bar{d} = \frac{1}{N} \sum_{r=1}^{k} f_r (x_r - a) = \bar{x} - a \tag{Eq 7}$$

Therefore:

$$\bar{x} = \bar{d} + a \tag{Eq 8}$$

which is useful in computing $\bar{x}$ quickly when a is near the mean.

Geometric Mean. The geometric mean of a set of N numbers is:

$$\bar{g} = \sqrt[N]{x_1 x_2 \ldots x_n} \tag{Eq 9}$$

If the numbers occur $f_1, f_2, \ldots, f_N$ times, respectively, then:

$$\bar{g} = \sqrt[N]{x_1^{f_1} x_2^{f_2} \ldots x_n^{f_n}} \tag{Eq 10}$$

where $n = f_1 + f_2 + \cdots + f_n$.

Harmonic Mean. The harmonic mean of a set of N numbers is:

$$\bar{h} = \frac{1}{(1/N)(1/x_1 + 1/x_2 + \cdots + 1/x_N)} = \frac{N}{\Sigma(1/x)} \tag{Eq 11}$$

If the numbers occur $f_1, f_2, \ldots, f_N$ times, respectively, then:

$$\bar{h} = \frac{1}{(1/N)(f_1/x_1 + f_2/x_2 + \cdots + f_N/x_N)} = \frac{N}{\Sigma(f/x)} \tag{Eq 12}$$

where $N = f_1 + f_2 + \cdots + f_N$.

Quadratic Mean. The quadratic mean of a set of N numbers is:

$$\bar{q} = \sqrt{\frac{x_1^2 + x_2^2 + \cdots + x_n^2}{N}} = \sqrt{\frac{\Sigma x^2}{N}} \tag{Eq 13}$$

SECOND MOMENTS

The mean $\bar{d}$ in Eq 7 is the first moment of a distribution about a of the variate x. If $a = \bar{x}$, from Eq 8, then the first moment $\bar{d} = 0$.

The second moment μ_2' of a distribution about a of the variate x is the average of the squares of the differences $d_r = x_r - a$ between a and values of x_r:

$$\mu_2' = \frac{1}{N} \sum_{r=1}^{k} f_r d_r{}^2 = \frac{1}{N} \sum_{r=1}^{k} f_r(x_r - a)^2 \qquad \text{(Eq 14)}$$

If most measured values of x are approximately equal to a, then μ_2' will be small. If a differs widely from x, then μ_2' will be large, because the terms in Eq 14 are positive. If for Eq 14, $a = \bar{x}$, the second moment about the mean $\bar{x}$ is termed the variance, μ_2, and is expressed as:

$$\mu_2 = \frac{1}{N} \sum_{r=1}^{n} f_r(x_r - \bar{x})^2 \qquad \text{(Eq 15)}$$

STANDARD DEVIATION

The standard deviation, σ, of the same set is the positive square root of μ_2, or:

$$\sigma^2 = \mu_2 = \frac{1}{N} \sum_{r=1}^{k} f_r(x_r - \bar{x})^2 = \frac{1}{N} \sum_{r=1}^{k} f_r(d_r - \bar{d})^2 \qquad \text{(Eq 16)}$$

Expanding Eq 16 produces:

$$\sigma^2 = \frac{1}{N} \left(\sum_{r=1}^{k} f_r d_r{}^2 - 2\bar{d} \sum_{r=1}^{k} f_r d_r + \bar{d}^2 \sum_{r=1}^{k} f_r \right)$$

$$= \frac{1}{N} (N\mu - 2_2'N\bar{d}^2 + N\bar{d}^2) \qquad \text{(Eq 17)}$$

Thus, μ_2 and μ_2' about a are related by:

$$\sigma^2 = \mu_2 = \mu_2' - \bar{d}^2 \qquad \text{(Eq 18)}$$

SIMPLE PROBABILITY

If E can occur in M ways or M times out of a total of N mutually exclusive and equally likely possibilities, then the probability of occurrence of E is:

$$P(E) = \frac{M}{N} = p \qquad \text{(Eq 19)}$$

where $O \leq P(E) \leq 1$. The probability of nonoccurrence or failure of E is:

$$P(\bar{E}) = 1 - \frac{M}{N} = q \qquad \text{(Eq 20)}$$

where $O \leq P(\bar{E}) \leq 1$.

PROBABILITY THEOREMS

If $P(A)$ is the probability of A occurring, with $P(A)$ between 0 and 1, then if $P(A) = 1$, the event A is certain to occur, and if $P(A) = 0$, the event A is certain not to happen. For N equally likely outcomes involving events A and B, the following notation may be used:

$$n_1 = \text{outcomes in which only } A \text{ occurs}$$
$$n_2 = \text{outcomes in which only } B \text{ occurs}$$
$$n_3 = \text{outcomes in which both occur}$$
$$n_4 = \text{outcomes in which neither occurs}$$

and

$$N = n_1 + n_2 + n_3 + n_4$$

The probability of A occurring is:

$$P(A) = \frac{n_1 + n_3}{N} \qquad \text{(Eq 21)}$$

The probability of B occurring is:

$$P(B) = \frac{n_2 + n_3}{N} \qquad \text{(Eq 22)}$$

The probability of either A or B (or both) occurring is:

$$P(A + B) = \frac{n_1 + n_2 + n_3}{N} \qquad \text{(Eq 23)}$$

The probability of the joint occurrence of A and B is:

$$P(AB) = \frac{n_3}{N} \qquad \text{(Eq 24)}$$

The conditional probability of the event A occurring after event B has occurred is:

$$P\left(\frac{A}{B}\right) = \frac{n_3}{n_2 + n_3} \qquad \text{(Eq 25)}$$

The conditional probability of the event B occurring after the event A has occurred:

$$P\left(\frac{B}{A}\right) = \frac{n_3}{n_1 + n_3} \qquad \text{(Eq 26)}$$

From this series of probabilities emerges the additive law of probability, expressed as:

$$P(A + B) = P(A) + P(B) - P(AB) \qquad \text{(Eq 27)}$$

and the multiplicative law of probability expressed as:

$$P(AB) = P(B)P\left(\frac{A}{B}\right) = P(A)P\left(\frac{B}{A}\right) \qquad \text{(Eq 28)}$$

Mutually Exclusive Events. If A and B are mutually exclusive events:

$$P(AB) = 0 \qquad \text{(Eq 29)}$$

For this case, Eq 27 becomes:

$$P(A + B) = P(A) + P(B) = P(A \text{ or } B) \qquad \text{(Eq 30)}$$

Statistical Independence. If A and B are statistically independent, then:

$$P\left(\frac{B}{A}\right) = P(B) \qquad \text{and} \qquad P\left(\frac{A}{B}\right) = P(A) \qquad \text{(Eq 31)}$$

For this case, Eq 28 becomes $P(AB) = P(A)P(B)$, and Eq 27 becomes $P(A + B) = P(A) + P(B) - P(A)P(B)$. Solving Eq 28 for $P(B/A)$ produces:

$$P\left(\frac{B}{A}\right) = \frac{P(AB)}{P(A)} \qquad \text{(Eq 32)}$$

Further, substituting:

$$P(AB) = P(B)P\left(\frac{A}{B}\right)$$

also taken from Eq 28, into Eq 32 produces:

$$P\left(\frac{B}{A}\right) = \frac{P(B)}{P(A)} P\left(\frac{A}{B}\right) \qquad \text{(Eq 33)}$$

Replacing B by a third event C gives:

$$P\left(\frac{C}{A}\right) = \frac{P(C)}{P(A)} P\left(\frac{A}{C}\right) \qquad \text{(Eq 34)}$$

Dividing Eq 33 by Eq 34 produces the result:

$$\frac{P(B/A)}{P(C/A)} = \frac{P(B)P(A/B)}{P(C)P(A/C)} \qquad \text{(Eq 35)}$$

a form of Bayes's theorem.

DISCRETE RANDOM VARIABLE

If a variable X can be described by a discrete set of values $x_1, x_2, \ldots, x_n$ with respect to probabilities $p_1, p_2, \ldots, p_n$, where $p_1 + p_2 + \cdots + p_n = 1$, then these values form a discrete probability distribution. Because with given probabilities x takes specific values, it is designated as a discrete random variable or change variable. The probability that X takes the value x_j is:

$$P(X = x_j) = f(x_j) \qquad \text{(Eq 36)}$$

where $j = 1, 2, \ldots, n$, and $f(x)$ is the probability function of the random variable X, with $f(x_j) \geq 0$. $\sum_1^n f(x_j) = 1$. The joint probability that X and Y take the values x_j and y_k, respectively, is:

$$P(X = x_j, Y = y_j) = f(x_j, y_k) \tag{Eq 37}$$

where $j = 1, 2, \ldots, n$ and $k = 1, 2, \ldots, r$ and where $f(x, y)$ is the probability function of a two-dimensional random variable:

$$\left[f(x_j, y_j) \geq 0, \sum_1^n f(x_j) = 1, \sum_1^r f(y_k) = 1 \right]$$

PERMUTATIONS AND COMBINATIONS

The number of arrangements, or permutations, of n objects is $n!$. The first position can be occupied by any of the n objects, the second by any of the remaining $(n - 1)$ objects, and so on. Denoting the number of permutations of n objects by $_nP_n$, then:

$$_nP_n = n(n - 1)(n - 2) \ldots (3)(2)(1) = n! \tag{Eq 38}$$

The permutations of n things taken r at a time is denoted by $_nP_r$. In any arrangement there are n choices for the first place, $(n - 1)$ for the second, and $(n - 2)$ for third, and on to the rth place, which has any of the remaining $(n - r + 1)$. Thus:

$$_nP_r = n(n - 1)(n - 2) \cdots (n - r + 1) = \frac{n!}{(n - r)!} = P(n, r) \tag{Eq 39}$$

The combinations of n things taken r at a time are all possible arrangements of r of the n things, without regard for the order of the arrangement. For example, the possible combinations of a, b, c, taking two at a time, are ab, ac, and bc.

The combinations of n things, taking r at a time, is denoted by $_nC_r$. Any combination of the r things can be arranged in $r!$ ways. Therefore:

$$_nC_r Xr! = {_nP_r} \tag{Eq 40}$$

Dividing Eq 40 by $r!$ gives:

$$_nC_r = \frac{_nP_r}{r!} = \frac{n!}{r!(n - r)!} \tag{Eq 41}$$

which is called the binomial coefficient. If n is a positive integer, then:

$$(a + b)^n = a^n + {_nC_1}a^{n-1}b + {_nC_2}a^{n-2}b^2 + {_nC_3}a^{n-3}b^3 + \cdots + {_nC_n}b^n \tag{Eq 42}$$

which, for $n = 2, 3, 4, \ldots$, is known as the binomial theorem.

The following are properties of the binomial coefficient:

$$_nC_r = \frac{n!}{r!\,(n-r)!} = {}_nC_{n-r} = C(n, r)$$

$$2^n = 1 + {}_nC_1 + {}_nC_2 + \cdots + {}_nC_n$$

$$0 = 1 - {}_nC_1 + {}_nC_2 - {}_nC_3 + \cdots$$

$$_nC_r + {}_nC_{r-1} = {}_{n+1}C_r$$

CONTINUOUS RANDOM VARIABLE

The random variable X (Fig. 1) is denoted as a continuous random variable if $f(x)$ is continuously differentiable, that is:

$$\frac{df(x)}{dx} = \lim_{\Delta x \to 0} \frac{P(X < x \le X + \Delta x)}{\Delta x} = \phi(x) \qquad \text{(Eq 43)}$$

where $\phi(x)$ is probability density, and the cumulative probability distributions are:

$$P(x \le X) = \int_{-\infty}^{X} \phi(x)\, dx$$

$$P(a < x \le b) = \int_{a}^{b} \phi(x)\, dx = f(b) - f(a)$$

$$P(-\infty < x \le \infty) = \int_{-\infty}^{\infty} \phi(x)\, dx = 1$$

A two-dimensional random variable is a continuous random variable if $f(x, y)$ is continuous for all x_j and y_k, and the joint probability density:

$$\phi(x, y) = \frac{\partial^2 f(x, y)}{\partial x\, \partial y} \qquad \text{(Eq 44)}$$

exists and is continuous in piecewise manner.

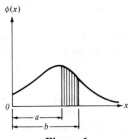

Figure 1

EXPECTATION AND MOMENTS

The mean of a probability distribution for a variate x is the expectation $E(x)$, defined by:

$$E(x) = \frac{p_1 x_1 + p_2 x_2 + \cdots + p_n x_n}{p_1 + p_2 + \cdots + p_n} \qquad \text{(Eq 45)}$$

Because the sum of the probabilities is unity, $p_1 + p_2 + p_3 + \cdots + p_n = 1$. Therefore, $E(x)$ as given in Eq 45 becomes:

$$E(x) = p_1 x_1 + p_2 x_2 + \cdots + p_n x_n = [x] \qquad \text{(Eq 46)}$$

The expectation of a probability distribution of a continuous variate is defined as:

$$E(x) = \int x \phi(x) \, dx = [x] \qquad \text{(Eq 47)}$$

where the integration covers the range of x. The second moment about a is defined by:

$$\mu_2' = \sum_{r=1}^{n} p_r (x_r - a)^2 \qquad \text{(Eq 48)}$$

for a discrete probability distribution μ_2' and by:

$$\mu_2' = \int \phi(x)(x - a)^2 dx = [(x - a)^2] \qquad \text{(Eq 49)}$$

for a continuous probability distribution.

Standard Deviation. The variance μ_2 is given by Eq 48 and Eq 49 with $a = [x]$. The standard deviation σ is given by:

$$\sigma^2 = \mu_2 = [(x - [x])^2] \qquad \text{(Eq 50)}$$

and is related to the second moment $\mu_2'(a)$ by:

$$\sigma^2 = \mu_2' - [d]^2 \qquad \text{(Eq 51)}$$

where $d = x - a$. Then:

$$[d] = [x] - a \qquad \text{(Eq 52)}$$

When $a = [x]$, then Eq 52 becomes $[x - [x]] = [x] - [x] = 0$.

For example, objects numbered 1, 2, 3, ..., n are placed in a box and thoroughly mixed. Then one is drawn at random. If each object is equally likely to be drawn, the probability is:

$$p_r = \frac{1}{n} \qquad r = 1, 2, 3, \ldots, n$$

and the expectation $E(x)$ of a specific object is:

$$E(x) = [x] = \frac{1 + 2 + 3 + \cdots + n}{n} = \frac{n + 1}{2}$$

The second moment about $x = 0$ of the probability distribution of x is, by Eq 48:

$$\mu_2' = [x^2] = n^{-1}(1^2 + 2^2 + \cdots + n^2) = \frac{1}{6}(n + 1)(2n + 1)$$

The variance defined by Eq 50 takes the form:

$$\sigma^2 = \mu_2 = [x^2] - [x]^2 = \frac{1}{12}(n^2 - 1)$$

For large values of n:

$$[x] = \frac{n}{2} \quad \text{and} \quad \sigma = \frac{n}{2(3)^{1/2}}$$

and the values of $[x]$ and σ will become proportional to n when n is large.

CHEBYSHEV'S INEQUALITY

The upper bounds for the probability that a random variable x, or its absolute deviation $|x - \xi|$ from the mean value $\xi = E\{x\}$, exceeds a given value $a > 0$ are specified by the expression:

$$P[x \ge a] \le \frac{\xi}{a} \quad (a > 0) \tag{Eq 53}$$

and by

$$P[|x - \xi| \ge a] \le \frac{\sigma^2}{a^2} \quad (a > 0) \tag{Eq 54}$$

which is known as Chebyshev's inequality.

BINOMIAL DISTRIBUTION

If a trial has only two possible results, success with probability p or failure with probability of $q = (1 - p)$ and if n independent trials are made, then the probability of a particular sequence of r successes and $(n - r)$ failures is $p^2 q^{n-r}$. The number of sequences with r successes and $(n - r)$ failures is:

$$C(n, r) = \frac{n!}{[r!(n - r)!]} \tag{Eq 55}$$

which is the binomial coefficient. The probability of exactly r successes in n trials is:

$$P(r) = C(n, r)p^r q^{n-r} = C(n, r)p^r(1 - p)^{n-r} \tag{Eq 56}$$

The term $P(r)$ contains p^r in the binomial expansion of $(p + q)^n$. The probability distribution in Eq 56 thus is known as the binomial distribution.

The expectation or the mean number of successes $E(x) = \bar{x}$ of the binomial distribution is taken from Eq 45 in the form:

$$\bar{x} = \frac{\sum\limits_{r=0}^{n} rp_r}{\sum\limits_{r=0}^{n} p_r} \qquad \text{(Eq 57)}$$

where $p_r = C(n, r)p^r q^{n-r}$ and, since $q = 1 - p$:

$$\sum_{r=0}^{n} p_r = \sum_{r=0}^{n} C(n, r)p^r q^{n-r} = (p + q)^n$$

$$= [p + (1 - p)]^n = 1^n = 1 \qquad \text{(Eq 58)}$$

If the partial derivative with respect to p is denoted by ∂_p, then:

$$rp^r = p\partial_p p^r \qquad \text{(Eq 59)}$$

Because the denominator of Eq 57 is unity:

$$\bar{x} = \sum_{r=0}^{n} C(n, r)rp^r q^{n-r} \qquad \text{(Eq 60)}$$

By treating p and q as independent variables in summing Eq 60, and using the result of Eq 59, Eq 60 may be written:

$$\bar{x} = p\partial_p \sum_{r=0}^{n} C(n, r)p^r q^{n-r}$$

$$= p\partial_p(p + q)^n = np(p + q)^{n-1} \qquad \text{(Eq 61)}$$

Substituting $q = 1 - p$ in Eq 61 produces:

$$\bar{x} = np[p + (1 - p)]^{n-1} = np \qquad \text{(Eq 62)}$$

the mean number of successes for the binomial distribution.

STANDARD DEVIATION OF THE BINOMIAL DISTRIBUTION

The variance of the binomial distribution can be computed by using Eq 51. The second moment μ_2' about $x = 0$ of the distribution of the number of successes is:

$$\mu_2' = np[1 + p(n - 1)] \qquad \text{(Eq 63)}$$

From Eq 51:

$$\sigma^2 = \mu_2' - \bar{x}^2 = np[1 + p(n - 1)] - (np)^2 = npq \qquad q = 1 - p \qquad \text{(Eq 64)}$$

Thus, the standard deviation of the total successes in n trials is:

$$\sigma = \sqrt{npq} \qquad \text{(Eq 65)}$$

POISSON DISTRIBUTION

The Poisson distribution is the limit of the binomial distribution when the number of trials n is very large and the probability of success p is very small. For the binomial distribution, the mean number of successes is $\bar{x} = np = m$. As n moves to infinity and p to zero, the limiting form becomes:

$$\lim_{\substack{n\to\infty \\ p\to 0}} (np) = m = \text{a constant} \qquad \text{or} \qquad p = \frac{m}{n} \tag{Eq 66}$$

for the binomial distribution. Substituting $p = m/n$ in Eq 56 for the binomial distribution produces:

$$P(r) = n(n-1)(n-2)\cdots(n-r+1)\left(\frac{m}{n}\right)^r \frac{(1 - m/n)^{n-r}}{r!} \tag{Eq 67}$$

which may be written in the form:

$$P(r) = \frac{m^r}{r!}\left(1 - \frac{1}{n}\right)\left(1 - \frac{2}{n}\right)\cdots\left(1 - \frac{(r-1)}{n}\right)\left(1 - \frac{m}{n}\right)^n\left(1 - \frac{m}{n}\right)^{-r} \tag{Eq 68}$$

For any fixed r, as n tends to infinity:

$$\lim_{n\to\infty}\left(1 - \frac{1}{n}\right)\left(1 - \frac{2}{n}\right)\cdots\left(1 - \frac{(r-1)}{n}\right) = 1$$

$$\lim_{n\to\infty}\left(1 - \frac{m}{n}\right)^{-r} = 1$$

$$\lim_{n\to\infty}\left(1 - \frac{m}{n}\right)^{n} = e^{-m}$$

The limiting form of Eq 68 as n tends to infinity is:

$$P(r) = \frac{m^r e^{-m}}{r!} \tag{Eq 69}$$

which is known as the Poisson distribution. The mean $\bar{x}$ of the Poisson distribution may be computed by:

$$\bar{x} = \sum_{r=0}^{\infty} \frac{rm^r e^{-m}}{r!} = me^{-m}\sum_{r=0}^{\infty}\frac{m^{r-1}}{(r-1)!} = me^{-m}e^{m} = m \tag{Eq 70}$$

The standard deviation of the Poisson distribution is:

$$\sigma = \sqrt{m} = \sqrt{np} \tag{Eq 71}$$

NORMAL DISTRIBUTION

The probability density function of the normal or gaussian distribution is:

$$\phi(x) = \frac{1}{\sigma\sqrt{2\pi}}e^{-(x-\mu)^2/2\sigma^2} \tag{Eq 72}$$

where μ = mean, σ = standard deviation of the random variable X, and σ^2 = variance. Moments about $x = \mu$ are $\mu_1 = 0$, $\mu_2 = \sigma^2$, $\mu_3 = 0$, $\mu_4 = 3\sigma^4$. Moments about $x = 0$ are $\nu_1 = \mu$, $\nu_2 = \mu^2 + \sigma^2$, $\nu_3 = \mu(\mu^2 + 3\sigma^2)$, $\nu_4 = \mu^4 + 6\mu^2\sigma^2 + 3\sigma^4$. The probability function:

$$P(X = x) = \int_{-\infty}^{x} \phi(x)\, dx = F(x) \qquad \text{(Eq 73)}$$

is the cumulative normal distribution function.

To evaluate the integral of $\phi(x)$ between finite values of x, let:

$$I = \int_{x_1}^{x_2} \phi(x)\, dx = \frac{(2\pi)^{-1/2}}{\sigma} \int_{x_1}^{x_2} e^{-(x-\mu)^2/2\sigma^2}\, dx \qquad \text{(Eq 74)}$$

To simplify the integral, let:

$$v = \frac{x - \mu}{\sigma} \qquad dx = \sigma\, dv \qquad \text{(Eq 75)}$$

With this change, Eq 74 becomes:

$$I = (2\pi)^{-1/2} \int_{v_1}^{v_2} e^{-v^2/2}\, dv \qquad \text{(Eq 76)}$$

where

$$v_1 = \frac{x_1 - \mu}{\sigma} \qquad v_2 = \frac{x_2 - \mu}{\sigma}$$

The function $F(z)$ is given by:

$$F(z) = (2\pi)^{-1/2} \int_{-\infty}^{z} e^{-y^2/2}\, dy \qquad \text{(Eq 77)}$$

and the integral is given by:

$$I = F(v_2) - F(v_1) \qquad \text{(Eq 78)}$$

in terms of the function $F(z)$.

STANDARD DEVIATION OF THE MEAN

To compute the standard deviation of the means for M sets of N measurements, each with its own mean and standard deviation, the following notations may be used:

σ = standard deviation of the individual measurements
σ_m = standard deviation of the means of various samples
x_{si} = measurement i in the set s
$\bar{x}_s$ = mean of the set s
$\bar{X}$ = mean of all measurements
d_{si} = deviation of x_{si}, $x_{si} - \bar{X} = d_{si}$
$D_s = x_s - \bar{X}$ = deviation of mean $\bar{x}_s$

For N measurements in each of M sets, there will be a total of $n = MN$ measurements. For individual measurements the variance is:

$$\sigma^2 = \sum_{s=1}^{M} \sum_{i=1}^{N} \frac{d_{si}^2}{MN} \qquad \text{(Eq 79)}$$

and the variance of the means is:

$$\sigma_m{}^2 = \sum_{s=1}^{m} \frac{D_s{}^2}{M} \qquad \text{(Eq 80)}$$

The deviations D_s of the means can be expressed in terms of the deviations d_{si} of the individual observations:

$$D_s = \bar{x}_s - \bar{X} = \frac{1}{N} \sum_{i=1}^{N} x_{si} - \bar{X} \qquad \text{(Eq 81)}$$

Substituting the square of the expression:

$$d_{si} = x_{si} - \bar{X} \qquad \text{(Eq 82)}$$

into Eq 79 gives:

$$\sigma^2 = \sum_{s=1}^{M} \sum_{i=1}^{N} \frac{(x_{si} - \bar{X})^2}{MN} \qquad \text{(Eq 83)}$$

Substituting the square of Eq 81 into Eq 80 gives:

$$\sigma_m{}^2 = \frac{1}{M} \sum_{s=1}^{M} \left(\frac{1}{N} \sum_{i=1}^{N} x_{si} - \bar{X} \right)^2 \qquad \text{(Eq 84)}$$

which can be reduced to:

$$\sigma_m{}^2 = \sum_{s=1}^{M} \sum_{i=1}^{N} \frac{(x_{si} - \bar{X})^2}{MN^2} \qquad \text{(Eq 85)}$$

Thus, from Eq 83 and Eq 85:

$$\sigma_m{}^2 = \frac{\sigma^2}{N} \qquad \text{or} \qquad \sigma_m = \frac{\sigma}{\sqrt{N}} \qquad \text{(Eq 86)}$$

APPROXIMATION WITH LEAST SQUARES METHOD

In experimental work, a need often arises for a curve to represent a set of data points that may form a trend that is linear, quadratic, or of higher order. The least squares method of computing a curve minimizes the error in fitting the curve at the data points.

For example, assume a set of n data points (x_i, y_i) through which a straight line is to be drawn. Data points and the line to be fitted are shown in Fig. 2. The line may be expressed as:

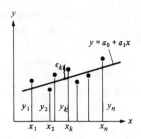

Figure 2

$$y = a_0 + a_1 x \qquad \text{(Eq 87)}$$

For the kth point, the ordinate is given as y_k. The ordinate at x_k is $a_0 + a_1 x_k$, and the difference between these values at the kth point is the error of fit:

$$\varepsilon_k = y_k - (a_0 + a_1 x_k) \qquad \text{(Eq 88)}$$

Summing the squares of all data point errors, the total error of fit becomes:

$$E = \sum_{k=1}^{n} \varepsilon_k^2 = \sum_{k=1}^{n} [y_k - (a_0 + a_1 x_k)]^2 \qquad \text{(Eq 89)}$$

with the errors squared to eliminate possible cancellation. To determine best fit, that is, to minimize total error, E is seen as a function of a_0 and a_1, and for E, the derivatives vanish. Therefore:

$$\frac{\partial E}{\partial a_0} = -2 \sum_{k=1}^{n} [y_k - (a_0 + a_1 x_k)] = 0 \qquad \text{(Eq 90)}$$

$$\frac{\partial E}{\partial a_1} = -2 \sum_{k=1}^{n} [y_k - (a_0 + a_1 x_k)] x_k = 0 \qquad \text{(Eq 91)}$$

If Eq 90 and 91 are divided by -2 and terms are rearranged, then:

$$n a_0 + a_1 \sum_{k=1}^{n} x_k = \sum_{k=1}^{n} y_k \qquad \text{(Eq 92)}$$

$$a_0 \sum_{k=1}^{n} x_k + a_1 \sum_{k=1}^{n} x_k^2 = \sum_{k=1}^{n} x_k y_k \qquad \text{(Eq 93)}$$

which are simultaneous algebraic equations for parameters a_0 and a_1. In matrix form, Eq 92 and 93 can be written:

$$[A](a) = (b) \qquad \text{(Eq 94)}$$

where

$$[A] = \begin{bmatrix} n & \sum_{k=1}^{n} x_k \\ \sum_{k=1}^{n} x_k & \sum_{k=1}^{n} x_k^2 \end{bmatrix}$$

$$(a) = \begin{pmatrix} a_0 \\ a_1 \end{pmatrix}$$

$$(b) = \begin{pmatrix} \sum_{k=1}^{n} y_k \\ \sum_{k=1}^{n} x_k y_k \end{pmatrix}$$

The solution to Eq 94 becomes:

$$(a) = [A]^{-1}(b) \qquad \text{(Eq 95)}$$

This method of least squares may be used to fit a polynomial of any order. To fit an mth-order curve to the n given data points (x_k, y_k), for example:

$$y = a_0 + a_1 x + a_2 x^2 + \cdots + a_m x^m \qquad \text{(Eq 96)}$$

the same derivation procedure is used. The general result becomes, from Eq 94:

$$[A] = \begin{bmatrix} n & \sum_{k=1}^{n} x_k & \sum_{k=1}^{n} x_k^2 \cdots & \sum_{k=1}^{n} x_k^m \\ \sum_{k=1}^{n} x_k & \sum_{k=1}^{n} x_k^2 & \sum_{k=1}^{n} x_k^3 \cdots & \sum_{k=1}^{n} x_k^{m+1} \\ \cdots\cdots\cdots\cdots\cdots\cdots\cdots\cdots\cdots\cdots \\ \sum_{k=1}^{n} x_k^m & \sum_{k=1}^{n} x_k^{m+1} & \sum_{k=1}^{n} x_k^{m+2} \cdots & \sum_{k=1}^{n} x_k^{2m} \end{bmatrix}$$

$$(a) = \begin{pmatrix} a_0 \\ a_1 \\ \vdots \\ a_m \end{pmatrix} \qquad (b) = \begin{pmatrix} \sum_{k=1}^{n} y_k \\ \sum_{k=1}^{n} y_k x_k \\ \vdots \\ \sum_{k=1}^{n} y_k x_k^m \end{pmatrix} \qquad \text{(Eq 97)}$$

Thus, to minimize error in fitting a curve to a set of data points, only the elements of the matrices $[A]$ and (b) need be computed. For example, the following data:

x	0.00	1.00	2.00	3.00	4.00
y	0.99	0.03	-1.02	-1.94	-3.04

follow a somewhat linear pattern. In determining the coefficients of $y = a_0 + a_1 x$ by the least squares method, it is found that $a_0 = 1.00999$ and $a_1 = -1.00299$. Applying the method to determine coefficients for $y = a_0 + a_1 x + a_2 x^2$, the result becomes:

$$a_0 = 0.98856 \qquad a_1 = -0.96013 \qquad a_2 = -0.01071$$

for the equation $y = a_0 + a_1 x + a_2 x^2 + a_3 x^3$ the result is:

$$a_0 = 0.99756 \qquad a_1 = -1.02463$$
$$a_2 = 0.03428 \qquad a_3 = -0.00749$$

MATRIX FORMULATION

For a set of n data points (x_i, y_i), where a determination of best fit is sought for the coefficients of:

$$y = a_0 + a_1 x + a_2 x^2 \tag{Eq 98}$$

the equation is written for every data point, that is:

$$y_1 = a_0 + a_1 x_1 + a_2 x_1^2$$
$$y_2 = a_0 + a_1 x_2 + a_2 x_2^2$$
$$\dots\dots\dots\dots\dots\dots$$
$$y_n = a_0 + a_1 x_n + a_2 x_n^2 \tag{Eq 99}$$

Defined in matrix notation, Eq 99 becomes:

$$[C] = \begin{bmatrix} 1 & 1 & 1 & \cdots & 1 \\ x_1 & x_2 & x_3 & \cdots & x_n \\ x_1^2 & x_2^2 & x_3^2 & \cdots & x_n^2 \end{bmatrix}$$

$$(y) = \begin{Bmatrix} y_1 \\ \vdots \\ y_n \end{Bmatrix} \qquad (a) = \begin{Bmatrix} a_0 \\ a_1 \\ a_2 \end{Bmatrix} \tag{Eq 100}$$

Written as a single matrix equation, Eq 99 becomes:

$$[C]'\{a\} = \{y\} \tag{Eq 101}$$

Reducing Eq 101 to a square system by premultiplying through by $[C]$ yields:

$$[C][C]'\{a\} = [C]\{y\} \tag{Eq 102}$$

By introducing in Eq 102 the notation, $[D] = [C][C]'$, the solution may be expressed as:

$$\{a\} = [D]^{-1}[C]\{y\} \tag{Eq 103}$$

15
Statics

FORCES AND EQUILIBRIUM

Mechanics. The branch of science that deals with forces and motion.

Statics. The branch of mechanics dealing with equilibrium of forces on bodies at rest or moving in a straight line at a uniform velocity.

Kinematics. The branch of mechanics dealing with motion of bodies without considering forces influencing their motion. Geometry and time are the only considerations.

Kinetics. The branch of mechanics that examines the effect of unbalanced external forces in changing the motion of bodies.

Weight. A force, related to mass by the formula $W = Mg$, where $W =$ weight, $M =$ mass, and $g =$ gravitational acceleration.

Force. That which represents the action of one body on another and tends to change the state of rest or motion of a body. It is specified by its magnitude, direction, and point of application.

Inertia. The property of a body that maintains it in the state of rest or motion until acted on by some force. Mass is a measure of inertia.

Reaction. The force exerted by a body that is equal and opposite to the force acting upon it.

Rigid Body. A body that cannot be deformed by the action of forces.

NEWTON'S LAWS—FOUNDATION OF RIGID BODY MECHANICS

First Law (Law of Equilibrium). A body will remain at rest or move in a straight line with a uniform velocity if there is no unbalanced force, **F**, acting on it. In addition, the body will remain at rest or rotate with a constant angular velocity if there is no unbalanced moment, **M**, acting on it:

$$\Sigma \mathbf{F} = 0 \qquad \Sigma \mathbf{M} = 0$$

Second Law. The linear acceleration of the center of mass of a body is proportional to the resultant force, **F**, acting on the body and is in the direction of that resultant force. The angular acceleration of a body is proportional to the resultant moment, **M**, about the center of mass and is in the direction of that resultant moment:

$$\Sigma \mathbf{F} = m\mathbf{a} \qquad \Sigma \mathbf{M} = I_G \alpha$$

where **a** is the linear and α the angular acceleration.

Third Law. For every force and moment acting on a body, the body exerts an equal, opposite, and collinear reactive force and moment.

Law of Gravitation. Two bodies are mutually attracted to one another with equal and opposite forces. The magnitude of this force is:

$$F = \frac{Gm_1 m_2}{r^2} \qquad \qquad \text{(Eq 1)}$$

where m_1, $m_2 \equiv$ masses of the two bodies
$r \equiv$ distance between the mass centers
$G \equiv$ constant of gravitation ($6.673 \times 10^{-11} m^3/\text{kg} \cdot \text{s}^2$)

Considering bodies on or near the earth, the force of attraction, the weight of the body, is expressed as:

$$W = mg \qquad \qquad \text{(Eq 2)}$$

where $g = \dfrac{MG}{r^2}$ (from Eq 1), $M \equiv$ the mass of the earth, and g is normally taken to be 32.174 ft/s^2 (9.81 m/s^2) at sea level. Statics uses the first and third laws and the law of gravitation.

RESULTANTS OF CONCURRENT FORCES

Concurrent Forces. Forces that pass through the same point in space.

Principle of Transmissibility. Forces on a rigid body may be applied at any point along the line of action of the force and still be equivalent to the original force.

System of Forces. Any number of forces taken collectively.

Equivalent System. Systems of forces are equivalent if they have the same net effect on the rigid body, for example, they have the same resultant force.

Resultant Force. A single force that is equivalent to or may replace a system of forces, sometimes called the resultant of the system.

Sense. One of the two directions along the line of action of the force.

Components of a Force. Two or more forces that are equivalent to a single force.

Resolution. The process of replacing a single force by a system of components. This single force is the resultant of its components.

RESULTANTS IN TWO DIMENSIONS

Given two concurrent forces, $\mathbf{F}_1$ and $\mathbf{F}_2$, the resultant is found using vector addition by applying the parallelogram or triangle laws. The sum is expressed as $\mathbf{R} = \mathbf{F}_1 + \mathbf{F}_2$. Using an appropriate scale, these laws may be used to determine the resultant graphically (see Fig. 1a and 2a).

Finding the resultant of $\mathbf{F}_1$ and a force having a sense opposite that of $\mathbf{F}_2$ but with the same magnitude requires the vector addition of $\mathbf{F}_1$ and $-\mathbf{F}_2$. This is equivalent to vector subtraction (see Fig. 1b and 2b):

$$\mathbf{R} = \mathbf{F}_1 + (-\mathbf{F}_2) = \mathbf{F}_1 - \mathbf{F}_2$$

To find the resultant for a system having more than two forces, successive vector additions must be performed by laying the force vectors end to end as shown in Fig. 3. The resultant is the vector, $\mathbf{R}$, that closes the diagram. The space diagram shows the orientation of the concurrent forces, where $\mathbf{R} = \mathbf{P} + \mathbf{Q} + \mathbf{S}$. This technique can be used as a graphical method or to visualize the vector addition process.

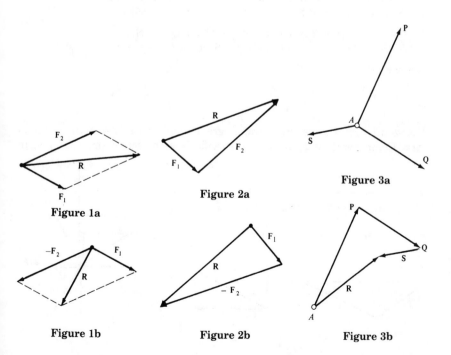

Figure 1a

Figure 2a

Figure 3a

Figure 1b

Figure 2b

Figure 3b

Algebraic computation of the magnitude of the resultant along with the computation of the angles shown in Fig. 4 may be performed using the law of cosines and the law of sines:

- Law of Cosines: $R^2 = F_1^2 + F_2^2 - 2F_1F_2 \cos \beta$

- Law of Sines: $\dfrac{R}{\sin \beta} = \dfrac{F_1}{\sin \alpha} = \dfrac{F_2}{\sin \theta}$

These laws may be applied to successive pairs of forces when dealing with resultants of more than two forces, as shown in Fig. 4.

The rectangular components of a force are found by using directions for the component forces that are perpendicular. The x and y directions are characterized by the $\mathbf{i}$ and $\mathbf{j}$ unit vectors (Fig. 5). Applying the parallelogram law gives $\mathbf{F}_1 = \mathbf{F}_x + \mathbf{F}_y$. In this case:

$$F_x = F_1 \cos \theta$$
$$F_y = F_1 \sin \theta$$
$$\theta = \tan^{-1} \frac{F_y}{F_x}$$
$$F_1 = \sqrt{F_x^2 + F_y^2}$$
$$\mathbf{F}_1 = F_x\mathbf{i} + F_y\mathbf{j}$$

Addition of the multiple forces in Fig. 6 is made easier by the use of rectangular components, as shown in Fig. 6. The resultant of the three forces is $\mathbf{R} = \mathbf{P} + \mathbf{Q} + \mathbf{S}$. Resolving each force into its rectangular components:

$$R_x\mathbf{i} + R_y\mathbf{j} = P_x\mathbf{i} + P_y\mathbf{j} + Q_x\mathbf{i} + Q_y\mathbf{j} + S_x\mathbf{i} + S_y\mathbf{j}$$
$$= (P_x + Q_x + S_x)\mathbf{i} + (P_y + Q_y + S_y)\mathbf{j}$$

from which

$$R_x = P_x + Q_x + S_x \qquad R_y = P_y + Q_y + S_y$$
or
$$= \Sigma F_x \qquad\qquad = \Sigma F_y$$

Resolution of a force into parallelogram components is sometimes necessary. Components of $\mathbf{F}$ along any specific lines of action (for example, in

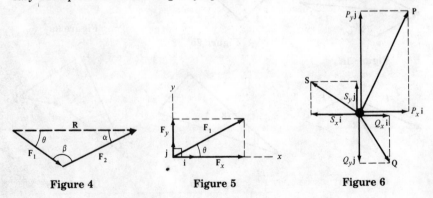

Figure 4   Figure 5   Figure 6

Fig. 7, $m_1 - m_2$ and $n_1 - n_2$ where θ and ϕ are given) may be found using the law of sines and the law of cosines to evaluate the magnitudes.

RESULTANTS IN THREE DIMENSIONS

It is difficult to visualize graphical methods of vector addition as well as the idea of parallelogram components in three dimensions. Therefore, only rectangular components are presented here (see Fig. 8). In the expressions:

$$F_x = F \cos \theta_x \qquad F = \sqrt{F_x^2 + F_y^2 + F_z^2}$$
$$F_y = F \cos \theta_y \qquad \mathbf{F} = F_x \mathbf{i} + F_y \mathbf{j} + F_z \mathbf{k}$$
$$F_z = F \cos \theta_z \qquad \mathbf{F} = F(\cos \theta_x \, \mathbf{i} + \cos \theta_y \, \mathbf{j} + \cos \theta_z \, \mathbf{k})$$

the unit vectors $\mathbf{i}$, $\mathbf{j}$, $\mathbf{k}$ are in the x-, y-, and z-directions, respectively. Introducing the direction cosines of $\mathbf{F}$, that is, $l = \cos \theta_x$, $m = \cos \theta_y$, and $n = \cos \theta_z$, the force may be written as:

$$\mathbf{F} = F(l\mathbf{i} + m\mathbf{j} + n\mathbf{k})$$

where $l^2 + m^2 + n^2 = 1$. The vector force can be viewed using the concept of the scalar (or dot) product; that is, the rectangular component is the scalar product of a force and the unit vector in the direction of the component desired. For example:

$$F_x = \mathbf{F} \cdot \mathbf{i} = F \cos \theta_x$$

which is the projection of $\mathbf{F}$ on the direction $\mathbf{i}$. More generally $F_n = \mathbf{F} \cdot \mathbf{n}$ where $\mathbf{n}$ is a general unit vector (magnitude of 1). If the vector in the $\mathbf{n}$-direction is desired, then $\mathbf{F}_n = (\mathbf{F} \cdot \mathbf{n})\mathbf{n}$. If $\mathbf{n}$ has direction cosines α, β, γ, it may be written in component form just as any other vector, $\mathbf{n} = \alpha\mathbf{i} + \beta\mathbf{j} + \gamma\mathbf{k}$, where its magnitude is unity. If $\mathbf{F}$ has direction cosines l, m, n with respect to the x-y-z axes then the $\mathbf{F}$ component in the $\mathbf{n}$-direction becomes:

$$F_n = \mathbf{F} \cdot \mathbf{n} = F(l\mathbf{i} + m\mathbf{j} + n\mathbf{k}) \cdot (\alpha\mathbf{i} + \beta\mathbf{j} + \gamma\mathbf{k})$$
$$= F(l\alpha + m\beta + n\gamma)$$

This result is based on the definitions of $\mathbf{i} \cdot \mathbf{i} = 1$ or $\mathbf{i} \cdot \mathbf{j} = 0$.

If θ is the angle between the force $\mathbf{F}$ and the direction of the unit vector $\mathbf{n}$, then from the definition of the dot product, $\mathbf{F} \cdot \mathbf{n} = F \cos \theta$. The angle between $\mathbf{F}$ and $\mathbf{n}$ is given by:

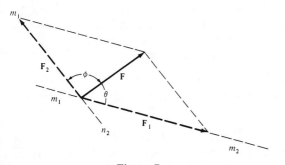

Figure 7

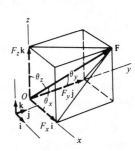

Figure 8

$$\theta = \cos^{-1} \frac{\mathbf{F} \cdot \mathbf{n}}{F}$$

To find three-dimensional resultants using rectangular components, given forces $\mathbf{F}_1$, $\mathbf{F}_2$, and $\mathbf{F}_3$, the following relationship is used:

$$\mathbf{R} = \mathbf{F}_1 + \mathbf{F}_2 + \mathbf{F}_3 = \Sigma \mathbf{F}$$
$$= R_x \mathbf{i} + R_y \mathbf{j} + R_z \mathbf{k}$$

where

$$R_x = \Sigma F_x = F_{1_x} + F_{2_x} + F_{3_x}$$
$$R_y = \Sigma F_y = F_{1_y} + F_{2_y} + F_{3_y}$$
$$R_z = \Sigma F_z = F_{1_z} + F_{2_z} + F_{3_z}$$

and

$$R = \sqrt{R_x^2 + R_y^2 + R_z^2}$$

Direction angles for the resultant, $\mathbf{R}$, are:

$$\theta_x = \cos^{-1} (\Sigma F_x/R) \qquad \theta_y = \cos^{-1} (\Sigma F_y/R) \qquad \theta_z = \cos^{-1} (\Sigma F_z/R)$$

The above analysis can be applied to other coordinate systems.

MOMENTS AND COUPLES

Moment of a Force (Torque) About a Point. The product of the magnitude of the force and the shortest distance (moment arm) from the point to the line of action of the force.

Couple. Two forces that are parallel, equal in magnitude and opposite in sense, that tend to produce only rotation.

TWO DIMENSIONAL MOMENTS AND COUPLES

Given a force $\mathbf{F}$ having a line of action a distance d from point O as in Fig. 9, the magnitude of the moment is given by $M_O = Fd$. The vector can be represented as $\mathbf{M}_O = (Fd)\mathbf{k}$. The moment is positive if the force tends to turn the body counterclockwise around the point O. Another way of expressing the vector form of the moment uses the vector, or cross, product. The moment is defined as $\mathbf{M}_O = \mathbf{r} \times \mathbf{F}$, which is rewritten as:

$$\mathbf{M}_O = (r_x \mathbf{i} + r_y \mathbf{j}) \times (F_x \mathbf{i} + F_y \mathbf{j})$$
$$= (r_x F_y - r_y F_x) \mathbf{k}$$

based upon the definition of the cross product. The magnitude is expressed as $M_O = r_x F_y - r_y F_x$.

Varignon's Theorem states that the moment of a force about a point is equal to the sum of the moments of its components about the point. Therefore, the system of Fig. 10 can be replaced by the one shown in Fig. 11 and yield the same scalar moment, $M_O = r_x F_y - r_y F_x$. This theorem can simplify the computation of moments for two-dimensional forces.

The couple is a pure moment produced by two equal, opposite, parallel forces. Given the two forces $\mathbf{F}$ and $-\mathbf{F}$, the magnitude of the couple is found by computing the moment about point O:

$$M = F(a + d) - Fa \qquad M = Fd \qquad \text{(Eq 3)}$$

where d is the shortest distance separating the line of action of the two forces (Fig. 12). The direction of the moment is perpendicular to the plane, its sense governed by the right-hand rule. The extended thumb follows the direction of the moment vector while the fingers rotate in the same direction that the couple would tend to rotate. Because the magnitude of Eq 3 does not depend on the location of point O, the couple or any moment applied to a rigid body is considered a free vector.

THREE-DIMENSIONAL MOMENTS AND COUPLES

The moment vector caused by force $\mathbf{F}$ acting about point O, as in Fig. 13, is perpendicular to the plane formed by the position vector $\mathbf{r}$ and the force, $\mathbf{F}$. The sense is again specified by the right-hand rule. The magnitude is given by $M_O = rF \sin \alpha$.

A moment is considered positive if the vector is directed in the positive direction along an axis. The direction of the moment vector is better defined by using the cross product definition of the moment of $\mathbf{F}$ about point O and computing the cross product using the determinant:

$$\mathbf{M}_O = \mathbf{r} \times \mathbf{F} = \begin{vmatrix} \mathbf{i} & \mathbf{j} & \mathbf{k} \\ r_x & r_y & r_z \\ F_x & F_y & F_z \end{vmatrix}$$

Expanding the determinant gives:

$$\begin{aligned} \mathbf{M}_O &= (r_y F_z - r_z F_y)\mathbf{i} + (r_z F_x - r_x F_z)\mathbf{j} + (r_x F_y - r_y F_x)\mathbf{k} \\ &= M_x \mathbf{i} + M_y \mathbf{j} + M_z \mathbf{k} \end{aligned} \qquad \text{(Eq 4)}$$

where M_x, M_y, and M_z are the scalar components of the $\mathbf{M}_O$ vector about the respective axes (Fig. 14). The magnitude of $\mathbf{M}_O$ becomes:

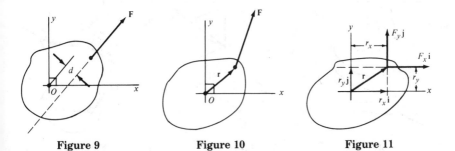

Figure 9   Figure 10   Figure 11

$$M_O = \sqrt{M_x^2 + M_y^2 + M_z^2}$$

Equation 4 automatically gives the proper sense of each component in a right-hand coordinate system.

The magnitude of a moment in a specific direction or along a specific axis (such as the λ axis shown in Fig. 15) can be determined by finding the moment $\mathbf{M}_O$ and obtaining its projection along the λ-direction using the dot product, $M_\lambda = (\mathbf{r} \times \mathbf{F}) \cdot \mathbf{n}$, where $\mathbf{n}$ is a unit vector in the direction λ. This unit vector is defined by using its direction cosines of α, β, and γ so that $\mathbf{n} = \alpha\mathbf{i} + \beta\mathbf{j} + \gamma\mathbf{k}$. The actual magnitude, M_λ, is given by the determinant:

$$|\mathbf{M}_\lambda| = M_\lambda = \begin{vmatrix} r_x & r_y & r_z \\ F_x & F_y & F_z \\ \alpha & \beta & \gamma \end{vmatrix}$$

Expanding this gives the result:

$$M_\lambda = (r_y F_z - r_z F_y)\alpha + (r_z F_x - r_x F_z)\beta + (r_x F_y - r_y F_x)\gamma$$

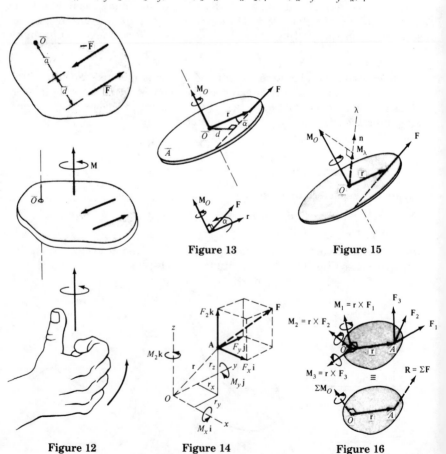

Figure 13

Figure 15

Figure 12

Figure 14

Figure 16

This magnitude can be multiplied by the unit vector to obtain the vector expression for $\mathbf{M}_\lambda$:

$$\mathbf{M}_\lambda = M_\lambda \mathbf{n} = ((\mathbf{r} \times \mathbf{F}) \cdot \mathbf{n})\mathbf{n}$$

The process is simplified if one of the three principal axes is parallel to the direction desired. For example, if the z axis is positioned parallel to the λ-direction, then M_z is the desired moment.

Varignon's theorem also applies to the three-dimensional problem so the sum of the moments of all the forces in a concurrent force system is equal to the moment of the resultant of the forces about the same point (Fig. 16). This means that if $\mathbf{R} = \mathbf{F}_1 + \mathbf{F}_2 + \mathbf{F}_3 + \ldots$, then:

$$\mathbf{r} \times \mathbf{F}_1 + \mathbf{r} \times \mathbf{F}_2 + \mathbf{r} \times \mathbf{F}_3 + \cdots = \mathbf{r} \times (\mathbf{F}_1 + \mathbf{F}_2 + \mathbf{F}_3 + \ldots) = \mathbf{r} \times \Sigma \mathbf{F}$$

or $\quad \Sigma \mathbf{M}_O = \mathbf{r} \times \mathbf{R}$

Conversely, the moment of a force about a point is the same as the sum of the moments of the components of the force about the same point.

Couples are treated in three dimensions in the same manner as for two dimensions (Fig. 17). The vector expression for the moment of the couple is determined by taking the sum of the moments of $\mathbf{F}$ and $-\mathbf{F}$ about point O which gives:

$$\mathbf{M} = \mathbf{r}_A \times \mathbf{F} + \mathbf{r}_B \times (-\mathbf{F}) = (\mathbf{r}_A - \mathbf{r}_B) \times \mathbf{F}$$

Since $\mathbf{r}_A - \mathbf{r}_B = \mathbf{r}$, all reference to the point O disappears. The moment of the couple becomes $\mathbf{M} = \mathbf{r} \times \mathbf{F}$. Hence $\mathbf{M}$, as stated before, is a free vector.

ADDITION OF MOMENTS

The same concepts of vector addition used with forces are used with moments. Addition of pure moments (couples) gives a resultant that is a pure moment.

RESULTANTS OF FORCE/MOMENT SYSTEMS

Force/Moment Systems. In practical terms, rigid bodies must be viewed as possibly having both nonconcurrent forces and pure moments applied to them. This is considered a force/moment system.

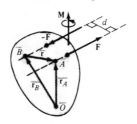

Figure 17

Resultant. The simplest system that is equivalent to and may replace a system of several nonconcurrent forces and couples is a single force and couple. In some instances, it is advantageous to reduce the resultant to a single force or possibly a single couple.

Coplanar Force System. Force vectors comprising the system lie in one plane and moment vectors are perpendicular to this plane (two dimensional system).

Collinear Forces. Forces that lie along the same line of action.

Parallel Force System. System composed of forces that have parallel lines of action. May be two- or three-dimensional system.

REPLACEMENT OF A FORCE BY AN EQUIVALENT FORCE/COUPLE COMBINATION

To obtain the resultant for a system that may contain several nonconcurrent forces in combination with several couples, a single force on a rigid body may be moved to a new point of contact by replacing it with the appropriate force/couple combination. If each force is moved to the same point, they may be added to obtain the resultant.

For two dimensions (coplanar forces), this replacement is shown as follows in moving force $\mathbf{F}$ to the point of attachment at B (Fig. 18). Given a force at point A, two equal and opposite forces are placed at B. This system in Fig. 18(b) is equivalent to that in Fig. 18(a). The force at A and the $-\mathbf{F}$ force at B form a couple of magnitude Fd. The final equivalent system is represented in Fig. 18(c). Force $\mathbf{F}$ at A was replaced with an equal force at B along with a couple having the magnitude of the moment of $\mathbf{F}$ about B.

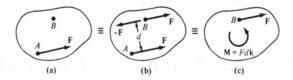

(a)   (b)   (c)

Figure 18

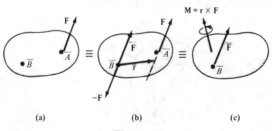

(a)   (b)   (c)

Figure 19

For three dimensions, the procedure is the same. Again applying the two opposing forces at B (Fig. 19), it is seen that the equivalent system in Fig. 19(c) is comprised of the force $\mathbf{F}$ at B and the couple $\mathbf{M} = \mathbf{r} \times \mathbf{F}$. This couple is the same as the moment of $\mathbf{F}$ at its original point of attachment about point B.

For two dimensions, the process of finding the resultant force/couple combination can be shown using the three forces, $(\mathbf{F}_1, \mathbf{F}_2, \mathbf{F}_3)$ and the couple $\mathbf{C}$ acting on the body (Fig. 20). Using the method described above, $\mathbf{F}_1$, $\mathbf{F}_2$, and $\mathbf{F}_3$ may be moved to point O accompanied by couples that have magnitudes equal to the moments of the forces about the point.

This new system is shown in Fig. 21. Since the couple $\mathbf{C}$ is a free vector, it may also be moved to point O. All the couples lie along the line of action perpendicular to the plane of the paper. The resultant force (Fig. 22) is found as before:

$$\mathbf{R} = \mathbf{F}_1 + \mathbf{F}_2 + \mathbf{F}_3 + \cdots = \Sigma \mathbf{F}$$

$$R_x = \Sigma F_x \qquad R_y = \Sigma F_y \qquad R = \sqrt{(\Sigma F_x)^2 + (\Sigma F_y)^2}$$

$$\theta = \tan^{-1}\frac{R_y}{R_x} = \tan^{-1}\frac{\Sigma F_y}{\Sigma F_x}$$

and the magnitude of the resultant moment is found by:

$$M_R = \Sigma M_O = -F_1 d_1 + F_2 d_2 - F_3 d_3 + C$$

It is arbitrarily assumed that the resultant moment in Fig. 22 is clockwise.

If $\mathbf{R}$ is moved to a parallel line of action an appropriate distance from point O, a system of a single resultant force without the accompanying moment can be found. This is shown in Fig. 23. Opposing forces are placed at point P. The original $\mathbf{R}$ at point O along with $-\mathbf{R}$ form a couple that opposes M_R. If $Rd = M_R$, then the couples cancel and the equivalent resultant system becomes that shown in Fig. 23.

For three dimensions (Fig. 24), the methods are the same except that no attempt is usually made to reduce the resultant system to a single force. Vector operations must normally be used instead of dealing with scalar magnitudes of the moments only. Assuming three forces are applied to the body, the moments of these about point O are found as shown in Fig. 24(b), where

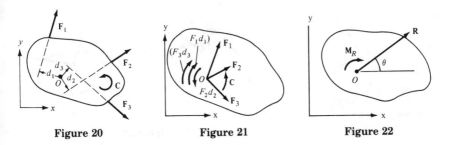

Figure 20   Figure 21   Figure 22

$$M_1 = r_1 \times F_1 \quad M_2 = r_2 \times F_2 \quad M_3 = r_3 \times F_3$$

The resultant force R, having a magnitude of R, and the resultant moment M_R with a magnitude M_R are described in the equations:

$$R_x = \Sigma F_x \quad R_y = \Sigma F_y \quad R_z = \Sigma F_z$$
$$R = \sqrt{(\Sigma F_x)^2 + (\Sigma F_y)^2 + (\Sigma F_z)^2}$$
$$M_{Rx} = \Sigma(r \times F)_x \quad M_{Ry} = \Sigma(r \times F)_y \quad M_{Rz} = \Sigma(r \times F)_z$$
$$M_R = \sqrt{M_{Rx}^2 + M_{Ry}^2 + M_{Rz}^2}$$

and

$$R = F_1 + F_2 + F_3 = \Sigma F$$
$$M_R = M_1 + M_2 + M_3 = \Sigma(r \times F)$$

EQUILIBRIUM

The study of equilibrium combines the concepts of resultants of force/moment systems with Newton's first law. A rigid body is in equilibrium when the net external forces and moments, that is, the resultant force and moment on the body equal zero.

GENERAL CONDITIONS FOR EQUILIBRIUM

As shown in the discussion on resultants, for a three-dimensional system, three components of a resultant force and three components of a resultant moment can be described. The following conditions must then apply for a general three-dimensional body to be in equilibrium:

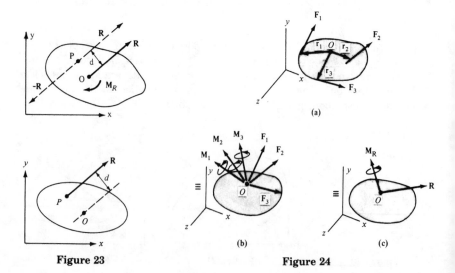

Figure 23

Figure 24

$$\left.\begin{array}{l} \Sigma F_x = R_x = 0 \\ \Sigma F_y = R_y = 0 \\ \Sigma F_z = R_z = 0 \end{array}\right\} \quad \Sigma \mathbf{F} = \mathbf{R} = 0$$

$$\left.\begin{array}{l} \Sigma M_x = M_{Rx} = 0 \\ \Sigma M_y = M_{Ry} = 0 \\ \Sigma M_z = M_{Rz} = 0 \end{array}\right\} \quad \Sigma \mathbf{M} = \mathbf{M}_R = 0$$

If a given system of forces is applied to a body, a maximum of six unknown quantities, such as forces or directions, can be found because there are six independent equations given. Because the net moment at any point on the body is zero, moment equations may be set up around other points or axes on the body and used instead of some or all of the force equations. If more than six forces on the body are required, however, the system cannot be analyzed using the static equations; that is, the system is statically indeterminate.

Different conditions and hence different numbers of available equations may apply in special cases such as a planar system or a parallel-force system. A list of some of these and the equilibrium conditions that apply are given in Table 1 for arbitrary points O, a, b, c shown in Fig. 25.

If a problem is being analyzed graphically, the use of a vector diagram of the forces will show the diagram closed ($\mathbf{R} = 0$) when the body is in equilibrium. The following special conditions may be applied to any coordinate system:

- If two forces are in equilibrium, they must be collinear
- If three forces are in equilibrium, they must be concurrent. Likewise, if four forces are in equilibrium, the resultant of two is concurrent with the other two

THE FREE-BODY DIAGRAM

This type of diagram isolates the body in question and shows all the external forces that act upon the body. Figure 26 shows a structure and the free-body diagram that results when all the external forces are shown. The types of forces included are:

- Applied loads L_1, L_2, and L_3
- The body forces, such as W, caused by gravity, magnetic, or electric fields (remote forces)

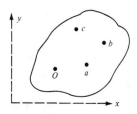

Figure 25

Table 1 Equilibrium systems and conditions

Force/moment system	No. of conditions or available equations	Conditions
Two dimensions (planar)		
Collinear	1	$\Sigma F = 0$
Concurrent at point O	2	$\Sigma F_x = 0$, $\Sigma F_y = 0$; $\Sigma F_x = 0$, $\Sigma M_a = 0$, if x direction not perpendicular to aO; $\Sigma M_a = 0$, $\Sigma M_b = 0$, if aOb not a straight line
Parallel	2	$\Sigma F = 0$, $\Sigma M = 0$; $\Sigma M_a = 0$, $\Sigma M_b = 0$, if line ab not parallel to forces
Nonparallel non-concurrent (general two-dimensional condition)	3	$\Sigma F_x = 0$, $\Sigma F_y = 0$, $\Sigma M = 0$; $\Sigma F_x = 0$, $\Sigma M_a = 0$, $\Sigma M_b = 0$, if x direction not perpendicular to ab; $\Sigma M_a = 0$, $\Sigma M_b = 0$, $\Sigma M_c = 0$, if abc not a straight line
Three dimensions (nonplanar)		
Concurrent at point O	3	$\Sigma F_x = 0$, $\Sigma F_y = 0$, $\Sigma F_z = 0$. Combinations of moment and force equations can be found, but are not common
Parallel	3	$\Sigma F_z = 0$, $\Sigma M_x = 0$, $\Sigma M_y = 0$, forces parallel to z axis. Other combinations possible but not common

- The reactions (such as forces at A and G), which are constraining forces and are exerted at points of support or attachment to other rigid bodies

Such forces as that resulting from the action of member DE on member $ACEG$ are internal forces and do not appear in the diagram. Since reactions must necessarily be included on free-body diagrams, the forces at reaction points must be properly interpreted. Some common modes of restraint and the forces that are associated with them are given in Tables 2 and 3.

ADEQUACY OF CONSTRAINT

Inspection of the system or the free-body diagram will normally indicate whether a rigid body is (a) improperly constrained by the reactions (inadequately supported); (b) adequately constrained; (c) redundantly constrained (having more reactions than needed, thus, statically indeterminate). A method for determining the adequacy of constraint for a rigid body when simple inspection is not sufficient is now described.

Three-Dimensional Body. There are six degrees of freedom for the general rigid body shown in Fig. 27, where n denotes a point where a restraint is attached, $\mathbf{S}_n$ is a unit vector representing that restraint which equals $S_{nx}\mathbf{i} + S_{ny}\mathbf{j} + S_{nz}\mathbf{k}$ and $\mathbf{r}_n = r_{nx}\mathbf{i} + r_{ny}\mathbf{j} + r_{nz}\mathbf{k}$ describes a position vector. For the rigid body to be completely fixed (adequately fixed), the determinant

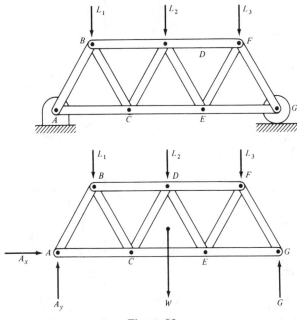

Figure 26

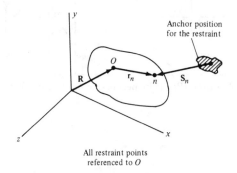

All restraint points
referenced to O

Figure 27

Table 2   Two-dimensional systems

Support or connection				Reaction	No. of unknowns
Rollers	Rocker	Smooth surface		Force with known line of action (Normal to surface)	1
Short cable		Short link		Force with known line of action	1
Collar on smooth rod		Pin in smooth slot		90° Force with known line of action	1
Smooth pin or hinge		Rough surface		or α Force of unknown direction	2
		Fixed support (Built-in or welded)		or α Force and couple	3

Source: Beer and Johnston (Ref 1) by permission of the publisher

Table 3 Three-dimensional systems

System	Reaction	No. of unknowns
Ball Smooth surface	F	1 Force with known line of action
Cable	F	1 Force with known line of action, force in direction of cable tension—applies to 2-dim. also)
Rough surface Ball and socket	F_y F_z F_x	3 Three force components
Roller on rough surface Wheel on rail	F_y F_z	2 Two force components
Fixed support	M_y F_y M_z F_z F_x M_x	6 Three force components and three couples
Universal joint	F_y M_x F_x F_z	4 Three force components and one couple
Hinge and bearing supporting radial load only	(M_y) F_y F_z (M_z)	4 Two force components and two couples
Pin and bracket Hinge and bearing supporting axial thrust and radial load	(M_y) F_y $\mathbf{F}_x$ F_z (M_z)	5 Three force components and two couples

Source: Beer and Johnston (Ref 1) by permission of the publisher

$$\begin{bmatrix} S_{1x} & S_{1y} & S_{1z} & (r_{1y}S_{1z} - r_{1z}S_{1y}) & (r_{1z}S_{1x} - r_{1x}S_{1z}) & (r_{1x}S_{1y} - r_{1y}S_{1x}) \\ S_{2x} & S_{2y} & S_{2z} & (r_{2y}S_{2z} - r_{2z}S_{2y}) & (r_{2z}S_{2x} - r_{2x}S_{2z}) & (r_{2x}S_{2y} - r_{2y}S_{2x}) \\ \vdots & \vdots & \vdots & \vdots & \vdots & \vdots \\ S_{nx} & S_{ny} & S_{nz} & (r_{ny}S_{nz} - r_{nz}S_{ny}) & (r_{nz}S_{nx} - r_{nx}S_{nz}) & (r_{nx}S_{ny} - r_{ny}S_{nx}) \end{bmatrix}$$

must not vanish (n = 1, 2, 3, 4, 5, 6). If the determinant vanishes, the rigid body is not adequately restrained. This analysis assumes that there are six restraints on the body. If the determinant does not vanish and an additional restraint is added, that reaction is redundant and the body would be statically indeterminate.

Two-Dimensional Body. For adequate constraints, the following determinant must not vanish:

$$\begin{bmatrix} S_{1x} & S_{1y} & (r_{1x}S_{1y} - r_{1y}S_{1x}) \\ S_{2x} & S_{2y} & (r_{2x}S_{2y} - r_{2y}S_{2x}) \\ S_{3x} & S_{3y} & (r_{3x}S_{3y} - r_{3y}S_{3x}) \end{bmatrix}$$

STRUCTURES

TRUSSES

A truss is a two- or three-dimensional framework used to carry loads. The following assumptions are used in the statical analysis of trusses:

• Members are connected by pinned joints (two-dimensional systems) or ball-and-socket joints (three-dimensional systems). The joints support forces but no moments
• Members have forces only acting at the joints and are thus two-force members that support only tension or compression. Each force acts on a line connecting the two joints on the member
• External loads are applied only at the joints. If a member has weight that is not negligible, it is taken to have one half the weight applied at each joint on the member
• Plane trusses are built upon a system of rigid triangular units (Fig. 28). Space trusses (three-dimensional) have the tetrahedron as the basic unit

Use of these assumptions gives reasonably good results away from the ends of a member as long as the axes of the members pass through a single point, such as point A of Fig. 28(a). There are two basic methods with which to analyze the forces in the members of a truss using the methods of statics (law of equilibrium).

Method of Joints. The truss is analyzed as a total rigid body to determine reactions caused by the external applied forces, that is, the loads and body forces. The load P in Fig. 29 is used along with the appropriate equilibrium conditions for a two-dimensional system to arrive at the values of the three reactions. For a space truss, six external reactions must be considered.

Equilibrium of each pinned joint in the structure is analyzed. Each joint is subject to the standard equilibrium condition for a two-dimensional concurrent force system (Fig. 30). For the space truss, the three-dimensional requirements are applied. Using the equations developed from the free-body diagrams in Fig. 29 and 30, the unknown reactions and forces in the members may be found. The opposing directions of forces at the pins (joints) and those on the members are dictated by Newton's third law.

Each member is analyzed to determine tension or compression. If a tension state is assumed on a member and if solution of the system of equations results in a negative force, then the member is in compression. Thus, the algebraic sign of the result determines the sense of the force.

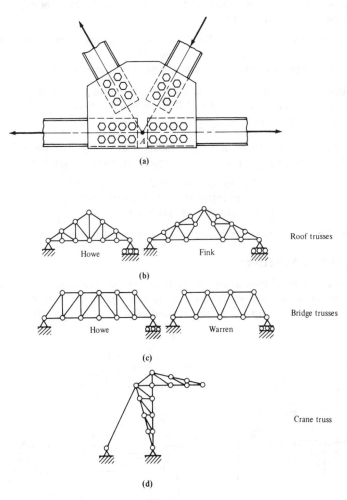

(a)

Howe   Fink   Roof trusses

(b)

Howe   Warren   Bridge trusses

(c)

Crane truss

(d)

Figure 28

Method of Sections. The entire truss is analyzed as a rigid body to get reactions, as done above with method of joints. The truss is cut so that the cut members provide the new external forces that will keep each section of the truss in equilibrium. Three members of a plane truss and six in a space truss can be cut, and two- or three-dimensional equilibrium equations for each rigid section can be used to analyze the forces in the cut members. An example of establishing a section through three members is shown in Fig. 31.

Static Determinancy of a Truss. The number of independent equations available for the solution of a plane truss is determined as follows: If m represents the number of members in the truss and each member represents one unknown force, j represents the number of joints, and 3 represents the number of external reactions that can be handled, then $2j$ is the number of equilibrium equations available and $m + 3$ equals the number of unknowns that must be determined. Thus:

$$m + 3 \begin{cases} >2j \text{ indicates a statically indeterminate truss (redundant members)} \\ =2j \text{ indicates a statically determinate truss} \\ <2j \text{ indicates an unstable truss (deficient number of internal members)} \end{cases}$$

The above expression deals with whether the proper number of internal members is present. There may still be problems with redundancy or incomplete fixity in reactions.

For space trusses, there are $3j$ equations available, ($\Sigma F_x = 0$, $\Sigma F_y = 0$, and $\Sigma F_z = 0$ for each joint) and $m + 6$ unknown forces. Therefore:

$$m + 6 \begin{cases} >3j \text{ indicates statically indeterminate truss} \\ =3j \text{ indicates statically determinate truss} \\ <3j \text{ indicates unstable truss} \end{cases}$$

Six reactions can be dealt with statically in three dimensions.

FRAMES/MACHINES

Frames and machines are general static structures that are not subject to the truss assumptions. To determine the reactions, a frame must be analyzed as a total rigid body if the total structure is rigid when the reac-

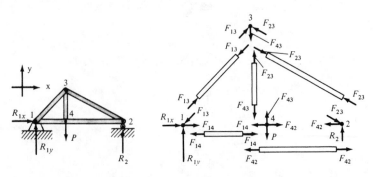

Figure 29   **Figure 30**

tions are removed. Then, each member of the frame is analyzed by using a free-body diagram for each. The members are not necessarily two-force members; that is, they may have weight acting at the cener of mass, and multiple forces and moments may also be applied. To solve unkown forces using the statical equations, the frame as a whole and each member are subject only to general equilibrium conditions.

For example, the frame shown in Fig. 32 supports a load of 200 lb. If joints A, B, C, and D are all pinned, the horizontal and vertical components of the force acting at each of these joints are found as follows.

A free-body diagram of the entire rigid frame is first constructed (Fig. 33a). Applying the three equilibrium equations gives:

$$\Sigma M_A = 0; \ -200 \text{ lb } (5 \text{ ft}) - 100 \text{ lb-ft} + F_E \ (7 \text{ ft}) = 0, F_E = 157 \text{ lb}$$
$$\Sigma F_x = 0; \ A_x = 0$$
$$\Sigma F_y = 0; \ A_y - 200 \text{ lb} + 157 \text{ lb} = 0, A_y = 43 \text{ lb}$$

Now, using these values for the reactions at A and E, a free-body diagram for each member of the frame is drawn (Fig. 33b). Because these are all multi-force members, there are two unknown components of force acting at each of the joints B, C, and D. According to Newton's third law, these components act with equal magnitude and opposite direction on adjacent free-body diagrams, as shown.

The 100 lb-ft couple is a free vector and can act at any point on the free-body diagram of member ABC, but this couple cannot act on the members CDE or BD. These have now been separated from member ABC, which is now a separate rigid body from the other members. Applying the equations of equilibrium to body ABC gives:

$$\Sigma M_B = 0; \ -43 \text{ lb } (1 \text{ ft}) - 100 \text{ lb-ft} + C_x \ (8 \text{ ft}) + C_y \ (6 \text{ ft}) = 0$$
$$\Sigma F_x = 0; \ -B_x - C_x = 0$$
$$\Sigma F_y = 0; \ 43 \text{ lb} + B_y + C_y = 0$$

and for member BD:

$$\Sigma M_B = 0; \ -200 \text{ lb } (4 \text{ ft}) + D_y \ (6 \text{ ft}) = 0$$
$$\Sigma F_x = 0; \ B_x - D_x = 0$$
$$\Sigma F_y = 0; \ D_y - 200 \text{ lb} - B_y = 0$$

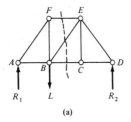
(a)

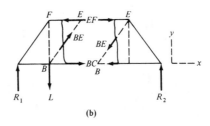
(b)

Figure 31

There are six independent equations and six unknowns. Due to the nature of the equations, the final solution comes rather easily:

$$B_x = 0.0 \qquad C_x = 0.0 \qquad D_x = 0.0$$
$$B_y = -66.7 \text{ lb} \qquad C_y = 23.7 \text{ lb} \qquad D_y = 133.3 \text{ lb}$$

Three additional equations may be set up using the member CDE. These are not new, independent equations, but could have been used instead of those obtained from the total frame. They may also be used to verify results.

DISTRIBUTED FORCE SYSTEMS

CENTROIDS AND CENTERS OF MASS

The center of mass of a body represents the point at which the mass is considered concentrated. It may be found by suspending a body at different points (Fig. 34). The line of force in the string passes through the center of mass or center of gravity. This assumes that forces exerted by gravity at all parts of the body are parallel.

To determine the location of the center of gravity mathematically, Varignon's theorem is applied to the parallel system of gravitational forces

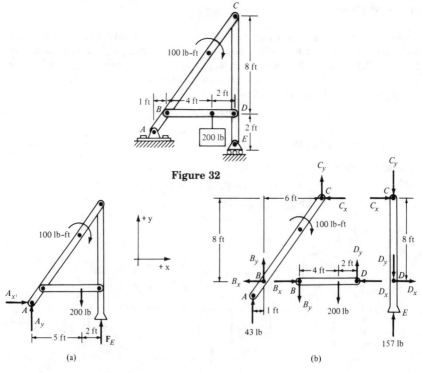

Figure 32

(a)   (b)

Figure 33

to locate its resultant. The moment of the resultant gravitational force W about any axis is equal to the sum of the moments about the axis of the gravitational forces dW acting on all particles (Fig. 34). The particles are considered as infinitesimal elements of the body. The resultant of gravitational forces acting on all elements is given by the sum $W = \int dW$, the weight of the body. About the y-axis, for example, the moment of the elemental weight is $x\, dW$, and the sum of these moments is $\int x\, dW$. This sum of moments equals $W\bar{x}$, the moment of the sum. Substituting $W = mg$ and $dW = g\, dm$, the moment expressions for two of the axes become:

$$\bar{x} = \frac{\displaystyle\int x\, dm}{m} \qquad \bar{y} = \frac{\displaystyle\int y\, dm}{m} \qquad\qquad\qquad \text{(Eq 5)}$$

The numerators represent the sum of the moments. The product of m and the corresponding coordinate of G represents the moment of the sum. If the body and axes are reoriented so the z-axis is horizontal, the third equation results:

$$\bar{z} = \frac{\displaystyle\int z\, dm}{m} \qquad\qquad\qquad\qquad\qquad \text{(Eq 6)}$$

To use these equations, expressions for the differential moment, xdm, ydm, and zdm, must be found and the integration performed.

Equations 5 and 6 may be expressed in vector form using Fig. 35, where the differential mass and the location of G are determined by their respective position vectors $\mathbf{r} = \mathbf{i}x + \mathbf{j}y + \mathbf{k}z$ and $\bar{\mathbf{r}} = \mathbf{i}\bar{x} + \mathbf{j}\bar{y} + \mathbf{k}\bar{z}$. Thus, Eq 5 and 6 are the components of the vector equation:

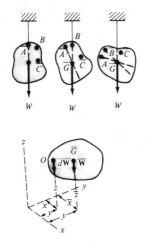

Figure 34

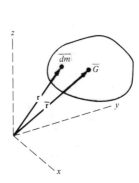

Figure 35

$$\overline{\mathbf{r}} = \frac{\int \mathbf{r}\, dm}{m}$$

If the density of a body is denoted by ρ, the mass of a differential element of volume dV becomes $dm = \rho\, dV$. If ρ is not constant throughout the body, but can be expressed as a function of the coordinates of the body, the above expressions are the written as:

$$\overline{x} = \frac{\int x\rho\, dV}{\int \rho\, dV} \qquad \overline{y} = \frac{\int y\rho\, dV}{\int \rho\, dV} \qquad \overline{z} = \frac{\int z\rho\, dV}{\int \rho\, dV}$$

If a homogeneous body (density constant in space) is symmetrical with respect to a point, line, or plane, its center of gravity is located at the point, in the line, or in the plane.

Centroids of Volumes. For a body of volume V and density ρ, the differential element has a mass $dm = \rho\, dV$. The density ρ cancels if it is homogeneous, that is, constant over the entire volume. The coordinates of the center of mass then become the coordinates of the centroid C:

$$\overline{x} = \frac{\int x\, dV}{V} \qquad \overline{y} = \frac{\int y\, dV}{V} \qquad \overline{z} = \frac{\int z\, dV}{V}$$

The centroid is the geometric center of the object.

Centroids of Areas (Planar Figures). When a body with density ρ has a small but constant thickness t, the body can be viewed as a surface area A (Fig. 36). The mass of an element is $dm = \rho t\, dA$. If ρ and t are constant over the area, the coordinates of the center of mass become the coordinates of the centroid C:

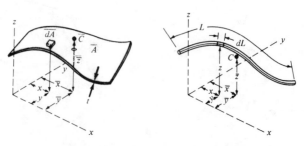

Figure 36   Figure 37

$$\bar{x} = \frac{\int x\, dA}{A} \qquad \bar{y} = \frac{\int y\, dA}{A} \qquad \bar{z} = \frac{\int z\, dA}{A}$$

The numerators above are the first moments of area. If the surface area is curved, all three coordinates are involved. For such a surface, the centroid C generally will not lie on the surface. If the area is a flat surface in the x-y plane, for example, only the coordinates in that plane will be considered unknown.

Centroids of Lines. For a slender rod or wire of length L, cross-sectional area A, and density ρ (Fig. 37), the body can be seen as a line segment where $dm = \rho A\, dL$. If ρ and A are constant, the coordinates of the center of mass are coordinates of the centroid C and:

$$\bar{x} = \frac{\int x\, dL}{L} \qquad \bar{y} = \frac{\int y\, dL}{L} \qquad \bar{z} = \frac{\int z\, dL}{L}$$

Generally, the centroid C does not lie on the line. Only two coordinates will require calculation if the rod lies in a single plane, such as the x-y plane.

Integration Method of Determining Centroids. To apply integration in determining centroids, expressions for the mass, volume, area, or length of the differential element must be found as well as the moment of that element about the necessary axes. Some general expressions for these differential elements are as follows:

$$dm = \rho\, dV$$
$$dV = dxdydz \quad \text{(requires triple integration)}$$
$$= \text{(area of element)}\, dx$$
$$= \text{(area of element)}\, dy$$
$$= \text{(length of element)}\, dxdy \quad \text{(requires double integration)}$$

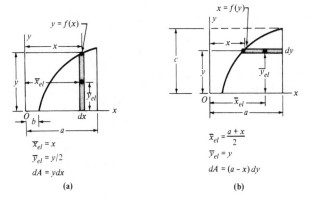

$$\bar{x}_{el} = x$$
$$\bar{y}_{el} = y/2$$
$$dA = y\,dx$$

(a)

$$\bar{x}_{el} = \frac{a+x}{2}$$
$$\bar{y}_{el} = y$$
$$dA = (a-x)\,dy$$

(b)

Figure 38

$$dA = dxdy \quad \text{(requires double integration)}$$
$$= \text{(length of element)}\, dx$$
$$= \text{(length of element)}\, dy$$
$$dL = \sqrt{1 + (dy/dx)^2}\, dx$$
$$= \sqrt{1 + (dx/dy)^2}\, dy$$
$$= \sqrt{r^2 + (dr/d\theta)^2}\, d\theta \quad \text{(polar coordinates)}$$

Although most of the above expressions deal with rectangular coordinates, similar expressions apply to other coordinate systems.

The integrand can be interpreted as follows:

$\int y\, dm \rightarrow y\, dm$ is the first moment of the mass dm about an axis from which y locates the center of mass of dm

$\int y\, dA \rightarrow y\, dA$ is the first moment of the area dA about an axis from which the centroid of the area dA is noted as y

For example, to set up the integration to compute centroids, where $\bar{y}_{el}$, $\bar{x}_{el}$, and $\bar{z}_{el}$ indicate centroids of the differential elements in Fig. 38, 39, and 40, the following relationships are employed. From Fig. 38(a):

$$\bar{y}A = \int \bar{y}_{el}\, dA = \int \frac{y}{2} y\, dx = \frac{1}{2} \int_b^a (f(x))^2\, dx$$

$$\bar{x}A = \int \bar{x}_{el}\, dA = \int x\, ydx = \int_b^a xf(x)\, dx$$

From Fig. 38(b):

$$\bar{y}A = \int \bar{y}_{el}\, dA = \int y(a - x)\, dy = \int_0^c y(a - f(y))\, dy$$

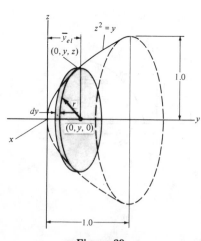

Figure 39

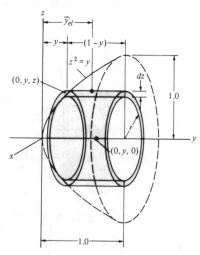

Figure 40

$$\bar{x}A = \int x_{el}\,dA = \int \left(\frac{a+x}{2}\right)(a-x)\,dy = \frac{1}{2}\int_a^c (a+f(y))(a-f(y))\,dy$$

For the plate element shown in Fig. 39:

$$\bar{y}_{el} = y$$
$$A = \pi r^2 \text{ (area of plate)}$$
$$dV = A\,dy = \pi r^2\,dy$$
$$r = z$$
$$y = z^2 \text{ (the equation of line that intersects}$$
$$\qquad y\text{-}z \text{ plane)}$$
$$z = y^{1/2}$$
$$\bar{y}V = \int \bar{y}_{el}\,dV = \int y\,\pi r^2\,dy$$
$$\bar{y}V = \pi \int_0^1 y^2\,dy$$

Centroidal positions $\bar{x}$ and $\bar{z}$ are determined by symmetry. For the shell element shown in Fig. 40:

$$\bar{y}_{el} = \frac{y+1}{2}$$

$$dA = 2\pi r\,(1-y) \text{ (surface area of shell)}$$
$$dV = 2\pi r\,(1-y)\,dz$$
$$r = z$$
$$y = z^2$$
$$z = y^{1/2}$$
$$\bar{y}V = \int \bar{y}_{el}\,dV = \int \frac{(y+1)}{2}\,2\pi r(1-y)\,dz$$

$$\bar{y}V = \pi \int_0^1 (y+1)(1-y)r\,dz$$

$$\bar{y}V = \pi \int_0^1 (z^2+1)(1-z^2)z\,dz$$

For a long, slender element, as shown in Fig. 41:

$$\bar{z}V = \int \bar{z}_{el}\,dV = \iint \frac{z}{2}\,z\,dx\,dy$$

$$\bar{z}V = \frac{1}{2}\iint \{f(x,y)\}^2\,dx\,dy$$

$$\bar{y}V = \int \bar{y}_{el}\,dV = \iint yz\,dx\,dy$$

$$\bar{y}V = \iint yf(x, y)\,dxdy$$

$$\bar{x}V = \int \bar{x}_{el}\,dV = \iint xz\,dxdy$$

$$\bar{x}V = \iint xf(x, y)\,dxdy$$

Limits of integration are determined by the specific surfaces involved.

Composite Bodies. The volume, mass, area, length, and the centroid of many common shapes are well known and tabulated. It is convenient to use this known information to compute the centroids of bodies with known shapes. This is done by replacing the integral forms with finite summations. For example, with a region made up of N segments, each of known mass and mass center:

$$\bar{x} = \frac{\displaystyle\sum_{i=1}^{N} x_i m_i}{\displaystyle\sum_{i=1}^{N} m_i}$$

where x_i is the mass center of m_i. For a plane region made up of N regions:

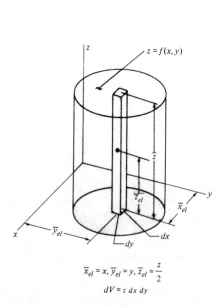

$$\bar{x}_{el} = x, \bar{y}_{el} = y, \bar{z}_{el} = \frac{z}{2}$$

$$dV = z\,dx\,dy$$

Figure 41

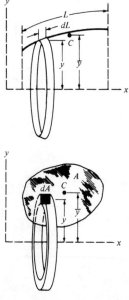

Figure 42

$$\bar{x} = \frac{\displaystyle\sum_{i=1}^{N} x_i A_i}{\displaystyle\sum_{i=1}^{N} A_i}$$

where x_i is the centroid of A_i.

Theorem of Pappus. This simple method is used to calculate the surface area formed by revolving a plane curve about a nonintersecting axis in the plane of the curve. The length L in the x-y plane of Fig. 42 revolves about the x-axis. An element of the surface formed is the ring denoted by dL. The ring area is its circumference times its slant height or $dA = 2\pi y\, dL$. The total area is:

$$A = 2\pi \int y\, dL$$

Because $\bar{y}L = \int y\, dL$, the area becomes:

$$A = 2\pi \bar{y} L \qquad\qquad\qquad\qquad (\text{Eq } 7)$$

where $\bar{y}$ is the y-coordinate of the centroid C for length L.

A volume may also be generated by revolving an area about a nonintersecting line in its plane. The element generated by revolving the area dA about the x-axis is the elemental ring of cross section dA and radius y. The volume becomes $dV = 2\pi y\, dA$. Total volume is therefore:

$$V = 2\pi \int y\, dA$$

Because $\bar{y}A = \int y\, dA$, the volume becomes:

$$V = 2\pi \bar{y} A \qquad\qquad\qquad\qquad (\text{Eq } 8)$$

where $\bar{y}$ is the y-coordinate of the centroid C of the revolved area A. If a line or an area is revolved through an angle θ less than 2π, the generated surface or volume may be found by replacing 2π by θ in Eq 7 and 8 where θ is in radians.

BEAM LOADING

A beam is a structural member that supports transverse loads, that is, loads perpendicular to the axis of the beam. Whether the load is concentrated at a point load or distributed over the surface affects the reaction of the beam to the load.

Statically indeterminate beams are those that cannot be analyzed using the static equilibrium equations, while statically determinate beams can be. A maximum of three reactions can be handled statically with a two-dimensional beam and a maximum of six with a three-dimensional beam. Examples of two-dimensional beams are given in Fig. 43.

Analysis of Shear and Bending Moment in Beams. Two-dimensional beams are considered here because they are usually encountered in practice. A beam may be loaded with point loads having very small regions of contact, with loads distributed over a certain length of the beam, and with torques. For a beam loaded as shown in Fig. 44(a), the reactions $\mathbf{R}_A$ and $\mathbf{R}_B$ are first determined using the entire beam in a free-body diagram (Fig. 44b). The forces resulting from the distributed loads of intensity w_1 (maximum value) and w_2 are seen to act at the centroid of the area under the load curve with a magnitude that equals the area under the curve $\left(\dfrac{w_1 L_1}{2}\text{ and } w_2 L_2\right)$. Intensity of a distributed load is the force per unit length applied to the beam. A section is cut at line C, and the beam may be considered in two portions as shown in Fig. 44(c). The left hand section must be kept in equilibrium by the force V (shear) and moment M (bending moment) applied by the right section. Likewise, the right hand section must be kept in equilibrium by the left hand side. M and V are internal reactions to the loading that are easily calculated using the equilibrium equations. They are related to the stresses occurring in a beam.

Shear and Moment Sign Conventions. When considering the internal reactions of the beam, the positive shear and bending moment convention is commonly shown as in Fig. 45(a). The pair of reactions at the left are those applied to the section of the beam to the left of the cut. Those on the right are applied to the right hand section.

If considering external forces on the beam, positive shear tends to cause movement of the parts of the beam adjacent to the cut line in the manner shown in Fig. 45(b). Positive bending moment tends to deform the beam into a concave upward curve as shown in Fig. 45(c).

Analysis of a series of free-body diagrams formed by using several sections of a beam will allow the variation of M and V across the beam to be

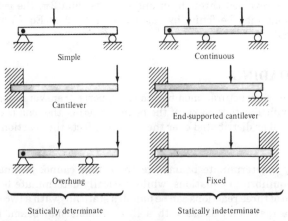

Figure 43

found. In the series of diagrams in Fig. 46, sections at C and E are taken and the free bodies of Fig. 46(c) and 46(d) are formed. Application of the equilibrium equations to the two free-body diagrams at the left side of Fig. 46(c) and 46(d) will allow the values of V and M in each half of the beam to be found. A diagram of V (Fig. 46e) and M (Fig. 46f) can then be drawn showing how these quantities vary across the beam and indicating the location of their maximum values.

A simpler way of evaluating the variation of M and V is to determine their mathematical relationships. Given the general load on the simple beam in Fig. 47(a), where the load intensity curve is a function of x, a small section of the beam can be isolated and the effect of the load examined (Fig. 47b). Assuming a positive bending moment and shear in this region and using these conventions in the free body in Fig. 47(b), the principles of equilibrium may be applied to the small section. Summing forces in the vertical direction gives:

$$V - (V + \Delta V) - w\Delta x = 0 \qquad \Delta V = -w\Delta x$$

Letting $\Delta x \to 0$ results in:

$$\frac{dV}{dx} = -w \qquad\qquad\qquad\qquad (Eq\ 9)$$

Separating variables and integrating:

$$V_D - V_C = -\int_{x_C}^{x_D} w\ dx \qquad\qquad\qquad (Eq\ 10)$$

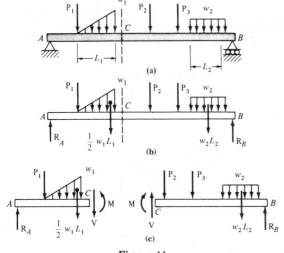

(a)

(b)

(c)

Figure 44

Left section $\qquad V \qquad$ Right section

(a) Internal force and moment section
(positive shear and positive bending moment)

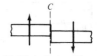

(b) Effect of external forces
(positive shear)

(c) Effect of external forces
(positive bending moment)

Figure 45

which may be interpreted as $V_D - V_C = -$ (area under load curve between C and D). Summing moments about point C' gives:

$$(M + \Delta M) - M - V\,\Delta x + w\,\Delta x\,\frac{\Delta x}{2} = 0$$

$$\Delta M = V\,\Delta x - \frac{1}{2}\,w(\Delta x)^2$$

Letting $\Delta x \to 0$ and knowing that $(\Delta x)^2$ terms are negligible, we get:

$$\frac{dM}{dx} = V \qquad\qquad\text{(Eq 11)}$$

Separating variables and integrating:

$$M_D - M_C = \int_{x_C}^{x_D} V\,dx \qquad\qquad\text{(Eq 12)}$$

which is equivalent to $M_D - M_C =$ area under shear curve between C and D.

Equations 9 to 12 must be applied in a region where $w(x)$ is continuous and may be easily used to generate shear and moment curves.

Because the above differential Equations 9 and 11 are linear, the effect of a combination of loadings can be found by superimposing the moment and shear curves that result from the loadings. Therefore, if w represents a load on one beam, which causes a shear V_1 and a moment M_1, and if V_2 and M_2 are caused by a load w_2, then:

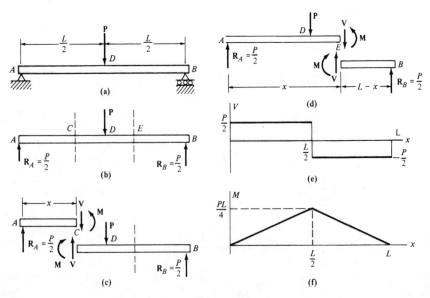

Figure 46

$$w_{total} = w_1 + w_2$$
$$V_{total} = V_1 + V_2$$
$$M_{total} = M_1 + M_2$$

The above relationships apply for any point in any portion of the beam.

FLEXIBLE CABLES

A cable may support a series of distinct loads as shown in Fig. 48(a) or it may support a continuously distributed load (Fig. 48b). The latter situation would be present when the cable weight is not negligible. If individual loads are rather close together, a continuous load may be used to approximate the load pattern in Fig. 48(a).

The intensity of the variable plus the continuous load applied to the cable in Fig. 48(b) is expressed as w units of force per unit length x. The resultant R of the vertical loading is:

$$R = \int dR = \int w \, dx$$

where the integration is taken over the desired interval. The position of R is found using moment so that:

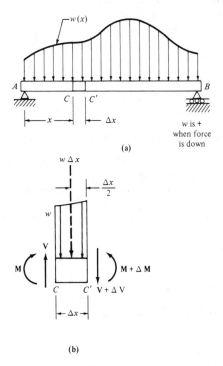

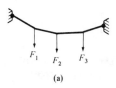

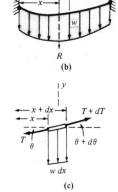

Figure 47   **Figure 48**

$$R\bar{x} = \int x \, dR \qquad \bar{x} = \frac{\int x \, dR}{R}$$

The differential load $dR = w \, dx$ in Fig. 48(c) represents a strip of vertical length w and width dx taken from under the load curve of Fig. 48(b). R represents the total area, with R passing through the centroid of the shaded area.

To satisfy equilibrium conditions, each element of the cable must be in equilibrium. At the position x, in Fig. 48(c), the tension in the cable is T, and the cable forms an angle θ with the horizontal. At section $x + dx$, the tension is $T + dT$, and the angle is $\theta + d\theta$. The changes in both T and θ are assumed positive with positive change in x. Applying Newton's first law to the x and y directions gives:

$$\Sigma F_y = 0 \qquad (T + dT) \sin(\theta + d\theta) = T \sin \theta + w \, dx$$
$$\Sigma F_x = 0 \qquad (T + dT) \cos(\theta + d\theta) = T \cos \theta$$

Using trigonometric expansions and the fact that $\sin(d\theta) = d\theta$ and $\cos(d\theta) = 1$ (as $d\theta \to 0$), we have:

$$d(T \sin \theta) = w \, dx \qquad \text{and} \qquad d(T \cos \theta) = 0$$

From the second expression, the horizontal component of T is seen to be constant. If $T_0 = T \cos \theta$ is used for this constant force, $T = T_0/\cos \theta$ can be inserted into the first of the two equations above to get $d(T_0 \tan \theta) = w \, dx$. Because $\tan \theta = dy/dx$, the equilibrium equation may be written in the form:

$$\frac{d^2 y}{dx^2} = \frac{w}{T_0} \qquad \qquad \text{(Eq 13)}$$

This is the basic differential equation for the flexible cable. The solution of Eq 13 must satisfy boundary conditions at the fixed ends of the cable.

SPECIAL (LIMITING) CASES OF DISTRIBUTED LOADING

Parabolic Cables. A suspension bridge where the uniform weight of the roadway must be supported is an application closely approximated by a constant vertical loading intensity, w. The mass of the cable is neglected. Figure 49 shows a suspension bridge of span L and sag h with origin of coordinates taken at the midpoint of the span which is the low point of the cable.

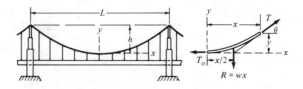

Figure 49

Equation 13 is solved subject to the boundary condition $dy/dx = 0$ when $x = 0$. This defines the deflection of the cable as:

$$y = \frac{wx^2}{2T_0}$$

which is a vertical parabola. Using the condition that $y = h$ at $x = L/2$ gives:

$$T_0 = \frac{wL^2}{8h} \qquad y = \frac{4hx^2}{L^2}$$

The tension T is found from the expression:

$$T = \sqrt{T_0^2 + w^2 x^2}$$

Eliminating T_0 then gives:

$$T = w \sqrt{x^2 + \left(\frac{L^2}{8h}\right)^2}$$

The maximum tension occurs at $x = L/2$ and is expressed as:

$$T_{max} = \frac{wL}{2} \sqrt{1 + \frac{L^2}{16h^2}}$$

The length of the cable is found using the differential relation $ds = \sqrt{(dx)^2 + (dy)^2}$. This gives:

$$\int_0^{S/2} ds = \frac{S}{2} = \int_0^{L/2} \sqrt{1 + \left(\frac{dy}{dx}\right)^2}\, dx = \int_0^{L/2} \sqrt{1 + \left(\frac{wx}{T_0}\right)^2}\, dx$$

Substituting a convergent series for the integrand and integrating term by term gives:

$$S = L\left[1 + \frac{8}{3}\left(\frac{h}{L}\right)^2 - \frac{32}{5}\left(\frac{h}{L}\right)^4 + \cdots\right]$$

This series converges for all values of $h/L \leq 1/4$. Since for most cases h is much smaller than $L/4$, the three terms should give a reasonably accurate approximation.

Catenary Cables. Consider a uniform cable suspended at two points in a horizontal plane and hanging under the action of its own weight only (Fig. 50). Due to curvature of the cable, the weight is not uniformly distributed with respect to the horizontal axis, x. The free-body diagram of a finite portion of the cable of length s is shown in Fig. 50(b). If the cable has a weight μ

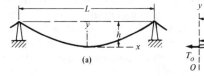

(a)　　　(b)

Figure 50

per unit length, the resultant R of the load between O and x is $R = \mu s$, and the differential vertical load is $\mu\ ds$. The resulting differential equation for this system is:

$$\frac{d^2y}{dx^2} = \frac{\mu}{T_0}\frac{ds}{dx} \qquad \text{(Eq 14)}$$

which is subject to the appropriate boundary conditions. Since $s = f(x, y)$ this equation must be changed so that it contains only the two variables x and y. The identity $(ds)^2 = (dx)^2 + (dy)^2$ is used for this purpose, and the differential equation becomes:

$$\frac{d^2y}{dx^2} = \frac{\mu}{T_0}\sqrt{1 + \left(\frac{dy}{dx}\right)^2}$$

Applying the boundary conditions, $\frac{dy}{dx} = 0$ and $y = 0$ at $x = 0$, gives the solution:

$$y = \frac{T_0}{\mu}\left(\cosh\frac{\mu x}{T_0} - 1\right) \qquad \text{(Eq 15)}$$

This is the equation of the curve (catenary) formed by a cable hanging under the action of its weight only. The cable length may be found to be:

$$s = \frac{T_0}{\mu}\sinh\frac{\mu x}{T_0} \qquad \text{(Eq 16)}$$

and the tension is determined from the equation:

$$T = T_0\cosh\frac{\mu x}{T_0} \qquad \text{(Eq 17)}$$

The value of T_0 can be found from Eq 15 if h is known. In terms of y, the tension is:

$$T = T_0 + \mu y \qquad \text{(Eq 18)}$$

Many problems concerning both the catenary and parabolic cable involve suspension points that are on different levels. The relationships developed here may be applied to the part of the cable on each side of the lowest point.

Cables with Concentrated Loads. A cable is attached to two fixed points A and B and supporting n given vertical concentrated loads $P_1, P_2, \ldots, P_n$ (Fig. 51a). It is assumed that the cable is flexible, that is, that its resistance to bending is small and therefore negligible and that the weight of the cable is negligible. The portion of cable between successive loads is considered as a two-force member, and the internal forces at any point in the cable are reduced to a tension force along the cable. Each of the loads is taken to lie in a given vertical line, so that the horizontal distance from support A to each of the loads is known. The horizontal and vertical distances between the supports are also known. The vertical distance from A to each of the points $C_1, C_2, \ldots, C_n$ must be found along with the tension T in each portion of the cable.

A free-body diagram of the entire cable is drawn (Fig. 51b). The reactions at A and B are represented by two components each since the slope of the cable is not known at those points. An additional equation must be obtained by considering the equilibrium of a portion of the cable. This is possible if the x and y coordinates of some point D of the cable are known. The free-body diagram of the portion of cable AD is shown in Fig. 51(c). The resulting system of equations may now be solved for the reactions at A and B.

When A_x and A_y have been determined, the vertical distance from A to any point of the cable may be easily found using the free-body diagram of Fig. 51(d). Because $\Sigma M_{C_2} = 0$, an equation can be obtained which may be solved for y_2. The horizontal component of the tension force is the same at any point of the cable, and the tension T is maximum when $\cos \theta$ is minimum.

DRY FRICTION (COULOMB FRICTION)

When a small horizontal force P is applied to the block shown in Fig. 52(a), a static-friction force F serves to balance P. F is the resultant of a great number of forces acting over the contact area between the block and the plane. These forces are caused by irregularities of the surfaces in contact and by molecular attraction to some extent.

When P is increased, F also increases, opposing P until it reaches a maximum value of F_m (Fig. 52b). If P is increased beyond this point, the friction force cannot balance it and the block starts to move. As soon as motion starts, the value of F drops from F_m to F_k. This is because motion reduces interaction

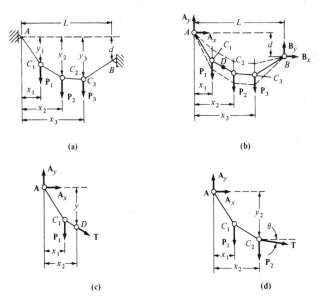

(a)   (b)

(c)   (d)

Figure 51

between the irregularities of the surfaces in contact. As P increases, the block slides with increasing velocity while the kinetic-friction force, F_k, remains approximately constant (as long as the velocities are not too great).

The maximum value of F_m has been shown experimentally to be proportional to the normal component of the reaction of the surface, N. Therefore:

$$F_m = \mu_s N$$

where μ_s is a constant called the coefficient of static friction. The kinetic-friction force is defined as:

$$F_k = \mu_k N$$

where μ_k is a constant called the coefficient of kinetic friction. These coefficients of friction do not depend upon the area of the surfaces in contact, but depend strongly on the nature of the surfaces.

FOUR SITUATIONS RELATED TO THE FRICTION FORCE

Four different situations relating to the friction problem are itemized below along with a description of the friction forces that are present. The situations are related to the diagrams of Fig. 53.

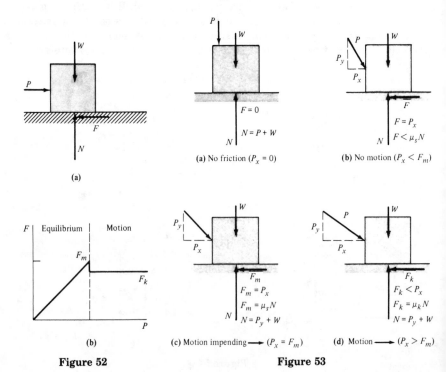

(a)

(a) No friction ($P_x = 0$)

(b) No motion ($P_x < F_m$)

(b)

(c) Motion impending ⟶ ($P_x = F_m$)

(d) Motion ⟶ ($P_x > F_m$)

Figure 52   **Figure 53**

- The forces do not tend to move the body along the surface; there is no friction force (Fig. 53a)
- The applied forces have a horizontal component but are not large enough to set the body in motion. The friction force **F** may be found by solving the equations of equilibrium for the body (Fig. 53b)
- The applied forces are such that the body is just about to slide. Motion is said to be impending. The friction force has reached its maximum value and both the equations of equilibrium and the equation $F_m = \mu_s N$ may be used (Fig. 53c)
- The body slides under the action of the applied forces, and Newton's second law applies. The equation $F_k = \mu_k N$ may be used (Fig. 53d)

For a two-dimensional body, the only equilibrium equations that can normally be used are $\Sigma F_x = 0$ and $\Sigma F_y = 0$. The moment equation is available only if a specific point of contact between the surfaces is known.

ANGLE OF FRICTION

The angle of static friction is denoted by ϕ_s and is defined as:

$$\tan \phi_s = \frac{F_m}{N} = \frac{\mu_s N}{N}$$

where

$$\tan \phi_s = \mu_s$$

The angle of kinetic friction is denoted by ϕ_k and defined by:

$$\tan \phi_k = \frac{F_k}{N} = \frac{\mu_k N}{N}$$

where

$$\tan \phi_k = \mu_k$$

These angles are more fully described by noting what happens to a block on an inclined plane that is subjected to no forces other than its own weight (Fig. 54). When the plane is inclined enough such that motion becomes impending, the angle between R and the normal will have reached its maximum value ϕ_s (Fig. 54a). The value of the angle of inclination corresponding to impending motion is called the angle of repose which is also the angle of static friction. If the angle of inclination θ is increased further, motion starts and the angle between R and the normal drops to ϕ_k (Fig. 54b). The forces acting on the block are now unbalanced.

WEDGES

Applying the principles of friction and the equations of equilibrium to these simple machines requires that a free-body diagram be set up for each component of the wedge system. Consider in Fig. 55 the example of block A (mass m) which rests against the vertical wall B. It is to be raised by forcing wedge C between A and a second wedge D. The minimum force P needed to raise the wedge is desired.

The free-body diagrams of A and C are drawn in Fig. 55(b) and (c). The magnitudes of the friction forces F_1, F_2, and F_3 on bodies A and C must be $\mu_s N_1$, $\mu_s N_2$, and $\mu_s N_3$, respectively, since motion must impend on all surfaces at the same time. Friction forces must be shown with their proper sense based upon the expected relative motion of the parts. Two equilibrium equations for each of the free bodies may now be set up and force P found.

SCREWS

These devices are used in a variety of applications such as fastening, adjustment, and transmission of power. To a great extent, the performance of the thread is governed by the internal friction. A simple static analysis of a square thread device gives some insight into screw thread forces.

A square-threaded jack shown in Fig. 56 is taken to have an axial load W and a moment M applied about the axis of the screw. Force R is exerted by the thread of the jack frame on a small portion of the screw thread. If M is just sufficient to turn the screw (impending motion), the thread of the screw will tend to slide around and up on the fixed thread of the frame. The angle ϕ is the angle of friction. The moment of R about the vertical axis is $Rr \sin(\alpha + \phi)$, and the total moment resulting from all reactions R becomes:

$$M = [r \sin(\alpha + \phi)] \Sigma R$$

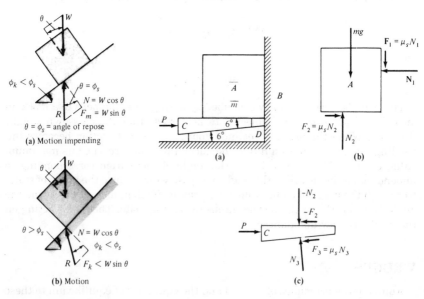

(a) Motion impending

$\phi_k < \phi_s$ $\theta = \phi_s$
$N = W \cos \theta$
R $F_m = W \sin \theta$
$\theta = \phi_s$ = angle of repose

(b) Motion

$\theta > \phi_s$ $N = W \cos \theta$
$\phi_k < \phi_s$
R $F_k < W \sin \theta$

Figure 54

(a)

(b) mg $F_1 = \mu_s N_1$ A N_1
$F_2 = \mu_s N_2$ N_2

(c) P C $-N_2$ $-F_2$ $F_3 = \mu_s N_3$ N_3

Figure 55

Equilibrium dictates that:

$$W = \Sigma R \cos (\alpha + \varphi) = [\cos (\alpha + \varphi)] \Sigma R$$

and dividing M by W gives:

$$M = Wr \tan (\alpha + \varphi)$$

FLEXIBLE BELTS

The impending movement of flexible belts and ropes over sheaves and drums is applicable to the design of belt drives, band brakes, and hoists. A drum subjected to the two belt tensions T_1 and T_2 is shown in Fig. 57(a) along with the torque M necessary to prevent rotation, and the bearing reaction R. T_2 is assumed greater than T_1. The free-body diagram of an element of the belt having length $r\,d\theta$ is shown in Fig. 57(b). The tension is seen to increase from T at angle θ to $T + dT$ at angle $\theta + d\theta$. The normal force is a differential value dN. The friction force is the differential quantity $\mu\,dN$ for impending motion. Summing forces in the t-direction gives:

$$\mu\,dN = dT$$

and summing in the n-direction gives:

$$dN = T\,d\theta$$

These two equations may be combined to get:

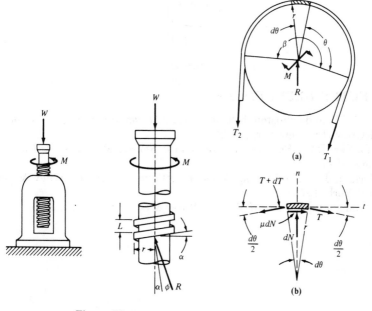

Figure 56   Figure 57

$$\frac{dT}{T} = \mu \, d\theta$$

Solution of this differential equation gives the following relationships between T_2 and T_1:

$$\ln \frac{T_2}{T_1} = \mu\beta \qquad\qquad\qquad\qquad \text{(Eq 19)}$$

and

$$T_2 = T_1 e^{\mu\beta} \qquad\qquad\qquad\qquad\qquad \text{(Eq 20)}$$

where β is the angle of wrap for the belt. The angle β may be greater than 2π and is always measured in radians. Equations 19 and 20 are to be used only for impending motion. The formulas may be applied to problems involving belt drives where the pulley and the belt rotate. The problem then becomes finding whether the belt will move with respect to the pulley. If the belt is actually slipping, similar formulas can be used which include the coefficient of kinetic friction, μ_k. For a V-belt, the cross-section being shown in Fig. 58, the relationship of the tensions T_2 and T_1 becomes:

$$\frac{T_2}{T_1} = e^{\mu\beta/\sin(\alpha/2)}$$

where α is the groove angle.

Figure 58

SELECTED REFERENCES

1. Beer, F.P. and Johnston, E.R., Jr., *Vector Mechanics for Engineers: Statics,* McGraw-Hill, New York, 1972
2. Hibbeler, R.C., *Engineering Mechanics: Statics,* Macmillan & Co., New York, 1974
3. Meriam, J.L., *Engineering Mechanics, Volume I: Statics,* Wiley & Sons, New York, 1978
4. Meriam, J.L., *Statics, SI Version,* Wiley & Sons, New York, 1975

16
Vibration Analysis

By Paul Lam, Ph.D.
Department of Mechanical
Engineering
University of Akron

The study of vibration involves analysis of oscillatory motions of mechanical systems and the dynamic conditions related to system responses. Vibration requires energy and power. This requirement reduces efficiency and causes high stresses in mechanical systems. Vibration analysis seeks to predict structural responses (displacement, velocity, or acceleration) of vibratory systems subjected to such excitations as harmonic force, rotating unbalance, and ground motion.

TERMINOLOGY

Free Vibration. Vibration that occurs without any influence of external force after initial displacement. The system vibrates under the action of forces inherent in the system itself.

Forced Vibration. Vibration that takes place under the influence of such external forces as harmonic force, rotating unbalance, and ground motion.

Natural Frequency. Property of the dynamic system. For a discrete mass system, there exists at least one natural frequency for each mass point. The fundamental frequency is the lowest natural frequency. For a continuous system, there is an infinite number of natural frequencies. Natural frequency is:

$$f_n = \frac{\omega}{2\pi}$$

where ω is given in rad/s.

Period of Vibration. The interval of time in which the vibratory motion repeats itself. It is expressed as $\tau = \frac{1}{f_n}$.

Resonance. The condition in which the frequency of the exciting force coincides with one of the natural frequencies of the system. This is a potentially dangerous situation because large amplitudes can result.

Damping. Dissipation of energy by friction or other viscous forces.

Degree of Freedom. The number of independent coordinates required to specify completely the motion of the structure at any instant of time.

Periodic Motion. Motion that repeats itself after an interval of time (Fig. 1). A common type of vibratory motion. Mathematically, it is represented by $f(t) = f(t + \tau)$, where $\tau \equiv$ period of motion.

UNDAMPED FREE VIBRATION

A simple vibration system is shown in Fig. 2. The most important parameters are (a) the mass, (b) the spring-restoring force, (c) the damper-dissipative force, and (d) the excitation. The response of this single degree of freedom (SDOF) vibration system is defined by the displacement x.

For an undamped free vibration system with a single degree of freedom (Fig. 3), the differential equation describing the motion becomes:

$$m\ddot{x} + kx = 0 \qquad \text{(Eq 1)}$$

where $\ddot{x}$ is the second derivative with respect to time. The general solution of this second order differential equation in terms of the initial displacement x_0 and initial velocity v_0 is:

$$x(t) = x_0 \cos \omega_n t + \frac{v_0}{\omega_n} \sin \omega_n t \qquad \text{(Eq 2)}$$

where $\omega_n = \sqrt{\dfrac{kg}{W}}$ = undamped natural frequency, rad/s, τ = period of free

vibration = $2\pi \sqrt{\dfrac{W}{gk}}$, and W = weight of vibrating mass.

The solution may also be written in the form:

$$x(t) = X \sin (\omega_n t + \theta) \qquad \text{(Eq 3)}$$

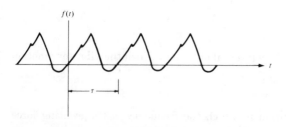

Figure 1   Periodic forcing function

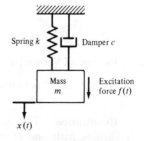

Figure 2   Vibration system with single degree of freedom

where

$$X = \text{amplitude of vibration}$$

$$X = \sqrt{x_0{}^2 + \left(\frac{v_0}{\omega_n}\right)^2}$$

$$\theta = \tan^{-1}\frac{\omega_n x_0}{v_0}$$

The natural frequency f_n can also be expressed in terms of the static deflection Δ of the system. In terms of Hz, or cycles per second, f_n is:

$$f_n = \frac{1}{2\pi}\sqrt{\frac{g}{\Delta}} \qquad \text{(Eq 4)}$$

where Δ is the static deflection due to weight W. Using $g = 386$ in./s^2, and Δ given in inches, the relationship between f_n and Δ may be expressed as:

$$f_n = \frac{3.127}{\sqrt{\Delta}}\text{ cps} \qquad \text{(Eq 5)}$$

or

$$f_n = \frac{187.6}{\sqrt{\Delta}}\text{ cpm} \qquad \text{(Eq 6)}$$

Figure 4 shows a natural frequency versus static deflection plot of Eq. 5.

The Energy Method. Energy considerations can be used to determine the natural frequency of a conservative system. When there is no energy dissipation, a system is termed conservative. At any instant, the energy of such a system in free vibration is partly kinetic and partly potential. Kinetic energy is a function of velocity and potential energy is a function of work done in elastic deformation or work done against a force field such as gravity. The total energy, which is termed mechanical energy, is constant, and in a conservative system, the rate of change of the total energy must be zero. That is, $T + U = $ constant and:

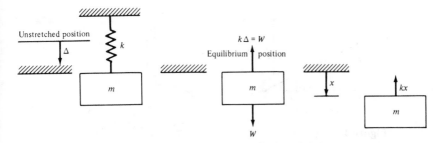

Figure 3 Spring mass system and free-body diagram

$$\frac{d}{dt}(T + U) = 0 \tag{Eq 7}$$

where T is kinetic energy and U is potential energy. The maximum kinetic energy must equal the maximum potential energy; that is:

$$T_{max} = U_{max} \tag{Eq 8}$$

The natural frequency of the system can then be determined if the vibration motion is assumed to be harmonic. The frequency depends on the accuracy of the assumed motion.

For example, the torsional pendulum of Fig. 5 consists of a disk having a mass moment of inertia J measured in lb · in./s², restrained in rotation by a wire of torsional stiffness K measured in in. · lb/rad. Assuming harmonic oscillatory motion expressed as $\theta = A \sin \omega_n t$, then:

$$T_{max} = \frac{1}{2} J \theta_{max}^2 = \frac{1}{2} J \omega_n^2 A^2 \text{ and } U_{max} = \frac{1}{2} K \theta_{max}^2 = \frac{1}{2} KA^2$$

Equating the maximum kinetic and potential energies, the natural frequency becomes $\omega_n = \sqrt{K/J}$.

In vibratory systems with distributed masses, such as the beam, or a spring with significant mass, the deflection configuration of the system is needed to evaluate the kinetic and potential energies. Rayleigh showed that the lowest frequency can be determined with acceptable accuracy by assuming any reasonable deflection curve. If the true deflection curve of the vibrating system is assumed, the fundamental frequency found is the correct frequency. For any other curve, the frequency determined will be higher than the correct frequency, because deviations from the true curve require additional constraints, which imply greater stiffness and higher frequency. Static deflection curves of the elastic body generally result in fairly accurate values for the frequency.

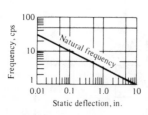

Figure 4 Natural frequency versus static deflection

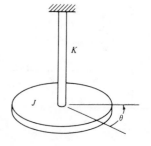

Figure 5 A torsional pendulum

Natural Frequencies of Simple Systems. A mechanical system can often be reduced to one of the simple systems shown in Fig. 6. The equations for the natural frequencies are given in ω_n rad/s $= 2\pi f_n$. The stiffness of elements presented in Fig. 7 can be used for the general equation, $\omega_n = \sqrt{k/m}$.

EQUIVALENT SPRINGS AND MASSES

In general, the equation of motion of a SDOF free-vibration system can be shown to be of the following form:

$$m_{eq}\ddot{x} + k_{eq}x = 0 \tag{Eq 9}$$

where m_{eq} and k_{eq} are the equivalent mass and spring constants. From energy considerations, k_{eq} can be obtained by expressing the total potential energy of the system in terms of a displacement, that is:

$$U = \frac{1}{2} k_{eq}x^2 \tag{Eq 10}$$

Similarly, m_{eq} is obtained by expressing the total kinetic energy of the system as:

$$T = \frac{1}{2} m_{eq}\ddot{x}^2 \tag{Eq 11}$$

In general, most complicated systems can be reduced to an equivalent single degree of freedom system. Some of the equivalent stiffness and mass systems are shown in Fig. 7 and 8.

DAMPED FREE VIBRATION (SDOF)

When the vibratory system of Fig. 1 is disturbed by an initial displacement or velocity, the equation of motion becomes:

$$m\ddot{x} + c\dot{x} + kx = 0 \tag{Eq 12}$$

which can be written as:

$$\ddot{x} + 2\xi\omega_n\dot{x} + \omega_n^2 x = 0 \tag{Eq 13}$$

where $\xi = \dfrac{c}{2m\omega_n}$ = damping ratio. The solution of the second order differential equation depends on the value of ξ. The three possible cases are:

Example 1. Overdamped. ($\xi > 1$, aperiodic motion)

$$x(t) = \frac{v_0}{2\sqrt{\xi^2 - 1}\,\omega_n}[e^{\omega_n\sqrt{\xi^2-1}\,t} - e^{-\omega_n\sqrt{\xi^2-1}\,t}] \tag{Eq 14}$$

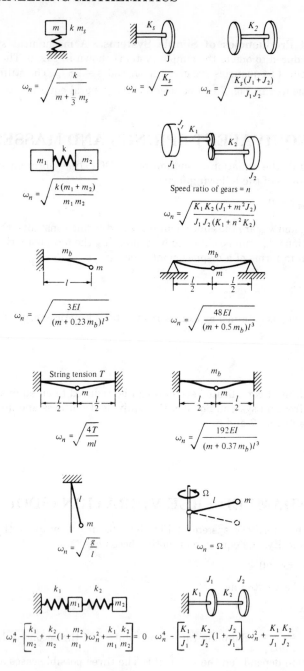

$$\omega_n = \sqrt{\frac{k}{m + \frac{1}{3} m_s}}$$

$$\omega_n = \sqrt{\frac{K_s}{J}}$$

$$\omega_n = \sqrt{\frac{K_s(J_1 + J_2)}{J_1 J_2}}$$

$$\omega_n = \sqrt{\frac{k(m_1 + m_2)}{m_1 m_2}}$$

Speed ratio of gears $= n$

$$\omega_n = \sqrt{\frac{K_1 K_2 (J_1 + m^2 J_2)}{J_1 J_2 (K_1 + n^2 K_2)}}$$

$$\omega_n = \sqrt{\frac{3EI}{(m + 0.23 m_b) l^3}}$$

$$\omega_n = \sqrt{\frac{48EI}{(m + 0.5 m_b) l^3}}$$

String tension T

$$\omega_n = \sqrt{\frac{4T}{ml}}$$

$$\omega_n = \sqrt{\frac{192EI}{(m + 0.37 m_b) l^3}}$$

$$\omega_n = \sqrt{\frac{g}{l}}$$

$$\omega_n = \Omega$$

$$\omega_n^4 - \left[\frac{k_1}{m_2} + \frac{k_2}{m_2}(1 + \frac{m_2}{m_1})\right]\omega_n^2 + \frac{k_1 k_2}{m_1 m_2} = 0$$

$$\omega_n^4 - \left[\frac{K_1}{J_1} + \frac{K_2}{J_2}(1 + \frac{J_2}{J_1})\right]\omega_n^2 + \frac{K_1 K_2}{J_1 J_2}$$

$$\omega^4 - \left[\frac{k_1(J_1 + J_2)}{J_1 J_2} + \frac{k_2(J_2 + J_3)}{J_2 J_3}\right]\omega^3 + \frac{k_1 k_2(J_1 + J_2 + J_3)}{J_1 J_2 J_3} = 0 \quad \text{where } k = \frac{GI_o}{l}$$

Figure 6   Natural frequencies

Example 2. Critically Damped. $(\xi = 1$, aperiodic motion)

$$x(t) = (x_0 + v_0 t)e^{-\omega_n t} \qquad\qquad\qquad\text{(Eq 15)}$$

Example 3. Underdamped. $(\xi < 1$, periodic motion)

$$x(t) = Xe^{-\xi\omega_n t}\sin(\omega_d t + \theta) \qquad\qquad\qquad\text{(Eq 16)}$$

where

$$\omega_d = \omega_n\sqrt{1 - \xi^2} = \text{damped natural frequency}$$

$$\tau_d = \frac{2\pi}{\omega_d} = \text{period of free vibration with damping } \xi$$

$$X = \sqrt{x_0{}^2 + \left(\frac{v_0 + \xi\omega_n x_0}{\omega_d}\right)^2} = \text{amplitude of vibration}$$

$$\theta = \tan^{-1}\frac{x_0\omega_d}{v_0 + \xi\omega_n x_0}$$

The solutions of the three cases are illustrated in Fig. 9. When $\xi \geqq 1$, aperiodic motions exist in the viscously damped vibration system. For the underdamped case, the system vibrates periodically. Also, when $\xi < 0.2$, the damped and undamped frequency ratio is near unity. The expression can be written as:

$$\left(\frac{\omega_d}{\omega_n}\right)^2 + \xi^2 = 1 \qquad\qquad\qquad\text{(Eq 17)}$$

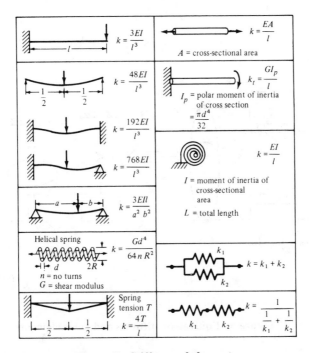

Figure 7   Stiffness of elements

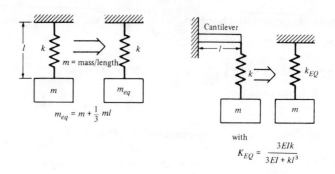

with

$$K_{EQ} = \frac{3EIk}{3EI + kl^3}$$

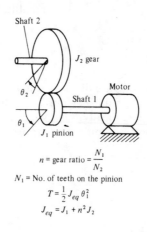

n = gear ratio = $\frac{N_1}{N_2}$

N_1 = No. of teeth on the pinion

$$T = \frac{1}{2} J_{eq} \theta_1^2$$

$$J_{eq} = J_1 + n^2 J_2$$

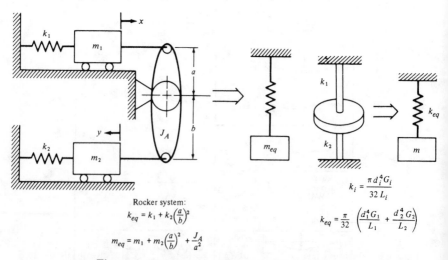

Rocker system:

$$k_{eq} = k_1 + k_2 \left(\frac{a}{b}\right)^2$$

$$m_{eq} = m_1 + m_2 \left(\frac{a}{b}\right)^2 + \frac{J_A}{a^2}$$

$$k_i = \frac{\pi d_i^4 G_i}{32 L_i}$$

$$k_{eq} = \frac{\pi}{32} \left(\frac{d_1^4 G_1}{L_1} + \frac{d_2^4 G_2}{L_2}\right)$$

Figure 8   Equivalent stiffness and mass elements

which is an equation of a unit circle (see Fig. 10). Typical damping ratios are:

Material	Damping ratio, ξ
Automobile shock absorbers	0.1-0.5
Rubber	0.04
Riveted steel structures	0.03
Concrete	0.02
Wood	0.003
Cold rolled steel	0.0006
Cold rolled aluminum	0.0002
Phosphor bronze	0.00007

Logarithmic Decrement ($\xi < 1$). To determine the amount of damping present in a vibration system, measure the rate of decay of free oscillations (Fig. 11). This is best expressed by the logarithmic decrement, δ, which is a measure of the rate of decay of a damped free vibration system. Logarithmic decrement is:

$$\delta = \ln \frac{x_i}{x_{i+1}} \qquad \text{(Eq 18)}$$

In terms of the damping ratio, δ can also be expressed as:

$$\delta = \frac{2\pi\xi}{\sqrt{1 - \xi^2}} \qquad \text{(Eq 19)}$$

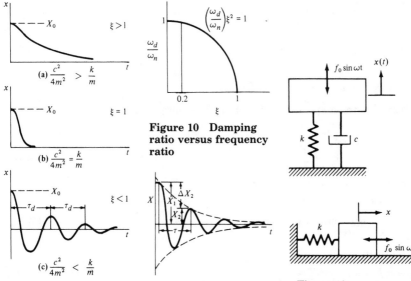

Figure 9 Damped free vibration responses

Figure 10 Damping ratio versus frequency ratio

Figure 11 Rate of decay

Figure 12
Harmonically excited SDOF system

The larger the damping ratio, the greater the rate of decay. For small ξ, the log decrement can be approximated by $\delta = 2\pi\xi$. The logarithmic decrement can also be obtained from the resonance curve of forced vibration as:

$$\delta = \frac{f_2 - f_1}{f_n}\pi \tag{Eq 20}$$

where f_n is the resonant frequency and f_1 and f_2 are frequencies on each side of resonance, for which the amplitude is 0.707 times the amplitude at resonance. The expression $f_n/(f_2 - f_1)$ is a measure of the sharpness of the resonance curve, and it is sometimes called the Q of the system:

$$Q = \frac{f_n}{f_2 - f_1} = \frac{1}{2\xi} \tag{Eq 21}$$

Equivalent Viscous Damping. In any vibratory system, other types of damping, such as Coulomb dry friction, fluid or air resistance, and internal molecular friction (structural damping), can exist. The equations of motion for these types of friction are nonlinear and difficult to solve. Problems of this type are usually solved numerically, but equivalent viscous damping coefficients can be used to represent these types of damping. The equation of the system of vibration can be reduced to a second order linear differential equation and can be expressed as:

$$m_{eq}\ddot{x} + c_{eq}\dot{x} + k_{eq}x = 0 \tag{Eq 22}$$

The major concern is to obtain c_{eq} which is the damping coefficient due to other nonlinear dissipative force systems. To derive the equivalent viscous damping coefficients, the energy input for harmonic force is first considered. For the SDOF system shown in Fig. 12, assuming that the motion lags the harmonic force by a phase angle θ, then:

$$f(t) = f_0 \sin \omega t \tag{Eq 23}$$

and

$$x(t) = X \sin (\omega t - \theta) \tag{Eq 24}$$

where X is the amplitude of vibration. The energy input per cycle is given by:

$$U = \int_0^t f\,dx = \int_0^{\frac{2\pi}{\omega}} f\frac{dx}{dt}\,dt \tag{Eq 25}$$

Since $\dot{x} = X\omega \cos (\omega t - \theta)$, then:

$$U = \int_0^{\frac{2\pi}{\omega}} \omega f_0 X \sin \omega t \cos (\omega t - \theta)\,dt \tag{Eq 26}$$

Integrating:

$$U = \pi f_0 X \sin \theta \tag{Eq 27}$$

The maximum energy input will occur at the resonance condition ($\theta = 90°$) represented by:

$$U = \pi f_0 X \tag{Eq 28}$$

To derive the equivalent viscous damping, energy dissipated by viscous damping is considered next. This energy is represented by:

$$U_d = \int_0^{\frac{2\pi}{\omega}} f_d dx = \int_0^{\frac{2\pi}{\omega}} f_d \dot{x} dt \tag{Eq 29}$$

where f_d is the damping force.

If:

$$f_d = c\dot{x} = cX\omega \cos(\omega t - \theta) \tag{Eq 30}$$

then

$$U_d = \int_0^{\frac{2\pi}{\omega}} cX\omega \cos(\omega t - \theta) X\omega \cos(\omega t - \theta) dt \tag{Eq 31}$$

With integration:

$$U_d = \pi c\omega X^2 \tag{Eq 32}$$

At the resonant condition, the energy input and the dissipated energy by viscous damping must be balanced, that is, $U_{\text{input}} = U_d$. Therefore:

$$\pi f_0 X = \pi c\omega_n X^2 \tag{Eq 33}$$

and

$$X = \frac{f_0}{c\omega_n} \tag{Eq 34}$$

For other types of damping, such as Coulomb or structural damping, the resonance amplitude is approximated as:

$$X_{\text{res}} = \frac{f_0}{c_{\text{eq}}\omega_n} \tag{Eq 35}$$

Since energy dissipated by nonviscous forces under harmonic excitation is defined as:

$$U_d = \pi c_{\text{eq}}\omega X^2 \tag{Eq 36}$$

then

$$c_{\text{eq}} = \frac{U_d}{\pi\omega X^2} \tag{Eq 37}$$

For the general case, if n damping forces exist, then the equivalent damping coefficient can be calculated by:

$$c_{\text{eq}} = \frac{\sum_{i=1}^{n} U_{di}}{\pi\omega X^2} \tag{Eq 38}$$

Nonviscous Damping Forces. The most common types of nonviscous damping are given below.

Example 4. Coulomb Dry Friction. Coulomb damping results from the friction produced by two sliding surfaces as shown in Fig. 12, where the damping force is represented by:

$$f_d = \mu N \tag{Eq 39}$$

with μ = coefficient of friction and N = normal force. The energy input for Coulomb damping is derived to be:

$$U_d = 4f_dX[\cos\theta + \sin\theta] \tag{Eq 40}$$

For Coulomb dry friction, the equivalent viscous damping coefficient is therefore given by:

$$c_{eq} = \frac{4f_d}{\pi\omega_n X} \tag{Eq 41}$$

Example 5. Structural Damping (Hysteresis Damping). When structural material such as steel or aluminum is cyclically stressed, energy is dissipated within the material. Experimentally, energy dissipated per cycle has been found to be proportional to the amplitude of motion and is given by:

$$U_d = \alpha X^\gamma \tag{Eq 42}$$

where d and γ are constants that are dependent on material characteristics and geometry. For example, γ is from 2 to 2.3 for steel. For $\gamma = 2$, the equivalent viscous damping coefficient is:

$$c_{eq} = \frac{\alpha}{\pi\omega} \tag{Eq 43}$$

and the equation of motion with structural damping becomes:

$$m\ddot{x} + \frac{\alpha}{\pi\omega}\dot{x} + kx = f_0\sin\omega t \tag{Eq 44}$$

Therefore, the steady-state amplitude can be expressed as:

$$X = \frac{f_0}{\sqrt{(k - m\omega^2)^2 + \left(\frac{\alpha}{\pi}\right)^2}} \tag{Eq 45}$$

Example 6. Damping Force Proportional to Square of Velocity. When objects moving with moderate speed (<20 m/s) in fluid are resisted by a damping force proportional to the square of the speed, the damping force is expressed as:

$$f_d = \pm a\dot{x}^2 \tag{Eq 46}$$

where the negative sign is used when speed is positive and vice versa. The energy dissipated per cycle is expressed as:

$$U_d = \int_0^{2\pi} aX^3\omega^2\sin^3 u\, du$$

Integrating:
$$U_d = \frac{8}{3} aX^3 \omega^2$$

Then, equivalent viscous damping is expressed as:

$$c_{eq} = \frac{8}{3\pi} a\omega X \qquad \text{(Eq 47)}$$

The equation of motion becomes:

$$m\ddot{x} + \frac{8}{3\pi} a\omega X\dot{x} + kx = f_0 \sin \omega t \qquad \text{(Eq 48)}$$

and the resonant amplitude becomes:

$$X = \sqrt{\frac{3\pi f_0}{8a\omega_n{}^2}} \qquad \text{(Eq 49)}$$

FORCED HARMONIC VIBRATION

When the vibratory system of Fig. 1 is excited by a harmonic force:

$$f(t) = f_0 \sin \omega t$$

The equation of motion becomes:

$$\ddot{x} + 2\xi\omega_n\dot{x} + \omega_n{}^2 x = \omega_n{}^2 \delta_{st} \sin \omega t \qquad \text{(Eq 50)}$$

where $\delta_{st} = f_0/k$ = static deflection or zero frequency deflection and ω = forcing or driving frequency. The general solution of the second order nonhomogeneous differential equation is:

$$x(t) = x_{\text{homogeneous}} + x_{\text{steady state}} \qquad \text{(Eq 51)}$$

As $t \to \infty$, the homogeneous portion of the solution vanishes because resisting forces such as structural damping or friction are always present. The steady-state solution always exists as long as energy is supplied to the system through the forcing function. So, in harmonic forced vibration, x_{88} is most critical. The steady state solution for the harmonic excited vibration system is:

$$x(t) = X \sin (\omega t - \phi) \qquad \text{(Eq 52)}$$

where the amplitude of vibration and phase angle are given by:

$$\frac{X}{\delta_{st}} = \frac{1}{\sqrt{(1 - r^2)^2 + (2\xi r)^2}} \qquad \text{(Eq 53)}$$

and

$$\phi = \tan^{-1} \frac{2\xi r}{1 - r^2} \qquad \text{(Eq 54)}$$

and where $r = \dfrac{\omega}{\omega_n}$ = frequency ratio. Figure 13 shows the relationship between the amplitude ratio $\dfrac{X}{\delta_{st}}$ and r.

ROTATING UNBALANCED FORCES

A common source of forced vibration is the unbalance of rotating parts. Electric motors, turbines, and automobile engines are some examples. An elastically mounted system with the exciting force the rotation of an unbalanced disk or wheel is shown in Fig. 14. Excitation is the inertia type. The force is supplied by rotation of an eccentric mass m with eccentricity e. If m rotates with angular velocity ω, vertical displacement of the mass becomes $x + e \sin \omega t$, where x represents the motion of the spring-supported mass. Using M to represent the total mass including m, the equation for system motion becomes:

$$(M - m)\frac{d^2x}{dt^2} + m\frac{d^2}{dt^2} \quad (x + e \sin \omega t) = -kx - c\frac{dx}{dt} \tag{Eq 55}$$

or, by rearranging terms:

$$M\frac{d^2x}{dt^2} + c\frac{dx}{dt} + kx = (me\omega^2) \sin \omega t \tag{Eq 56}$$

The maximum displacement can be expressed as:

$$X = \frac{me\omega^2}{\sqrt{(k - M\omega^2)^2 + (c\omega)^2}} \tag{Eq 57}$$

$$\tan \phi = \frac{c\omega}{k - M\omega^2} \tag{Eq 58}$$

If the numerator and denominator of Eq 57 and Eq 58 are divided by k, and $\sqrt{k/M}$ is replaced by ω_n, the natural frequency of the system, Eq 57 and Eq 58 may be expressed as:

$$X = \frac{\dfrac{m}{M}er^2}{\sqrt{[1 - r^2]^2 + [2\xi r]^2}} \tag{Eq 59}$$

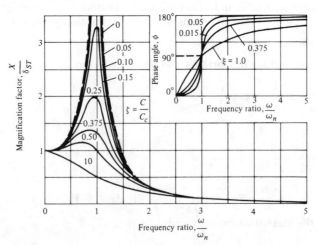

Figure 13   Static deflection versus frequency ratio

$$\tan \phi = \frac{2\xi r}{1 - r^2} \qquad \text{(Eq 60)}$$

where $r = \dfrac{\omega}{\omega_n}$ = frequency ratio and ξ = the damping factor. For convenience, MX/me and ϕ can be plotted against ω/ω_n for various values of the damping factor ξ. At low speeds, the exciting force $me\omega^2$ is small. When $\omega/\omega_n = 1.0$, $MX/me = \frac{1}{2}\xi$, and the amplitude is limited only by damping. When ω/ω_n is very large, the ratio MX/me approaches 1.0, and the mass $(M - m)$ has an amplitude $X = me/M$, 180° out of phase with m.

Example 7. The moving parts of a reciprocating engine produce dynamic forces that may cause undesirable vibrations. Although rotating parts such as the crankshaft can be balanced, more complex motions, like those of the piston and connecting rod, cannot be balanced so easily. In calculating un-balanced forces in a single-cylinder engine, the moving parts are divided into reciprocating and rotating weights. The connecting-rod weight is divided into two portions, the piston end and the crank end. Although this division into two lumped masses will lead to errors in the moment of inertia and conse-quently in the torque equation, the force analysis can be considered exact. With the rotating weight assumed to be counterbalanced, the force equation for the single-cylinder engine becomes:

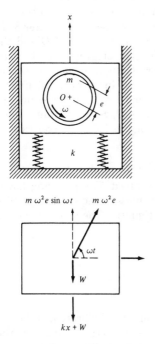

Figure 14 Rotating
unbalance machine

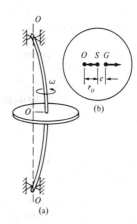

Figure 15 Whirling of
shaft due to unbalance

$$F = m_{rec} r \omega^2 (\cos \omega t + \frac{r}{l} \cos 2\omega t) = f_1 + f_2 \qquad \text{(Eq 61)}$$

where m_{rec} is the mass of the reciprocating weight and where f_1, which alternates once per revolution, is the primary force and f_2, which alternates twice per revolution, is the secondary force. For the in-line engine or one block of the V engine, Eq 61 can be added for each crank position ϕ_n so that the equation becomes:

$$F = m_{rec} r \omega^2 \sum_n [\cos (\omega t + \phi_n) + \frac{r}{l} \cos 2(\omega t + \phi_n)] \qquad \text{(Eq 62)}$$

By proper angular spacing ϕ_h of the n cylinders, the vibration force F can be eliminated.

WHIRLING OF ROTATING SHAFTS

At certain speeds, called critical, whirling, or whipping speed, rotating shafts tend to bow out and whirl. This effect is caused by such factors as the mass unbalance, hysteresis damping in the shaft, gyroscopic forces, oil friction in the journal bearings, and unsymmetrical stiffness of the shaft or bearings. Synchronous whirl in an idealized system is shown in Fig. 15. A single disk of mass m is symmetrically located on a shaft supported by two bearings. The center of mass G is at a radial distance e from the geometric center S. The center line of the bearings intersects the plane of the disk at O and the shaft center is deflected by $OS = r_0$. If the effects of gravity and friction are neglected, the disk is influenced by two forces, the restoring force of the shaft from S to O, and the centrifugal force through G in the outward direction. For equilibrium to be achieved, these two forces must be collinear, equal in magnitude, and opposite in direction. Thus, points O, S, and G must lie along a straight line. A discussion of the effects of the forces in two cases of synchronous whirling follows.

Example 8. Synchronous Whirling. The lateral deflection r_0 can be determined by equating the two forces involved. The restoring force of the shaft is kr_0, where k equals the lateral stiffness of the shaft at the disk, and $m\omega^2(r_0 + e)$ equals the centrifugal force. Equating the two expressions:

$$kr_0 = m\omega^2(r_0 + e) \qquad \text{(Eq 63)}$$

or

$$r_0 = \frac{m\omega^2 e}{k - m\omega^2} = \frac{(\omega/\omega_n)^2 e}{1 - (\omega/\omega_n)^2} \qquad \text{(Eq 64)}$$

where $\omega_n = \sqrt{k/m}$, the natural frequency of lateral vibration of the shaft and disk at zero speed. Equation 64 shows that the critical speed of the shaft equals the natural frequency of lateral vibration ω_n of the shaft and disk. Thus, r_0 is positive below the critical speed and negative for speeds greater than ω_n. Figure 16 shows two conditions: (a) for ω less than ω_n the system rotates with the heavy side G outside S, and (b) for ω greater than ω_n the light side, or the side opposite G, is outside S. Because $\dfrac{\omega}{\omega_n} = r =$ frequency ratio, Eq 64 can be further reduced to:

$$r_0 = \frac{er^2}{1 - r^2} \tag{Eq 65}$$

Example 9. Synchronous Whirling, Friction Included. Forces such as air friction opposing the whirl (described in Case 1) can be resolved into a force F and a moment about the shaft center, with the moment overcome by the driving torque of the shaft. The damping force F acting at S is assumed to be viscous. Thus, F is proportional to the tangential velocity $r\omega$, and may be expressed as:

$$F = cr_0\omega \tag{Eq 66}$$

where c is the coefficient of viscous friction. The frictional force F enables the radial distance line e to lead the lateral deflection line r_0 by the angle ϕ (Fig. 17). Intersection point O, geometric center S, and center of mass G are fixed relative to each other, and the system rotates together about O with speed ω. Summing forces along r_0 and perpendicular to r_0 produces:

$$\begin{aligned} -kr_0 + m\omega^2\rho \cos \alpha &= 0 \\ -cr_0\omega + m\omega^2\rho \sin \alpha &= 0 \end{aligned} \tag{Eq 67}$$

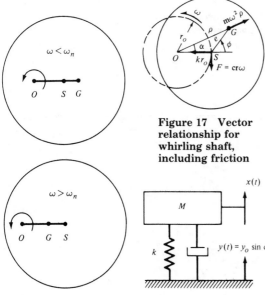

Figure 17 Vector relationship for whirling shaft, including friction

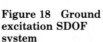

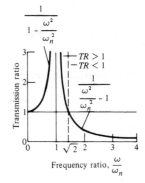

Figure 16 Undamped system

Figure 18 Ground excitation SDOF system

Figure 19 Transmissibility ratio versus frequency ratio

From Fig. 17, α and ϕ are related as follows:

$$\rho \sin \alpha = e \sin \phi$$
$$\rho \cos \alpha = r_0 + e \cos \phi \qquad \text{(Eq 68)}$$

Substituting, the equilibrium equations become:

$$-kr_0 + m\omega^2 (r_0 + e \cos \phi) = 0$$
$$-cr_0\omega + m\omega^2 e \sin \phi = 0 \qquad \text{(Eq 69)}$$

Solving simultaneously for ϕ and r_0:

$$\tan \phi = \frac{c\omega}{k - m\omega^2} = \frac{2\xi(\omega/\omega_n)}{1 - (\omega/\omega_n)^2} \qquad \text{(Eq 70)}$$

and

$$r_0 = \frac{m\omega^2 e \cos \phi}{k - m\omega^2} = \frac{m\omega^2 e}{\sqrt{(k - m\omega^2)^2 + (c\omega)^2}}$$

$$= \frac{e(\omega/\omega_n)^2}{\sqrt{[1 - (\omega/\omega_n)^2]^2 + [2\xi(\omega/\omega_n)]^2}} \qquad \text{(Eq 71)}$$

FORCED VIBRATION FROM HARMONIC GROUND MOTION

An elastic structure may be influenced by unwanted vibration if the base or foundation of the structure moves. For example, consider the elastically supported system shown in Fig. 18, with the spring and mass system subjected to the movement $y(t) = y_0 \sin \omega t$, where y = maximum ground amplitude. The equation of motion for the harmonic ground excited system is:

$$M\ddot{x} + c(\dot{x} - \dot{y}) + k(x - y) = 0 \qquad \text{(Eq 72)}$$

where $x(t) \equiv$ absolute displacement of mass M and $y(t) \equiv$ absolute displacement of foundation. Assuming $x > y$ and $z = x - y \equiv$ relative displacement of M, the equation can be rewritten as:

$$\ddot{z} + 2\xi\omega_n\dot{z} + \omega_n^2 z = -y_0\omega^2 \sin \omega t \qquad \text{(Eq 73)}$$

The steady-state solution of the above equation becomes:

$$z = Z \sin(\omega t - \phi) - y_0 \sin \omega t \qquad \text{(Eq 74)}$$

where

$$Z = y_0 \sqrt{\frac{1 + (2\xi r)^2}{(1 - r^2)^2 + (2\xi r)^2}}$$

and

$$\phi = \tan^{-1} \frac{2\xi r^3}{1 - r^2 + (2\xi r)^2}$$

VIBRATION TRANSMISSIBILITY ISOLATION

With properly designed springs, which are referred to as isolators, excessive vibratory forces generated by machines and engines can be reduced substantially. Two cases of vibration transmissibility, or vibration isolation, are discussed below.

Example 10. Force Excitation. If F_t is defined as the transmitted force through the spring/damper system, then the foundation force is:

$$|F_t| = X\sqrt{k^2 + c^2\omega^2} \qquad \text{(Eq 75)}$$

Transmissibility is defined as the ratio of the foundation and input forces, that is:

$$TR = \left|\frac{F_t}{F_0}\right| = \sqrt{\frac{1 + (2\xi r)^2}{(1 - r^2)^2 + (2\xi r)^2}} \qquad \text{(Eq 76)}$$

Example 11. Harmonic Base Motion. For harmonic base motion as shown in Fig. 18, the transmissibility is given by:

$$TR = \left|\frac{z}{y_0}\right| = \sqrt{\frac{1 + (2\xi r)^2}{(1 - r^2)^2 + (2\xi r)^2}} \qquad \text{(Eq 77)}$$

Some of the important properties of transmissibility are as follows and can be observed from Fig. 19:

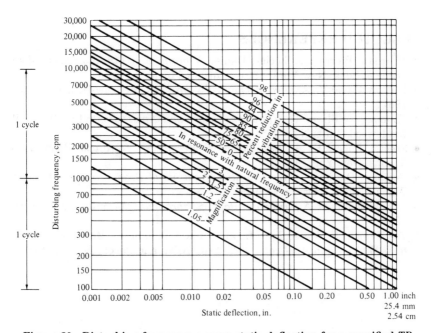

Figure 20 Disturbing frequency versus static deflection for a specified _TR_

- Vibration isolation is possible when the frequency ratio is greater than $\sqrt{2}$. In this case $TR < 1$
- For $r > \sqrt{2}$, TR with damping is greater than TR without damping
- When the damping is negligible, the transmissibility equation is reduced to the following:

$$TR = \frac{1}{(\omega/\omega_n)^2 - 1} \tag{Eq 78}$$

where ω/ω_n is always greater than $\sqrt{2}$. By replacing ω_n^2 in Eq 78 with g/Δ, where Δ is the static deflection of the system, transmissibility becomes:

$$TR = \frac{1}{\frac{(2\pi f)^2 \Delta}{g} - 1} \tag{Eq 79}$$

Solving for f, we obtain with Δ in millimeters:

$$f = 15.76 \sqrt{\frac{1}{\Delta}\left(\frac{1}{TR} + 1\right)} \, \text{Hz} \tag{Eq 80}$$

Defining the reduction in TR as $R = 1 - TR$, Eq 80 can be written as:

$$f = 15.76 \sqrt{\frac{1}{\Delta}\left(\frac{2 - R}{1 - R}\right)} \, \text{Hz}$$

Fig. 20 shows an f vs Δ plot with R as parameter.

SELECTED REFERENCES

- Thureau, Pierre and Lecler, Daniel, *Vibrations of Linear Systems,* John Wiley & Sons, New York, 1981, translated by J. Grosjeau
- Hutton, David V., *Applied Mechanical Vibrations,* McGraw-Hill, New York, 1981
- Thomson, William T., *Vibration Theory and Applications,* Prentice-Hall, Englewood Cliffs, NJ, 1965
- Steidel, Robert F., *An Introduction to Mechanical Vibrations,* John Wiley & Sons, New York, 1971
- Gorman, Daniel J., *Free Vibration Analysis of Beams and Shafts,* John Wiley & Sons, New York, 1975
- Anderson, Roger A., *Fundamentals of Vibrations,* Macmillan, New York, 1967
- Tse, Francis S., Morse, Ivan E., and Hinkle, Rolland T., *Mechanical Vibrations, Theory and Applications,* 2nd ed., Allyn and Bacon, Boston, 1978

17
Kinematics

By Mamerto L. Chu, Ph.D.
Department of Mechanical Engineering
University of Akron

KINEMATICS OF A PARTICLE

Coordinate Systems. The five coordinate systems, classified according to two or three dimensions, are shown in Fig. 1 through 5. When the two-dimensional Cartesian and polar coordinate systems of Fig. 1 and 4 are placed in a plane, with their origins in coincidence, then the Cartesian and polar coordinates of a point $P(x, y)$ and $P(\rho, \phi)$ are related as follows:

$$x = \rho \cos \phi \tag{Eq 1}$$

$$y = \rho \sin \phi \tag{Eq 2}$$

Example 1. Figures 1 and 4 show by inspection that $x = \rho \cos \phi$ and $y = \rho \sin \phi$. Because $\cos^2 \phi + \sin^2 \phi = 1$, squaring and adding the expressions produces:

$$x^2 + y^2 = \rho^2 \tag{Eq 3}$$

Dividing Eq 2 by Eq 1 gives:

$$\phi = \tan^{-1}\left(\frac{y}{x}\right) \tag{Eq 4}$$

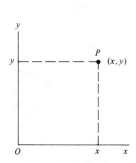

Figure 1 Cartesian coordinates—two dimensions

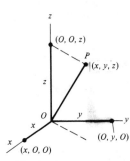

Figure 2 Cartesian coordinates—three dimensions

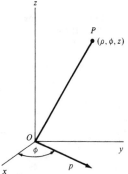

Figure 3 Cylindrical coordinates

Figures 2 and 3 establish the relationship between two coordinate systems when their origins and z-axes coincide. Because the two sets of coordinates of a point P are (x, y, z) and (ρ, ϕ, z), then:

$$x = \rho \cos \phi \qquad y = \rho \sin \phi \qquad z = z \qquad \text{(Eq 5)}$$

From this, $x^2 + y^2 + z^2 = \rho^2 + z^2$. Eliminating z^2, $x^2 + y^2 = \rho^2$. The unit vectors for the coordinate systems of Fig. 1 through 5 are shown graphically in Fig. 6 through 9.

Example 2. To express the polar unit vectors ρ and ϕ in terms of Cartesian unit vectors $\mathbf{i}$ and $\mathbf{j}$, use the components of ρ and ϕ along $\mathbf{i}$ and $\mathbf{j}$, shown in Fig. 10:

$$\rho = \mathbf{i} \cos \phi + \mathbf{j} \cos (90 - \phi) = \mathbf{i} \cos \phi + \mathbf{j} \sin \phi$$
$$\phi = \mathbf{i} \cos (90 - \phi) + \mathbf{j} \cos \phi = -\mathbf{i} \sin \phi + \mathbf{j} \cos \phi$$

The components $\mathbf{i}$ and $\mathbf{j}$ along ρ and ϕ are expressed as:

$$\mathbf{i} = \rho \cos \phi - \phi \cos (90 - \phi) = \rho \cos \phi - \phi \sin \phi$$
$$\mathbf{j} = \rho \sin \phi + \phi \cos \phi$$

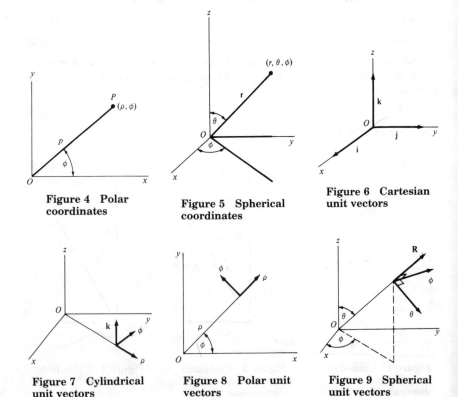

Figure 4 Polar coordinates

Figure 5 Spherical coordinates

Figure 6 Cartesian unit vectors

Figure 7 Cylindrical unit vectors

Figure 8 Polar unit vectors

Figure 9 Spherical unit vectors

Example 3. To express the cylindrical unit vectors ρ, φ, and **k** in terms of Cartesian unit vectors **i**, **j**, and **k**, use the components of ρ, φ, and **k** along i, j, and k, shown in Fig. 6 and 7:

$$\rho = \mathbf{i} \cos \phi + \mathbf{j} \sin \phi$$
$$\phi = -\mathbf{i} \sin \phi + \mathbf{j} \cos \phi$$
$$\mathbf{k} = \mathbf{k}$$

Similarly:

$$\mathbf{i} = \rho \cos \phi - \phi \sin \phi$$
$$\mathbf{j} = \rho \sin \phi + \phi \cos \phi$$
$$\mathbf{k} = \mathbf{k}$$

Displacement of a Particle. A moving particle generates a path. In Fig. 11(a), for a particle R initially located at R_1 and later at R_2, the displacement of R is the directed line segment R_1 to R_2. Having both magnitude and direction, it is a vector quantity. Displacement is the net position change. Fig. 11(b) shows particle R moving by a circuitous route from R_1 to R_2. Nevertheless, the displacement of R is the vector from R_1 to R_2, designated as $\mathbf{\Delta R}$.

Figure 12 illustrates the general case of the plane motion of a particle. R_1 and R_2 are two positions of R, defined by the rectangular coordinates $R_1(x_1, y_1)$ and $R_2(x_2, y_2)$ or the polar coordinates $R_1(\rho_1, \phi_1)$ and $R_2(\rho_2, \phi_2)$. The points may be defined by the position vectors $\mathbf{R}_1$ and $\mathbf{R}_2$. If the position vectors are now placed, then $\mathbf{\Delta R}$ is defined by the vector equations:

$$\mathbf{R}_2 = \mathbf{R}_1 + \mathbf{\Delta R} \qquad \mathbf{\Delta R} = \mathbf{R}_2 - \mathbf{R}_1 \qquad \text{(Eq 6)}$$

Relative Displacement. The vectors $\mathbf{R}_A$ and $\mathbf{R}_B$ in Fig. 13(a) are position vectors which describe the positions of A and B in the xy coordinate system. The vector $\mathbf{R}_{BA}$ describes the position of B relative to A in the same xy system. The combined vectors are related by:

$$\mathbf{R}_B = \mathbf{R}_A + \mathbf{R}_{BA} \qquad \text{(Eq 7)}$$

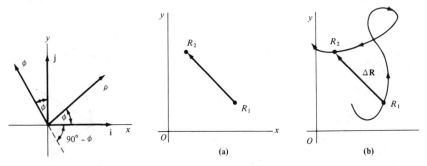

(a)　　　　(b)

Figure 10　Diagram for polar and Cartesian unit vectors

Figure 11　Displacement of a particle

In Fig. 13(b) the same three vectors are shown in polar form. If A and B are fixed in the same rigid body, then the body may translate, rotate, or it may be affected by both translation and rotation, as shown in Fig. 14. A moving $x'y'$ system is attached to the body with origin at A. With pure translation, the $x'y'$ system moves from position 1 to position 2, as shown in Fig. 14(a), displacements of A and B are identical, and $\Delta \mathbf{R}_B = \Delta \mathbf{R}_A$. With $\mathbf{R}_{B_2A} = \mathbf{R}_{B_1A}$, the displacement of B relative to A, $\Delta \mathbf{R}_{BA}$, is zero. Thus using Eq 7:

$$\Delta \mathbf{R}_B = \Delta \mathbf{R}_A + \Delta \mathbf{R}_{BA}$$
$$\Delta \mathbf{R}_{BA} = \Delta \mathbf{R}_B - \Delta \mathbf{R}_A = 0 \tag{Eq 8}$$

With the $x'y'$ system in pure rotation, as shown in Fig. 14b, point B has an absolute displacement $\Delta \mathbf{R}_B$ because B is fixed in the rotating $x'y'$ system. The relative-position vector $\mathbf{R}_{BA}$ also is fixed. Thus:

$$\mathbf{R}_{B_1A} = \mathbf{R}_{B_2A} \tag{Eq 9}$$

The displacement of B relative to A is zero. If B_1 and B_2 are referred to the $x_1'y_1'$ system, then:

$$\Delta \mathbf{R}_B = \mathbf{R}_{B_2A} - \mathbf{R}_{B_1A} = \Delta \mathbf{R}_{BA} \tag{Eq 10}$$

Therefore, in Eq 8, $\Delta \mathbf{R}_A = 0$, and $\Delta \mathbf{R}_{BA} = \Delta \mathbf{R}_B$. Equation 10 demonstrates that when both A and B are fixed to a body, the displacement of B relative to A, $\Delta \mathbf{R}_{BA}$, denotes the displacement of B in a nonrotating coordinate system with origin at A. Figure 14(c) shows a system with both translation and rotation. Displacement of B has the components $\Delta \mathbf{R}_A$, the translational component, and $\Delta \mathbf{R}_{BA}$, the rotational component. Thus:

$$\Delta \mathbf{R}_B = \Delta \mathbf{R}_A + \Delta \mathbf{R}_{BA} \tag{Eq 11}$$

Figure 15 shows a point P moving relative to another moving body. Consider points B and A as fixed to the same rigid body, and point P as instantaneously coincident with point B in the B_1 position. In Fig. 15(a), the $x'y'$ system with fixed points A and B moves in pure translation from position 1 to position 2. Point P moves from P_1 to P_2. From an observer fixed to the $x'y'$ system, the displacement of P is:

$$\Delta \mathbf{R}_P{}^R = \mathbf{R}_{P_2} - \mathbf{R}_{P_1} \tag{Eq 12}$$

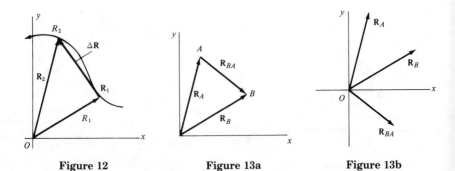

| Figure 12 | Figure 13a | Figure 13b |

a relative displacement. The absolute displacement of P is then:

$$\Delta\mathbf{R}_P = \Delta\mathbf{R}_A + \Delta\mathbf{R}_P{}^R \qquad\text{(Eq 13)}$$

where P moves relative to a translating system. For motion of P in a reference system with pure rotation, as shown in Fig. 15(b), $\Delta\mathbf{R}_A$ is zero; the absolute displacement of P has two components: $\Delta\mathbf{R}_{BA}$, the displacement of point B, and $\Delta\mathbf{R}_P{}^R$, the relative displacement of P in the rotating $x'y'$ system. Thus, the absolute displacement of P becomes:

$$\Delta\mathbf{R}_P = \Delta\mathbf{R}_{BA} + \Delta\mathbf{R}_P{}^R \qquad\text{(Eq 14)}$$

Figure 15(c) shows the $x'y'$ system in translation from position 1 to position 2 and in rotation from position 2 to position 3.

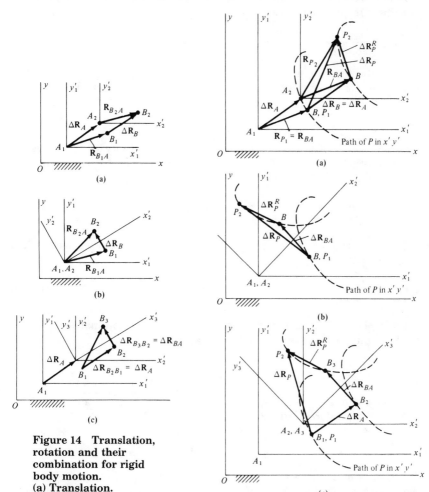

Figure 14 Translation,
rotation and their
combination for rigid
body motion.
(a) Translation.
(b) Rotation.
(c) Translation and
rotation

Figure 15 Motion of a point relative
to another moving body

The displacement of P consists of three components:

$\Delta \mathbf{R}_A$ = component due to translation of $x'y'$
$\Delta \mathbf{R}_{BA}$ = relative rotational displacement of point B fixed in $x'y'$
$\Delta \mathbf{R}_P{}^R$ = relative displacement of P in $x'y'$

Thus:

$$\Delta \mathbf{R}_P = \Delta \mathbf{R}_A + \Delta \mathbf{R}_{BA} + \Delta \mathbf{R}_P{}^R \tag{Eq 15}$$

Substituting Eq 11 for the displacement of the coincident point B, produces:

$$\Delta \mathbf{R}_P = \Delta \mathbf{R}_B + \Delta \mathbf{R}_P{}^R \tag{Eq 16}$$

Linear velocity is motion along a straight line. If the x-axis is the line of of motion, the average velocity is:

$$v_{av} = \bar{v} = \frac{x_2 - x_1}{t_2 - t_1} = \frac{\Delta x}{\Delta t} \tag{Eq 17}$$

with Δx the distance in time Δt. If the object is at x_1 and x_2 at times t_1 and t_2, instantaneous velocity is:

$$v = \lim_{\Delta t \to 0} \frac{\Delta x}{\Delta t} = \frac{dx}{dt} \tag{Eq 18}$$

If the position x is a function of time t, instantaneous velocity v is the derivative of x with respect to t. The distance d moved between times t_1 and t_2 is obtained by integrating Eq 18:

$$d = x_2 - x_1 = \int_{t_1}^{t_2} v(t)\,dt \tag{Eq 19}$$

Velocity also is defined as the time rate of change of the position vector of the body. Velocity $\mathbf{v}$ of a point specified by position vector $\mathbf{r}$ is:

$$\mathbf{v} = \frac{d\mathbf{r}}{dt} \tag{Eq 20}$$

Example 4. To express $\mathbf{v}$ in terms of $\mathbf{r}$ in Cartesian coordinates, use Eq 20. In Cartesian coordinates, $\mathbf{r} = x\mathbf{i} + y\mathbf{j} + z\mathbf{k}$. Differentiating produces:

$$\mathbf{v} = \frac{d\mathbf{r}}{dt} = \mathbf{i}\frac{dx}{dt} + \mathbf{j}\frac{dy}{dt} + \mathbf{k}\frac{dz}{dt}$$

To express $\mathbf{v}$ in terms of $\mathbf{r}$ in polar coordinates, using the result above, $\mathbf{r} = x\mathbf{i} + y\mathbf{j} = \rho\boldsymbol{\rho}$. With differentiation:

$$\mathbf{v} = \frac{d\mathbf{r}}{dt} = \frac{d}{dt}(\rho\boldsymbol{\rho}) = \boldsymbol{\rho}\frac{d\rho}{dt} + \rho\frac{d\boldsymbol{\rho}}{dt}$$

As the position vector $\mathbf{r}$ changes in time, the unit vector $\boldsymbol{\rho}$ also changes direction. In Cartesian coordinates, the unit vectors $\mathbf{i}$, $\mathbf{j}$, and $\mathbf{k}$ remain constant in magnitude and direction, but the direction of $\boldsymbol{\rho}$ changes. The change $d\boldsymbol{\rho}$ in $\boldsymbol{\rho}$ is $|\boldsymbol{\rho}|d\phi = d\phi$ since $|\boldsymbol{\rho}| = 1$ (Fig. 16). Because $d\boldsymbol{\rho}$ is along $\boldsymbol{\phi}$, $d\boldsymbol{\rho} = \boldsymbol{\phi}d\phi$. Thus:

$$\frac{d\boldsymbol{\rho}}{dt} = \boldsymbol{\phi}\,\frac{d\phi}{dt}$$

Substituting this expression for **v** above:

$$\mathbf{v} = \boldsymbol{\rho}\,\frac{d\rho}{dt} + \boldsymbol{\phi}\rho\,\frac{d\phi}{dt}$$

Setting $\dfrac{d\phi}{dt} = \omega$ produces $\mathbf{v} = \boldsymbol{\rho}\,\dfrac{d\rho}{dt} + \boldsymbol{\phi}\,\rho\omega$. In this way, velocity **v** is resolved into one component along the radius vector **r** and another component perpendicular to it; dr/dt corresponds to the rate of change of **r**, and $r\omega$ represents the rate of change of the direction of **r**.

Linear acceleration a is the time rate of change of linear velocity **v**:

$$\mathbf{a} = \frac{d\mathbf{v}}{dt} \qquad \text{(Eq 21)}$$

Average acceleration is:

$$\mathbf{a}_{av} = \mathbf{a} = \frac{\mathbf{v}_2 - \mathbf{v}_1}{t_2 - t_1} = \frac{\Delta \mathbf{v}}{\Delta t} \qquad \text{(Eq 22)}$$

when at time t_1, the velocity is $\mathbf{v}_1$, and at t_2, it is $\mathbf{v}_2$. Equation 21 represents the limit of $\mathbf{a}_{av}$ as Δt goes to zero; that is:

$$\mathbf{a} = \lim_{\Delta t \to 0} \frac{\Delta \mathbf{v}}{\Delta t} = \frac{d\mathbf{v}}{dt} \qquad \text{(Eq 23)}$$

Example 5. To find the position and velocity of a point moving along the x-axis at a constant acceleration of **a** ft/s^2 at time t if at $t = 0$, $v = v_0$ and $x = x_0$, use Eq 21, $d\mathbf{v} = \mathbf{a}\,dt$. If v is the velocity at time t:

$$\int_{v_0}^{v} d\mathbf{v} = \int_{0}^{t} \mathbf{a}\,dt$$

Integrating produces $v - v_0 = \mathbf{a}t$. Solving for v, $v = v_0 + \mathbf{a}t$. From Eq 18, $dx = v\,dt$. Using the above result for v:

$$\int_{x_0}^{x} dx = \int_{t=0}^{t} (v_0 + \mathbf{a}t)\,dt$$

With integration:

$$x - x_0 = v_0 t + \tfrac{1}{2}\mathbf{a}t^2$$

Expressions for Velocity and Accelerations in Various Coordinate Systems. In three dimensional Cartesian coordinates, the velocity vector **v** is:

$$\mathbf{v} = \mathbf{i}\,\frac{dx}{dt} + \mathbf{j}\,\frac{dy}{dt} + \mathbf{k}\,\frac{dz}{dt} \qquad \text{(Eq 24)}$$

In cylindrical coordinates:

$$\mathbf{v} = \rho\frac{d\rho}{dt} + \boldsymbol{\phi}\rho\frac{d\phi}{dt} + \mathbf{k}\frac{dz}{dt} \tag{Eq 25}$$

In spherical coordinates:

$$\mathbf{v} = \mathbf{R}\frac{dr}{dt} + \boldsymbol{\theta}r\frac{d\theta}{dt} + \boldsymbol{\phi}r\sin\theta\frac{d\phi}{dt} \tag{Eq 26}$$

If a dot above a quantity indicates its time derivative, the velocity vector in Cartesian coordinates is:

$$\mathbf{v} = \mathbf{i}\,\dot{x} + \mathbf{j}\,\dot{y} + \mathbf{k}\,\dot{z} \tag{Eq 27}$$

In cylindrical coordinates:

$$\mathbf{v} = \rho\,\dot{\rho} + \boldsymbol{\phi}\,\rho\dot{\phi} + \mathbf{k}\,\dot{z} \tag{Eq 28}$$

In spherical coordinates:

$$\mathbf{v} = \mathbf{R}\,\dot{r} + \boldsymbol{\theta}r\,\dot{\theta} + \boldsymbol{\phi}r\sin\theta\,\dot{\phi} \tag{Eq 29}$$

Acceleration is:

$$\mathbf{a} = \frac{d\mathbf{v}}{dt} = \frac{d^2\mathbf{r}}{dt^2} = \ddot{\mathbf{r}} \tag{Eq 30}$$

Differentiating Eq 27, 28, and 29 with respect to time:

In Cartesian coordinates:

$$\mathbf{a} = \mathbf{i}\,\ddot{x} + \mathbf{j}\,\ddot{y} + \mathbf{k}\,\ddot{z} = a_x\mathbf{i} + a_y\mathbf{j} + a_z\mathbf{k} \tag{Eq 31}$$

In cylindrical coordinates:

$$\mathbf{a} = \rho\,(\ddot{\rho} - \rho\,\dot{\phi}^2) + \boldsymbol{\phi}(\rho\,\ddot{\phi} + 2\,\dot{\rho}\,\dot{\phi}) + \mathbf{k}\,\ddot{z} \tag{Eq 32}$$

In spherical coordinates:

$$\mathbf{a} = \mathbf{R}\,(\ddot{r} - r\dot{\theta}^2 - r\sin\theta\,\dot{\phi}^2) + \boldsymbol{\theta}(r\,\ddot{\theta} + 2\dot{r}\,\dot{\theta} - r\sin\theta\cos\theta\,\dot{\phi}^2)$$
$$+ \boldsymbol{\phi}(2\dot{\phi}\dot{r}\sin\theta + 2r\dot{\theta}\,\dot{\phi}\cos\theta + r\,\ddot{\phi}\sin\theta) \tag{Eq 33}$$

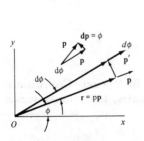

Figure 16

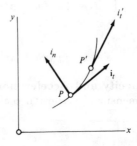

Figure 17a

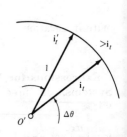

Figure 17b

CURVILINEAR MOTION—TANGENTIAL
AND NORMAL COMPONENTS

Plane Motion of a Particle. For a particle moving along a curve in Fig. 17, let P be the initial instantaneous position of the particle. At P, a unit vector $\mathbf{i}_t$ is tangent to the path of the particle in the direction of motion (Fig. 17a). The unit vector $\mathbf{i}_t'$ corresponds to the position P' of the particle at a later instant. From the same origin O', the vector $\Delta\mathbf{i}_t = \mathbf{i}_t' - \mathbf{i}_t$ (Fig. 17b). The magnitude of $\Delta\mathbf{i}_t$ is $2\sin(\Delta\theta/2)$. As $\Delta\theta$ approaches zero, the vector $\Delta\mathbf{i}_t/\Delta\theta$ becomes tangent to the unit circle of Fig. 17(b) and perpendicular to $\mathbf{i}_t$, and its magnitude approaches:

$$\lim_{\Delta\theta\to 0} \frac{2\sin(\Delta\theta/2)}{\Delta\theta} = \lim_{\Delta\theta\to 0} \frac{\sin(\Delta\theta/2)}{\Delta\theta/2} = 1$$

Thus, the vector $\Delta\mathbf{i}_t$ at the limit is a unit vector along the normal to the path of the particle. Thus $\mathbf{i}_n$, the normal unit vector (Fig. 17a), is:

$$\mathbf{i}_n = \lim_{\Delta\theta\to 0} \frac{\Delta\mathbf{i}_t}{\Delta\theta}$$

$$\mathbf{i}_n = \frac{d\mathbf{i}_t}{d\theta} \qquad \text{(Eq 34)}$$

Because the particle velocity $\mathbf{v}$ is tangent to the path, it may be expressed as the product of the scalar v and the unit vector $\mathbf{i}_t$:

$$\mathbf{v} = v\mathbf{i}_t \qquad \text{(Eq 35)}$$

Differentiating Eq 35 with respect to t, to obtain the acceleration of the particle:

$$\mathbf{a} = \frac{d\mathbf{v}}{dt} = \frac{dv}{dt}\mathbf{i}_t + v\frac{d\mathbf{i}_t}{dt} \qquad \text{(Eq 36)}$$

But:

$$\frac{d\mathbf{i}_t}{dt} = \frac{d\mathbf{i}_t}{d\theta}\frac{d\theta}{ds}\frac{ds}{dt}$$

and $\dfrac{ds}{dt} = v, \dfrac{d\theta}{ds} = \dfrac{1}{\rho}$, where ρ is the radius of curvature of the path at P in Fig. 18, and

$$\frac{d\mathbf{i}_t}{d\theta} = i_n$$

Therefore:

$$\frac{d\mathbf{i}_t}{dt} = \frac{v}{\rho}\mathbf{i}_n \qquad \text{(Eq 37)}$$

Substituting this expression into Eq 36:

$$\mathbf{a} = \frac{dv}{dt}\mathbf{i}_t + \frac{v^2}{\rho}\mathbf{i}_n \qquad \text{(Eq 38)}$$

or $\mathbf{a} = a_t \mathbf{i}_t + a_n \mathbf{i}_n$. Thus, the scalar components of the acceleration are:

$$a_t = \frac{dv}{dt} \qquad a_n = \frac{v^2}{\rho} \qquad \text{(Eq 39)}$$

Depending upon whether particle speed increases or decreases, a_t is positive or negative and the direction of vector component $\mathbf{a}_t$ is in the direction of motion or against it. The vector component $\mathbf{a}_n$ is always directed toward the center of curvature C (Fig. 19).

ANGULAR MOTION

Angular velocity is the time rate of change of angular position. A moving point is specified by its position in polar coordinates (ρ, ϕ). For circular motion, ρ is constant. If at time t_1, the angular position is ϕ_1, and at time t_2, it is ϕ_2, the average angular velocity is expressed as:

$$\omega_{av} = \overline{\omega} = \frac{\phi_2 - \phi_1}{t_2 - t_1} = \frac{\Delta\phi}{\Delta t} \qquad \text{(Eq 40)}$$

Instantaneous angular velocity is:

$$\omega = \lim_{\Delta t \to 0} \frac{\Delta\phi}{\Delta t} = \frac{d\phi}{dt} \qquad \text{(Eq 41)}$$

If ω is a function of time t, then the angle formed by vector ρ in time Δt is:

$$\phi = \phi_2 - \phi_1 = \int_{t_1}^{t_2} \frac{d\phi}{dt}\, dt = \int_{t_1}^{t_2} \omega(t)\, dt \qquad \text{(Eq 42)}$$

Angular velocity typically is expressed in radians per second (rad/s). A radian is the angle subtended by an arc equal in length to the radius of a circle; therefore, there are 2π radians in $360°$. If 3θ is the angle subtended by an arc with length s at the center of a circle with radius R, then $\theta = \frac{s}{R}$ radians. Since angular velocity is $\omega = \frac{d\theta}{dt}$ and θ is expressed in radians, angular velocity is expressed in rad/s.

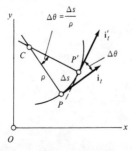

Figure 18

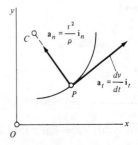

Figure 19

The frequency f of periodic motion is the number of cycles completed in 1 s. If T is the number of seconds required to complete one cycle or revolution, the frequency is:

$$f = \frac{1}{T} \qquad \text{(Eq 43)}$$

with the dimensions of per second, s^{-1}. The relationship between the angular velocity ω of the motion and f and T is:

$$\omega = \frac{2\pi}{T} \text{ rad/s} = 2\pi f \text{ rad/s} \qquad \text{(Eq 44)}$$

When the angular position of a point moving in a circle of radius r changes by $\Delta\phi$, the point moves a distance $r\Delta\phi$ (Fig. 20). The distance $r\Delta\phi$ is the arc length when $\Delta\phi$ is expressed in radians. Thus, the velocity of the point tangent to the circle is $v_t = \frac{r\Delta\phi}{\Delta t} = r\frac{\Delta\phi}{\Delta t}$. Because $\frac{\Delta\phi}{\Delta t} = \omega$, tangential velocity with ω expressed in rad/s is:

$$v_t = r\omega \qquad \text{(Eq 45)}$$

In Fig. 21, the angular velocity is represented by a vector $\boldsymbol{\omega}$ perpendicular to the plane of motion. The direction of $\boldsymbol{\omega}$ is determined by the right-hand rule. From Eq 45, the tangential velocity v_t of a point moving in a circle of radius a is $v_t = a\omega$. With the position vector $\mathbf{r}$, the radius is $a = \mathbf{r} \sin\phi$. Thus, $v_t = \omega \mathbf{r} \sin\phi$. In terms of the vectors $\mathbf{v}_t$, $\boldsymbol{\omega}$, and $\mathbf{r}$, the tangential velocity vector $\mathbf{v}_t$ is:

$$\mathbf{v}_t = \boldsymbol{\omega} \times \mathbf{r} \qquad \text{(Eq 46)}$$

with magnitude $v_t = |\mathbf{v}_t| = |\boldsymbol{\omega} \times \mathbf{r}| = \omega r \sin\phi$, and the direction of $\boldsymbol{\omega} \times \mathbf{r}$ is that of $\mathbf{v}_t$.

Angular acceleration is the rate of change of angular velocity. If ω is the angular velocity at time t, and α the angular acceleration, then:

$$\alpha = \frac{d\omega}{dt} \qquad \text{(Eq 47)}$$

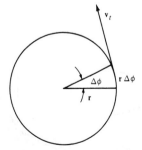

Figure 20 Tangential velocity v_t

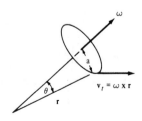

Figure 21 Angular velocity vector

If the angular velocity is ω_1 at time t_1 and ω_2 at time t_2, then the average angular acceleration is:

$$\alpha_{av} = \bar{\alpha} = \frac{\omega_2 - \omega_1}{t_2 - t_1} = \frac{\Delta \omega}{\Delta t} \qquad \text{(Eq 48)}$$

Equation 47 represents the limit of α_{av} as Δt goes to zero, that is, $\alpha = \lim_{\Delta t \to 0} \frac{\Delta \omega}{\Delta t} = \frac{d\omega}{dt}$.

Example 6. To relate the angular velocity of a point at constant speed to its radial acceleration, note that in Fig. 22 the change in the direction of v is $d\phi$. Thus, the change in v is $dv = v\,d\phi$. Dividing by dt, $\frac{dv}{dt} = v\frac{d\phi}{dt}$. Acceleration dv/dt is directed along ρ toward the center of the circle; thus it is a radial acceleration. Since $v = \omega\rho$, $\frac{dv}{dt} = v\frac{d\phi}{dt} = v\,\omega = \omega^2\rho = \frac{v^2}{\rho}$. If ω changes in magnitude only, then the α direction is along ω, as shown in Fig. 23. The magnitude of the tangential acceleration $\mathbf{a}_t$ is:

$$a_t = r\frac{d\omega}{dt} = r\alpha \qquad \text{(Eq 49)}$$

In vector form:

$$\mathbf{a}_t = \boldsymbol{\alpha} \times \mathbf{r} \qquad \text{(Eq 50)}$$

RELATIVE MOTION IN A PLANE

Translating Reference Axes. In analyzing the plane curvilinear motion of two particles in Fig. 24, motion of A is observed from a translating frame of reference x-y with origin at B. The position vector of A relative to an observer at B is $\mathbf{r}_{A/B} = \mathbf{i}x + \mathbf{j}y$ where $\mathbf{i}$ and $\mathbf{j}$ are unit vectors along the x- and y-axes. The position of B is measured by its vector $\mathbf{r}_B$. The absolute position of A in the fixed system X-Y is:

$$\mathbf{r}_A = \mathbf{r}_B + \mathbf{r}_{A/B} \qquad \text{(Eq 51)}$$

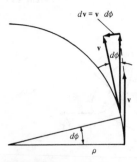

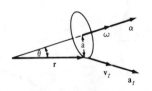

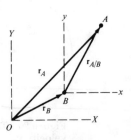

Figure 22
Relationship of
angular velocity and
radial acceleration

Figure 23   Angular
acceleration vector α
with ω constant in
direction

Figure 24

Velocity is:

$$\dot{\mathbf{r}}_A = \dot{\mathbf{r}}_B + \dot{\mathbf{r}}_{A/B}$$
$$\mathbf{v}_A = \mathbf{v}_B + \mathbf{v}_{A/B}$$

(Eq 52)

and acceleration is:

$$\ddot{\mathbf{r}}_A = \ddot{\mathbf{r}}_B + \ddot{\mathbf{r}}_{A/B}$$
$$\mathbf{a}_A = \mathbf{a}_B + \mathbf{a}_{A/B}$$

(Eq 53)

The velocity of A measured relative to x-y is $\dot{\mathbf{r}}_{A/B} = \mathbf{v}_{A/B} = \mathbf{i}\dot{x} + \mathbf{j}\dot{y}$, and the acceleration of A measured relative to x-y is $\ddot{\mathbf{r}}_{A/B} = \dot{\mathbf{v}}_{A/B} = \mathbf{a}_{A/B} = \mathbf{i}\ddot{x} + \mathbf{j}\ddot{y}$. In these differentiations, unit vectors have no derivatives because their directions and magnitudes remain unchanged.

Rotating Reference Axes. A rotating reference system aids in solving problems where motion occurs in a system that itself is rotating. For example, the path of a fluid particle moving along the curved vane of a centrifugal pump can be important in design. Fig. 25(a) shows the curvilinear plane motion of two particles A and B in a fixed X-Y plane. The motion of A is observed from a moving reference frame x-y with origin at B and rotating with an angular velocity $\omega = \dot{\theta}$. Angular velocity may be expressed as the vector $\boldsymbol{\omega} = \mathbf{k}\omega = \mathbf{k}\dot{\theta}$ normal to the plane of motion and with its positive sense in the positive Z-direction as established by the right-hand rule. The absolute position of A is given by $\mathbf{r}_A = \mathbf{r}_B + \mathbf{r} = \mathbf{r}_B + (\mathbf{i}x + \mathbf{j}y)$, where $\mathbf{r}$ stands for $\mathbf{r}_{A/B}$. Because the unit vectors $\mathbf{i}$ and $\mathbf{j}$ are rotating, their time derivatives must be evaluated. Fig. 25(b) shows the change in each unit vector during time dt when the reference axes rotate through an angle $d\theta = \omega\,dt$. The differential change in $\mathbf{i}$ is $d\mathbf{i}$, in the direction of $\mathbf{j}$ and with a magnitude $d\theta$ times the unit vector $\mathbf{i}$. Thus, $d\mathbf{i} = \mathbf{j}\,d\theta$. Similarly, the unit vector $\mathbf{j}$ has a change $d\mathbf{j}$ in the negative x-direction, so that $d\mathbf{j} = -\mathbf{i}\,d\theta$. Dividing by dt and replacing $d\mathbf{i}/dt$ by $\dot{\mathbf{i}}$, $d\mathbf{j}/dt$ by $\dot{\mathbf{j}}$, and $d\theta/dt$ by $\dot{\theta} = \omega$ produces $\dot{\mathbf{i}} = \mathbf{j}\omega$ and $\dot{\mathbf{j}} = -\mathbf{i}\omega$. When the cross product is introduced, $\boldsymbol{\omega} \times \mathbf{i} = \mathbf{j}\omega$ and $\boldsymbol{\omega} \times \mathbf{j} = -\mathbf{i}\omega$ (Fig. 25c). Time derivatives of the unit vectors are:

$$\dot{\mathbf{i}} = \boldsymbol{\omega} \times \mathbf{i} \qquad \dot{\mathbf{j}} = \boldsymbol{\omega} \times \mathbf{j}$$

(Eq 54)

Using these expressions, the position-vector equation for A and B may be differentiated to obtain the relative velocity equation, $\dot{\mathbf{r}}_A = \dot{\mathbf{r}}_B + (\dot{\mathbf{i}}x + \dot{\mathbf{j}}y) + (\mathbf{i}\dot{x} + \mathbf{j}\dot{y})$. Because $\dot{\mathbf{i}}x + \dot{\mathbf{j}}y = \boldsymbol{\omega} \times \mathbf{i}x + \boldsymbol{\omega} \times \mathbf{j}y = \boldsymbol{\omega} \times \mathbf{r}$ and $\mathbf{i}\dot{x} + \mathbf{j}\dot{y} = \mathbf{v}_{\text{rel}}$, the velocity measured by a fixed observer on the x-y frame of reference, the relative velocity equation therefore becomes:

$$\mathbf{v}_A = \mathbf{v}_B + \boldsymbol{\omega} \times \mathbf{r} + \mathbf{v}_{\text{rel}}$$

(Eq 55)

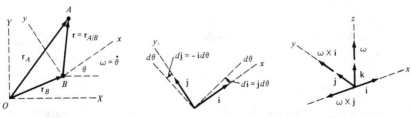

Figure 25a   Figure 25b   Figure 25c

Relative acceleration may be determined by differentiating Eq 55:

$$\mathbf{a}_A = \mathbf{a}_B + \dot{\boldsymbol{\omega}} \times \mathbf{r} + \boldsymbol{\omega} \times \dot{\mathbf{r}} + \dot{\mathbf{v}}_{rel} \qquad \text{(Eq 56)}$$

The third term on the right of Eq 56 becomes:

$$\boldsymbol{\omega} \times \dot{\mathbf{r}} = \boldsymbol{\omega} \times \frac{d}{dt}(\mathbf{i}x + \mathbf{j}y) = \boldsymbol{\omega} \times (\boldsymbol{\omega} \times \mathbf{r}) + \boldsymbol{\omega} \times \mathbf{v}_{rel}$$

The last term on the right of Eq 56 is:

$$\begin{aligned}
\dot{\mathbf{v}}_{rel} &= \frac{d}{dt}(\mathbf{i}\dot{x} + \mathbf{j}\dot{y}) = (\mathbf{i}\dot{x} + \mathbf{j}\dot{y}) + (\mathbf{i}\ddot{x} + \mathbf{j}\ddot{y}) \\
&= \boldsymbol{\omega} \times (\mathbf{i}\dot{x} + \mathbf{j}\dot{y}) + (\mathbf{i}\ddot{x} + \mathbf{j}\ddot{y}) \\
&= \boldsymbol{\omega} \times \mathbf{v}_{rel} + \mathbf{a}_{rel} \qquad \text{(Eq 57)}
\end{aligned}$$

Substitution into Eq 56 and collection of terms produce:

$$\mathbf{a}_A = \mathbf{a}_B + \dot{\boldsymbol{\omega}} \times \mathbf{r} + \boldsymbol{\omega} \times (\boldsymbol{\omega} \times \mathbf{r}) + 2\boldsymbol{\omega} \times \mathbf{v}_{rel} + \mathbf{a}_{rel} \qquad \text{(Eq 58)}$$

which is the general vector expression for the absolute acceleration of a particle A in terms of its acceleration measured relative to a coordinate system rotating with an angular velocity $\boldsymbol{\omega}$. The terms $\dot{\boldsymbol{\omega}} \times \mathbf{r}$ and $\boldsymbol{\omega} \times (\boldsymbol{\omega} \times \mathbf{r})$, shown in Fig. 26, represent the t- and n-components of $\mathbf{a}_{P/B}$, respectively, of point P in circular motion with respect to B. This motion is observed from nonrotating axes moving with B. The magnitude of $\dot{\boldsymbol{\omega}} \times \mathbf{r}$ is $r\ddot{\theta}$, with direction tangent to the circle. The magnitude of $\boldsymbol{\omega} \times (\boldsymbol{\omega} \times \mathbf{r})$ is $r\omega^2$, with direction from P to B along the normal to the circle. The term $2\boldsymbol{\omega} \times \mathbf{v}_{rel}$ is called Coriolis acceleration, which is the difference between the acceleration of A relative to P as measured from nonrotating axes and from rotating axes.

Example 7. To determine the magnitude and direction of Coriolis acceleration for a body constrained to move along a groove in a rotating disk, as shown in Fig. 27, assume the body moves outward at a velocity $\mathbf{v}$, constant in magnitude. From the expression for Coriolis acceleration, $\mathbf{a}_c = 2\boldsymbol{\omega} \times \mathbf{v}$, and since $\boldsymbol{\omega}$ and $\mathbf{v}$ are perpendicular, the magnitude of $\mathbf{a}_c$ is $a_c = 2\omega v$. As shown in Fig. 27, the Coriolis acceleration is directed perpendicular to $\mathbf{v}$ and $\boldsymbol{\omega}$.

Example 8. Particle A moves in the circular groove of 80-mm radius in Fig. 28(a). Simultaneously, the grooved plate rotates about point O at a rate of $\omega = \dot{\theta}$. To determine the absolute velocity of A at a position for which $\theta = 45°$ and

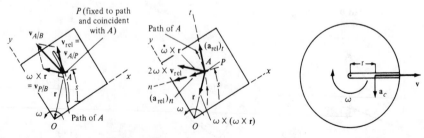

Figure 26   Figure 27

$\beta = 45°$, when at this instant $\dot{\theta} = 3$ rad/s and $\dot{\beta} = 5$ rad/s, assume that axes x-y, attached to the plate with origin at B, form the rotating reference system. The terms of Eq 55, $\mathbf{v}_A = \mathbf{v}_B + \boldsymbol{\omega} \times \mathbf{r} + \mathbf{v}_{rel}$, shown in Fig. 28(b), can be evaluated in the following way: Point B moves in a circular arc around O; its velocity has the magnitude $|\mathbf{v}_B| = r_B\omega = 0.10\sqrt{2}(3) = 0.424$ m/s. To determine the absolute acceleration of particle A when $\ddot{\theta} = 7$ rad/s^2 and $\ddot{\beta} = 12$ rad/s^2 for the position indicated in Fig. 28(a), use Eq 58, $\mathbf{a}_A = \mathbf{a}_B + \dot{\boldsymbol{\omega}} \times \mathbf{r} + \boldsymbol{\omega} \times (\boldsymbol{\omega} \times \mathbf{r}) + 2\boldsymbol{\omega} \times \mathbf{v}_{rel} + \mathbf{a}_{rel}$. The term $\mathbf{a}_B$ is the acceleration of B in its circular motion about O. Its components are:

$$(a_B)_n = r_B\dot{\theta}^2 = 0.10\sqrt{2}(3^2) = 1.273 \text{ m/s}^2$$
$$(a_B)_t = r_B\ddot{\theta} = 0.10\sqrt{2}(7) = 0.990 \text{ m/s}^2$$

shown in Fig. 29(a). The acceleration of point P with respect to B when P is attached to the plate and momentarily coincident with A, is caused by rotation of the x-y axes and has the components:

$$|\dot{\boldsymbol{\omega}} \times \mathbf{r}| = (a_{P/B})_t = r\ddot{\theta} = 0.08(7) = 0.56 \text{ m/s}^2$$

and

$$|\boldsymbol{\omega} \times (\boldsymbol{\omega} \times \mathbf{r})| = (a_{P/B})_n = r\dot{\theta}^2 = 0.08(3^2) = 0.72 \text{ m/s}^2$$

The Coriolis acceleration takes the positive X-direction as determined by the cross product $\boldsymbol{\omega} \times \mathbf{v}_{rel}$ and has magnitude of:

$$|2\boldsymbol{\omega} \times \mathbf{v}_{rel}| = 2(3)(0.40) = 2.40 \text{ m/s}^2$$

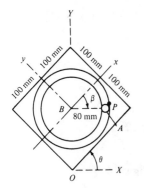

Figure 28a

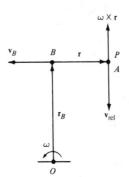

Figure 28b

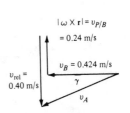

Figure 28c

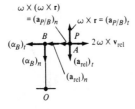

Figure 29a

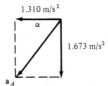

Figure 29b

Example 9. Pin A of link AC of Fig. 30 has movement confined in the rotating slot of link BO. The clockwise angular velocity of BO is $\omega = 2$ rad/s and constant. Where $\theta = 45°$ with AC in the horizontal position, the following method can be used to determine the angular velocity of AC, the velocity of A relative to the slot in BO, the angular acceleration of AC, and the acceleration of A relative to the slot in BO. A point P attached to the rotating slot and coincident with A is designated. The velocity of A is $\mathbf{v}_A = \mathbf{v}_P + \mathbf{v}_{A/P}$. Velocity of the point P on member BO is, where $v = r\omega$, $v_P = \overline{OP}\omega = 225\sqrt{2}(2) = 450\sqrt{2}$ mm/s. The relative velocity $\mathbf{v}_{A/P}$ equal to $\mathbf{v}_{rel}$ is along the slot toward O, as seen in Fig. 30(b). The velocity of A is tangent to its circular arc about C. The vector equation may now be solved since only two scalar unknowns remain, the magnitude of $\mathbf{v}_{A/P}$ and the magnitude of $\mathbf{v}_A$. For the 45° position in Fig. 30(c), $v_{A/P} = v_{rel} = 450\sqrt{2} \tan 45° = 450\sqrt{2}$ mm/s and $v_A = 450\sqrt{2}(\sqrt{2}) = 900$ mm/s, each in the direction shown. The angular velocity of AC is determined as:

$$\left[\omega = \frac{v}{r}\right] \quad \omega_{AC} = \frac{v_A}{AC} = \frac{900}{225} = 4 \text{ rad/s counterclockwise}$$

The accelerations are $\mathbf{a}_A = \mathbf{a}_P + 2\boldsymbol{\omega} \times \mathbf{v}_{rel} + \mathbf{a}_{rel}$. The terms in the equation are:

$$(a_A)_n = \overline{AC}\omega_{AC}^2 = 225(4)^2 = 3600 \text{ mm/s}^2 \text{ directed toward } C$$

$$(a_A)_t = \overline{AC}\alpha_{AC} = 225\alpha_{AC} \text{ normal to } AC, \text{ sense unknown}$$

$$(a_P)_n = \overline{OP}\omega^2 = 225\sqrt{2}(2)^2 = 900\sqrt{2} \text{ mm/s}^2 \text{ directed toward } O$$

$$(a_P)_t = \overline{OP}\alpha = 0 \text{ since } \alpha = \dot{\omega} = 0$$

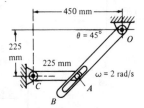

Figure 30a

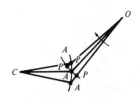

Figure 30b

Figure 30c

Figure 30d

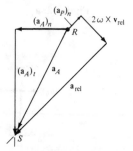

Figure 30e

$|2\omega \times \mathbf{v}_{\text{rel}}| = 2\omega v_{\text{rel}} = 2(2)(450\sqrt{2}) = 1800\sqrt{2}$ mm/s^2 directed as in Fig. 29(d)

$\mathbf{a}_{\text{rel}}$ = vector measured along slot

The vector equation may be solved because only two scalar unknowns remain, the magnitudes of $(\mathbf{a}_A)_t$ and $\mathbf{a}_{\text{rel}}$. The solution begins at point R of Fig. 30(e) and ends at point S where $(\mathbf{a}_A)_t$ and $\mathbf{a}_{\text{rel}}$ intersect. The two magnitudes are $(a_A)_t = 7200$ mm/s^2 and $a_{\text{rel}} = 8910$ mm/s^2, from which:

$$\alpha_{AC} = \frac{(a_A)_t}{AC} = \frac{7200}{225} = 32 \text{ rad/s}^2$$

KINEMATICS OF A RIGID BODY

The Velocity of a Rigid Body. In Fig. 31, if a rigid body has an angular velocity ω and point A on the body has a velocity $\mathbf{v}_A$, then the body has motion combining translation and rotation. The position of B, which is any other fixed point in the body, is defined by:

$$\mathbf{r}_B = \mathbf{r}_A + \mathbf{r}_{BA} \tag{Eq 59}$$

The velocity of B is:

$$\dot{\mathbf{r}}_B = \dot{\mathbf{r}}_A + \dot{\mathbf{r}}_{BA} \tag{Eq 60}$$

Since $\dot{\mathbf{r}}_A = \mathbf{v}_A$, which is given, and $\mathbf{r}_{BA}$ is a position vector in a rigid body and thus its length cannot change:

$$\dot{\mathbf{r}}_{BA} = \omega \times \mathbf{r}_{BA} \tag{Eq 61}$$

Therefore:

$$\mathbf{v}_B = \mathbf{v}_A + \omega \times \mathbf{r}_{BA} \tag{Eq 62}$$

where $\mathbf{v}_A$ is the absolute velocity of A and represents translation. Eq 62 is often written in the form:

$$\mathbf{v}_B = \mathbf{v}_A + \mathbf{v}_{BA} \tag{Eq 63}$$

where $\mathbf{v}_B$ is the absolute velocity of B, $\mathbf{v}_A$ is the absolute velocity of A, and $\mathbf{v}_{BA}$ is the velocity of B relative to A. The velocity of B relative to A is the velocity of B in a reference system with A as the origin fixed to the rigid body. To compute the velocity of B in Fig. 32 by employing point C instead of A, use ω'

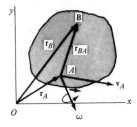

Figure 31 Translation
and rotation of rigid body

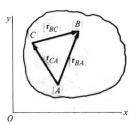

Figure 32

as the angular velocity of the body and v_C as the velocity of point C, to which B is referred. Equation 62 becomes:

$$\mathbf{v}_B = \mathbf{v}_C + \boldsymbol{\omega}' \times \mathbf{r}_{BC} \qquad \text{(Eq 64)}$$

Because

$$\mathbf{v}_C = \mathbf{v}_A + \boldsymbol{\omega} \times \mathbf{r}_{CA} \qquad \text{(Eq 65)}$$

and $\mathbf{r}_{BA} = \mathbf{r}_{CA} + \mathbf{r}_{BC}$, as shown in Fig. 32, Eq 62 can be written:

$$\mathbf{v}_B = \mathbf{v}_A + \boldsymbol{\omega} \times (\mathbf{r}_{CA} + \mathbf{r}_{BC}) = \mathbf{v}_A + \boldsymbol{\omega} \times \mathbf{r}_{CA} + \boldsymbol{\omega} \times \mathbf{r}_{BC} \qquad \text{(Eq 66)}$$

Substituting Eq 65 into Eq 64 produces:

$$\mathbf{v}_B = \mathbf{v}_A + \boldsymbol{\omega} \times \mathbf{r}_{CA} + \boldsymbol{\omega}' \times \mathbf{r}_{BC} \qquad \text{(Eq 67)}$$

Therefore, $\boldsymbol{\omega} \times \mathbf{r}_{BC} = \boldsymbol{\omega}' \times \mathbf{r}_{BC}$ and:

$$\boldsymbol{\omega} = \boldsymbol{\omega}' \qquad \text{(Eq 68)}$$

The velocity of a rigid body is the sum of a rotational velocity $\boldsymbol{\omega}$ about any reference axis in the body and the velocity of that reference axis. The velocity of the reference is the translational component of total velocity, and this differs for each reference. But the angular velocity $\boldsymbol{\omega}$ remains the same and does not depend upon choice of the reference axis.

Acceleration of a Rigid Body. The velocity of any point B in a rigid body is, from Eq 62, $\mathbf{v}_B = \mathbf{v}_A + \boldsymbol{\omega} \times \mathbf{r}_{BA}$, where $\boldsymbol{\omega}$ is the angular velocity, $\mathbf{v}_A$ is the velocity of the reference and the translational component of $\mathbf{v}_B$, and $\mathbf{r}_{BA}$ is the position vector fixed in the body which defines the position of B relative to the reference A. In Fig. 33, the reference axis has an acceleration $\mathbf{a}_A$ and the body has an angular acceleration $\boldsymbol{\alpha}$. Generally, $\dot{\boldsymbol{\omega}}$ does not have the same direction as $\boldsymbol{\omega}$. The acceleration of B is determined by taking the derivative of Eq 62:

$$\dot{\mathbf{v}}_B = \dot{\mathbf{v}}_A + \boldsymbol{\alpha} \times \mathbf{r}_{BA} + \boldsymbol{\omega} \times \dot{\mathbf{r}}_{BA} \qquad \text{(Eq 69)}$$

Because $\dot{\mathbf{v}}_B = \mathbf{a}_B$, $\dot{\mathbf{v}}_A = \mathbf{a}_A$, and $\dot{\mathbf{r}}_{BA} = \boldsymbol{\omega} \times \mathbf{r}_{BA}$, Eq 69 can be expressed as:

$$\mathbf{a}_B = \mathbf{a}_A + \boldsymbol{\alpha} \times \mathbf{r}_{BA} + \boldsymbol{\omega} \times (\boldsymbol{\omega} \times \mathbf{r}_{BA}) \qquad \text{(Eq 70)}$$

where $\mathbf{a}_A$ is the acceleration of the reference and the translational component of total acceleration of B. The remaining two components result from the rotation of the body.

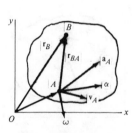

Figure 33

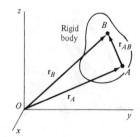

Figure 34

Example 10. If a rigid body undergoes pure translation, as shown in Fig. 34, the relationship required between the time rate of change of r_A and that of r_B, if A and B are fixed points in the rigid body, can be determined by $r_B = r_A + r_{AB}$. On differentiation:

$$\frac{dr_B}{dt} = \frac{dr_A}{dt} + \frac{dr_{AB}}{dt}$$

Because pure translation in a rigid body requires that r_{AB} move parallel to itself and that the magnitude of r_{AB} be constant:

$$\frac{dr_{AB}}{dt} = 0$$

$$\frac{dr_B}{dt} = \frac{dr_A}{dt}$$

Thus under pure translation, the velocity is the same for all points of the body and equal to the translational velocity. Thus, for a body in pure translation, every point of the moving body simultaneously has the same velocity and acceleration relative to a given point. With pure translation, ω and α are both zero. If a body undergoes pure translation, and since $\alpha = \omega = 0$, Eq 62 becomes $\bar{v}_B = v_A$, and Eq 70 reduces to $a_B = a_A$.

Example 11. For a body in pure rotation, every point in the moving body has simultaneously the same angular velocity and angular acceleration about a given point A. For a body undergoing pure rotation, v_A and a_A are identically zero. Then Eq 62 becomes $v_B = \omega \times r_{BA}$ and Eq 70 becomes $a_B = \alpha \times r_{BA} + \bar{\omega} \times (\omega \times r_{BA})$, or $a_B = a_t + a_r$. Thus, for any point B, the velocity is its tangential velocity; the acceleration is the vector sum of the tangential and radial accelerations.

Example 12. To find the velocity and acceleration of any point in a body rotating about the z-axis, as shown in Fig. 35, which runs through the body, with an angular velocity ω and an angular acceleration α, choose an origin at Q within the body. Point P is located relative to Q by the position vector r. The velocity of the point is given by $v_P = \omega \times r = v_t$, and acceleration is given by

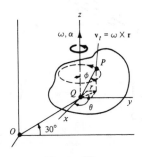

Figure 35

$\mathbf{a}_P = \boldsymbol{\alpha} \times \mathbf{r} + \boldsymbol{\omega} \times (\boldsymbol{\omega} \times \mathbf{r})$. The speed is $v_P = \omega r \sin \phi$, and the magnitude of the acceleration is:

$$a_P = \sqrt{(\alpha r \sin \phi)^2 + (\omega^2 r \sin \phi)^2}$$
$$= \sqrt{a_r{}^2 + a_r{}^2}$$

With β the angle between the tangent to the circle of motion of P and $\mathbf{a}_P$:

$$\tan \beta = \frac{a_r}{a_t} = \frac{\alpha}{\omega^2}$$

Example 13. As shown in Fig. 36, crank OB of the linkage oscillates about O through a limited arc, causing crank AC to oscillate about C. When the linkage passes the position shown with OB normal to the x-axis and CA normal to the y-axis, the angular velocity of OB is 2 rad/s clockwise and constant. For this instant calculate the angular accelerations of CA and AB. To solve this, the motions of the three links may be described by equating the motion of A in its absolute circular path about C to the motion of A determined from its motion relative to B. The corresponding equations are:

$$\mathbf{V}_A = \mathbf{V}_B + \mathbf{V}_{A/B} \qquad \mathbf{a}_A = \mathbf{a}_B + \mathbf{a}_{A/B}$$

The velocity equation may be written as:

$$\omega_{CA} \times \mathbf{r}_A = \omega_{OB} \times \mathbf{r}_B + \omega_{AB} \times \mathbf{r}_{A/B}$$

where

$$\omega_{CA} = \omega_{CA}\mathbf{k} \qquad \omega_{OB} = 2\mathbf{k} \text{ rad/s} \qquad \omega_{AB} = \omega_{AB}\mathbf{k}$$
$$\mathbf{r}_A = 75\mathbf{i} \text{ mm} \qquad \mathbf{r}_B = 100\mathbf{j} \text{ mm} \qquad \mathbf{r}_{A/B} = -175\mathbf{i} + 100\mathbf{j} \text{ mm}$$

Substitution gives:

$$(\omega_{CA}\mathbf{k} \times 75\mathbf{i}) = (2\mathbf{k} \times 100\mathbf{j}) + \omega_{AB}\mathbf{k} \times (-175\mathbf{i} + 100\mathbf{j})$$
$$75\omega_{CA}\mathbf{j} = -200\mathbf{i} - 175\omega_{AB}\mathbf{j} - 100\omega_{AB}\mathbf{i}$$

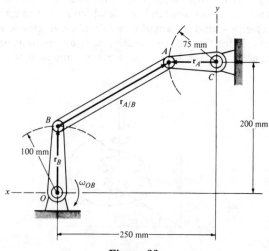

Figure 36

Equating the respective coefficients of the **i**- and **j**-terms gives:

$$0 = -200 - 100\omega_{AB} \quad \text{and} \quad 75\omega_{CA} = -175\omega_{AB}$$

The solutions of which are:

$$\omega_{AB} = -2 \text{ rad/s} \quad \text{and} \quad \omega_{CA} = 4.67 \text{ rad/s}$$

Because the unit vector **k** points into the paper in the positive z-direction, it is seen that the angular velocity of AB is counterclockwise and that of CA is clockwise. The acceleration equation is now solved in a similar manner. Its terms are:

$$\begin{aligned}
\mathbf{a}_A &= \boldsymbol{\alpha}_{CA} \times \mathbf{r}_A + \boldsymbol{\omega}_{CA} \times (\boldsymbol{\omega}_{CA} \times \mathbf{r}_A) \\
&= \alpha_{CA}\mathbf{k} \times 75\mathbf{i} + 4.67\mathbf{k} \times (4.67\mathbf{k} \times 75\mathbf{i}) \\
&= 75\alpha_{CA}\mathbf{j} - 1633\mathbf{i} \text{ mm/s}^2 \\
\mathbf{a}_B &= \boldsymbol{\alpha}_{OB} \times \mathbf{r}_B + \boldsymbol{\omega}_{OB} \times (\boldsymbol{\omega}_{OB} \times \mathbf{r}_B) \\
&= \mathbf{0} \times 100\mathbf{j} + 2\mathbf{k} \times (2\mathbf{k} \times 100\mathbf{j}) \\
&= -400\mathbf{j} \text{ mm/s}^2 \\
\mathbf{a}_{A/B} &= \boldsymbol{\alpha}_{AB} \times \mathbf{r}_{A/B} + \boldsymbol{\omega}_{AB} \times (\boldsymbol{\omega}_{AB} \times \mathbf{r}_{A/B}) \\
&= \alpha_{AB}\mathbf{k} \times (-175\mathbf{i} + 100\mathbf{j}) + (-2\mathbf{k}) \times [(-2\mathbf{k}) \times (-175\mathbf{i} + 100\mathbf{j})] \\
&= -175\alpha_{AB}\mathbf{j} - 100\alpha_{AB}\mathbf{i} + 700\mathbf{i} - 400\mathbf{j} \text{ mm/s}^2
\end{aligned}$$

Substitution into the acceleration equation and equating the respective coefficients of the **i**- and **j**-terms give:

$$\begin{aligned}
-1633 &= 700 - 100\alpha_{AB} \\
75\alpha_{CA} &= -800 - 175\alpha_{AB}
\end{aligned}$$

The solutions of which are:

$$\alpha_{AB} = 23.3 \text{ rad/s}^2 \quad \text{and} \quad \alpha_{CA} = -65.1 \text{ rad/s}^2$$

Because the unit vector **k** points into the paper in the positive z-direction, it is seen that the angular acceleration of AB is clockwise and that of CA is counterclockwise.

SELECTED REFERENCES

- Beer, Ferdinand P. and Johnston, E. Russell, Jr., Vector Mechanics for Engineers, *Dynamics,* 3rd ed., McGraw-Hill, New York, 1977
- Hibbeler, R. C., Engineering Mechanics, *Dynamics,* 2nd ed., Macmillan, New York, 1978
- Shames, Irving H., Engineering Mechanics, *Dynamics,* Vol. II, 2nd ed., Prentice-Hall, Englewood Cliffs, NJ, 1966
- Ginsberg, Jerry H. and Genin, Joseph, *Dynamics,* John Wiley and Sons, New York, 1977
- Higdon, Archie, Stiles, William B., Davis, Arthur W., Evces, Charles R. and Weese, John A., *Engineering Dynamics,* 2nd ed., Prentice-Hall, Englewood Cliffs, NJ
- Shigley, Joseph E., *Kinematic Analysis of Machines,* 2nd ed., McGraw-Hill, New York, 1969
- Branson, Lane K., *Engineering Mechanics, Statics and Dynamics,* Simon and Schuster, New York, 1970

18
Kinetics

By Mamerto L. Chu, Ph.D.
Department of Mechanical Engineering
University of Akron

SYSTEMS OF UNITS

U.S. Customary System. The pound, lb, is the unit of mass. It is defined as the standard preserved by the British government and also as $\frac{1}{2.2}$ kilogram. The slug is still sometimes used as the unit of mass, and is interchangeable with the current pound. Acceleration is measured in feet per second per second, ft/s^2. The poundal is defined as the force that gives an acceleration of 1 ft/s^2 to a pound mass: 1 poundal = 1 lb $\times$ 1 ft/s^2. A pound-weight is defined as a mass of one pound under the acceleration of gravity: 1 lb-wt = 1 lb $\times$ 32 ft/s^2 = 32 poundals.

International System (SI). The kilogram, kg, is defined as the mass of a particular cylinder of platinum-iridium alloy kept by the International Bureau of Weights and Measures, and also, approximately, as the mass of a liter of pure water. Acceleration is measured in meters per second per second, m/s^2. The newton, N, is the force that gives an acceleration of 1 m/s^2 to a 1 kg mass: 1 N = 1 kg $\times$ 1 m/s^2. Also, 1 N = 7.14 poundals.

KINETICS OF PARTICLES

When a force **F** acts on a particle of mass m, the force **F** and the acceleration **a** of the particle satisfy the relationship:

$$\mathbf{F} = m\mathbf{a} \qquad \text{(Eq 1)}$$

which is an expression of Newton's second law. The magnitudes of **F** and **a** are proportional, and vectors **F** and **a** have the same direction (Fig. 1). When **F** varies with t in magnitude or direction, Eq 1 still holds. Magnitudes of **F** and **a** remain proportional, and the two vectors have the same direction at any given instant. However, they will not, in general, be tangent to the path of the particle. When several forces act simultaneously on a particle, Eq 1 becomes:

$$\Sigma\mathbf{F} = m\mathbf{a} \qquad \text{(Eq 2)}$$

where $\Sigma\mathbf{F}$ represents the resultant of forces acting on the particle.

Equations of Motion. In solving problems, Eq 2 is usually expressed in component form that depends on the coordinate system. The coordinate system is dictated by the motion involved. In rectangular coordinates x, y, z, Eq 2 will have the components:

$$\Sigma F_x = ma_x \qquad \Sigma F_y = ma_y \qquad \Sigma F_z = ma_z \qquad \text{(Eq 3)}$$

where

$$|\mathbf{\Sigma F}| = \sqrt{(\Sigma F_x)^2 + (\Sigma F_y)^2 + (\Sigma F_z)^2}$$

and

$$|\mathbf{a}| = \sqrt{a_x^2 + a_y^2 + a_z^2}$$

For rectilinear motion, the x-axis may be chosen to coincide with the direction of the acceleration $\mathbf{a}$, and the several motion equations become $\Sigma F_x = ma$, $\Sigma F_y = 0$, $\Sigma F_z = 0$. The equation of motion may also be expressed as the differential equation $\Sigma F_x = m\ddot{x}$, where ΣF_x is a function of time, displacement, or velocity. To express x as a function of t, two successive integrations would be required.

For plane curvilinear motion, where n- and t-components are used, components of Eq 2 may be expressed as:

$$\Sigma F_n = ma_n \qquad \Sigma F_t = ma_t \qquad \text{(Eq 4)}$$

where $a_n = v\dot{\theta} = \rho\dot{\theta}^2 = v^2/\rho$ and $a_t = \dot{v} = \ddot{s}$.

For plane curvilinear motion where r- and θ-components are used, the components of Eq 2 may be expressed as:

$$\Sigma F_r = ma_r \qquad \Sigma F_\theta = ma_\theta \qquad \text{(Eq 5)}$$

where $a_r = \ddot{r} - r\dot{\theta}^2$ and $a_\theta = r\ddot{\theta} + 2\dot{r}\dot{\theta}$.

For spatial curvilinear motion, cylindrical coordinates may be used with:

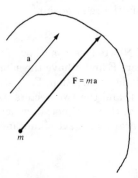

Figure 1

$$\Sigma F_r = ma_r \qquad \Sigma F_\theta = ma_\theta \qquad \Sigma F_z = ma_z \tag{Eq 6}$$

or spherical coordinates may be used with:

$$\Sigma F_R = ma_R \qquad \Sigma F_\theta = ma_\theta \qquad \Sigma F_\phi = ma_\phi \tag{Eq 7}$$

In rectangular coordinates, resolving each force **F** and acceleration **a** into rectangular components produces:

$$\Sigma(F_x\mathbf{i} + F_y\mathbf{j} + F_z\mathbf{k}) = m(a_x\mathbf{i} + a_y\mathbf{j} + a_z\mathbf{k}) \tag{Eq 8}$$

from which $\Sigma F_x = ma_x$, $\Sigma F_y = ma_y$, $\Sigma F_z = ma_z$. Because the components of the acceleration equal the second derivatives of the coordinates of the particle:

$$\Sigma F_x = m\ddot{x} \qquad \Sigma F_y = m\ddot{y} \qquad \Sigma F_z = m\ddot{z}$$

Example 1. Two blocks shown in Fig. 2 start from rest. Assumed are a frictionless horizontal plane and pulley and a pulley with negligible mass. To determine the acceleration of each block and the tension in each cord, denote the tension in cord ACD by T_1 and the tension in cord BC by T_2. If block A moves through s_A, block B moves through $s_B = 1/2s_A$. Differentiating twice with respect to t produces:

$$a_B = \frac{1}{2}s_A \tag{Eq 9}$$

Applying Newton's second law successively to block A:

$$\overset{+}{\rightarrow}\Sigma F_x = m_A a_A \qquad T_1 = 100a_A \tag{Eq 10}$$

Observing that the weight of block B is:

$$W_B = m_B g = (300 \text{ kg})(9.81 \text{ m/s}^2) = 2940 \text{ N}$$

and applying Newton's second law, then:

$$+ \downarrow \Sigma F_y = m_B a_B \qquad 2940 - T_2 = 300a_B$$

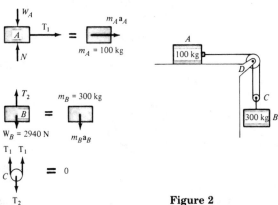

Figure 2

or, substituting for a_B from Eq 9, $2940 - T_2 = 300\left(\dfrac{1}{2}a_A\right)$, and $T_2 = 2940 -$
$150a_A$. For Pulley C, since m_C is assumed to be zero:

$$+\downarrow \Sigma F_y = m_C a_C = 0 \qquad T_2 - 2T_1 = 0 \tag{Eq 11}$$

Substituting for T_1 and T_2 from Eq 9 and 10 into Eq 11, $2940 - 150a_A -$
$2(100a_A) = 0$, $2940 - 350a_A = 0$, and $a_A = 8.40$ m/s^2. Substituting this value
for a_A into Eq 9 and Eq 10:

$$a_B = \frac{1}{2}a_A = \frac{1}{2}(8.40 \text{ m/s}^2) = 4.20 \text{ m/s}^2$$

$$T_1 = 100a_A = (100\text{kg})(8.40\text{m/s}^2) = 840 \text{ N}$$

From Eq 11, $T_2 = 2T_1 = 2(840 \text{ N}) = 1680$ N.

Tangential and Normal Components. Resolving the forces and the acceleration of the particle into components, as shown in Fig. 3, and substituting into Eq 2, two scalar equations are obtained:

$$\Sigma F_t = ma_t \qquad \Sigma F_n = ma_n \tag{Eq 12}$$

Substituting derivatives for a_t and a_n:

$$\Sigma F_t = m\frac{dv}{dt} \qquad \Sigma F_n = m\frac{v^2}{\rho} \tag{Eq 13}$$

The equations then may be solved for two unknowns.

Example 2. For a bob of a 2-m pendulum in a vertical plane, the tension in
the cord is 2.5 times the weight of the bob for the position shown in Fig. 4.
To find the velocity and acceleration of the bob, consider the weight of the bob
to be $W = mg$. The tension in the cord is 2.5 mg. With $\mathbf{a}_n$ directed toward O
and assuming $\mathbf{a}_t$ as shown in Fig. 5, Newton's second law produces:

$$+\swarrow \Sigma F_t = ma_t$$
$$mg \sin 30° = ma_t$$
$$a_t = g \sin 30° = +4.90 \text{ m/s}^2$$

Thus:

$$a_t = 4.90 \text{ m/s}^2\swarrow$$

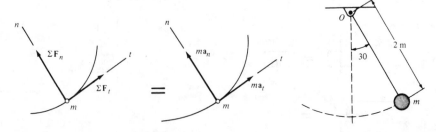

Figure 3   Figure 4

For:

$$+\nwarrow \Sigma F_n = ma_n$$
$$2.5\ mg - mg\ \cos 30° = ma_n$$
$$a_n = 1.634\ g = +16.03\ \text{m/s}^2$$

Thus:

$$a_n = 16.03\ \text{m/s}^2 \nwarrow$$

Since:

$$a_n = v^2/\rho$$
$$v^2 = \rho a_n = (2\ \text{m})(16.03\ \text{m/s}^2)$$
$$v = \pm 5.66\ \text{m/s}$$
$$\mathbf{v} = 5.66\ \text{m/s}\ \nearrow\ (\text{up or down})$$

Transverse Components. For a particle P, in reference to polar coordinates r and θ and moving in a plane under the action of several forces, the forces and acceleration of the particle can be resolved into radial and transverse components (Fig. 6). Substituting into Eq 2 produces two scalar equations:

$$\Sigma F_r = ma_r \qquad \Sigma F_\theta = ma_\theta \tag{Eq 14}$$

Substituting for a_r and a_θ:

$$\Sigma F_r = m(\ddot{r} - r\dot{\theta}^2) \tag{Eq 15}$$

and

$$\Sigma F_\theta = m(r\ddot{\theta} + 2\dot{r}\dot{\theta}) \tag{Eq 16}$$

which may be solved for two unknowns.

Example 3. The 3-ft bar OA in Fig. 7 rotates about O. The rotation is defined by the relationship $\theta = 0.15t^2$, with θ expressed in radians and t in seconds. Block B slides along the arm in such a way that its distance from $O = r = 3 - 0.40t^2$, with r expressed in feet and t in seconds. To find total velocity and total acceleration of block B after OA has rotated through 30°, first determine the time t for which $\theta = 30°$. Substituting $\theta = 30° = 0.524$ rad for θ, $\theta = 0.15t^2$, $0.524 = 0.15t^2$, and $t = 1.869$ s. Substituting $t = 1.869$ s in equations for r, θ, and their first and second derivatives:

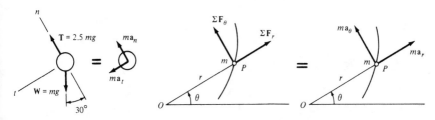

Figure 5   **Figure 6**

360/ENGINEERING MATHEMATICS

$$r = 3 - 0.40t^2 = 1.603 \text{ ft} \qquad \theta = 0.15t^2 = 0.524 \text{ rad}$$
$$\dot{r} = -0.80t = -1.495 \text{ ft/s} \qquad \dot{\theta} = 0.30t = 0.561 \text{ rad/s}$$
$$\ddot{r} = -0.80 = -0.800 \text{ ft/s}^2 \qquad \ddot{\theta} = 0.30 = 0.300 \text{ rad/s}^2$$

When $t = 1.869$ s, the velocity of B becomes:

$$v_r = \dot{r} = -1.495 \text{ ft/s}$$
$$v_\theta = r\dot{\theta} = 1.603(0.561) = 0.899 \text{ ft/s}$$

Solving the right triangle in Fig. 8 produces the magnitude and direction of the velocity, $v = 1.744$ ft/s and $\beta = 31.0°$. The acceleration of B is determined by:

$$a_r = \ddot{r} - r\dot{\theta}^2$$
$$= -0.800 - 1.603(0.561)^2 = -1.304 \text{ ft/s}^2$$
$$a_\theta = r\ddot{\theta} + 2\dot{r}\dot{\theta}$$
$$= 1.603(0.300) + 2(-1.495)(0.561) = -1.196 \text{ ft/s}^2$$

So $a = 1.770$ ft/s and $\gamma = 42.5°$.

WORK, POWER, AND ENERGY

Work of a constant force is the product of the force and the effective displacement of the point where force is applied. Effective displacement is the component of displacement parallel to the force. For example, in Fig. 9 the work of force F on application point $AB = F \times AC$. Work of a variable force on a body moving through distance $\Delta S = (s_2 - s_1)$ is expressed as:

$$W = \int_{s_1}^{s_2} F \cos \alpha \, ds = \int_{s_1}^{s_2} F_t \, ds$$

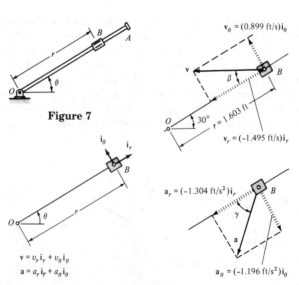

Figure 7

Figure 8

in which F is the variable force, ds the elementary length of path, α the angle between force and element ds, and F_t the tangential component of force. The sign of work is positive if force and effective displacement have the same sense, and negative if they differ. The unit of work equals any distance unit times any force unit, such as foot-pound, or any power unit times any time unit, such as watt-hour. A typical work diagram is shown in Fig. 10. Values of F_t are plotted as ordinates; corresponding values of s as abscissas. Curve AB is drawn through ends of ordinates. Area $ABDC$ times mn equals the work done by F_t over distance $s_2 - s_1$. Work of gravity on a body equals the product of the body weight and change in the height of the mass center. Work of a central force F directed toward a fixed point in any displacement of its application point, is:

$$\int_{r_1}^{r_2} F\,dr$$

with r_2 and r_1 the distances of the point from the center at the beginning and end of the displacement. Work of a torque T on a rotating body undergoing angular displacement of $\theta = (\theta_2 - \theta_1)$ radians is:

$$W = \int_{\theta_1}^{\theta_2} T\,d\theta$$

With T constant, $W = T(\theta_2 - \theta_1)$. Mechanical efficiency of a machine is expressed as W_u/W_a, with W_u = useful work performed and W_a = work applied to the machine to provide useful work and to overcome resistance such as friction. Power of a force is its time rate of doing work. With P = power and W = work, instantaneous $P = dW/dt = F_t(ds/dt) = F_t v$, where v is instantaneous velocity of application point of force F. Instantaneous power of a torque is $P = dW/dt = T(d\theta/dt) = T\omega$, where ω is the body's instantaneous angular velocity.

ENERGY AND MOMENTUM METHODS

Kinetic Energy of a Particle. For a particle of mass m acted upon by a force F and moving along a rectilinear and/or curved path, as shown in Fig. 11, Newton's second law is expressed in terms of the tangential components of the force and of the acceleration $F_t = ma_t$ or $F_t = m(dv/dt)$, where v is the particle speed. Since $v = ds/dt$:

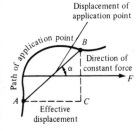

Figure 9

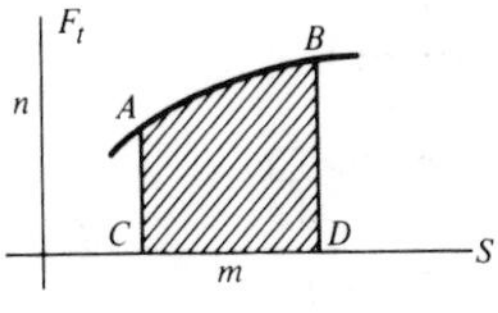

Figure 10

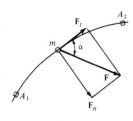

Figure 11

$$F_t = m \frac{dv}{ds} \frac{ds}{dt} = mv \frac{dv}{ds}$$

and $F_t ds = mv \, dv$. Integrating from A_1, where $s = s_1$ and $v = v_1$, to A_2, where $s = s_2$ and $v = v_2$:

$$\int_{s_1}^{s_2} F_t ds = m \int_{r_1}^{r_2} v \, dv = \frac{1}{2} mv_2{}^2 - \frac{1}{2} mv_1{}^2 \qquad \text{(Eq 17)}$$

The left-hand member of Eq 17 represents the work $U_{1 \to 2}$ of the force F exerted during particle displacement from A_1 to A_2. The work $U_{1 \to 2}$ and the expression $\frac{1}{2} mv^2$ are scalar quantities. Kinetic energy of the particle, denoted by T, is:

$$T = \frac{1}{2} mv^2 \qquad \text{(Eq 18)}$$

Substituting into Eq 17:

$$U_{1 \to 2} = T_2 - T_1 \qquad \text{(Eq 19)}$$

which defines a particle moving from A_1 to A_2 under force $\mathbf{F}$. The work of the force $\mathbf{F}$ is equal to the change in kinetic energy of the particle. Kinetic energy is measured in joules if SI metric units are used, and in ft·lb when U.S. customary units are used. In SI units:

$$T = \frac{1}{2} mv^2 = \mathrm{kg\,(m/s)^2} = \mathrm{(kg \cdot m/s^2)\ m} = \mathrm{N \cdot m} = \mathrm{J}$$

In customary units:

$$T = \frac{1}{2} mv^2 = \mathrm{(lb \cdot s^2/ft)\,(ft/s)^2} = \mathrm{lb \cdot ft}$$

Work of the Force Exerted by a Linear Spring. For a body A attached to a fixed point B by a spring, the spring is assumed to be undeformed when the body is at A_0 (Fig. 12a). The magnitude of the force $\mathbf{F}$ exerted by the spring on body A is proportional to the deflection x from the position A_0:

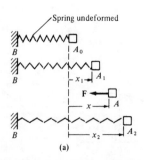
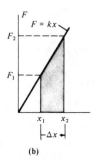

(a)   (b)

Figure 12

$$F = kx \tag{Eq 20}$$

where k is the spring constant, expressed in N/m or kN/m in the SI system and in lb/ft or lb/in. in the U.S. customary system of units. The relationship $F = kx$ is accurate under static conditions. Under dynamic conditions, it should take the inertia of the spring into account. If the mass of the spring is small compared with the other masses in motion, however, the error introduced by using $F = kx$ in the solution of kinetics problems is small. The work of force $\mathbf{F}$ exerted by the spring during displacement from $A_1(x = x_1)$ to $A_2(x = x_2)$ is obtained by:

$$dU = -F\,dx = -kx\,dx \qquad U_{1\to2} = -\int_{x_1}^{x_2} kx\,dx = \frac{1}{2}kx_1{}^2 - \frac{1}{2}kx_2{}^2 \tag{Eq 21}$$

The work of the force $\mathbf{F}$ exerted by the spring is positive when $x_2 < x_1$, that is, when the spring is returning to its undeformed position. Because Eq 20 defines a straight line of slope k passing through the origin, the work $U_{1\to2}$ of $\mathbf{F}$ from A_1 to A_2 may be obtained by evaluating the area of the trapezoid shown in Fig. 12(b). The base Δx of the trapezoid is multiplied by its mean height $1/2(F_1 + F_2)$. Because the work of the force $\mathbf{F}$ exerted by the spring is positive for a negative value of Δx:

$$U_{1\to2} = -\frac{1}{2}(F_1 + F_2)\Delta x \tag{Eq 22}$$

Conservation of Energy. When a particle is affected by the action of conservative forces, the work can be expressed as a change in potential energy, and the principle of work and energy may be modified. Equation 19 may be written:

$$V_1 - V_2 = T_2 - T_1 \qquad T_1 + V_1 = T_2 + V_2 \tag{Eq 23}$$

According to Eq 23, when a particle is moved by conservative forces, the sum of the kinetic energy and of the potential energy of the particle remains constant. The sum $T + V$ represents the total mechanical energy of the particle and is denoted by E.

For a pendulum shown in Fig. 13, released with no velocity from A_1 and allowed to swing in a vertical plane, potential energy is measured from the level of A_2; when the particle is at A_1, $T_1 = 0$, $V_1 = Wl$ and $T_1 + V_1 = Wl$. At A_2, the speed of the pendulum is $v_2 = \sqrt{2gl}$. Thus:

$$T_2 = \frac{1}{2}mv_2{}^2 = \frac{1}{2}\frac{W}{g}(2\,gl) = Wl$$

$$V_2 = 0$$

$$T_2 + V_2 = Wl$$

Potential Energy. For a body of weight $\mathbf{W}$ moving along a curved path from a point A_1, y_1 to a point A_2, y_2 (Fig. 14), the work of the weight $\mathbf{W}$ during displacement is:

$$U_{1\to 2} = Wy_1 - Wy_2 \qquad \text{(Eq 24)}$$

with functions Wy_1 and Wy_2 corresponding to the first and second positions of the body. The function Wy is the potential energy of the body with respect to the force of gravity $\mathbf{W}$ and is denoted by V_g. Thus:

$$U_{1\to 2} = (V_g)_1 - (V_g)_2 \qquad \text{(Eq 25)}$$

with $V_g = Wy$. If $(V_g)_2 > (V_g)_1$, that is, if the potential energy increases during the displacement, the work $U_{1\to 2}$ is negative. If $\mathbf{W}$ is positive, the potential energy decreases. For a body attached to a spring as shown in Fig. 12(a) and moving from a position A_1 with a deflection x_1, to a position A_2 with a deflection x_2, the work of the force $\mathbf{F}$ exerted by the spring on the body is:

$$U_{1\to 2} = \frac{1}{2}\,kx_1{}^2 - \frac{1}{2}\,kx_2{}^2 \qquad \text{(Eq 26)}$$

The work of the elastic force is determined by subtracting the value of $1/2\,kx^2$ for the second position from its value for the first position. The function V_e is the potential energy with respect to the elastic force $\mathbf{F}$, thus $U_{1\to 2} = (V_e)_1 - (V_e)_2$, with:

$$V_e = \frac{1}{2}\,kx^2 \qquad \text{(Eq 27)}$$

During displacement, the work of the force $\mathbf{F}$ exerted by the spring is negative and potential energy V_e increases. Although the expression for V_e is valid only when the deflection of the spring is measured from its undeformed position, Eq 27 is valid even when the spring is rotated about its fixed end as shown in Fig. 15(a). The work of the elastic force is determined by the initial and final deflections of the spring (Fig. 15b).

Conservative Forces. Force $\mathbf{F}$ acting on a particle A is conservative if its work $U_{1\to 2}$ is independent of the path of particle A from A_1 to A_2 (Fig. 16a). Thus:

$$U_{1\to 2} = V(x_1, y_1, z_1) - V(x_2, y_2, z_2) \qquad \text{(Eq 28)}$$

or $U_{1\to 2} = V_1 - V_2$. The function $V(x, y, z)$ represents the potential energy,

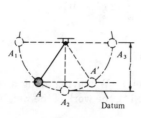

Figure 13

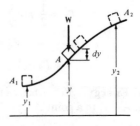

Figure 14

or potential function, of **F**. If A_2 coincides with A_1, that is, if the particle describes a closed path (Fig. 16b), $V_1 = V_2$ and the work becomes zero. Thus, for any conservative force **F**:

$$\oint \mathbf{F} \cdot d\mathbf{r} = 0 \qquad \text{(Eq 29)}$$

where the circle overlaid on the integral symbol indicates a closed path. Applying Eq 28 between two neighboring points $A(x, y, z)$ and $A'(x + dx, y + dy, z + dz)$, the work dU that corresponds to the displacement $d\mathbf{r}$ from A to A' is $dU = V(x, y, z) - V(x + dx, y + dy, z + dz)$, or:

$$dU = -dV(x, y, z) \qquad \text{(Eq 30)}$$

Thus, the elementary work of a conservative force is described by an exact differential. Substituting for dU in Eq 30:

$$F_x dx + F_y dy + F_z dz = -\left(\frac{\partial V}{\partial x} dx + \frac{\partial V}{\partial y} dy + \frac{\partial V}{\partial z} dz\right)$$

and

$$F_x = -\frac{\partial V}{\partial x} \qquad F_y = -\frac{\partial V}{\partial y} \qquad F_z = -\frac{\partial V}{\partial z} \qquad \text{(Eq 31)}$$

The components of **F** are functions of the coordinates x, y, z. The relationships of Eq 31 may be expressed as:

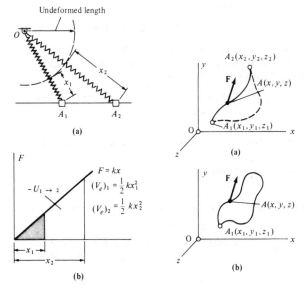

Undeformed length

x_2

x_1

A_1　A_2

(a)

F

$F = kx$

$-U_1 \rightarrow 2$

$(V_e)_1 = \frac{1}{2}kx_1^2$

$(V_e)_2 = \frac{1}{2}kx_2^2$

x_1

x_2

(b)

Figure 15

$A_2(x_2, y_2, z_2)$

$\mathbf{F}$　$A(x, y, z)$

O　$A_1(x_1, y_1, z_1)$　x

z

(a)

$\mathbf{F}$

$A(x, y, z)$

O　$A_1(x_1, y_1, z_1)$　x

z

(b)

Figure 16

$$\mathbf{F} = F_x \mathbf{i} + F_y \mathbf{j} + F_z \mathbf{k} = -\left(\frac{\partial V}{\partial x}\mathbf{i} + \frac{\partial V}{\partial y}\mathbf{j} + \frac{\partial V}{\partial z}\mathbf{k}\right) \qquad \text{(Eq 32)}$$

The vector in the right side of Eq 32, the gradient of the scalar function V, is denoted by **grad V**. Thus, for any conservative force:

$$\mathbf{F} = -\mathbf{grad}\ \mathbf{V} \qquad \text{(Eq 33)}$$

Example 4. With the spring in Fig. 17 compressed 75 mm, a 200-g pellet is released from rest at A and travels around the loop $ABCDE$. To determine the smallest value of the spring constant that will enable the pellet to travel around the loop while maintaining contact, use the following procedure. As the pellet reaches the highest point C, its potential energy with respect to gravity is maximum; its kinetic energy and speed are minimum. The force $\mathbf{N}$ exerted on the pellet by the loop must equal, or be greater than, zero. With $\mathbf{N} = 0$, the smallest possible speed v_c is computed as follows. $+\downarrow\Sigma F_n = ma_n$. Since $W = ma_n$, $mg = ma_n$, $a_n = g$, and:

$$a_n = \frac{v_c^2}{r}$$

then

$$v_c^2 = ra_n = rg = (0.150\ \text{m})(9.81\ \text{m/s}^2) = 1.472\ \text{m}^2/\text{s}^2$$

Because the spring in Position 1 of Fig. 17 is compressed 0.075 m from its undeformed position, potential energy is determined by:

$$V_e = \frac{1}{2}kx^2 = \frac{1}{2}k(0.075\ \text{m})^2 = (0.00281\ \text{m}^2)k$$

At Point A, $V_g = 0$; therefore:

$$V_1 = V_e + V_g = (0.00281\ \text{m}^2)k$$

Since the pellet is released from rest, $v_A = 0$ and $T_1 = 0$. Because the spring in Position 2 is undeformed, $V_e = 0$. Since the pellet is 0.450 m above Point A, and $W = (0.200\ \text{kg})(9.81\ \text{m/s}^2) = 1.962\ \text{N}$:

$$V_g = Wy = (1.962\ \text{N})(0.450\ \text{m}) = 0.883\ \text{N}\cdot\text{m} = 0.883\ \text{J}$$
$$V_2 = V_e + V_g = 0.883\ \text{J}$$

To determine kinetic energy, use the value of v_c^2 above; thus:

$$T_2 = \frac{1}{2}mv_c^2 = \frac{1}{2}(0.200\ \text{kg})(1.472\ \text{m}^2/\text{s}^2) = 0.1472\ \text{N}\cdot\text{m} = 0.1472\ \text{J}$$

Applying the principle of conservation of energy between Positions 1 and 2:

$$T_1 + V_1 = T_2 + V_2$$
$$0 + (0.00281\ m^2)k = 0.1472\ \text{J} + 0.883\ \text{J}$$
$$k = 367\ \text{J/m}^2 = 367\ \text{N/m}$$

Thus, the minimum value of k is $k = 367$ N/m.

Linear Momentum of a Particle. In the Newtonian expression, $\mathbf{F} = m\mathbf{a}$, replacing the acceleration $\mathbf{a}$ by the derivative $d\mathbf{v}/dt$ gives $\mathbf{F} = m(d\mathbf{v}/dt)$. Because the mass m of the particle is constant:

$$\mathbf{F} = \frac{d}{dt}(m\mathbf{v}) \tag{Eq 34}$$

The vector $m\mathbf{v}$ is the linear momentum, or simply the momentum, of the particle, having the same direction as the particle velocity and magnitude equal to the product of the mass m and the particle speed v (Fig. 18). The resultant of the forces acting on the particle equals the rate of change of the linear momentum of the particle, as expressed in Eq 34. Denoting by $\mathbf{L}$ the linear momentum of the particle:

$$\mathbf{L} = m\mathbf{v} \tag{Eq 35}$$

Using $\dot{\mathbf{L}}$ as derivative with respect to t, Eq 34 can be written:

$$\mathbf{F} = \dot{\mathbf{L}} \tag{Eq 36}$$

Impulse and Momentum. The principle of impulse and momentum may be used to solve problems involving force, mass, velocity, and time. For a particle of mass m acted upon by a force $\mathbf{F}$, Newton's second law may be expressed as:

$$\mathbf{F} = \frac{d}{dt}(m\mathbf{v}) \tag{Eq 37}$$

where $m\mathbf{v}$ is the linear momentum. Multiplying both sides of this equation by dt and integrating from a time t_1 to a time t_2, $\mathbf{F}\,dt = d(m\mathbf{v})$ and:

$$\int_{t_1}^{t_2} \mathbf{F}\,dt = m\mathbf{v}_2 - m\mathbf{v}_1$$

or

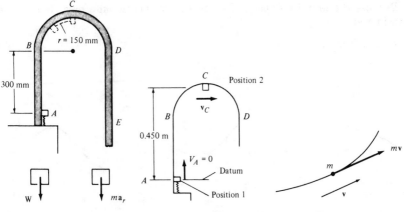

Figure 17   Figure 18

$$m\mathbf{v}_1 + \int_{t_1}^{t_2} \mathbf{F}\, dt = m\mathbf{v}_2 \tag{Eq 38}$$

The integral in Eq 38 is a vector, the linear impulse or impulse of the force **F** during the time interval. Resolving **F** into rectangular components:

$$\mathbf{Imp}_{1\to2} = \int_{t_1}^{t_2} \mathbf{F}\, dt$$

$$= \mathbf{i} \int_{t_1}^{t_2} F_x dt + \mathbf{j} \int_{t_1}^{t_2} F_y dt + \mathbf{k} \int_{t_1}^{t_2} F_z dt \tag{Eq 39}$$

The components of the impulse of the force **F** are equal to the areas formed by the curves of components F_x, F_y, and F_z plotted against t (Fig. 19). For a force **F** with constant magnitude and direction, the impulse is represented by the vector $\mathbf{F}(t_2 - t_1)$. The vector has the same direction as **F**.

For a particle described by Eq 38, the final momentum $m\mathbf{v}_2$ may be determined by vector addition of its initial momentum $m\mathbf{v}_1$ and the impulse of the force **F**, as shown in Fig. 20. It may be written:

$$m\mathbf{v}_1 + \mathbf{Imp}_{1\to2} = m\mathbf{v}_2 \tag{Eq 40}$$

Kinetic energy and work are scalar quantities; momentum and impulse are vector quantities. Analytically, Eq 40 may be expressed by equivalent component equations:

$$(mv_x)_1 + \int_{t_1}^{t_2} F_x dt = (mv_x)_2$$

$$(mv_y)_1 + \int_{t_1}^{t_2} F_y dt = (mv_y)_2$$

$$(mv_z)_1 + \int_{t_1}^{t_2} F_z dt = (mv_z)_2 \tag{Eq 41}$$

Because the impulse of each of several forces acting on a particle must be considered:

$$m\mathbf{v}_1 + \Sigma\, \mathbf{Imp}_{1\to2} = m\mathbf{v}_2 \tag{Eq 42}$$

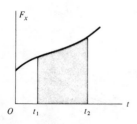 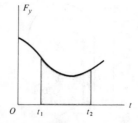 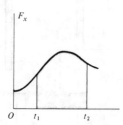

Figure 19

Impulsive Motion. A large force acting during a very short time interval on a particle to produce a definite change in momentum is called an impulsive force. The motion is impulsive motion. For example, when contact is made between bat and baseball during time interval Δt, the average value of the force $\mathbf{F}$ delivered by the bat is very large, and the impulse $\mathbf{F}\,\Delta t$ is large enough to redirect motion of the ball (Fig. 21). When impulsive forces act on a particle, Eq 42 then becomes:

$$m\mathbf{v}_1 + \Sigma\,\mathbf{F}\,\Delta t = m\mathbf{v}_2 \qquad\qquad \text{(Eq 43)}$$

Example 5. A 2000-kg cannon, shown in Fig. 22, fires a 10-kg shell with an initial velocity of 600 m/s at an angle of 30°. The cannon moves horizontally. The cannon has no recoil mechanism and the shell leaves the barrel 6 ms after firing. To determine the recoil velocity of the cannon and the resultant $\mathbf{R}$ of the vertical impulsive forces exerted by the ground on the cannon, first apply the principle of impulse and momentum to find the impulse $\mathbf{F}\,\Delta t$ exerted by the cannon on the shell. Then apply the principle to the cannon. To determine the final momentum of the cannon and the impulse $\mathbf{R}\,\Delta t$ exerted by the ground on the cannon, all nonimpulsive forces may be neglected because the time interval $\Delta t = 6$ ms $= 0.006$ s is very short. For the shell as a free body:

$$(m_S\mathbf{v}_S)_1 + \Sigma\,\mathbf{Imp}_{1\to2} = (m_S\mathbf{v}_S)_2$$
$$0 + F\,\Delta t = (10\text{ kg})(600\text{ m/s})$$
$$F\,\Delta t = 6000\text{ kg}\cdot\text{m/s} = 6000\text{ N}\cdot\text{s}$$

For the cannon as a free body:

$$(m_C\mathbf{v}_C)_1 + \Sigma\,\mathbf{Imp}_{1\to2} = (m_C\mathbf{v}_C)_2$$

The $\xrightarrow{+} x$ component is $0 - (F\,\Delta t)\cos 30° = -m_C v_C$, so:

$$0 - (6000\text{ kg}\cdot\text{m/s})\cos 30° = -(2000\text{ kg})v_C$$

and we get $v_C = +2.60$ m/s and $\mathbf{v}_C = 2.60$ m/s $\leftarrow$. The $+\uparrow y$ component is $0 + R\,\Delta t - (F\,\Delta t)\sin 30° = 0$, $R\,\Delta t = (6000\text{ N}\cdot\text{s})\sin 30° = 3000\text{ N}\cdot\text{s}$, and:

$$R = \frac{3000\text{ N}\cdot\text{s}}{0.006\text{ s}} = +500\,000\text{ N} \qquad R = 500\text{ kN}\uparrow$$

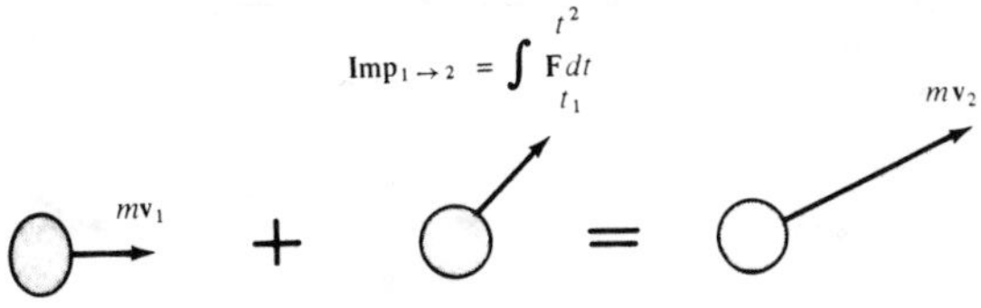

$$\text{Imp}_{1\to2} = \int_{t_1}^{t_2} \mathbf{F}\,dt$$

Figure 20

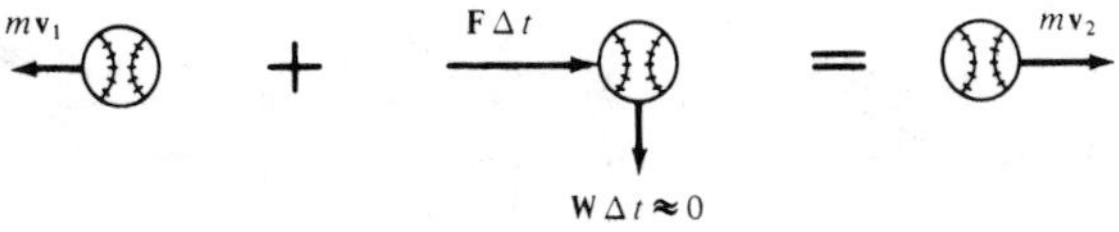

Figure 21

Impact. When two bodies collide in a very small time interval with relatively large forces, the result is called an impact. The common normal to the colliding surfaces is the line of impact. Central impact occurs when the mass centers of two colliding bodies are located on this line. Velocities of the two particles directed along the line of impact produce direct impact (Fig. 23a). Oblique impact is shown in Fig. 23(b).

Direct Central Impact. For two particles A and B, of mass m_A and m_B, moving along the same straight line and to the right with velocities v_A and v_B, as shown in Fig. 24(a), if v_A is larger than v_B, particle A will eventually strike particle B. The two particles deform and, after deformation, reach the same velocity u (Fig. 24b). After restitution, the particles will either regain their original shape or will remain deformed. To determine the particle velocities v_A' and v_B' after restitution (Fig. 24c), consider first the two particles together. Because there is no impulsive, external force, total particle momentum is conserved, and $m_A \mathbf{v}_A + m_B \mathbf{v}_B = m_A \mathbf{v}_A' + m_B \mathbf{v}_B'$. Because the velocities are directed along the same axis, this equation may be expressed in scalar components:

$$m_A v_A + m_B v_B = m_A v_A' + m_B v_B' \qquad \text{(Eq 44)}$$

Positive values for any of the scalar quantities v_A, v_B, v_A', or v_B' indicate the corresponding vector is directed to the right; negative values indicate that the vector is directed to the left. Because the impulsive force acting on A during this period is the force $\mathbf{P}$ exerted by B (Fig. 25a):

$$m_A v_A - \int P \, dt = m_A u \qquad \text{(Eq 45)}$$

where the integral defines the deformation period. With $\mathbf{R}$ the force of B on A during restitution (Fig. 25b):

$$m_A u - \int R \, dt = m_A v_A' \qquad \text{(Eq 46)}$$

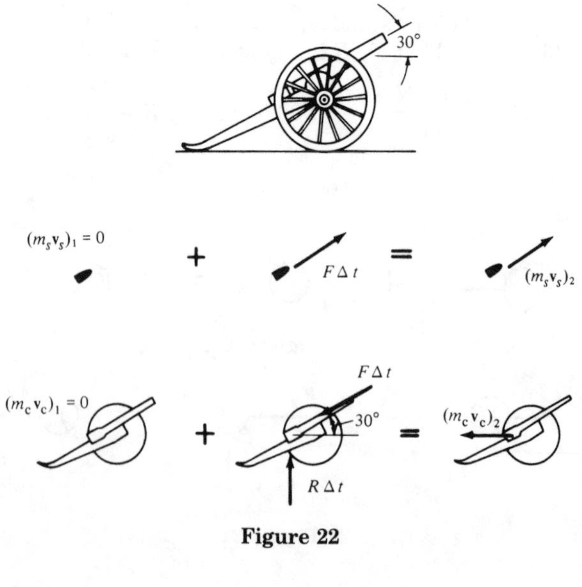

Figure 22

where the integral defines the restitution period. The ratio of the magnitudes of the impulses during restitution and deformation is called the coefficient of restitution, denoted by e:

$$e = \frac{\int R\, dt}{\int P\, dt} \qquad \text{(Eq 47)}$$

The value of the coefficient e, always between 0 and 1, depends on materials involved, impact velocity, and the shape and size of the colliding bodies. Solving Eq 45 and 46 and substituting into 47, we write:

$$e = \frac{u - v'_A}{v_A - u} \qquad \text{(Eq 48)}$$

For particle B:

$$e = \frac{v'_B - u}{u - v_B} \qquad \text{(Eq 49)}$$

Therefore, from Eq 48 and 49:

$$e = \frac{(u - v'_A) + (v'_B - u)}{(v_A - u) + (u - v_B)} = \frac{v'_B - v'_A}{v_A - v_B}$$

and

$$v'_B - v'_A = e(v_A - v_B) \qquad \text{(Eq 50)}$$

When $e = 0$, perfectly plastic impact results, and Eq 50 yields $v'_B = v'_A$, with no period of restitution. Both particles stay together after impact. Substituting $v'_B = v'_A = v'$ into Eq 44 produces:

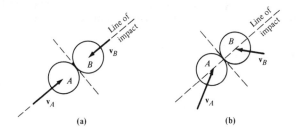

(a)   (b)

Figure 23 (a) Direct central impact. (b) Oblique central impact

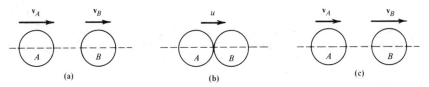

(a)   (b)   (c)

Figure 24 (a) Before impact. (b) At maximum deformation. (c) After impact

$$m_A v_A + m_B v_B = (m_A + m_B) v' \qquad \text{(Eq 51)}$$

which can be solved for the common velocity v' of the two particles after impact.

Angular Momentum of a Particle. For particle P with mass m moving with respect to a Newtonian frame of reference $Oxyz$, linear momentum at a given instant is defined as the vector $m\mathbf{v}$, the particle velocity $\mathbf{v}$ multiplied by its mass m. The moment about O of the vector $m\mathbf{v}$ is $\mathbf{H}_O$, the moment of momentum, or angular momentum, of the particle about O at that instant. Denoting by $\mathbf{r}$ the position vector of P:

$$\mathbf{H}_O = \mathbf{r} \times m\mathbf{v} \qquad \text{(Eq 52)}$$

which describes a vector perpendicular to the plane containing $\mathbf{r}$ and $m\mathbf{v}$, with magnitude:

$$H_O = rmv \sin \phi \qquad \text{(Eq 53)}$$

where ϕ is the angle between $\mathbf{r}$ and $m\mathbf{v}$ (Fig. 26). The sense of $\mathbf{H}_O$ may be determined from the sense of $m\mathbf{v}$ by applying the right-hand rule. Units of angular momentum are obtained by multiplying the units of length and linear momentum. The vectors $\mathbf{r}$ and $m\mathbf{v}$ may be resolved into components and expressed as:

$$\mathbf{H}_O = \begin{vmatrix} \mathbf{i} & \mathbf{j} & \mathbf{k} \\ x & y & z \\ mv_x & mv_y & mv_z \end{vmatrix} \qquad \text{(Eq 54)}$$

The components of $\mathbf{H}_O$ also represent the moments of the linear momentum $m\mathbf{v}$ about the coordinate axes. Expanding the determinant in Eq 54 gives:

$$H_x = m(yv_z - zv_y) \qquad H_y = m(zv_x - xv_z) \qquad H_z = m(xv_y - yv_x) \qquad \text{(Eq 55)}$$

For a particle moving in the xy plane, $z = v_z = 0$; the components H_x and H_y become zero. Angular momentum perpendicular to the xy plane is defined by the scalar:

$$H_O = H_z = m(xv_y - yv_x) \qquad \text{(Eq 56)}$$

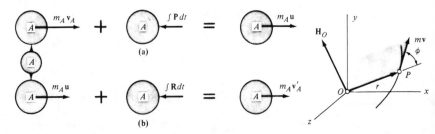

Figure 25 (a) Period of deformation. (b) Period of restitution   **Figure 26**

which is positive or negative, depending on the sense in which the particle is observed to move from O. In polar coordinates, linear momentum of the particle is resolved into radial and transverse components, as shown in Fig. 27, and is expressed as:

$$H_O = rmv \sin \phi = rmv_\theta \qquad \text{(Eq 57)}$$

Because $v_\theta = r\dot{\theta}$:

$$H_O = mr^2\dot{\theta} \qquad \text{(Eq 58)}$$

To compute the derivative with respect to t of $\mathbf{H}_O$ of a moving particle P, differentiate both sides of Eq 52, $\dot{\mathbf{H}}_O = \dot{\mathbf{r}} \times m\mathbf{v} + \mathbf{r} \times m\dot{\mathbf{v}} = \mathbf{v} \times m\mathbf{v} + \mathbf{r} \times m\mathbf{a}$. Because the vectors $\mathbf{v}$ and $m\mathbf{v}$ are collinear, the first term of the expression is zero, and $m\mathbf{a}$ equals the sum $\Sigma \mathbf{F}$ of the forces acting on P. Because $\mathbf{r} \times \Sigma \mathbf{F}$ represents the sum $\Sigma \mathbf{M}_O$ of the moments about O:

$$\Sigma \mathbf{M}_O = \dot{\mathbf{H}}_O \qquad \text{(Eq 59)}$$

Angular Momentum of a Rigid Body in Plane Motion. For a rigid slab in plane motion, with η particles P_i of mass Δm_i the angular momentum $\mathbf{H}_G$ about its mass center G of the slab may be determined by taking the moments about G of the momenta of the particles in motion with respect to either frame Oxy or $Gx'y'$. Using $Gx'y'$:

$$\mathbf{H}_G = \sum_{i=1}^{n} (\mathbf{r}_i' \times \mathbf{v}_i' \Delta m_i) \qquad \text{(Eq 60)}$$

where $\mathbf{r}_i'$ and $\mathbf{v}_i' \Delta m_i$ denote the position vector and the linear momentum of the particle P_i relative to the centroidal frame of reference $Gx'y'$ (Fig. 28). Because the particle belongs to the slab, $\mathbf{v}_i' = \boldsymbol{\omega} \times \mathbf{r}_i'$, where $\boldsymbol{\omega}$ is the instantaneous angular velocity of the slab, and:

$$\mathbf{H}_G = \sum_{i=1}^{n} [\mathbf{r}_i' \times (\boldsymbol{\omega} \times \mathbf{r}_i')\Delta m_i]$$

This expression represents a vector of the same direction as $\boldsymbol{\omega}$, perpendicular to the slab, with magnitude equal to $\omega \Sigma r_i'^2 \Delta m_i$. The sum $\Sigma r_i'^2 \Delta m_i$ represents the moment of inertia $\bar{I}$ of the slab about a centroidal axis perpendicular to the slab. Thus the angular momentum $\mathbf{H}_G$ about the mass center is:

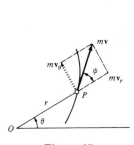

Figure 27

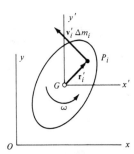

Figure 28

$$\mathbf{H}_G = \bar{I}\boldsymbol{\omega} \qquad\qquad\qquad\qquad\qquad\qquad\qquad\qquad \text{(Eq 61)}$$

Differentiating both members of Eq 61 produces:

$$\dot{\mathbf{H}}_G = \bar{I}\dot{\boldsymbol{\omega}} = \bar{I}\boldsymbol{\alpha} \qquad\qquad\qquad\qquad\qquad\qquad \text{(Eq 62)}$$

KINETICS OF RIGID BODIES

Equations of Motion for a Rigid Body. For a rigid body acted upon by several forces $\mathbf{F}_1, \mathbf{F}_2, \mathbf{F}_3, \ldots \mathbf{F}_n$, as shown in Fig. 29, consider first the motion of the mass center G of the body with respect to the Newtonian frame of reference $Oxyz$, which can be expressed by:

$$\Sigma \mathbf{F} = m\bar{\mathbf{a}} \qquad\qquad\qquad\qquad\qquad\qquad\qquad\qquad \text{(Eq 63)}$$

where m is the mass and $\bar{\mathbf{a}}$ the acceleration of mass center G. Motion relative to the centroidal frame of reference $Gx'y'z'$ may be expressed as:

$$\Sigma \mathbf{M}_G = \dot{\mathbf{H}}_G \qquad\qquad\qquad\qquad\qquad\qquad\qquad \text{(Eq 64)}$$

where $\dot{\mathbf{H}}_G$ is the rate of change of $\mathbf{H}_G$, the angular momentum about G of the rigid body. Taken together, Eq 63 and 64 describe a system of the external forces equipollent to the system consisting of the vector $m\bar{\mathbf{a}}$ attached at G and the couple of moment $\dot{\mathbf{H}}_G$ (Fig. 30). Now $\bar{\mathbf{a}}$, the acceleration of the center of mass in Eq 63, can be expressed in any coordinate system depending on the motion of the center of mass of the body, that is, Cartesian, polar, normal-tangential, cylindrical, or spherical.

Plane Motion of a Rigid Body. For a rigid mass m moved by forces $\mathbf{F}_1, \mathbf{F}_2, \mathbf{F}_3, \ldots \mathbf{F}_n$, as shown in Fig. 31, contained in the plane of the body, substituting for $\mathbf{H}_G$ from Eq 62 into Eq 64, and writing Eq 63 and Eq 64 in scalar form:

$$\Sigma F_x = m\bar{a}_x \qquad \Sigma F_y = m\bar{a}_y \qquad \Sigma M_G = \bar{I}\alpha \qquad\qquad \text{(Eq 65)}$$

The coordinates $\bar{x}$ and $\bar{y}$ of the mass center and the angular coordinate θ of the slab may be obtained at any instant t by integration. Similar expressions to those of Eq 65 can be derived for polar motion:

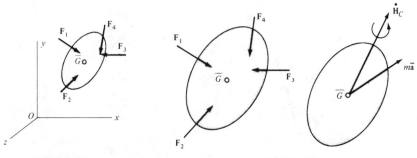

Figure 29   Figure 30

$$\Sigma \mathbf{F}_r = m\bar{\mathbf{a}}_r \qquad \Sigma \mathbf{F}_\theta = m\bar{\mathbf{a}}_\theta \qquad \Sigma \mathbf{M}_G = \bar{I}\alpha$$

and for normal-tangential coordinates:

$$\Sigma \mathbf{F}_m = m\bar{\mathbf{a}}_n \qquad \Sigma \mathbf{F}_t = m\bar{\mathbf{a}}_t \qquad \Sigma \mathbf{M}_G = \bar{I}\alpha$$

Noncentroidal Rotation. The motion of a rigid body that rotates about a fixed axis placed outside its mass center is called a noncentroidal rotation. The mass center G moves in a circle of radius $\bar{r}$ about point O, where the axis of rotation intersects the reference plane (Fig. 32). With ω the angular velocity and α angular acceleration of the line OG, the tangential and normal components of the acceleration of G are:

$$\bar{a}_t = \bar{r}\alpha \qquad\qquad\qquad \text{(Eq 66)}$$

$$\bar{a}_n = \bar{r}\omega^2 \qquad\qquad\qquad \text{(Eq 67)}$$

Because line OG is part of the body, ω and α also represent the angular velocity and the angular acceleration of the body in its motion relative to G. Eq 66 and 67 define the kinematic relationship of the motions of the mass center G and the body about G and can be used to eliminate $\bar{a}_t$ and $\bar{a}_n$ by applying D'Alembert's principle (Fig. 33) or the method of dynamic equilibrium (Fig. 34). By equating the moments about the fixed point O of the forces and vectors shown in Fig. 33:

$$+\curvearrowleft \Sigma M_O = \bar{I}\alpha + (m\bar{r}\alpha)\bar{r} = (\bar{I} + m\bar{r}^2)\alpha$$

Because $\bar{I} + m\bar{r}^2 = I_O$, with I_O the moment of inertia of the rigid body about the fixed axis O:

$$\Sigma M_O = I_O\alpha \qquad\qquad\qquad \text{(Eq 68)}$$

Example 6. A pendulum with mass of 7.5 kg and center of mass at G has a radius of gyration about O of 295 mm (Fig. 35). The pendulum is released at $\theta = 0$. Friction is negligible. To determine the total force on the bearing at the instant when $\theta = 30°$, find the normal component O_n from a force equation in the n-direction, which involves the normal acceleration $\bar{r}\omega^2$. The angular velocity ω of the pendulum is found from the integral of the angular acceleration, and O_t depends on the tangential acceleration $\bar{r}\alpha$. The moment equation about O gives:

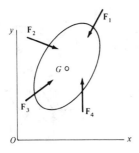

Figure 31

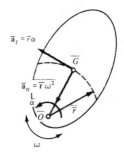

Figure 32

$$[\Sigma M_O = I_O \alpha]$$
$$7.5\,(9.81)\,(0.25)\,\cos\theta = 7.5\,(0.295)^2\alpha$$
$$\alpha = 28.2\,\cos\theta\ \text{rad/s}^2$$

For $\theta = 30°$:

$$[\omega\,d\omega = \alpha\,d\theta]$$
$$\int_0^\omega \omega\,d\omega = \int_0^{\pi/6} 28.2\,\cos\theta\,d\theta$$
$$\omega^2 = 28.2\ (\text{rad/s})^2$$

The equations of motion applied to the 30° position yield:

$$[\Sigma \dot{F}_n = m\bar{r}\omega^2]$$
$$O_n - 7.5\,(9.81)\,(0.5) = 7.5\,(0.25)\,(28.2)$$
$$O_n = 89.6\ \text{N}$$
$$[\Sigma F_t = m\bar{r}\alpha]$$
$$7.5\,(9.81)\,(0.866) - O_t = 7.5\,(0.25)\,(28.2)\,(0.866)$$
$$O_t = 17.96\ \text{N}$$

Thus, the total force on the bearing at O is:

$$O = \sqrt{(89.6)^2 + (17.96)^2} = 91.4\ \text{N}$$

Rolling Motion. For a balanced disk or wheel that rolls without sliding, as shown in Fig. 36, mass center and geometric center coincide. Acceleration $\bar{\mathbf{a}}$ of mass center G and its angular acceleration $\boldsymbol{\alpha}$ are not independent. The distance $\bar{x}$ traveled by G during a rotation θ is $\bar{x} = r\theta$, where r is the disk radius. Differentiating this relationship twice:

$$\bar{a} = r\alpha \qquad\qquad\qquad\qquad\qquad\qquad\qquad\qquad\quad (\text{Eq } 69)$$

Because effective forces in plane motion reduce to a vector $m\bar{\mathbf{a}}$ and a couple $\bar{I}\alpha$, these forces are reduced to a vector of magnitude $mr\alpha$ attached at G and to a couple of magnitude $\bar{I}\alpha$, as shown in Fig. 36.

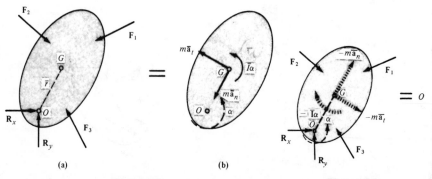

(a)

(b)

Figure 33   **Figure 34**

When the disk rotates and slides at the same time, a relative motion exists between the point of the disk which is in contact with the ground and the ground itself, and the force of friction has the magnitude $F_k = \mu_k N$, where μ_k is the coefficient of kinetic friction. In this case, however, the motion of the mass center G of the disk and the rotation of the disk about G are independent, and $\bar{a}$ is not equal to $r\alpha$. These three different cases may be summarized as follows:

Rolling, no sliding: $\qquad\quad F \le \mu_s N \qquad \bar{a} = r\alpha$
Rolling, sliding impending: $\quad F = \mu_s N \qquad \bar{a} = r\alpha$
Rotating and sliding: $\qquad\quad F = \mu_k N \qquad \bar{a}$ and α independent

When it is not known whether a disk slides or not, it should first be assumed that the disk rolls without sliding. If F is found smaller than, or equal to, $\mu_s N$, the assumption is proved correct. If F is found larger than $\mu_s N$, the assumption is incorrect and the problem should be started again, assuming rotating and sliding.

For an unbalanced disk or wheel, mass center G does not coincide with geometric center O, and Eq 69 does not hold between $\bar{a}$ and α. A similar relation will hold, however, between the magnitude a_O of acceleration of the geometric center and the angular acceleration α. The following similar relationship holds:

$$a_O = r\alpha \qquad\qquad\qquad\qquad\qquad\qquad\qquad\text{(Eq 70)}$$

To determine $\bar{a}$ in terms of α and the angular velocity ω, a relative-acceleration formula may be used:

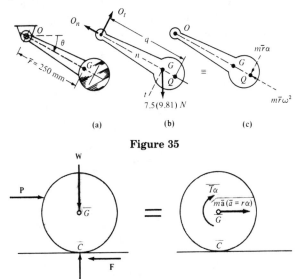

(a)   (b)   (c)

Figure 35

Figure 36

$$\bar{\mathbf{a}} = \mathbf{a}_G = \mathbf{a}_O + \mathbf{a}_{G/O}$$
$$= \mathbf{a}_O + (\mathbf{a}_{G/O})_t + (\mathbf{a}_{G/O})_n \qquad \text{(Eq 71)}$$

where the three component accelerations are directed as shown in Fig. 37 and the magnitudes $a_O = r\alpha$, $(a_{G/O})_t = (OG)\alpha$, and $(a_{G/O})_n = (OG)\omega^2$.

Example 7. The 30-kg wheel in Fig. 38 has a mass center at G and a radius of gyration of $k_G = 0.15$ m. A 200-N force is applied at the center. With the wheel initially at rest, static and kinetic coefficients of friction between the wheel and horizontal plane at A are $\mu = 0.45$. To determine the acceleration of the center O, use the free-body and kinetic diagrams of Fig. 38(b). The mass center G is located outside the geometric center O, and the initial path of motion for G is unknown. The components $m(\mathbf{a}_G)_x$ and $m(\mathbf{a}_G)_y$ act in the x and y directions. Using the radius of gyration and the mass, the moment of inertia about the mass center is:

$$I_G = k_G{}^2 m = (0.15)^2 30 = 0.675 \text{ kg} \cdot \text{m}^2$$

Applying the equations of motion gives:

$$\overset{+}{\rightarrow} \Sigma F_x = m(a_G)_x \qquad 200 - F_A = 30(a_G)_x \qquad \text{(Eq 72)}$$

$$+ \uparrow \Sigma F_y = m(a_G)_y \qquad N_A - 294.3 = 30(a_G)_y \qquad \text{(Eq 73)}$$

$$\curvearrowright + \Sigma M_G = I_G \alpha \qquad F_A(0.25) - N_A(0.1) = 0.675\alpha \qquad \text{(Eq 74)}$$

Thus, the unknowns are F_A, N_A, $(a_G)_x$, $(a_G)_y$, and α.

If the wheel rolls without slipping, the acceleration components $(\mathbf{a}_G)_x$ and $(\mathbf{a}_G)_y$ can be related to angular acceleration $\boldsymbol{\alpha}$. Acceleration of the center has a magnitude of $a_O = \alpha r = \alpha(0.25)$ and is directed to the right. Because the wheel is originally at rest, $\omega = 0$. Using kinematic diagrams in Fig. 39, with O as the base point, accelerations of points G and O can be related by:

$$\mathbf{a}_G = \mathbf{a}_O + (\mathbf{a}_{G/O})_t + (\mathbf{a}_{G/O})_n$$

or

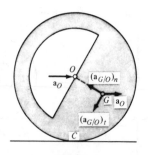

Figure 37

$$(a_G)_x + (a_G)_y = (0.25)\alpha + \alpha(0.1) + 0$$
$$\rightarrow \quad \uparrow \quad \rightarrow \quad \uparrow$$

Equating horizontal and vertical components:

$$(a_G)_x = 0.25\alpha \tag{Eq 75}$$

$$(a_G)_y = 0.1\alpha \tag{Eq 76}$$

Equations 72 through 76 are solved for the five unknowns:

$$F_A = 146.0 \text{ N}$$
$$N_A = 316.0 \text{ N}$$
$$(a_G)_x = 1.80 \text{ m/s}^2$$
$$(a_G)_y = 0.722 \text{ m/s}^2$$
$$\alpha = 7.22 \text{ rad/s}^2$$

The result contradicts the original assumption of no slipping, since $146.0 > 0.45(316.0) = 142.2$ N. Therefore, with slipping:

$$\mathbf{a}_G = \mathbf{a}_O + (\mathbf{a}_{G/O})_t + (\mathbf{a}_{G/O})_n$$
$$(a_G)_x + (a_G)_y = a_O + \alpha(0.1) + 0$$
$$\rightarrow \quad \uparrow \quad \rightarrow \quad \uparrow$$

that is, $\mathbf{a}_O$ and $\boldsymbol\alpha$ are independent and $F_A = 0.45\,N_A = 140.2$ N. Thus, $(a_G)_x = a_O$ and $(a_G)_y = 0.1\alpha$. Reusing Eq 72 through 74 gives:

$$(a_G)_x = 1.99 \text{ m/s}^2$$
$$(a_G)_y = 0.577 \text{ m/s}^2$$
$$\alpha = 5.77 \text{ rad/s}^2$$
$$a_O = 1.99 \text{ m/s}^2$$

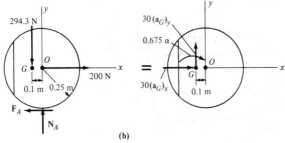

Figure 38

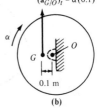

Figure 39 (a) Absolute motion. (b) Relative motion

Principle of Work and Energy for a Rigid Body. To apply the principle of work and energy to the motion of a rigid body, assume that the rigid body contains a large number n of particles of mass Δm_i, and let:

$$T_1 + U_{1\to2} = T_2 \tag{Eq 77}$$

where T_1, T_2 = initial and final values of total kinetic energy of the particles and $U_{1\to2}$ = work of all forces acting on the particles. Total kinetic energy:

$$T = \frac{1}{2} \sum_{i=1}^{n} (\Delta m_i) v_i^2 \tag{Eq 78}$$

which is a positive scalar quantity.

Forces Acting on a Rigid Body. The work of a force $\mathbf{F}$ during a displacement from A_1 to A_2 is:

$$U_{1\to2} = \int_{A_1}^{A_2} \mathbf{F} \cdot d\mathbf{r} \tag{Eq 79}$$

or

$$U_{1\to2} = \int_{s_1}^{s_2} (F \cos \alpha)\, ds \tag{Eq 80}$$

where F equals the magnitude of the force, α the angle formed by the direction of motion at A, and s the variable of integration that is the measure of distance traveled by A. The forces $\mathbf{F}$ and $-\mathbf{F}$ in Fig. 40 form a couple of moment $\mathbf{M}$ acting on a rigid body. Displacement of points A and B to positions A' and B'' may be divided into two parts. Points A and B in one part undergo equal displacements $d\mathbf{r}_1$. In the other part of the displacement, A' remains fixed while B' moves to B'' through displacement $d\mathbf{r}_2$ of magnitude $ds_2 = r\, d\theta$. In the first part, the work of $\mathbf{F}$ equals $-\mathbf{F}$ in magnitude and is opposite in sign; their sum is zero. In the second part, the work of force $\mathbf{F}$ is $dU = F\, ds_2 = Fr\, d\theta$.

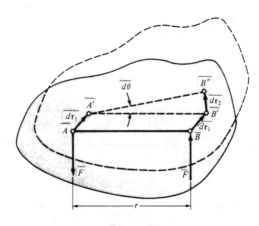

Figure 40

Because the product Fr equals the magnitude M of the moment of the couple, the work of a couple of moment $\mathbf{M}$ is:

$$dU = M\,d\theta \tag{Eq 81}$$

where $d\theta$ represents the angle of rotation expressed in radians. Integrating both members of Eq 81 from θ_1 to θ_2 produces the work of the couple during a finite rotation of the rigid body:

$$U_{1\to2} = \int_{\theta_1}^{\theta_2} M\,d\theta \tag{Eq 82}$$

When the moment $\mathbf{M}$ is constant, Eq 82 becomes:

$$U_{1\to2} = M(\theta_2 - \theta_1) \tag{Eq 83}$$

Kinetic Energy of a Rigid Body in Plane Motion. If the absolute velocity $\mathbf{v}_i$ of each particle P_i of a rigid body of mass m in plane motion is expressed as the sum of the velocity $\bar{\mathbf{v}}$ of the mass center G of the body and the velocity v_i' of the particle relative to a frame $Gx'y'$ attached to G and of fixed orientation, as shown in Fig. 41, the kinetic energy of this system may be expressed as:

$$T = \frac{1}{2}\,m\bar{v}^2 + \frac{1}{2}\sum_{i=1}^{n}(\Delta m_i)v_i'^2 \tag{Eq 84}$$

The magnitude v_i' of the relative velocity of P_i equals $r_i'\omega$ which is the product of the distance r_i' and P_i from the axis through G perpendicular to the plane of motion and the magnitude ω of the angular velocity of the body. Substituting into Eq 84:

$$T = \frac{1}{2}\,m\bar{v}^2 + \frac{1}{2}\left(\sum_{i=1}^{n} r_i'^2 \Delta m_i\right)\omega^2 \tag{Eq 85}$$

Expressed in terms of the moment of inertia $\bar{I}$ of the body about the axis through G:

$$T = \frac{1}{2}\,m\bar{v}^2 + \frac{1}{2}\,\bar{I}\omega^2 \tag{Eq 86}$$

For a body in translation, that is, $\omega = 0$, the expression reduces to $\frac{1}{2}\,m\bar{v}^2$. For a body in centroidal rotation ($\bar{v} = 0$), it reduces to $\frac{1}{2}\,\bar{I}\omega^2$.

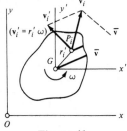

Figure 41

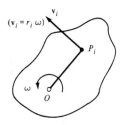

Figure 42

Noncentroidal Rotation. The kinetic energy of a rigid body rotating with an angular velocity ω about a fixed axis through O, as shown in Fig. 42, may be expressed by noting that the speed v_i of the particle P_i equals the product of the distance r_i of P_i from the fixed axis and the magnitude ω of the angular velocity at the instant considered. Substituting into Eq 78:

$$T = \frac{1}{2} \sum_{i=1}^{n} (\Delta m_i)(r_i \omega)^2 = \frac{1}{2} \left(\sum_{i=1}^{n} r_i^2 \Delta m_i \right) \omega^2 \qquad \text{(Eq 87)}$$

Expressed in terms of the moment of inertia I_O about the fixed axis through O:

$$T = \frac{1}{2} I_O \omega^2 \qquad \text{(Eq 88)}$$

Example 8. A 240-lb block hangs from a cable wound around a drum of 1.25-ft radius attached to a flywheel (Fig. 43). The combined centroidal moment of inertia $\bar{I} = 10.5$ lb·ft·s² for the drum and flywheel. The downward velocity of the block is 6 ft/s. Given the bearing friction equivalent to the couple **M** of magnitude 60 lb·ft, determine the velocity of the block after 4 ft of downward movement. The kinetic energy of Position 1 is expressed in terms of $\bar{v}_1 = 6$ ft/s, and:

$$\omega_1 = \frac{\bar{v}_1}{r} = \frac{6 \text{ ft/s}}{1.25 \text{ ft}} = 4.80 \text{ rad/s}$$

Thus: $T_1 = \frac{1}{2} m \bar{v}_1^2 + \frac{1}{2} \bar{I} \omega_1^2$

$$= \frac{1}{2} \frac{240 \text{ lb}}{32.2 \text{ ft/s}^2} (6 \text{ ft/s})^2 + \frac{1}{2} (10.5 \text{ lb·ft·s}^2)(4.80 \text{ rad/s})^2$$

$$= 255 \text{ ft·lb}$$

For Position 2, $\omega_2 = \bar{v}_2/1.25$, and:

$$T_2 = \frac{1}{2} m \bar{v}_2^2 + \frac{1}{2} \bar{I} \omega_2^2$$

$$= \frac{1}{2} \frac{240}{32.2} (\bar{v}_2)^2 + \left(\frac{1}{2} \right) (10.5) \left(\frac{\bar{v}_2}{1.25} \right)^2 = 7.09 \bar{v}_2^2$$

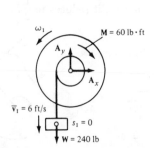

Figure 43

During motion, work is done only by the weight $\mathbf{W}$ and the friction couple $\mathbf{M}$, $\mathbf{W}$ in a positive sense and $\mathbf{M}$ in a negative sense. Thus $s_1 = 0$, $s_2 = 4$ ft, $\theta_1 = 0$, and:

$$\theta_2 = \frac{s_2}{r} = \frac{4 \text{ ft}}{1.25 \text{ ft}} = 3.20 \text{ rad}$$

Therefore:
$$\begin{aligned} U_{1 \to 2} &= W(s_2 - s_1) - M(\theta_2 - \theta_1) \\ &= (240 \text{ lb})(4 \text{ ft}) - (60 \text{ lb} \cdot \text{ft})(3.20 \text{ rad}) \\ &= 768 \text{ ft} \cdot \text{lb} \end{aligned}$$

According to the principle of work and energy:

$$T_1 + U_{1 \to 2} = T_2$$
$$255 \text{ ft} \cdot \text{lb} + 768 \text{ ft} \cdot \text{lb} = 7.09 \bar{v}_2{}^2$$
$$\bar{v}_2 = 12.01 \text{ ft/s}$$
$$\bar{\mathbf{v}}_2 = 12.01 \text{ ft/s} \downarrow$$

Impulse and Momentum for the Plane Motion of a Rigid Body. Because the vectors associated with a rigid body may be considered sliding vectors, vectors shown in Fig. 44 are not only equipollent but equivalent; the vectors on the left-hand side of the equals sign may be transformed into the vectors on the right-hand side. Therefore:

Syst Momenta$_1$ + Syst Ext Imp$_{1 \to 2}$ = Syst Momenta$_2$ (Eq 89)

But momenta $\mathbf{v}_i \Delta m_i$ may be reduced to a vector attached at G:

$$\mathbf{L} = \sum_{i=1}^{n} \mathbf{v}_i \Delta m_i \qquad \text{(Eq 90)}$$

and to a couple with moment equal to the sum of moments about G:

$$H_G = \sum_{i=1}^{n} \mathbf{r}_i' \times \mathbf{v}_i \Delta m_i \qquad \text{(Eq 91)}$$

The expressions $\mathbf{L}$ and H_G define linear momentum and the angular momentum about G of the system of particles. Further, because $\mathbf{L} = m\bar{\mathbf{v}}$ and $\mathbf{H}_G = \bar{I}\omega$, the system of the momenta $\mathbf{v}_i \Delta m_i$ is equivalent to the linear momentum vector

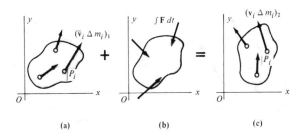

(a)   (b)   (c)

Figure 44

$m\bar{\mathbf{v}}$ attached at G and to the angular momentum couple $\bar{I}\omega$, as indicated in Fig. 45. The system of momenta reduces to the vector $m\bar{\mathbf{v}}$ when the body is in translation ($\omega = 0$) and to the couple $\bar{I}\omega$ during centroidal rotation ($\mathbf{v} = 0$).

Impulsive Motion.   Problems involving impulsive motion are well adapted to solution by the method of impulse and momentum. Because the time involved is very short, the bodies may be assumed to occupy the same positions during that time interval.

Eccentric Impact.   To analyze eccentric impact of two rigid bodies, denote by $\mathbf{v}_A$ and $\mathbf{v}_B$ the velocities before impact of the two points of contact A and B, as shown in Fig. 46(a). Under the impact, the two bodies deform. After deformation, the velocities $\mathbf{u}_A$ and $\mathbf{u}_B$ of A and B will have equal components along the line of impact nn (Fig. 46b). After a period of restitution, A and B will have velocities $\mathbf{v}'_A$ and $\mathbf{v}'_B$ (Fig. 46c). Assuming the bodies to be frictionless, the forces exerted by each on the other are directed along the line of impact. With $\int P\, dt$ representing the magnitude of the impulse of one of these forces during deformation and $\int R\, dt$ the magnitude of the impulse of the same force during the period of restitution, the coefficient of restitution e is defined as the ratio:

$$e = \frac{\int R\, dt}{\int P\, dt} \tag{Eq 92}$$

The relative velocities of two particles before and after impact remain the same between the components along the line of impact of the two points of contact A and B. Therefore:

$$(v'_B)_n - (v'_A)_n = e[(v_A)_n - (v_B)_n] \tag{Eq 93}$$

Example 9.   The 2-kg sphere moving with an initial velocity of 5 m/s strikes an 8-kg rigid rod AB as shown in Fig. 47(a). The rod hinged at A is initially at rest. The coefficient of restitution between the rod and sphere is 0.80. To determine the angular velocity of the rod and the velocity of the sphere after impact, consider the rod and sphere as a single system. The initial momenta of the rod and sphere and the impulses of the external forces are equipollent to the final system momenta. The only external impulsive force is the impulsive reaction at A. The $+\circlearrowleft$ moments about A are:

$$m_s v_s (1.2 \text{ m}) = m_s v'_s (1.2 \text{ m}) + m_R \bar{v}'_R (0.6 \text{ m}) + \bar{I}\omega' \tag{Eq 94}$$

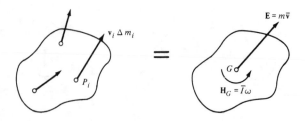

Figure 45

Since the rod rotates about A:

$$\bar{v}_R' = \bar{r}\omega' = (0.6 \text{ m})\,\omega'$$

and

$$\bar{I} = \frac{1}{12}\,mL^2 = \frac{1}{12}\,(8 \text{ kg})(1.2 \text{ m})^2 = 0.96 \text{ kg}\cdot\text{m}^2$$

Substituting these values into Eq 94:

$(2 \text{ kg})(5 \text{ m/s})(1.2 \text{ m})$
$\quad = (2 \text{ kg})\,v_s'(1.2 \text{ m}) + (8 \text{ kg})(0.6 \text{ m})\,\omega'(0.6 \text{ m}) + (0.96 \text{ kg}\cdot\text{m}^2)\,\omega'$
$12 = 2.4v_s' + 3.84\omega'$ (Eq 95)

To determine relative velocities, with positive direction to the right:

$$v_B' - v_s' = e(v_s - v_B)$$

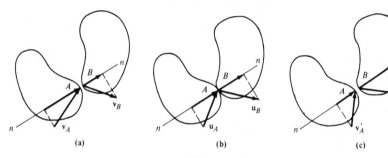

Figure 46

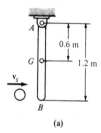

(a)

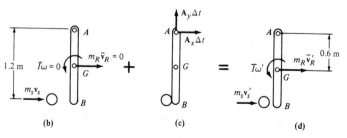

Figure 47

Substituting $v_s = 5$ m/s, $v_B = 0$, and $e = 0.80$:

$$v'_B - v'_s = 0.80 \,(5 \text{ m/s}) \qquad \text{(Eq 96)}$$

Because the rod rotates about A:

$$v'_B = (1.2 \text{ m})\,\omega' \qquad \text{(Eq 97)}$$

Solving Eq 95 to 97 simultaneously:

$$\omega' = +3.21 \text{ rad/s} \qquad \boldsymbol{\omega}' = 3.21 \text{ rad/s} \,\circlearrowleft$$
$$v'_s = -0.143 \text{ m/s} \qquad \mathbf{v}'_s = 0.143 \text{m/s} \leftarrow$$

SPATIAL KINETICS OF A RIGID BODY

Translational Motion. The translational motion of a body is defined in terms of the acceleration of the body's mass center, $\mathbf{a}_G$, measured from an inertial X, Y, Z reference. In vector form, the translational motion for the body can be written:

$$\Sigma \mathbf{F} = m\mathbf{a}_G \qquad \text{(Eq 98)}$$

or by the three scalar equations:

$$\Sigma F_x = m\,(a_G)_x \qquad \Sigma F_y = m\,(a_G)_y \qquad \Sigma F_z = m\,(a_G)_z \qquad \text{(Eq 99)}$$

The expression $\Sigma \mathbf{F} = \Sigma F_x \mathbf{i} + \Sigma F_y \mathbf{j} + \Sigma F_z \mathbf{k}$ represents the sum of all the external forces acting on the body.

Equations of Rotational Motion. The rotational motion of a body can be considered with respect to point O, which is fixed to an inertial reference and does not accelerate, or the body's center of mass G. The equations:

$$\Sigma \mathbf{M}_O = \frac{d\mathbf{H_O}}{dt} \qquad \text{(Eq 100)}$$

$$\Sigma \mathbf{M}_G = \frac{d\mathbf{H}_G}{dt} \qquad \text{(Eq 101)}$$

describe the relationships of the moments of the external forces applied to a system of particles or a rigid body and the angular momentum of the particles measured with respect to either point O or the center of mass G.

The scalar components of the angular momentum $\mathbf{H}_O$ or $\mathbf{H}_G$ are defined by:

$$\begin{aligned} H_x &= I_{xx}\omega_x - I_{xy}\omega_y - I_{xz}\omega_z \\ H_y &= -I_{yx}\omega_x + I_{yy}\omega_y - I_{yz}\omega_z \\ H_z &= -I_{zx}\omega_x - I_{zy}\omega_y + I_{zz}\omega_z \end{aligned} \qquad \text{(Eq 102)}$$

or by:

$$H_x = I_x\omega_x \qquad H_y = I_y\omega_y \qquad H_z \doteq I_z\omega_z \qquad \text{(Eq 103)}$$

if principal axes of inertia are used at either point O or point G. If these components are computed about x, y, z axes that are rotating with an angular velocity $\boldsymbol{\Omega}$, which may differ from angular velocity $\boldsymbol{\omega}$, the time derivative $\mathbf{H} = d\mathbf{H}/dt$, as used in Eq 100 and 101, must account for the rotation of the x, y, z

axes as measured from the inertial X, Y, Z axes. Thus, the time derivative of **H** becomes:

$$\Sigma \mathbf{M}_O = (\dot{\mathbf{H}}_O)_{xyz} + \boldsymbol{\Omega} \times \mathbf{H}_O \qquad \Sigma \mathbf{M}_G = (\dot{\mathbf{H}}_G)_{xyz} + \boldsymbol{\Omega} \times \mathbf{H}_G \qquad \text{(Eq 104)}$$

where $(\dot{\mathbf{H}})_{xyz}$ is the time rate of change of **H** measured from the x, y, z reference.

For a body having general motion, as shown in Fig. 48(a), the x, y, z axes with origin at G can be seen to translate only relative to the inertial X, Y, Z frame of reference, thus simplifying Eq 104, since $\boldsymbol{\Omega} = 0$.

For x, y, z axes having motion $\boldsymbol{\Omega} = \boldsymbol{\omega}$, the axes may be chosen in such a way that they are fixed in and move with the body having a fixed point O as shown in Fig. 48(b). The moments and products of inertia of the body relative to these axes are constant during motion. Since $\boldsymbol{\Omega} = \boldsymbol{\omega}$, the expressions of Eq 104 become:

$$\Sigma \mathbf{M}_O = (\dot{\mathbf{H}}_O)_{xyz} + \boldsymbol{\omega} \times \mathbf{H}_O \qquad \Sigma \mathbf{M}_G = (\dot{\mathbf{H}}_G)_{xyz} + \boldsymbol{\omega} \times \mathbf{H}_G \qquad \text{(Eq 105)}$$

These vector equations may also be expressed in scalar terms:

$$\begin{aligned}
\Sigma M_x \mathbf{i} + \Sigma M_y \mathbf{j} + \Sigma M_z \mathbf{k} = {} & (I_{xx}\dot{\omega}_x - I_{xy}\dot{\omega}_y - I_{xz}\dot{\omega}_z)\mathbf{i} \\
& + (-I_{yx}\dot{\omega}_x + I_{yy}\dot{\omega}_y - I_{yz}\dot{\omega}_z)\mathbf{j} \\
& + (-I_{zx}\dot{\omega}_x - I_{zy}\dot{\omega}_y + I_{zz}\dot{\omega}_z)\mathbf{k} \\
& + (\omega_x\mathbf{i} + \omega_y\mathbf{j} + \omega_z\mathbf{k}) \times (I_{xx}\omega_x - I_{xy}\omega_y - I_{xz}\omega_z)\mathbf{i} \\
& + (\omega_x\mathbf{i} + \omega_y\mathbf{j} + \omega_z\mathbf{k}) \times (-I_{yx}\omega_x + I_{yy}\omega_y - I_{yz}\omega_z)\mathbf{j} \\
& + (\omega_x\mathbf{i} + \omega_y\mathbf{j} + \omega_z\mathbf{k}) \times (-I_{zx}\omega_x - I_{zy}\omega_y + I_{zz}\omega_z)\mathbf{k}
\end{aligned}$$

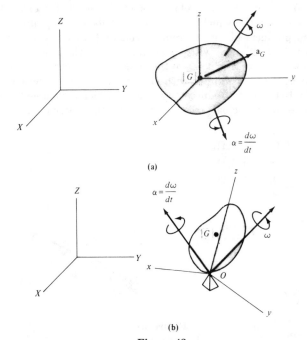

(a)

(b)

Figure 48

Computing the cross products and equating the respective **i**, **j**, and **k** components:

$$\Sigma M_x = I_{xx}\dot\omega_x - (I_{yy} - I_{zz})\omega_y\omega_z - I_{xy}(\dot\omega_y - \omega_z\omega_x) - I_{yz}(\omega_y{}^2 - \omega_z{}^2)$$
$$\qquad - I_{zx}(\dot\omega_z + \omega_x\omega_y)$$
$$\Sigma M_y = I_{yy}\dot\omega_y - (I_{zz} - I_{xx})\omega_z\omega_x - I_{yz}(\dot\omega_z - \omega_x\omega_y) - I_{zx}(\omega_z{}^2 - \omega_x{}^2)$$
$$\qquad - I_{xy}(\dot\omega_x + \omega_y\omega_z)$$
$$\Sigma M_z = I_{zz}\dot\omega_z - (I_{xx} - I_{yy})\omega_x\omega_y - I_{zx}(\dot\omega_x - \omega_y\omega_z) - I_{xy}(\omega_x{}^2 - \omega_y{}^2)$$
$$\qquad - I_{yz}(\dot\omega_y + \omega_z\omega_x) \qquad\qquad\qquad\text{(Eq 106)}$$

If the x, y, and z axes are considered principal axes of inertia, the products of inertia are zero, $I_{xx} = I_x$, and so on, and the above expressions reduce to:

$$\Sigma M_x = I_x\dot\omega_x - (I_y - I_z)\omega_y\omega_z$$
$$\Sigma M_y = I_y\dot\omega_y - (I_z - I_x)\omega_z\omega_x$$
$$\Sigma M_z = I_z\dot\omega_z - (I_x - I_y)\omega_x\omega_y \qquad\qquad\text{(Eq 107)}$$

which are the Euler equations of motion. Both Eq 106 and 107 are applicable only to moments summed either about point O or G.

The terms $\dot\omega_x$, $\dot\omega_y$, and $\dot\omega_z$ represent the time derivatives of x, y, z components of $\boldsymbol\omega$. Since the x, y, z axes are rotating at $\boldsymbol\Omega = \boldsymbol\omega$, then $(\dot{\boldsymbol\omega})_{XYZ} = (\dot{\boldsymbol\omega})_{xyz} + \boldsymbol\omega \times \boldsymbol\omega$. Since $\boldsymbol\omega \times \boldsymbol\omega = 0$, then $(\dot{\boldsymbol\omega})_{XYZ} = (\dot{\boldsymbol\omega})_{xyz}$. Computing $\dot\omega_x$, $\dot\omega_y$, and $\dot\omega_z$ on the basis of finding $(\boldsymbol\omega)_{XYZ}$ is generally simpler. For x, y, z axes having motion $\boldsymbol\Omega \neq \boldsymbol\omega$, it is often convenient to choose the x, y, z axes having an angular velocity $\boldsymbol\Omega$ different from the angular velocity $\boldsymbol\omega$ of the body, for example, spinning tops and gyroscopes, which are symmetrical about the spinning axis. The moments and products of inertia remain constant during the motion (Fig. 49). Although the disk spins with a constant rate $\boldsymbol\omega$, the moments of inertia of the disk about the x, y, z axes are the same for any angular velocity $\boldsymbol\Omega$ of the x, y, z axes, if $\boldsymbol\Omega$ is collinear with $\boldsymbol\omega$. For such a set of chosen axes, the vectors of Eq 104 may be reduced to scalar equations. Frequently, because the x, y, z axes are principal axes for the body, the Euler equations of motion become:

$$\Sigma M_x = I_x\dot\omega_x - I_y\Omega_z\omega_y + I_z\Omega_y\omega_z$$
$$\Sigma M_y = I_y\dot\omega_y - I_z\Omega_x\omega_z + I_x\Omega_z\omega_x$$
$$\Sigma M_z = I_z\dot\omega_z - I_x\Omega_y\omega_x + I_y\Omega_x\omega_y \qquad\qquad\text{(Eq 108)}$$

Figure 49

when Ω_x, Ω_y, Ω_z are the x, y, z components of $\boldsymbol{\Omega}$, measured from the inertial frame of reference.

Example 10. The gear in Fig. 50(a) has a mass of 10 kg. The gear is mounted at an angle of 10° with a rotating shaft of negligible mass. The moment of inertia of the gear about the z axis is $I_z = 0.1$ kg·m². About the x and y axes, $I_x = I_y = 0.05$ kg·m². For such a shaft rotating with a constant angular velocity of $\omega_{AB} = 30$ rad/s, determine the reactions of the bearing supports A and B at the instant the gear reaches the position shown.

Because the x, y, z axes are fixed to the flywheel, Eq 105 may be used. To determine first the components of the angular velocity $\boldsymbol{\omega}$ and the angular momentum $\mathbf{H}_G$ of the flywheel with respect to the x, y, z axes, use:

$$H_x = I_x \omega_x = 0$$
$$H_y = I_y \omega_y = 0.05 \, (-30 \sin 10°) = -0.260 \text{ kg·m}^2\text{/s}$$
$$H_z = I_z \omega_z = 0.1 \, (30 \cos 10°) = 2.95 \text{ kg·m}^2\text{/s}$$

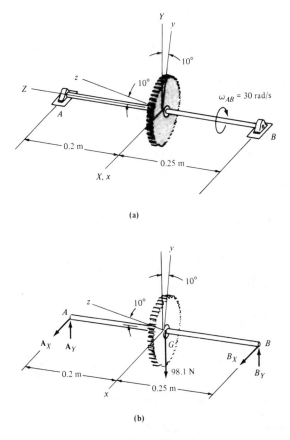

(a)

(b)

Figure 50

390/ENGINEERING MATHEMATICS

Thus: $\qquad$ $\mathbf{H}_G = \{-0.260\mathbf{j} + 2.95\mathbf{k}\}\,\mathrm{kg\cdot m^2/s}$

Since the x, y, z reference axes rotate with the same constant angular velocity as the flywheel, the angular momentum of the flywheel, $\mathbf{H}_G$, remains constant with respect to this rotating frame. Therefore, $(\mathbf{H}_G)_{xyz} = 0$, and Eq 105 becomes:

$$\Sigma\mathbf{M}_G = \boldsymbol{\omega} \times \mathbf{H}_G \qquad \mathbf{r}_A \times \mathbf{F}_A + \mathbf{r}_B \times \mathbf{F}_B = \boldsymbol{\omega} \times \mathbf{H}_G \tag{Eq 109}$$

which may be applied in terms of the inertial X, Y, Z frame of reference because the vectors, except $\mathbf{H}_G$, are simply expressed in these directions. Representing the directions of the X, Y, and Z axes by the unit vectors $\mathbf{I}$, $\mathbf{J}$, and $\mathbf{K}$, respectively, $\boldsymbol{\omega} = \{30\mathbf{K}\}$ rad/s and:

$$\mathbf{H}_G = H_y\,(\cos 10°\mathbf{J} - \sin 10°\mathbf{K}) + H_z\,(\sin 10°\mathbf{J} + \cos 10°\mathbf{K})$$

Substituting in Eq 109:

$$0.2\mathbf{K} \times (A_X\mathbf{I} + A_Y\mathbf{J}) + (-0.25\mathbf{K}) \times (B_X\mathbf{I} + B_Y\mathbf{J}) =$$
$$(30\mathbf{K}) \times [-0.260\,(\cos 10°\mathbf{J} - \sin 10°\mathbf{K}) + 2.95\,(\sin 10°\mathbf{J} + \cos 10°\mathbf{K})] \tag{Eq 110}$$

Expanding Eq 110 and equating the respective unit-vector components yields

$$-0.2A_Y + 0.25B_Y = -7.70 \tag{Eq 111}$$

$$A_X = 1.25B_X \tag{Eq 112}$$

Application of vector equation $(\Sigma\mathbf{F} = m\mathbf{a}_G)$ yields the scalar equations:

$$\Sigma F_X = m(a_G)_X \qquad A_X + B_X = 0 \tag{Eq 113}$$
$$\Sigma F_Y = m(a_G)_Y \qquad A_Y + B_Y - 98.1 = 0 \tag{Eq 114}$$
$$\Sigma F_Z = m(a_G)_Z \qquad 0 = 0 \tag{Eq 115}$$

Solving Eq 111 through 115 simultaneously gives $A_X = B_X = 0$, $A_Y = 71.6$ N, $B_Y = 26.4$ N.

SELECTED REFERENCES

- Beer, Ferdinand P. and Johnston, E. Russell, Jr., Vector Mechanics for Engineers, *Dynamics*, 3rd ed., McGraw-Hill, New York, 1977
- Hibbeler, R.C., Engineering Mechanics, *Dynamics*, 2nd ed., Macmillan, New York, 1978
- Shames, Irving H., Engineering Mechanics, *Dynamics*, Vol. II, 2nd ed., Prentice-Hall, Englewood Cliffs, NJ, 1966
- Ginsberg, Jerry H. and Genin, Joseph, *Dynamics*, John Wiley and Sons, New York, 1977
- Higdon, Archie, Stiles, William B., Davis, Arthur W., Evces, Charles R. and Weese, John A., *Engineering Dynamics*, 2nd ed., Prentice-Hall, Englewood Cliffs, NJ
- Shigley, Joseph E., *Kinematic Analysis of Machines*, 2nd ed., McGraw-Hill, New York, 1969
- Branson, Lane K., Engineering Mechanics, *Statics and Dynamics*, Simon and Schuster, New York, 1970

19
Stress-Strain
(Constitutive)
Relationships

By Samuel J. Brown, Ph.D.
President, Quest Engineering & Development Corp.

ELASTIC SOLIDS

Generalized Stress Equation. In most branches of continuum mechanics, it is sometimes assumed that the stress tensor is composed of two parts:

$$\sigma_{ij} = \bar{\sigma}_{ij} + \bar{\bar{\sigma}}_{ij} \qquad \text{(Eq 1)}$$

where $\bar{\sigma}_{ij}$ = conservative stress tensor and $\bar{\bar{\sigma}}_{ij}$ = dissipative stress tensor, with $\bar{\sigma}_{ij}$ associated with the reversible behavior of the material and $\bar{\bar{\sigma}}_{ij}$ related to the material dissipation (i.e., mechanical energy dissipation) resulting from momentum transport in the medium. The irreversible nature of a process is not completely characterized by $\bar{\bar{\sigma}}_{ij}$. From nonequilibrium statistical mechanics, the conservative stress tensor $\bar{\sigma}_{ij}$ is assumed to be related algebraically to the strain tensor in the medium and temperature, except perhaps in certain discussions of viscoelasticity. This relationship is called the kinetic equation of state and is expressed as:

$$\bar{\sigma}_{ij} = \bar{\sigma}_{ij}(A_{11}, A_{12}, \ldots, A_{33}, T) \qquad \text{(Eq 2)}$$

where A_{ij} = one form of the strain tensor and T = absolute temperature.

The dissipative stress tensor $\bar{\bar{\sigma}}_{ij}$ is usually related to the strain tensor through a differential equation that may be linear or nonlinear. Special forms for $\bar{\sigma}_{ij}$ and $\bar{\bar{\sigma}}_{ij}$ are presented here to illustrate the different forms of $\bar{\sigma}_{ij}$ and $\bar{\bar{\sigma}}_{ij}$. For example, the dissipative stress tensor vanishes everywhere in a thermoelastic medium, whether in an elastic medium or a medium with no material dissipation. The stress tensor σ_{ij} is described by the conservative part of the stress tensor alone. For an isotropic, linear, thermoelastic medium:

$$\bar{\bar{\sigma}}_{ij} = 0 \qquad \text{(Eq 3)}$$

and $\sigma_{ij} = \bar{\sigma}_{ij} = 2G\mathrm{E}_{ij} + \lambda\delta_{ij}\mathrm{E}_{kk} - (3\lambda + 2G)\alpha(T - \bar{T})\delta_{ij}$, where

$\mathrm{E}_{ij}(y, t)$ = Lagrangian linear strain tensor
$T(y, t)$ = absolute temperature
$\bar{T}$ = constant reference temperature
α, λ, G = constants

If $i = j$, then $\delta_{ij} = 1$ in Eq 3; and if $i \neq j$, then $\delta_{ij} = 0$. For a linear elastic solid with constant density and known body force, the equations of motion and strain-displacement relationships result in 9 basic equations and 15 unknowns, σ_{ij}, E_{ij}, and u_i. Six additional equations relating the same unknowns are required and are given by the kinetic equation of state. These additional equations are called the *constitutive equations or stress-strain equations*. For a uniaxial stress state, such as that produced by pulling a prismatic bar in uniaxial tension:

$$\sigma_{ij} = 0 \quad \text{for } i, j \neq 1 \qquad \text{(Eq 4)}$$

The nonvanishing stress component, σ_{11}, is related to the Lagrangian strain component E_{11} by the following relationship:

$$\sigma_{11} = E\mathrm{E}_{11} \qquad \text{(Eq 5)}$$

where E is a constant, Young's modulus of elasticity. Equation 5 indicates a linear relationship for which the stress σ_{11} is assumed to vanish when E_{11} vanishes. Since σ_{11} and E_{11} are uniquely related, there cannot be energy dissipation by the stress component during loading and unloading. Such a solid is called a linear elastic solid, or Hookean solid. For a Hookean solid, no dissipation of energy implies that the dissipative stress tensor vanishes. Therefore:

$$\bar{\bar{\sigma}}_{ij} = 0 \qquad \sigma_{ij} = \bar{\sigma}_{ij} \qquad \text{(Eq 6)}$$

where, in general, the existence of a certain kinetic equation of state is assumed:

$$\sigma_{ij} = \sigma_{ij}(\mathrm{E}_{11}, \mathrm{E}_{12}, \dots, \mathrm{E}_{33}, T) \qquad \text{(Eq 7)}$$

Generalized Hooke's Law. In the classical theory of linear elasticity, the temperature effect is neglected and the stress components σ_{ij} are uniquely related to the strain components. As a tensor equation, the generalized Hooke's law may be written in the form:

$$\sigma_{ij} = C_{ijkl}\mathrm{E}_{kl} \qquad \text{(Eq 8)}$$

where σ_{ij} is the stress tensor, E_{kl} is the strain tensor, and C_{ijkl} is the tensor of the elastic constants, or moduli, of the material. Inasmuch as $\sigma_{ij} = \sigma_{ji}$, then:

$$C_{ijkl} = C_{jikl} \qquad \text{(Eq 9)}$$

Since $\mathrm{E}_{kl} = \mathrm{E}_{lk}$, and the indices k and l in Eq 8 are dummies, C_{ijkl} can be made symmetric with respect to k and l without altering the sum. Without loss of generality, it may be assumed that:

$$C_{ijkl} = C_{ijlk} \qquad \text{(Eq 10)}$$

According to these symmetry properties, the maximum number of the independent elastic constants is 36.

If a strain energy function W exists, then:

$$W = \frac{1}{2} C_{ijkl} E_{ij} E_{kl}$$ (Eq 11)

with the property:

$$\frac{\partial W}{\partial e_{ij}} = \sigma_{ij}$$ (Eq 12)

Because the quadratic form in Eq 11 can be considered symmetric, then:

$$C_{ijkl} = C_{klij}$$ (Eq 13)

Under this symmetry condition, the number of independent elastic constants is reduced to 21, which in the generalized Hooke's law is the most general form of anisotropy. Thus, the general stress-strain relationship for anisotropic media can be written $\sigma_{ij} = C_{ijkl} E_{kl}$, where C_{ijkl} are the elastic constants. Since the stress tensor and strain tensor are symmetric, the relationship can be expressed in terms of a second order elastic coefficient matrix as:

$$\begin{bmatrix} \sigma_{11} \\ \sigma_{22} \\ \sigma_{33} \\ \sigma_{12} \\ \sigma_{23} \\ \sigma_{13} \end{bmatrix} = \begin{bmatrix} C_{11} & C_{12} & \cdots & C_{16} \\ C_{21} & C_{22} & & \\ \cdot & & \cdot & \\ \cdot & & & \cdot \\ \cdot & & & \cdot \\ C_{61} & & & C_{66} \end{bmatrix} \begin{bmatrix} E_{11} \\ E_{22} \\ E_{33} \\ E_{12} \\ E_{23} \\ E_{13} \end{bmatrix}$$ (Eq 14)

In formulating the notion of the components of strain E_{ij}, the components of displacement u_i were assumed functions of the coordinates (y_1, y_2, y_3) of the body in its undeformed state. In defining the stress tensor σ_{ij}, the components of σ_{ij} were assumed functions of the coordinates (y'_1, y'_2, y'_3) of the stressed (and hence deformed) medium. If the displacements u_i and their derivatives are small, then values of $\sigma_{ij}(y)$ and $\sigma_{ij}(y')$ cannot greatly differ. If $y'_k = y_k + u_k$, for example, then:

$$\frac{\partial \sigma_{ij}}{\partial y_k} = \frac{\partial \sigma_{ij}}{\partial y'_l} \frac{\partial y'_l}{\partial y_k} = \frac{\partial \sigma_{ij}}{\partial y'_l}\left(\delta_{kl} + \frac{\partial u_l}{\partial y_k}\right) = \frac{\partial \sigma_{ij}}{\partial y'_k} + \frac{\partial \sigma_{ij}}{\partial y'_l}\frac{\partial u_l}{\partial y_k}$$ (Eq 15)

Hence, in writing $\dfrac{\partial \sigma_{ij}}{\partial y_k} = \dfrac{\partial \sigma_{ij}}{\partial y'_k}$, we assume that the displacement derivatives are small compared with unity.

CONSTITUTIVE LAWS FOR ANISOTROPIC ELASTIC SOLIDS

The various types of anisotropic symmetry presented in this section hold for both elastic constants and coefficients of viscosity. To reduce the tensor C_{ijkl} to various *classifications of symmetry, the following definitions are used:*

Equivalent Axes. Two sets of Cartesian axes y_i and y_i are equivalent when the elastic constants C_{ijkl} and C'_{ijkl} are the same for both sets

Covering Operation. A transformation from one set of equivalent axes to another

Some familiar classifications of anisotropic symmetry are the following:

Plane Symmetry. Exists if the covering operation is a reflection through a plane

Axial Symmetry. Exists if the covering operation is a rotation about a certain axis through any arbitrary angle

Orthotropic Symmetry. A body has orthotropic symmetry if there exist three mutually perpendicular planes of symmetry

N-gonal Symmetry. Exists when the covering operation is a rotation about a certain axis through an angle of $2\pi/N$ and is usually described as:

2-gonal = digonal	6-gonal = hexagonal
3-gonal = trigonal	8-gonal = octagonal
4-gonal = tetragonal	

N-gonal Alternating. Exists when the covering operation is a rotation about an axis through an angle of $2\pi/N$ and a reflection through a plane perpendicular to the axis

Central Symmetry. Exists if the covering operation is a reflection through a point; equivalent to digonal alternating

To evaluate the independent elastic constants for each type of symmetry, the strain energy per unit volume W is used. Expressing W as a function of E_{ij} and retaining only the quadratic term, then:

$$W = \frac{1}{2} C_{ijkl} E_{ij} E_{kl} \tag{Eq 16}$$

which is a general expression for a linear, elastic solid. The symmetry conditions of Eq 13:

$$C_{ijkl} = C_{klij} \qquad C_{ijkl} = C_{jikl} \qquad C_{ijkl} = C_{ijlk} \tag{Eq 17}$$

indicate that there exist, at most, 21 independent elastic constants in C_{ijkl}. Reindexing the stress tensor σ_{ij} and strain tensor E_{ij} produces:

$$\sigma_1 = \sigma_{11} = \sigma_{\alpha\alpha} \quad \sigma_3 = \sigma_{33} = \sigma_{\gamma\gamma} \quad \sigma_5 = \sigma_{31} = \sigma_{\gamma\alpha}$$
$$\sigma_2 = \sigma_{22} = \sigma_{\beta\beta} \quad \sigma_4 = \sigma_{23} = \sigma_{\beta\gamma} \quad \sigma_6 = \sigma_{12} = \sigma_{\alpha\beta} \tag{Eq 18}$$

and

$$E_1 = E_{11} = E_{\alpha\alpha} \quad E_3 = E_{33} = E_{\gamma\gamma} \quad E_5 = E_{31} = E_{\gamma\alpha}$$
$$E_2 = E_{22} = E_{\beta\beta} \quad E_4 = E_{23} = E_{\beta\gamma} \quad E_6 = E_{12} = E_{\alpha\beta} \tag{Eq 19}$$

where 1, 2, and 3 or alternately α, β, and γ are triorthonormal coordinates.

From this:

$$W = \frac{1}{2} C_{\xi\phi} E_\xi E_\phi \quad (\xi, \phi = 1, 2, 3, 4, 5, 6) \tag{Eq 20}$$

This process satisfies symmetry properties automatically and suggests that:

$$C_{\xi\phi} = C_{\phi\xi} \tag{Eq 21}$$

In terms of stress, Eq 20 becomes:

$$W = \frac{1}{2} a_{11}\sigma_1{}^2 + \sigma_1(a_{12}\sigma_2 + a_{13}\sigma_3 + a_{14}\sigma_4 + a_{15}\sigma_5 + a_{16}\sigma_6) +$$

$$\frac{1}{2} a_{22}\sigma_2{}^2 + \sigma_2(a_{23}\sigma_3 + a_{24}\sigma_4 + a_{25}\sigma_5 + a_{26}\sigma_6) +$$

$$\frac{1}{2} a_{33}\sigma_3{}^2 + \sigma_3(a_{34}\sigma_4 + a_{35}\sigma_5 + a_{36}\sigma_6) +$$

$$\frac{1}{2} a_{44}\sigma_4{}^2 + \sigma_4(a_{45}\sigma_5 + a_{46}\sigma_6) +$$

$$\frac{1}{2} a_{55}\sigma_5{}^2 + \sigma_5 a_{56}\sigma_6 +$$

$$\frac{1}{2} a_{66}\sigma_6{}^2 \tag{Eq 22}$$

Therefore, there exist only (1 + 2 + 3 + 4 + 5 + 6) = 21 independent constants for $C_{\xi\phi}$. These constants replace the tensor C_{ijkl} in Eq 15. To express the strain energy function W for different types of anisotropic symmetry, and stress-strain law may be found from W by using:

$$\sigma_{ij} = \frac{\partial W}{\partial E_{ij}} \tag{Eq 23}$$

or equivalently:

$$\sigma_\xi = \frac{\partial W}{\partial E_\xi} \tag{Eq 24}$$

where $\xi = 1, 2, 3, 4, 5, 6$.

The derivations that follow are based on the equivalency of two sets of coordinate axes when the strain energy function W is the same function of the strain components referred to both sets of axes. The solid elastic body is assumed to undergo small deformations and obey the generalized Hooke's law. In the general case of a uniform curvilinearly anisotropic body, the generalized Hooke's law in the system of triorthogonal coordinates α, β, and γ has the following form:

$$E_{\alpha\alpha} = a_{11}\sigma_{\alpha\alpha} + a_{12}\sigma_{\beta\beta} + a_{13}\sigma_\gamma + a_{14}\sigma_{\beta\gamma} + a_{15}\sigma_{\alpha\gamma} + a_{16}\sigma_{\alpha\beta}$$
$$E_{\beta\beta} = a_{12}\sigma_{\alpha\alpha} + a_{22}\sigma_{\beta\beta} + \dots\dots\dots\dots\dots\dots\dots\dots + a_{26}\sigma_{\alpha\beta}$$
$$\dots\dots\dots\dots\dots\dots\dots\dots\dots\dots\dots\dots\dots\dots\dots\dots\dots\dots\dots$$
$$E_{\alpha\beta} = a_{16}\sigma_{\alpha\alpha} + a_{26}\sigma_{\beta\beta} + \dots\dots\dots\dots\dots\dots\dots\dots, + a_{66}\sigma_{\alpha\beta} \qquad \text{(Eq 25)}$$

where a_{jk} are the elastic constants (coefficients of deformation). There are 21 independent elastic constants. Expressed in terms of engineering constants:

$$a_{11} = \frac{1}{E_\alpha} \qquad a_{22} = \frac{1}{E_\beta} \qquad a_{33} = \frac{1}{E_\gamma}$$

$$a_{12} = -\frac{\nu_{\beta\alpha}}{E_\alpha} = -\frac{\nu_{\alpha\beta}}{E_\beta} \qquad a_{23} = -\frac{\nu_{\gamma\beta}}{E_\beta} = -\frac{\nu_{\beta\gamma}}{E_\gamma}$$

$$a_{13} = -\frac{\nu_{\alpha\gamma}}{E_\gamma} = -\frac{\nu_{\gamma\alpha}}{E_\alpha}$$

$$a_{44} = \frac{1}{G_{\beta\gamma}} \qquad a_{55} = \frac{1}{G_{\alpha\gamma}} \qquad a_{66} = \frac{1}{G_{\alpha\beta}}$$

$$a_{56} = \frac{\mu_{\alpha\beta,\,\gamma\alpha}}{G_{\alpha\gamma}} = \frac{\mu_{\gamma\alpha,\,\alpha\beta}}{G_{\alpha\beta}} \qquad a_{46} = \frac{\mu_{\alpha\beta,\,\beta\gamma}}{G_{\beta\gamma}} = \frac{\mu_{\beta\gamma,\,\alpha\beta}}{G_{\alpha\beta}}$$

$$a_{45} = \frac{\mu_{\gamma\alpha,\,\beta\gamma}}{G_{\beta\gamma}} = \frac{\mu_{\beta\gamma,\,\gamma\alpha}}{G_{\alpha\gamma}}$$

$$a_{14} = \frac{\eta_{\beta\gamma,\,\alpha}}{E_\alpha} = \frac{\eta_{\alpha,\,\beta\gamma}}{G_{\beta\gamma}} \qquad a_{25} = \frac{\eta_{\gamma\alpha,\,\beta}}{E_\beta} = \frac{\eta_{\beta,\,\gamma\alpha}}{G_{\alpha\gamma}} \qquad a_{36} = \frac{\eta_{\alpha\beta,\,\gamma}}{E_\gamma} = \frac{\eta_{\gamma,\,\alpha\beta}}{G_{\alpha\beta}}$$

$$a_{24} = \frac{\eta_{\beta\gamma,\,\beta}}{E_\beta} = \frac{\eta_{\beta,\,\beta\gamma}}{G_{\beta\gamma}} \qquad a_{35} = \frac{\eta_{\gamma\alpha,\,\gamma}}{E_\gamma} = \frac{\eta_{\gamma,\,\gamma\alpha}}{G_{\alpha\gamma}} \qquad a_{16} = \frac{\eta_{\alpha\beta,\,\alpha}}{E_\alpha} = \frac{\eta_{\alpha,\,\alpha\beta}}{G_{\alpha\beta}}$$

$$a_{34} = \frac{\eta_{\beta\gamma,\,\gamma}}{E_\gamma} = \frac{\eta_{\gamma,\,\beta\gamma}}{G_{\beta\gamma}} \qquad a_{15} = \frac{\eta_{\gamma\alpha,\,\alpha}}{E_\alpha} = \frac{\eta_{\alpha,\,\gamma\alpha}}{G_{\alpha\gamma}} \qquad a_{26} = \frac{\eta_{\alpha\beta,\,\beta}}{E_\beta} = \frac{\eta_{\beta,\,\alpha\beta}}{G_{\alpha\beta}}$$

E_α, E_β, and E_γ are Young's moduli in directions α, β, and γ, respectively. $G_{\beta\gamma}$, $G_{\alpha\gamma}$, $G_{\alpha\beta}$ are the shear moduli for the planes parallel at each point to the coordinate surfaces $\alpha = $ const, $\beta = $ const, and $\gamma = $ const. $\nu_{\beta\alpha}$, $\nu_{\gamma\beta}$, $\nu_{\alpha\gamma}$, $\nu_{\alpha\beta}$, $\nu_{\beta\gamma}$, $\nu_{\gamma\alpha}$ are Poisson's ratios characterizing the transverse compression in the presence of tension in the direction of the coordinate axes. The first subscript indicates the direction of transverse compression and the second subscript indicates the direction of the force.

$\mu_{\gamma\alpha,\,\beta\gamma}$, $\mu_{\alpha\beta,\,\beta\gamma}$, $\dots$, $\mu_{\beta\gamma,\,\alpha\beta}$ are Chentsov coefficients indicating the shear in planes tangent to the coordinate surfaces and caused by shearing stresses acting in planes tangent to the other coordinate surfaces. For example, $\mu_{\gamma\alpha,\,\beta\gamma}$ is the shear in a plane tangent to the coordinate surface $\beta = $ const and is caused by stress $\sigma_{\beta\gamma}$.

The notations $\eta_{\beta\gamma,\,\alpha}$, $\eta_{\gamma\alpha,\,\alpha}$, $\dots$, $\eta_{\beta\alpha,\,\gamma}$ are the coefficients of interaction of the first kind and $\eta_{\alpha,\,\beta\gamma}$, $\eta_{\beta,\,\beta\gamma}$, $\dots$, $\eta_{\gamma,\,\alpha\beta}$ are the coefficients of interaction of the second kind. The first coefficients characterize the shear in planes tangent to the coordinate surfaces, caused by normal stresses. The second coefficients characterize elongation in the directions of the coordinates, caused by shearing stresses.

If symmetry exists in the internal structure of the material of an anisotropic body, then its elastic properties exhibit a certain elastic symmetry. Such bodies possess symmetrical directions for which the elastic properties of the material are identical, and therefore symmetrical directions are known as equivalent directions. When an anisotropic body possesses elastic symmetry, the equations of Hooke's law in general form are simplified.

Plane Symmetry. At each point of the body, there is assumed a plane for which any two directions are symmetrical relative to this plane and are equivalent with respect to their elastic properties. Assume, for example, that coordinate γ at each point of a curvilinearly anisotropic body is perpendicular to the plane of elastic symmetry and that the plane at each point is parallel to the coordinate surface γ = const.

Digonal Symmetry. The covering operation for digonal symmetry is a rotation about the y_3-axis of π radians. The transformation matrix is:

$$a_{ij} \Rightarrow \begin{pmatrix} -1 & 0 & 0 \\ 0 & -1 & 0 \\ 0 & 0 & 1 \end{pmatrix}$$

From the transformation equations:

$$E_{ij} = a_{mi}a_{nj}E'_{mn} \tag{Eq 26}$$

It follows that:

$$
\begin{array}{ll}
E_{11} = E'_{11} & E_{\alpha\alpha} = E'_{\alpha\alpha} \\
E_{22} = E'_{22} & E_{\beta\beta} = E'_{\beta\beta} \\
E_{33} = E'_{33} \quad \text{or alternately} & E_{\gamma\gamma} = E'_{\gamma\gamma} \\
E_{23} = -E'_{23} & E_{\beta\gamma} = E'_{\beta\gamma} \\
E_{31} = -E'_{31} & E_{\gamma\alpha} = E'_{\gamma\alpha} \\
E_{12} = E'_{12} & E_{\alpha\beta} = E'_{\alpha\beta}
\end{array} \tag{Eq 27}
$$

or

$$
\begin{array}{lll}
E_1 = E'_1 & E_3 = E'_3 & E_5 = -E'_5 \\
E_2 = E_2 & E_4 = -E'_4 & E_6 = E'_6
\end{array} \tag{Eq 28}
$$

The strain energy function W must have the same form for E_{ij} and E'_{ij} or E_ξ and E'_ξ. Therefore, the terms containing the negative signs must vanish, or:

$$C_{14} = C_{24} = C_{34} = C_{15} = C_{25} = C_{35} = C_{46} = C_{56} = 0 \tag{Eq 29}$$

Thus, for a linear elastic solid, there are only 13 *independent elastic constants*. The matrix of the coefficients of the linear forms can be written as follows:

$$\begin{pmatrix} C_{11} & C_{12} & C_{13} & 0 & 0 & C_{16} \\ C_{21} & C_{22} & C_{23} & 0 & 0 & C_{26} \\ C_{31} & C_{32} & C_{33} & 0 & 0 & C_{36} \\ 0 & 0 & 0 & C_{44} & C_{45} & 0 \\ 0 & 0 & 0 & C_{54} & C_{55} & 0 \\ C_{61} & C_{62} & C_{63} & 0 & 0 & C_{66} \end{pmatrix}$$

(Eq 30)

The following strain-stress equations for the generalized Hooke's law can thus be obtained:

$$E_{\alpha\alpha} = a_{11}\sigma_{\alpha\alpha} + a_{12}\sigma_{\beta\beta} + a_{13}\sigma_{\gamma\gamma} + a_{16}\sigma_{\alpha\beta}$$
$$E_{\beta\beta} = a_{12}\sigma_{\alpha\alpha} + a_{22}\sigma_{\beta\beta} + a_{23}\sigma_{\gamma\gamma} + a_{26}\sigma_{\alpha\beta}$$
$$E_{\gamma\gamma} = a_{13}\sigma_{\alpha\alpha} + a_{23}\sigma_{\beta\beta} + a_{33}\sigma_{\gamma\gamma} + a_{36}\sigma_{\alpha\beta}$$
$$E_{\beta\gamma} = a_{44}\sigma_{\beta\gamma} + a_{45}\sigma_{\alpha\gamma}$$
$$E_{\gamma\alpha} = a_{45}\sigma_{\beta\gamma} + a_{55}\sigma_{\alpha\gamma}$$
$$E_{\alpha\beta} = a_{16}\sigma_{\alpha\alpha} + a_{26}\sigma_{\beta\beta} + a_{36}\sigma_{\gamma\gamma} + a_{66}\sigma_{\alpha\beta}$$

(Eq 31)

and the number of independent elastic constants a_{ik} reduced to 13. Equation 31 may also be represented in the following form:

$$E_{\alpha\alpha} = \frac{1}{E_1}\sigma_{\alpha\alpha} - \frac{\nu_{12}}{E_2}\sigma_{\beta\beta} - \frac{\nu_{13}}{E_3}\sigma_{\gamma\gamma} + \frac{\eta_{1,12}}{G_{12}}\sigma_{\alpha\beta}$$

$$E_{\beta\beta} = -\frac{\nu_{21}}{E_1}\sigma_{\alpha\alpha} + \frac{1}{E_2}\sigma_{\beta\beta} - \frac{\nu_{23}}{E_3}\sigma_{\gamma\gamma} + \frac{\eta_{2,12}}{G_{12}}\sigma_{\alpha\beta}$$

$$E_{\gamma\gamma} = -\frac{\nu_{31}}{E_1}\sigma_{\alpha\alpha} - \frac{\nu_{32}}{E_2}\sigma_{\beta\beta} + \frac{1}{E_3}\sigma_{\gamma\gamma} + \frac{\eta_{3,12}}{G_{12}}\sigma_{\alpha\beta}$$

$$E_{\beta\gamma} = \frac{1}{G_{23}}\sigma_{\beta\gamma} + \frac{\mu_{23,31}}{G_{13}}\sigma_{\alpha\gamma}$$

$$E_{\alpha\gamma} = \frac{\mu_{31,12}}{G_{23}}\sigma_{\beta\gamma} + \frac{1}{G_{13}}\sigma_{\alpha\gamma}$$

$$E_{\alpha\beta} = \frac{\eta_{12,1}}{E_1}\sigma_{\alpha\alpha} + \frac{\eta_{12,2}}{E_2}\sigma_{\beta\beta} + \frac{\eta_{12,3}}{E_3}\sigma_{\gamma\gamma} + \frac{1}{G_{12}}\sigma_{\alpha\beta}$$

(Eq 32)

Subscripts of the engineering constants are replaced by numeral subscripts: α by 1, β by 2, and γ by 3. Directions perpendicular to the plane of elastic symmetry are the principal directions of elasticity, and one principal direction passes through each point of the body. For a solid with digonal symmetry, the strain energy W has the form:

$$2W = E_1(C_{11}E_1 + 2C_{12}E_2 + 2C_{13}E_3 + 2C_{16}E_6) +$$
$$E_2(C_{22}E_2 + 2C_{23}E_3 + 2C_{26}E_6) +$$
$$E_3(C_{33}E_3 + 2C_{36}E_6) +$$
$$E_4(C_{44}E_4 + 2C_{45}E_5) +$$
$$C_{55}E_5^2 + C_{66}E_6^2$$

(Eq 33)

The same result describes a body with plane symmetry.

Orthotropic Symmetry. For a body with orthotropic symmetry, there are nine independent constants and W becomes:

$$2W = E_1(C_{11}E_1 + 2C_{12}E_2 + 2C_{13}E_5) + E_2(C_{22}E_2 + 2C_{23}E_4)$$
$$+ C_{33}E_3^2 + C_{44}E_4^2 + C_{55}E_5^2 + C_{66}E_6^2 \qquad \text{(Eq 34)}$$

Such materials as wood have three mutually orthogonal planes of elastic symmetry and are described as orthotropic. The axes of coordinates are chosen so that the coordinate planes and planes of elastic symmetry coincide. In this case, some of the coefficients C_{ij} in Eq 29 vanish. Besides the symmetry with respect to the y_1y_2-plane (Eq 29), the elastic constants C_{ij} must also be invariant under the coordinate transformation defined by the following direction cosines:

	y_1	y_2	y_3
y_1'	-1	0	0
y_2'	0	1	0
y_3'	0	0	1

This transformation of coordinates is a reflection in the y_2y_3-plane and leaves the σ_i and E_i unchanged with the following exceptions:

$$\sigma_5' = -\sigma_5 \qquad \sigma_6' = -\sigma_6$$
$$E_5' = -E_5 \qquad E_6' = -E_6 \qquad \text{(Eq 35)}$$

From Eq 29, $\sigma_1 = C_{11}E_1 + C_{12}E_2 + C_{13}E_3 + C_{16}E_6$, which becomes $\sigma_1' = C_{11}E_1' + C_{12}E_2' + C_{13}E_3' + C_{16}E_6'$, or $\sigma_1 = C_{11}E_1 + C_{12}E_2 + C_{13}E_3 - C_{16}E_6$. Thus, $C_{16} = 0$. Elastic symmetry in the y_1y_2-plane and in the y_2y_3-plane implies elastic symmetry in the y_1y_3-plane; therefore by considering the transformed expressions for $\sigma_2, \ldots, \sigma_6$:

$$C_{26} = C_{36} = C_{45} = C_{54} = C_{61} = C_{62} = C_{63} = 0 \qquad \text{(Eq 36)}$$

Thus, for orthotropic media, the matrix of the C_{ij} takes the form:

$$\begin{pmatrix} C_{11} & C_{12} & C_{13} & 0 & 0 & 0 \\ C_{21} & C_{22} & C_{23} & 0 & 0 & 0 \\ C_{31} & C_{32} & C_{33} & 0 & 0 & 0 \\ 0 & 0 & 0 & C_{44} & 0 & 0 \\ 0 & 0 & 0 & 0 & C_{55} & 0 \\ 0 & 0 & 0 & 0 & 0 & C_{66} \end{pmatrix} \qquad \text{(Eq 37)}$$

For a curvilinear anisotropic body, if three planes of elastic symmetry are perpendicular to the corresponding orthogonal coordinate directions α, β, γ, that is, the planes at each point of the body are parallel to the coordinate surfaces $\alpha = $ const, $\beta = $ const, and $\gamma = $ const, we obtain the following strain-stress equations for the generalized Hooke's law:

$$E_{\alpha\alpha} = a_{11}\sigma_\alpha + a_{12}\sigma_\beta + a_{13}\sigma_\gamma \qquad E_{\beta\gamma} = a_{44}\sigma_{\beta\gamma}$$
$$E_{\beta\beta} = a_{12}\sigma_\alpha + a_{22}\sigma_\beta + a_{23}\sigma_\gamma \qquad E_{\gamma\alpha} = a_{55}\sigma_{\gamma\alpha}$$
$$E_{\gamma\gamma} = a_{13}\sigma_\alpha + a_{23}\sigma_\beta + a_{33}\sigma_\gamma \qquad E_{\alpha\beta} = a_{66}\sigma_{\alpha\beta} \qquad \text{(Eq 38)}$$

The number of independent elastic constants a_{ik} is nine, and such a body is called orthogonally anisotropic or orthotropic. Equation 37 may also be presented as:

$$E_{\alpha\alpha} = \frac{1}{E_1}\sigma_{\alpha\alpha} - \frac{\nu_{12}}{E_2}\sigma_{\beta\beta} - \frac{\nu_{13}}{E_3}\sigma_{\gamma\gamma} \qquad E_{\beta\gamma} = \frac{1}{G_{23}}\sigma_{\beta\gamma}$$

$$E_{\beta\beta} = -\frac{\nu_{21}}{E_1}\sigma_{\alpha\alpha} + \frac{1}{E_2}\sigma_{\beta\beta} - \frac{\nu_{23}}{E_3}\sigma_{\gamma\gamma} \qquad E_{\gamma\alpha} = \frac{1}{G_{13}}\sigma_{\gamma\alpha}$$

$$E_{\gamma\gamma} = -\frac{\nu_{31}}{E_1}\sigma_{\alpha\alpha} - \frac{\nu_{32}}{E_2}\sigma_{\beta\beta} + \frac{1}{E_3}\sigma_{\gamma\gamma} \qquad E_{\alpha\beta} = \frac{1}{G_{12}}\sigma_{\alpha\beta} \qquad \text{(Eq 39)}$$

where, from Eq 37:

$$E_2\nu_{21} = E_1\nu_{12} \qquad E_3\nu_{32} = E_2\nu_{23} \qquad E_1\nu_{13} = E_3\nu_{31} \qquad \text{(Eq 40)}$$

Octagonal Symmetry. A body with octagonal symmetry has five independent elastic constants:

$$2W = C_{11}(E_1 + E_2)^2 + 2C_{13}(E_1 + E_2)^2 + C_{33}E_3^2$$
$$+ C_{44}(E_4^2 + E_5^2) + C_{66}E_6(E_6 - E_1) \qquad \text{(Eq 41)}$$

The same result describes a body with axial symmetry.

For a curvilinear anisotropic body, if it is assumed that coordinate γ is perpendicular at each point to the plane of isotropy, which at each point is parallel to the coordinate surface γ = const, the following strain-stress equations for Hooke's law in general form are obtained:

$$E_{\alpha\alpha} = a_{11}\sigma_{\alpha\alpha} + a_{12}\sigma_{\beta\beta} + a_{13}\sigma_{\gamma\gamma} \qquad E_{\beta\gamma} = a_{44}\sigma_{\beta\gamma}$$
$$E_{\beta\beta} = a_{12}\sigma_{\alpha\alpha} + a_{22}\sigma_{\beta\beta} + a_{13}\sigma_{\gamma\gamma} \qquad E_{\gamma\alpha} = a_{44}\sigma_{\gamma\alpha}$$
$$E_{\gamma\gamma} = a_{13}(\sigma_{\alpha\alpha} + \sigma_{\beta\beta}) + a_{33}\sigma_{\gamma\gamma} \qquad E_{\alpha\beta} = 2(a_{11} - a_{12})\sigma_{\alpha\beta} \qquad \text{(Eq 42)}$$

which may also be given in the form:

$$E_{\alpha\alpha} = \frac{1}{E}(\sigma_{\alpha\alpha} - \nu\sigma_{\beta\beta}) - \frac{\nu'}{E'}\sigma_{\gamma\gamma} \qquad E_{\beta\gamma} = \frac{1}{G'}\sigma_{\beta\gamma}$$

$$E_{\beta\beta} = \frac{1}{E}(\sigma_{\beta\beta} - \nu\sigma_{\alpha\alpha}) - \frac{\nu'}{E'}\sigma_{\gamma\gamma} \qquad E_{\gamma\alpha} = \frac{1}{G'}\sigma_{\gamma\alpha}$$

$$E_{\gamma\gamma} = -\frac{\nu'}{E'}(\sigma_{\alpha\alpha} + \sigma_{\beta\beta}) + \frac{1}{E'}\sigma_{\gamma\gamma} \qquad E_{\alpha\beta} = \frac{2(1+\nu)}{E}\sigma_{\alpha\beta} \qquad \text{(Eq 43)}$$

In this form:

E = Young's modulus for directions in the plane of isotropy
E' = Young's modulus for directions perpendicular to the plane of isotropy
ν = Poisson's ratio for contraction in the plane of isotropy due to tension in this plane

v' = Poisson's ratio for contraction in the plane of isotropy due to tension in the direction perpendicular to this plane

G' = shear modulus for planes normal to the plane of isotropy

$G = \dfrac{E}{2(1 + v)}$ = shear modulus for planes parallel to the plane of isotropy

A body possessing the above elastic properties is known as a transversely isotropic body.

Tetragonal Symmetry. For a body with tetragonal symmetry, there are seven independent elastic constants:

$$2W = C_{11}(E_1^2 + E_2^2) + 2C_{12}E_1E_2 + 2C_{13}E_3(E_1 + E_2)$$
$$+ 2C_{16}E_6(E_1 - E_2) + C_{33}E_3^2 + C_{44}(E_4^2 + E_5^2)$$
$$+ C_{66}E_6^2 \qquad \text{(Eq 44)}$$

ISOTROPIC MEDIA

Structural materials ordinarily are crystalline and cannot be regarded as being isotropic when viewed in small quantities. But the assumption of isotropy, when applied to an entire body, often does not lead to serious errors. Many cast metals are exceptions, and rolling and drawing also frequently produce crystal orientation, and therefore anisotropic character, to rolled and drawn metals. However, dimensions of most crystals are so small and chaotically distributed that in large bodies, the substance behaves as though it were isotropic; that is, its elastic properties are independent of the orientation of coordinate axes. The coefficients C_{ij} remain invariant when new coordinate axes y_1', y_2', y_3', are introduced by rotating the y_1, y_2, y_3-system through a right angle about the y_1-axis. The stress components become σ_1' and $C_{12} = C_{13}$, $C_{31} = C_{21}$, $C_{32} = C_{23}$, $C_{33} = C_{22}$, $C_{66} = C_{55}$. Rotation of axes through a right angle about the y_3-axis leads to $C_{21} = C_{12}$, $C_{22} = C_{11}$, $C_{23} = C_{13}$, $C_{31} = C_{32}$, $C_{55} = C_{44}$. The coordinate system y_1', y_2', y_3', derived from the y_1, y_2, y_3-system by rotation through an angle of 45' about the y_3-axis produces:

$$\sigma_{12}' = -\frac{1}{2}\sigma_{11} + \frac{1}{2}\sigma_{22} \qquad E_{12}' = -\frac{1}{2}E_{11} + \frac{1}{2}E_{22} \qquad \text{(Eq 45)}$$

or

$$\sigma_6' = -\frac{1}{2}\sigma_1 + \frac{1}{2}\sigma_2 \qquad E_6' = -E_1 + E_2 \qquad \text{(Eq 46)}$$

From Eq 35, and the relationship $C_{66} = C_{44}$:

$$\sigma_6 = C_{44}E_6 \qquad \text{(Eq 47)}$$

which becomes $\sigma_6' = C_{44}E_6'$ or:

$$-\frac{1}{2}\sigma_1 + \frac{1}{2}\sigma_2 = C_{44}(-E_1 + E_2) \qquad \text{(Eq 48)}$$

when referred to the y_1', y_2', y_3'-axes. From Eq 35:

$$\sigma_1 = C_{11}E_1 + C_{12}E_2 + C_{13}E_3 \qquad \sigma_2 = C_{21}E_1 + C_{22}E_2 + C_{23}E_3$$

and from the relationships $C_{22} = C_{11}$ and $C_{23} = C_{13} = C_{21} = C_{12}$, the following expression is derived:

$$-\frac{1}{2}\sigma_1 + \frac{1}{2}\sigma_2 = \frac{1}{2}(C_{11}-C_{12})(-E_1 + E_2) \qquad \text{(Eq 49)}$$

From Eq 48 and Eq 47:

$$C_{44} = \frac{1}{2}(C_{11} - C_{12}) \equiv G \qquad \text{(Eq 50)}$$

and $\sigma_6 = GE_6$. From this, the generalized Hooke's law for an isotropic body can be written in terms of the constants λ and G, where G is defined by Eq 50 and where:

$$C_{12} = \lambda \qquad \text{(Eq 51)}$$

From Eq 35:

$$\begin{aligned}
\sigma_{11} &= C_{11}E_{11} + C_{12}E_{22} + C_{12}E_{33} \\
&= C_{12}(E_{11} + E_{22} + E_{33}) + (C_{11} - C_{12})E_{11} \\
&= \lambda\phi + 2GE_{11}
\end{aligned}$$

Thus, the generalized Hooke's law for a homogeneous isotropic body becomes:

$$\sigma_{ij} = \lambda\delta_{ij}\phi + 2GE_{ij} \qquad \text{(Eq 52)}$$

where i, $j = 1, 2, 3$ and δ is the Kronecker delta. Eq 52 connects the invariants $\phi = E_{ii}$ and $\Theta = \sigma_{ii}$.

Substituting $j = i$ in Eq 52 and noting that $\delta_{ii} = \delta_{11} + \delta_{22} + \delta_{33} = 3$:

$$\Theta \equiv \sigma_{ii} = 3\lambda\phi + 2GE_{ii}$$

or:

$$\Theta = (3\lambda + 2G)\phi \qquad \text{(Eq 53)}$$

Solutions of Eq 52 are easily found for the strains E_{ij} in terms of the stresses σ_{ij}, by using:

$$E_{ij} = \frac{-\lambda}{2G}\delta_{ij}\phi + \frac{1}{2G}\sigma_{ij}$$

or

$$E_{ij} = \frac{-\lambda\delta_{ij}}{2G(3\lambda + 2G)}\Theta + \frac{1}{2G}\sigma_{ij} \qquad \text{(Eq 54)}$$

where $G \neq 0$ and $3\lambda + 2G \neq 0$. The constants λ and G are called the Lamé constants. Thus, for complete isotropy, there are just two independent constants, and:

$$2W = \left(C_{11} - \frac{1}{2}C_{44}\right)(E_1 + E_2 + E_3)^2 + \frac{C_{44}}{2}E_\xi E_\xi$$

$$= \left(C_{11} - \frac{1}{2}C_{44}\right)\phi^2 + \frac{C_{44}}{2}E_{ij}E_{ij} \qquad \text{(Eq 55)}$$

where $C_{11} = \lambda + 2G$, $C_{44} = 4G$ and $\xi = 1, 2, 3, 4, 5, 6$.

Simple Tension. For a right cylinder with the axis parallel to the y_1-axis subjected to longitudinal forces, applied to the ends of the cylinder, that produce a uniform tension σ_0 in every cross section of the cylinder:

$$\sigma_{11} = \sigma_0 = \text{const} \qquad \sigma_{22} = \sigma_{33} = \sigma_{12} = \sigma_{23} = \sigma_{31} = 0 \qquad \text{(Eq 56)}$$

The substitution from Eq 56 in Eq 54 yields the values of strains:

$$E_{11} = \frac{(\lambda + G)\sigma_0}{G(3\lambda + 2G)}$$

$$E_{12} = E_{23} = E_{31} = 0$$

$$E_{22} = E_{33} = \frac{-\lambda\sigma_0}{2G(3\lambda + 2G)} \qquad \text{(Eq 57)}$$

From the expression:

$$\frac{E_{22}}{E_{11}} = \frac{-\lambda}{2(\lambda + G)}$$

the following abbreviations are derived:

$$\nu \equiv \frac{\lambda}{2(\lambda + G)} \qquad \text{(Eq 58)}$$

and

$$E \equiv \frac{G(3\lambda + 2G)}{\lambda + G} \qquad \text{(Eq 59)}$$

Equation 57 can be written as:

$$E_{11} = \frac{1}{E}\sigma_0$$

$$E_{22} = E_{33} = \frac{-\nu}{E}\sigma_0 = -\nu E_{11}$$

$$E_{12} = E_{23} = E_{31} = 0 \qquad \text{(Eq 60)}$$

If stress σ_0 represents tension and $\sigma_0 > 0$, tensile stress produces extension in the direction of the cylinder axis and contraction in its cross section. For $\sigma_0 > 0$, then $E_{11} > 0$, $E_{22} < 0$, $E_{33} < 0$ and E and ν are positive. From Eq 60, the derived quantity:

$$E = \frac{\sigma_0}{E_{11}}$$

represents the ratio of tensile stress σ_0 to the extension E_{11} produced by σ_0. From Eq 60 also:

$$\nu = \left| \frac{E_{22}}{E_{11}} \right| = \left| \frac{E_{33}}{E_{11}} \right|$$

The quantity E is Young's modulus, and ν is the Poisson ratio. The constants λ and G are expressed in terms of Young's modulus and Poisson's ratio as:

$$\lambda = \frac{E\nu}{(1 + \nu)(1 - 2\nu)} \qquad G = \frac{E}{2(1 + \nu)} \tag{Eq 61}$$

Pure Shear. Pure shear is characterized by the stress components $\sigma_{23} = \tau_0 = \text{const}$ and $\sigma_{11} = \sigma_{22} = \sigma_{33} = \sigma_{12} = \sigma_{31} = 0$. Substituting these values in Eq 54 yields:

$$E_{23} = \frac{1}{2G}\tau_0 \qquad E_{11} = E_{22} = E_{33} = E_{12} = E_{31} = 0 \tag{Eq 62}$$

These equations describe a rectangular parallelepiped $OPQR$, with faces parallel to the coordinate planes, sheared in the $y_2 y_3$-plane so that the right angle between the edges of the parallelepiped parallel to the y_2- and y_3-axes is diminished, for $\tau_0 > 0$, by the angle $\alpha_{23} = 2E_{23}$. From Eq 62:

$$G = \frac{\tau_0}{\alpha_{23}}$$

with G called the modulus of rigidity or shear modulus. Because E and ν are positive, G is also positive (see Eq 61).

Hydrostatic Pressure. For a body σ subjected to a hydrostatic pressure of uniform intensity p distributed over its surface, the components $\overset{n}{P}_i$ of the stress vector acting on the surface are:

$$\overset{n}{P}_i = -pn_i$$

where n_i represents direction cosines of the normal n to the surface.

The stresses:

$$\sigma_{11} = \sigma_{22} = \sigma_{33} = -p$$

$$\sigma_{12} = \sigma_{23} = \sigma_{31} = 0$$

$$\Theta = \sigma_{11} + \sigma_{22} + \sigma_{33} = -3p \tag{Eq 63}$$

satisfy the equilibrium equation in the interior of σ and on its surface. From Eq 54 can be derived:

$$E_{11} = E_{22} = E_{33} = -\frac{p}{3\lambda + 2G} \qquad E_{12} = E_{23} = E_{31} = 0 \tag{Eq 64}$$

From Eq 64 is obtained:

$$\phi = E_{11} + E_{22} + E_{33} = -\frac{p}{\lambda + \frac{2}{3}G} \tag{Eq 65}$$

By introducing:

$$K = \lambda + \frac{2}{3}G \tag{Eq 66}$$

Eq 65 becomes $\phi = -\dfrac{p}{K}$ or $K = -\dfrac{p}{\phi}$.

Modulus of Compression.   The quantity K is the ratio of the compressive stress to the cubical compression and is called the modulus of compression. For all physical substances, K is positive. Substituting the expressions for λ and G from Eq 61 into Eq 66 gives:

$$K = \frac{E}{3(1 - 2\nu)} \tag{Eq 67}$$

For most structural materials, ν does not deviate much from one-third. For highly incompressible materials such as rubber, ν is nearly one-half and $G \doteq E/3$. The stress-strain relationships assume the simple form:

$$E_{ij} = \frac{1 + \nu}{E} \sigma_{ij} - \frac{\nu}{E} \delta_{ij} \Theta \tag{Eq 68}$$

where $\Theta = \sigma_{ii}$. Table 1 gives average values of E, G, and ν for several elastic materials.

Deviator.   For an isotropic elastic material for which there is no change of temperature, Hooke's law referred to rectangular Cartesian coordinates may be written in the form:

$$\begin{aligned} \sigma_{kk} &= 3KE_{kk} \\ \sigma'_{ij} &= 2GE'_{ij} \qquad i, j, k = 1, 2, \text{ and } 3 \end{aligned} \tag{Eq 69}$$

where K and G are constants and where σ'_{ij} and E'_{ij} are the stress deviation and strain deviation, expressed as:

$$\sigma'_{ij} = \sigma_{ij} - \frac{1}{3} \sigma_{kk} \delta_{ij} \qquad E'_{ij} = E_{ij} - \frac{1}{3} E_{kk} \delta_{ij} \tag{Eq 70}$$

With $\dfrac{1}{3} \sigma_{kk}$, the mean stress at a point and with infinitesimal strain, E_{kk} is the change of volume per unit volume.

Various Coordinate Descriptions (Isotropic Material).   If the coordinate axes coincide with the principal axes for a homogeneous, isotropic material, the shear strains and shear stresses are zero, and the invariants of

Table 1 Modulus of compression

Material	E	G	ν (experimental)	$\nu = \dfrac{E}{2G} - 1$
Carbon steels	29.5	11.5	0.29	0.283
Wrought iron	28.0	11.0	0.28	0.273
Cast iron	16.5	6.5	0.25	0.269
Aluminum alloys...........	10.0	2.4	0.31	$\cdots$
Magnesium alloys	6.5	2.4	0.35	$\cdots$
Copper (hot-rolled).........	15.0	5.6	0.33	0.339
Brass, 2:1 (cold-drawn)	13.0	4.9	0.33	0.327
Glass.....................	8.0	3.2	0.25	0.250
Spruce (along the grain)	1.5	0.08	$\cdots$	$\cdots$
Plastics:				
Cellulose acetate	0.22	$\cdots$	$\cdots$	$\cdots$
Vinylchloride acetate	0.46	$\cdots$	$\cdots$	$\cdots$
Phenolic laminates	1.23	$\cdots$	0.25	$\cdots$
Concrete..................	4.0	$\cdots$	0.2	$\cdots$

stress and strain are related by $\theta = (3\lambda + 2G)\phi$. Expressing the generalized Hooke's law for homogeneous isotropic material in terms of Cartesian tensors (or orthogonal curvilinear):

$$\sigma_{ij} = \lambda \delta_{ij}\phi + 2G E_{ij} = \frac{E\nu\phi}{(1+\nu)(1-2\nu)} \delta_{ij} + \frac{E}{1+\nu} E_{ij} \qquad \text{(Eq 71)}$$

where δ_{ij} is the Kronecker delta and ϕ is the dilatation. Expressed in terms of strain, Eq 69 becomes:

$$E_{ij} = -\frac{\lambda}{2G(3\lambda + 2G)} \delta_{ij}\theta + \frac{1}{2G}\sigma_{ij} = \frac{1+\nu}{E}\sigma_{ij} - \frac{\nu}{E}\theta\delta_{ij} \qquad \text{(Eq 72)}$$

where θ is the stress invariant, $\theta = \sigma_{11} + \sigma_{22} + \sigma_{33}$.

In Cartesian coordinates:

$$\sigma_{xx} = \frac{E}{(1+\nu)(1-2\nu)} [(1-\nu)E_{xx} + \nu(E_{yy} + E_{zz})]$$

$$\sigma_{yy} = \frac{E}{(1+\nu)(1-2\nu)} [(1-\nu)E_{yy} + \nu(E_{zz} + E_{xx})]$$

$$\sigma_{zz} = \frac{E}{(1+\nu)(1-2\nu)} [(1-\nu)E_{zz} + \nu(E_{xx} + E_{yy})]$$

$$\sigma_{yz} = \sigma_{zy} = \frac{E}{1+\nu} E_{yz} = 2G E_{yz} = G\gamma_{yz}$$

$$\sigma_{zx} = \sigma_{xz} = \frac{E}{1 + v} E_{zx} = 2G E_{zx} = G \gamma_{zx}$$

$$\sigma_{xy} = \sigma_{yx} = \frac{E}{1 + v} E_{xy} = 2G E_{xy} = G \gamma_{xy} \qquad \text{(Eq 73)}$$

In terms of strain:

$$E_{xx} = \frac{1}{E} [\sigma_{xx} - v(\sigma_{yy} + \sigma_{zz})]$$

$$E_{yy} = \frac{1}{E} [\sigma_{yy} - v(\sigma_{xx} + \sigma_{zz})]$$

$$E_{zz} = \frac{1}{E} [\sigma_{zz} - v(\sigma_{xx} + \sigma_{yy})]$$

$$E_{yz} = \frac{1 + v}{E} \sigma_{yz} = \frac{1}{2G} \sigma_{yz} = \frac{1}{2} \gamma_{yz}$$

$$E_{zx} = \frac{1 + v}{E} \sigma_{zx} = \frac{1}{2G} \sigma_{zx} = \frac{1}{2} \gamma_{zx}$$

$$E_{xy} = \frac{1 + v}{E} \sigma_{xy} = \frac{1}{2G} \sigma_{xy} = \frac{1}{2} \gamma_{xy} \qquad \text{(Eq 74)}$$

In cylindrical coordinates:

$$\sigma_{rr} = \frac{E}{(1 + v)(1 - 2v)} [(1 - v) E_{rr} + v(E_{\theta\theta} + E_{zz})]$$

$$\sigma_{\theta\theta} = \frac{E}{(1 + v)(1 - 2v)} [(1 - v) E_{\theta\theta} + v(E_{rr} + E_{zz})]$$

$$\sigma_{zz} = \frac{E}{(1 + v)(1 - 2v)} [(1 - v) E_{zz} + v(E_{rr} + E_{\theta\theta})]$$

$$\sigma_{r\theta} = \frac{E}{(1 + v)} E_{r\theta} = 2G E_{r\theta} = G \gamma_{r\theta}$$

$$\sigma_{rz} = \frac{E}{(1 + v)} E_{rz} = 2G E_{rz} = G \gamma_{rz}$$

$$\sigma_{\theta z} = \frac{E}{(1 + v)} E_{\theta z} = 2G E_{\theta z} = G \gamma_{\theta z} \qquad \text{(Eq 75)}$$

In terms of strain:

$$E_{rr} = \frac{1}{E} [\sigma_{rr} - v(\sigma_{\theta\theta} + \sigma_{zz})]$$

$$E_{\theta\theta} = \frac{1}{E} [\sigma_{\theta\theta} - v(\sigma_{rr} + \sigma_{zz})]$$

$$E_{zz} = \frac{1}{E}[\sigma_{zz} - \nu(\sigma_{\theta\theta} + \sigma_{rr})]$$

$$E_{r\theta} = \frac{1+\nu}{E}\sigma_{r\theta} = \frac{1}{2G}\sigma_{r\theta} = \frac{1}{2}\gamma_{r\theta}$$

$$E_{rz} = \frac{1+\nu}{E}\sigma_{rz} = \frac{1}{2G}\sigma_{rz} = \frac{1}{2}\gamma_{rz}$$

$$E_{\theta z} = \frac{1+\nu}{E}\sigma_{\theta z} = \frac{1}{2G}\sigma_{\theta z} = \frac{1}{2}\gamma_{\theta z} \qquad \text{(Eq 76)}$$

In spherical coordinates:

$$\sigma_{rr} = \frac{E}{(1+\nu)(1-2\nu)}[(1-\nu)E_{rr} + \nu(E_{\theta\theta} + E_{\phi\phi})]$$

$$\sigma_{\theta\theta} = \frac{E}{(1+\nu)(1-2\nu)}[(1-\nu)E_{\theta\theta} + \nu(E_{rr} + E_{\phi\phi})]$$

$$\sigma_{\phi\phi} = \frac{E}{(1+\nu)(1-2\nu)}[(1-\nu)E_{\phi\phi} + \nu(E_{rr} + E_{\theta\theta})]$$

$$\sigma_{r\theta} = \frac{E}{1+\nu}E_{r\theta} = 2GE_{r\theta} = G\gamma_{r\theta}$$

$$\sigma_{\theta\phi} = \frac{E}{1+\nu}E_{\theta\phi} = 2GE_{\theta\phi} = G\gamma_{\theta\phi}$$

$$\sigma_{r\phi} = \frac{E}{1+\nu}E_{r\phi} = 2GE_{r\phi} = G\gamma_{r\phi} \qquad \text{(Eq 77)}$$

In terms of strain:

$$E_{rr} = \frac{1}{E}[\sigma_{rr} - \nu(\sigma_{\theta\theta} + \nu_{\phi\phi})]$$

$$E_{\theta\theta} = \frac{1}{E}[\sigma_{\theta\theta} - \nu(\sigma_{rr} + \sigma_{\phi\phi})]$$

$$E_{\phi\phi} = \frac{1}{E}[\sigma_{\phi\phi} - \nu(\sigma_{rr} + \sigma_{\theta\theta})]$$

$$E_{r\theta} = \frac{1+\nu}{E}\sigma_{r\theta} = \frac{1}{2G}\sigma_{r\theta} = \frac{1}{2}\gamma_{r\theta}$$

$$E_{r\phi} = \frac{1+\nu}{E}\sigma_{r\phi} = \frac{1}{2G}\sigma_{r\phi} = \frac{1}{2}\gamma_{r\phi}$$

$$E_{\theta\phi} = \frac{1+\nu}{E}\sigma_{\theta\phi} = \frac{1}{2G}\sigma_{\theta\phi} = \frac{1}{2}\gamma_{\theta\phi} \qquad \text{(Eq 78)}$$

Plane strain, in Cartesian coordinates:

$$\sigma_{xx} = \frac{E}{(1 + v)(1 - 2v)}\left[(1 - v)E_{xx} + vE_{yy}\right]$$

$$\sigma_{yy} = \frac{E}{(1 + v)(1 - 2v)}\left[(1 - v)E_{yy} + vE_{xx}\right]$$

$$\sigma_{zz} = \frac{Ev}{(1 + v)(1 - 2v)}\left[E_{xx} + E_{yy}\right]$$

$$\sigma_{xy} = \frac{E}{(1 + v)}E_{xy} = 2GE_{xy} = G\gamma_{xy}$$

$$\sigma_{yz} = \sigma_{xz} = 0 \qquad\qquad\qquad (\text{Eq } 79)$$

In terms of strain:

$$E_{xx} = \frac{1 + v}{E}\left[(1 - v)\sigma_{xx} - v\sigma_{yy}\right]$$

$$E_{yy} = \frac{1 + v}{E}\left[(1 - v)\sigma_{yy} - v\sigma_{xx}\right]$$

$$E_{zz} = 0$$

$$E_{xy} = \frac{1 + v}{E}\sigma_{xy} = \frac{1}{2G}\sigma_{xy} = \frac{1}{2}\gamma_{xy}$$

$$E_{yz} = E_{xz} = 0 \qquad\qquad\qquad (\text{Eq } 80)$$

Plane strain, in polar coordinates:

$$\sigma_{rr} = \frac{E}{(1 + v)(1 - 2v)}\left[(1 - v)E_{rr} + vE_{\theta\theta}\right]$$

$$\sigma_{\theta\theta} = \frac{E}{(1 + v)(1 - 2v)}\left[(1 - v)E_{\theta\theta} + vE_{rr}\right]$$

$$\sigma_{zz} = \frac{Ev}{(1 + v)(1 - 2v)}\left[E_{rr} + E_{\theta\theta}\right]$$

$$\sigma_{r\theta} = \frac{E}{1 + v}E_{r\theta} = 2GE_{r\theta} = G\gamma_{r\theta}$$

$$\sigma_{rz} = \sigma_{z\theta} = 0 \qquad\qquad\qquad (\text{Eq } 81)$$

In terms of strain:

$$E_{rr} = \frac{1 + v}{E}\left[(1 - v)\sigma_{rr} - v\sigma_{\theta\theta}\right]$$

$$E_{\theta\theta} = \frac{1 + v}{E}\left[(1 - v)\sigma_{\theta\theta} - v\sigma_{rr}\right]$$

$$E_{zz} = 0$$

$$E_{r\theta} = \frac{1 + \nu}{E} \sigma_{r\theta} = \frac{1}{2G} \sigma_{r\theta} = \frac{1}{2} \gamma_{r\theta}$$

$$E_{rz} = E_{\theta z} = 0 \qquad \text{(Eq 82)}$$

Plane stress, Cartesian coordinates:

$$\sigma_{xx} = \frac{E}{1 - \nu^2} (E_{xx} + \nu E_{yy})$$

$$\sigma_{yy} = \frac{E}{1 - \nu^2} (E_{yy} + \nu E_{xx})$$

$$\sigma_{zz} = 0$$

$$\sigma_{xy} = \frac{E}{1 + \nu} E_{xy} = 2G E_{xy} = G \gamma_{xy}$$

$$\sigma_{yz} = \sigma_{xz} = 0 \qquad \text{(Eq 83)}$$

In terms of strain:

$$E_{xx} = \frac{1}{E} (\sigma_{xx} - \nu \sigma_{yy})$$

$$E_{yy} = \frac{1}{E} (\sigma_{yy} - \nu \sigma_{xx})$$

$$E_{zz} = \frac{1}{E} (\sigma_{xx} + \sigma_{yy})$$

$$E_{xy} = \frac{1 + \nu}{E} \sigma_{xy} = \frac{1}{2G} \sigma_{xy} = \frac{1}{2} \gamma_{xy}$$

$$E_{yz} = E_{xz} = 0 \qquad \text{(Eq 84)}$$

Plane stress, polar coordinates:

$$\sigma_{rr} = \frac{E}{1 - \nu^2} (E_{rr} + \nu E_{\theta\theta})$$

$$\sigma_{\theta\theta} = \frac{E}{1 - \nu^2} (E_{\theta\theta} + \nu E_{rr})$$

$$\sigma_{zz} = 0$$

$$\sigma_{r\theta} = \frac{E}{1 + \nu} E_{r\theta} = 2G E_{r\theta} = G \gamma_{r\theta}$$

$$\sigma_{rz} = \sigma_{\theta z} = 0 \qquad \text{(Eq 85)}$$

In terms of strain:

$$E_{rr} = \frac{1}{E} (\sigma_{rr} - \nu \sigma_{\theta\theta})$$

$$E_{\theta\theta} = \frac{1}{E} (\sigma_{\theta\theta} - \nu \sigma_{rr})$$

$$E_{zz} = \frac{1}{E} (\sigma_{rr} + \sigma_{\theta\theta})$$

$$E_{r\theta} = \frac{1 + \nu}{E} \sigma_{r\theta} = \frac{1}{2G} \sigma_{r\theta} = \frac{1}{2} \gamma_{r\theta}$$

$$E_{rz} = E_{\theta z} = 0 \qquad\qquad\qquad\qquad\qquad \text{(Eq 86)}$$

Elastic Constants. The more common relationships among the elastic constants are given in Table 2. E is the Young's modulus, and ν is the Poisson ratio. The Lamé constants are denoted by λ and G, which is sometimes called the modulus of rigidity, or shear modulus. The bulk modulus is denoted by K.

NEWTONIAN FLUIDS

Because a fluid at rest or in uniform flow cannot sustain shear stress, the maximum shear stress for such a fluid is zero, and the stress is purely hydrostatic. In a state of thermodynamic equilibrium, the static pressure in a pure fluid substance is assumed to be related to the density ρ and the absolute temperature T by an equation of state $F(\bar{p}_0, \rho, T) = 0$. The thermodynamic pressure p is the quantity given by the same functional relation to ρ and T that gives the static pressure $\bar{p}_0$ in an equilibrium state.

Barotropic flows satisfy the relationship $f(p, \rho) = 0$, which is independent of the temperature. The functional form of f depends on the special conditions of the flow, an isothermal flow with T a constant, for example. Another example is the reversible adiabatic flow (isentropic flow) of a gas. An ideal incompressible fluid is governed by the special barotropic equation $\rho = \text{const}$, and an ideal frictionless (nonviscous) fluid can sustain no shear stresses even in motion. In many flow fields, the pressure and body-force effects predominate over the viscous effects, and the flow can be analyzed by assuming the fluid to be nonviscous everywhere except in the boundary layer. This layer appears near a solid object in the flow field or near a container wall, where viscous effects are of the same order of magnitude as other effects.

The constitutive equation for the ideal nonviscous fluid is $P_{ij} = -p\,\delta_{ij}$, where p is the thermodynamic pressure. When the equation of state is $p = p(\rho)$, the frictionless fluid is called an elastic fluid. In an ideal frictionless fluid, $\bar{p} = p$, where p is the thermodynamic pressure.

Linear stress-strain rate relationships are shown in Fig. 1 for a fluid, although in some physical situations viscoelastic and nonlinear relationships may be useful. In Fig. 1, the stress components σ_{21}, σ_{22}, and σ_{23} denote the $y_1 y_3$ normal plane on which the stress acts, and σ_{11}, σ_{21}, and σ_{31} denote the direction of stress, and so on. The stress tensor must be symmetrical to satisfy equilibrium requirements. The second coefficient of viscosity is denoted by $\tilde{\lambda}$

Table 2 Elastic constants

Young's modulus, E	Lamé constants	
	G	λ
$\dfrac{G(3\lambda + 2G)}{\lambda + G}$	$\dfrac{\sqrt{(E+\lambda)^2 + 8\lambda^2} + (E - 3\lambda)}{4}$	$\dfrac{G(2G - E)}{E - 3G}$
$\dfrac{\lambda(1 + \nu)(1 - 2\nu)}{\nu}$	$\dfrac{\lambda(1 - 2\nu)}{2\nu}$	$\dfrac{2G\nu}{1 - 2\nu}$
$\dfrac{9K(K - \lambda)}{3K - \lambda}$	$\dfrac{3(K - \lambda)}{2}$	$\dfrac{3K - 2G}{3}$
$2G(1 + \nu)$	$\dfrac{E}{2(1 + \nu)}$	$\dfrac{\nu E}{(1 + \nu)(1 - 2\nu)}$
$\dfrac{9KG}{3K + G}$	$\dfrac{3EK}{9K - E}$	$\dfrac{3K(3K - E)}{9K - E}$
$3K(1 - 2\nu)$	$\dfrac{3K(1 - 2\nu)}{2(1 + \nu)}$	$\dfrac{3K\nu}{1 + \nu}$

Poisson's ratio, ν	Bulk modulus, K
$\dfrac{\lambda}{2(\lambda + G)}$	$\dfrac{3\lambda + 2G}{3}$
$\dfrac{\sqrt{(E+\lambda)^2 + 8\lambda^2} - (E + \lambda)}{4\lambda}$	$\dfrac{\sqrt{(E+\lambda)^2 + 8\lambda^2} + (3\lambda + E)}{6}$
$\dfrac{\lambda}{3K - \lambda}$	$\dfrac{\lambda(1 + \nu)}{3\nu}$
$\dfrac{E - 2G}{2G}$	$\dfrac{GE}{3(3G - E)}$
$\dfrac{3K - 2G}{2(3K + G)}$	$\dfrac{2G(1 + \nu)}{3(1 - 2\nu)}$
$\dfrac{3K - E}{6K}$	$\dfrac{E}{3(1 - 2\nu)}$

and ζ. For a monatomic gas, the second coefficient of viscosity $\tilde{\lambda}$ is $-\frac{2}{3}\tilde{\mu}$, where $\tilde{\mu}$ is the ordinary coefficient of viscosity and ζ is defined as $\zeta = \tilde{\lambda} + \frac{2}{3}\tilde{\mu}$. For a monatomic gas, $\zeta = 0$. The kinematic viscosity v is $\tilde{\mu}/\rho$, where ρ is the mass density. The Kronecker delta, δ_{ij}, is defined as $\delta_{ij} = 1$, $i = j$, and $\delta_{ij} = 0$, $i \neq j$. As shown in Eq 1, the stress tensor, σ_{ij}, may be separated into:

$$\sigma_{ij} = \bar{\sigma}_{ij} + \bar{\bar{\sigma}}_{ij} \tag{Eq 87}$$

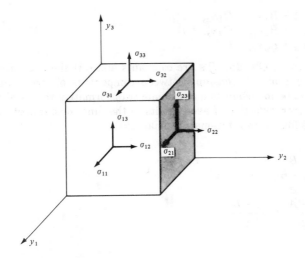

Figure 1 Stress state on an elemental cube. Note: A surface is denoted by the axis to which it is perpendicular. Stresses are on the positive surfaces

where

$\bar{\sigma}_{ij}$ = conservative part of the stress tensor
$\bar{\bar{\sigma}}_{ij}$ = dissipative part of the stress tensor

The conservative part of the stress tensor $\bar{\sigma}_{ij}$ may be represented by a simple scalar p, the fluid pressure, so that:

$$\bar{\sigma}_{ij} = -p\delta_{ij} \tag{Eq 88}$$

The negative sign means that the fluid pressure will be positive.

The dissipative portion of the stress tensor $\bar{\bar{\sigma}}_{ij}$ is given by:

$$\bar{\bar{\sigma}}_{ij} = \sigma_{ij} + p\delta_{ij} \tag{Eq 89}$$

and is termed the viscous stress tensor, and is denoted by σ'_{ij}. The stress tensor σ_{ij} at a point in a fluid medium thus is composed of two parts:

$$\sigma_{ij} = -p\delta_{ij} + \sigma'_{ij} \tag{Eq 90}$$

Because the viscous stress tensor σ'_{ij} is assumed to contribute the material dissipation, its relationship to the velocity strain tensor ϵ_{ij} is assumed. If the relationship is linear, then the fluid is called a Newtonian viscous fluid, for which:

$$\sigma'_{ij} = \tilde{C}_{ijkl}\epsilon_{kl} \text{ and } \epsilon_{ij} = \partial E_{ij}/\partial t = \dot{E}_{ij} \tag{Eq 91}$$

where the constants $\tilde{C}_{ijkl}$ are called the viscosity coefficients. With the assumption that the stress components may be expressed as a linear function of the rates of strain components, the stress-rate of strain relationship may be expressed as:

$$\sigma'_{xx} = A_1 \epsilon_{xx} + B_1 \epsilon_{yy} + C_1 \gamma_{xy} + D_1$$
$$\sigma'_{yy} = A_2 \epsilon_{xx} + B_2 \epsilon_{yy} + C_2 \gamma_{xy} + D_2$$
$$\sigma'_{xy} = A_3 \epsilon_{xx} + B_3 \epsilon_{yy} + C_3 \gamma_{xy} + D_3 \qquad \text{(Eq 92)}$$

where A's, B's, C's, and D's are constants and ϵ is the rate of strain. The assumption that relationships between components of stress and rates of strain must be invariant to a coordinate transformation that is either a rotation or mirror reflection of axes results in the nine constants of Eq 92 being reduced to four from rotational invariance:

$$A_1 = B_2 = A$$
$$B_1 = A_2 = B$$
$$C_1 = -A_3 = B_3 = -C_2 = C$$
$$D_1 = D_2 = D$$
$$C_3 = \frac{A_1 - A_2}{2} = \frac{A - B}{2}$$
$$D_3 = 0 \qquad \text{(Eq 93)}$$

From this, Eq 92 can be rewritten as:

$$\sigma'_{xx} = A\epsilon_{xx} + B\epsilon_{yy} + C\gamma_{xy} + D$$
$$\sigma'_{yy} = B\epsilon_{xx} + A\epsilon_{yy} - C\gamma_{xy} + D$$
$$\sigma'_{xy} = -C(\epsilon_{xx} - \epsilon_{yy}) + \frac{A - B}{2}\gamma_{xy} \qquad \text{(Eq 94)}$$

According to the assumption of invariance due to mirror reflection transformation, the stress-rate of strain relationship should be independent of the coordinate system; hence:

$$C = 0 \qquad \text{(Eq 95)}$$

It can also be assumed that stress components must also reduce to the hydrostatic pressure p when all the velocity gradients are zero. Accordingly, for σ'_{xx} in Eq 94:

$$D = -p \qquad \text{(Eq 96)}$$

The constant $(A - B)/2$ in the last equation of Eq 94 is the proportionality constant connecting the shearing stress and rate of shearing strain. This constant is generally denoted by the dynamic coefficient of viscosity $\tilde{\mu}$. The relationships between stress and rate of strain in the two-dimensional case given in Eq 94 are reduced to:

$$\sigma'_{xx} = 2\tilde{\mu}\epsilon_{xx} + B\epsilon_{kk}\delta_{ij} - p$$
$$\sigma'_{yy} = 2\tilde{\mu}\epsilon_{yy} + B\epsilon_{kk}\delta_{ij} - p$$
$$\sigma'_{xy} = \tilde{\mu}\gamma_{xy} = 2\tilde{\mu}\epsilon_{xy} \qquad \text{(Eq 97)}$$

where $B = -\frac{2}{3}(\tilde{\mu} - \tilde{\mu}_1)$ and $\tilde{\mu}_1$ is the second viscosity coefficient, which is significant only when molecular energy is exchanged between translational degrees of freedom and vibrational and rotational degrees of freedom. For a perfect gas, the second viscosity coefficient $\tilde{\mu}_1$ has been verified to be negligibly small. The stress-rate of strain relationships of Eq 97 can be extended to three-dimensional flows.

From Eq 90 and Eq 91, it can be seen that, unlike an elastic solid, a fluid at rest ($\epsilon_{ij} = 0$) has a static stress state characterized by the hydrostatic pressure, $-p\delta_{ij}$. For an isotropic, homogeneous, Newtonian fluid, Eq 91 can be reduced to:

$$\sigma'_{ij} = 2\tilde{\mu}\epsilon_{ij} + \tilde{\lambda}\epsilon_{kk}\delta_{ij} \qquad \text{(Eq 98)}$$

where $\tilde{\mu}$ and $\tilde{\lambda}$ are the first and second coefficients of viscosity, respectively. Thus:

$$\sigma'_{ii} = (2\tilde{\mu} + 3\tilde{\lambda})\epsilon_{ii} = K\epsilon_{ii} \qquad \text{(Eq 99)}$$

where $K = 2\tilde{\mu} + 3\tilde{\lambda}$ is the bulk coefficient of viscosity.

For incompressible flow, the continuity equation is:

$$u_{i,i} = 0 \qquad \text{(Eq 100)}$$

or

$$\epsilon_{ii} = 0 \qquad \text{(Eq 101)}$$

Therefore:

$$\sigma'_{ii} = 0 \qquad \text{(Eq 102)}$$

If the fluid pressure p follows the usual form of the ideal gas law:

$$p = \rho RT \qquad \text{(Eq 103)}$$

where R is the gas constant, then the viscous stress tensor for a monatomic gas also has the property $\sigma'_{ii} = 0$. Thus:

$$\tilde{\lambda} = -\frac{2}{3}\tilde{\mu} \qquad \text{(Eq 104)}$$

From Eq 90 and Eq 102:

$$p = -\frac{1}{3}\sigma_{ii} \qquad \text{(Eq 105)}$$

for incompressible flow of an isotropic, homogeneous, Newtonian fluid or flow of a monatomic ideal gas (with allowable fluctuations). This result does not hold exactly for other types of fluid media. The effect of the viscous stress tensor can be neglected when:

- The magnitudes of the viscosity coefficients $\tilde{C}_{ijkl}$ of a fluid medium and the magnitudes of the local velocity gradients are small
- A fluid medium is in equilibrium with its surroundings
- A medium is accelerating as a rigid body and the velocity gradients $q_{i,j}$ vanish everywhere in the medium

In such cases:

$$\sigma'_{ij} = 0 \qquad \text{(Eq 106)}$$

everywhere, and the stress tensor σ'_{ij} is expressible in terms of a simple scalar:

$$\sigma_{ij} = -p\,\delta_{ij} \qquad \text{(Eq 107)}$$

Further, in such cases where the viscous stress tensor can be neglected, the stress vector σ_i acting on a plane defined by a unit normal vector n_i at a point P in a fluid medium is:

$$\sigma_i = \sigma_{ji}n_j = -p\delta_{ji}n_j = -pn_i \qquad \text{(Eq 108)}$$

COORDINATE SYSTEMS

Expansions of the stress-strain rate relationships for various coordinate systems are given below.

Cartesian Tensor. Velocity is denoted by u_i in the y_i direction, and ϕ is dilatation, $\nabla \cdot \mathbf{u}$ or $\delta_{ij}\epsilon_{kk}$:

$$\sigma_{ij} = -P\delta_{ij} + \sigma'_{ij} = -P\delta_{ij} + 2\tilde{\mu}\epsilon_{ij} + \delta_{ij}\tilde{\lambda}\phi$$

$$= -P\delta_{ij} + \tilde{\mu}\left(\frac{\partial u_i}{\partial y_j} + \frac{\partial u_j}{\partial y_i}\right) + \tilde{\lambda}\delta_{ij}\frac{\partial u_k}{\partial y_k}$$

$$= -P\delta_{ij} + \tilde{\mu}\left(\frac{\partial u_i}{\partial y_j} + \frac{\partial u_j}{\partial y_i} - \frac{2}{3}\,\delta_{ij}\,\frac{\partial u_k}{\partial y_k}\right) + \zeta\delta_{ij}\frac{\partial u_k}{\partial y_k} \qquad \text{(Eq 109)}$$

Orthogonal Curvilinear. Velocities are denoted by u_1, u_2, and u_3 in the y_1, y_2, and y_3 directions respectively and h_1, h_2, and h_3 are defined by the line element:

$$\sigma_{11} = -P + \sigma'_{11} = -P + 2\tilde{\mu}\epsilon_{11} + \tilde{\lambda}\nabla\cdot\mathbf{u}$$

$$= -P + 2\mu\left(\frac{1}{h_1}\frac{\partial u_1}{\partial y_1} + \frac{u_2}{h_1 h_2}\frac{\partial h_1}{\partial y_2} + \frac{u_3}{h_3 h_1}\frac{\partial h_1}{\partial y_3}\right)$$

$$+ \lambda\frac{1}{h_1 h_2 h_3}\left\{\frac{\partial}{\partial y_1}(h_2 h_3 u_1) + \frac{\partial}{\partial y_2}(h_3 h_1 u_2) + \frac{\partial}{\partial y_3}(h_1 h_2 u_3)\right\}$$

$$\sigma_{22} = -P + \sigma'_{22} = -P + 2\tilde{\mu}\epsilon_{22} + \tilde{\lambda}\nabla\cdot\mathbf{u}$$

$$= -P + 2\mu\left(\frac{1}{h_2}\frac{\partial u_2}{\partial y_2} + \frac{u_3}{h_2 h_3}\frac{\partial h_2}{\partial y_3} + \frac{u_1}{h_1 h_2}\frac{\partial h_2}{\partial y_1}\right)$$

$$+ \lambda\frac{1}{h_1 h_2 h_3}\left\{\frac{\partial}{\partial y_1}(h_2 h_3 u_1) + \frac{\partial}{\partial y_2}(h_3 h_1 u_2) + \frac{\partial}{\partial y_3}(h_1 h_2 u_3)\right\}$$

$$\sigma_{33} = -P + \sigma'_{33} = -P + 2\tilde{\mu}\epsilon_{33} + \tilde{\lambda}\nabla\cdot\mathbf{u}$$

$$= -P + 2\mu\left(\frac{1}{h_3}\frac{\partial u_3}{\partial y_3} + \frac{u_1}{h_3 h_1}\frac{\partial h_3}{\partial y_1} + \frac{u_2}{h_2 h_3}\frac{\partial h_3}{\partial y_2}\right)$$

$$+ \lambda\frac{1}{h_1 h_2 h_3}\left\{\frac{\partial}{\partial y_1}(h_2 h_3 u_1) + \frac{\partial}{\partial y_2}(h_3 h_1 u_2) + \frac{\partial}{\partial y_3}(h_1 h_2 u_3)\right\}$$

$$\sigma_{23} = \sigma_{32} = 2\tilde{\mu}\epsilon_{23} = \mu \left\{ \frac{h_3}{h_2} \frac{\partial}{\partial y_2} \left(\frac{u_3}{h_3} \right) + \frac{h_2}{h_3} \frac{\partial}{\partial y_3} \left(\frac{u_2}{h_2} \right) \right\}$$

$$\sigma_{13} = \sigma_{31} = 2\tilde{\mu}\epsilon_{13} = \mu \left\{ \frac{h_1}{h_3} \frac{\partial}{\partial y_3} \left(\frac{u_1}{h_1} \right) + \frac{h_3}{h_1} \frac{\partial}{\partial y_1} \left(\frac{u_3}{h_3} \right) \right\}$$

$$\sigma_{12} = \sigma_{21} = 2\tilde{\mu}\epsilon_{12} = \mu \left\{ \frac{h_2}{h_1} \frac{\partial}{\partial y_1} \left(\frac{u_2}{h_2} \right) + \frac{h_1}{h_2} \frac{\partial}{\partial y_2} \left(\frac{u_1}{h_1} \right) \right\} \qquad \text{(Eq 110)}$$

Cartesian. The velocities are denoted by u, v, and w in the x, y, and z directions respectively:

$$\sigma_{xx} = -P + \sigma'_{xx} = -P + 2\tilde{\mu}\epsilon_{xx} + \tilde{\lambda}\mathbf{\nabla} \cdot \mathbf{V}$$

$$= -P + 2\tilde{\mu}\frac{\partial u}{\partial x} + \tilde{\lambda}\left(\frac{\partial u}{\partial x} + \frac{\partial v}{\partial y} + \frac{\partial w}{\partial z} \right)$$

$$\sigma_{yy} = -P + \sigma'_{yy} = -P + 2\tilde{\mu}\epsilon_{yy} + \tilde{\lambda}\mathbf{\nabla} \cdot \mathbf{V}$$

$$= -P + 2\tilde{\mu}\frac{\partial v}{\partial y} + \tilde{\lambda}\left(\frac{\partial u}{\partial x} + \frac{\partial v}{\partial y} + \frac{\partial w}{\partial z} \right)$$

$$\sigma_{zz} = -P + \sigma'_{zz} = -P + 2\tilde{\mu}\epsilon_{zz} + \tilde{\lambda}\mathbf{\nabla} \cdot \mathbf{V}$$

$$= -P + 2\tilde{\mu}\frac{\partial w}{\partial z} + \tilde{\lambda}\left(\frac{\partial u}{\partial x} + \frac{\partial v}{\partial y} + \frac{\partial w}{\partial z} \right)$$

$$\sigma_{xy} = \sigma_{yx} = 2\tilde{\mu}\epsilon_{xy} = \tilde{\mu}\left(\frac{\partial u}{\partial y} + \frac{\partial v}{\partial x} \right)$$

$$\sigma_{xz} = \sigma_{zx} = 2\tilde{\mu}\epsilon_{xz} = \tilde{\mu}\left(\frac{\partial w}{\partial x} + \frac{\partial u}{\partial z} \right)$$

$$\sigma_{yz} = \sigma_{zy} = 2\tilde{\mu}\epsilon_{yz} = \tilde{\mu}\left(\frac{\partial v}{\partial z} + \frac{\partial w}{\partial y} \right) \qquad \text{(Eq 111)}$$

Cylindrical. The velocities are denoted by v_r, v_θ, and v_z in the r, θ, and z directions respectively:

$$\sigma_{rr} = -P + \sigma'_{rr} = -P + 2\tilde{\mu}\epsilon_{rr} + \tilde{\lambda}\mathbf{\nabla} \cdot \mathbf{V}$$

$$= -P + 2\tilde{\mu}\frac{\partial v_r}{\partial r} + \tilde{\lambda}\left\{ \frac{1}{r}\frac{\partial}{\partial r}(rv_r) + \frac{1}{r}\frac{\partial v_\theta}{\partial \theta} + \frac{\partial v_z}{\partial z} \right\}$$

$$\sigma_{\theta\theta} = -P + \sigma'_{\theta\theta} = -P + 2\tilde{\mu}\epsilon_{\theta\theta} + \tilde{\lambda}\mathbf{\nabla} \cdot \mathbf{V}$$

$$= -P + 2\tilde{\mu}\left(\frac{1}{r}\frac{\partial v_\theta}{\partial \theta} + \frac{v_r}{r} \right) + \tilde{\lambda}\left\{ \frac{1}{r}\frac{\partial}{\partial r}(rv_r) + \frac{1}{r}\frac{\partial v_\theta}{\partial \theta} + \frac{\partial v_z}{\partial z} \right\}$$

$$\sigma_{zz} = -P + \sigma'_{zz} = -P + 2\tilde{\mu}\epsilon_{zz} + \tilde{\lambda}\mathbf{\nabla} \cdot \mathbf{V}$$

$$= -P + 2\tilde{\mu}\frac{\partial v_z}{\partial z} + \tilde{\lambda}\left\{ \frac{1}{r}\frac{\partial}{\partial r}(rv_r) + \frac{1}{r}\frac{\partial v_\theta}{\partial \theta} + \frac{\partial v_z}{\partial z} \right\}$$

$$\sigma_{r\theta} = \sigma_{\theta r} = 2\tilde{\mu}\epsilon_{r\theta} = \tilde{\mu}\left(\frac{1}{r}\frac{\partial v_r}{\partial \theta} + \frac{\partial v_\theta}{\partial r} - \frac{v_\theta}{r}\right)$$

$$\sigma_{rz} = \sigma_{zr} = 2\tilde{\mu}\epsilon_{rz} = \tilde{\mu}\left(\frac{\partial v_r}{\partial z} + \frac{\partial v_z}{\partial r}\right)$$

$$\sigma_{\theta z} = \sigma_{z\theta} = 2\tilde{\mu}\epsilon_{\theta z} = \tilde{\mu}\left(\frac{1}{r}\frac{\partial v_z}{\partial \theta} + \frac{\partial v_\theta}{\partial z}\right) \tag{Eq 112}$$

Spherical. v_r, v_θ, and v_ϕ are the velocities in the r, θ, and ϕ directions respectively:

$$\sigma_{rr} = -P + \sigma'_{rr} = -P + 2\tilde{\mu}\epsilon_{rr} + \tilde{\lambda}\boldsymbol{\nabla}\cdot\mathbf{V}$$

$$= -P + 2\tilde{\mu}\frac{\partial v_r}{\partial r} + \tilde{\lambda}\left\{\frac{1}{r^2}\frac{\partial}{\partial r}(r^2 v_r) + \frac{1}{r\sin\theta}\frac{\partial}{\partial \theta}(v_\theta \sin\theta) + \frac{1}{r\sin\theta}\frac{\partial v_\phi}{\partial \phi}\right\}$$

$$\sigma_{\theta\theta} = -P + \sigma'_{\theta\theta} = -P + 2\tilde{\mu}\epsilon_{\theta\theta} + \tilde{\lambda}\boldsymbol{\nabla}\cdot\mathbf{V}$$

$$= -P + 2\tilde{\mu}\left(\frac{1}{r}\frac{\partial v_\theta}{\partial \theta} + \frac{v_r}{r}\right) + \tilde{\lambda}\left\{\frac{1}{r^2}\frac{\partial}{\partial r}(r^2 v_r)\right.$$

$$\left. + \frac{1}{r\sin\theta}\frac{\partial}{\partial \theta}(v_\theta \sin\theta) + \frac{1}{r\sin\theta}\frac{\partial v_\phi}{\partial \phi}\right\}$$

$$\sigma_{\phi\phi} = -P + \sigma'_{\phi\phi} = -P + 2\tilde{\mu}\epsilon_{\phi\phi} + \tilde{\lambda}\boldsymbol{\nabla}\cdot\mathbf{V}$$

$$= -P + 2\tilde{\mu}\left(\frac{1}{r\sin\theta}\frac{\partial v_\phi}{\partial \phi} + \frac{v_r}{r} + \frac{v_\theta \cot\theta}{r}\right)$$

$$+ \tilde{\lambda}\left\{\frac{1}{r^2}\frac{\partial}{\partial r}(r^2 v_r) + \frac{1}{r\sin\theta}\frac{\partial}{\partial \theta}(v_\theta \sin\theta) + \frac{1}{r\sin\theta}\frac{\partial v_\phi}{\partial \phi}\right\}$$

$$\sigma_{r\theta} = \sigma_{\theta r} = 2\tilde{\mu}\epsilon_{r\theta} = \tilde{\mu}\left\{r\frac{\partial}{\partial r}\left(\frac{v_\theta}{r}\right) + \frac{1}{r}\frac{\partial v_r}{\partial \theta}\right\}$$

$$\sigma_{r\phi} = \sigma_{\phi r} = 2\tilde{\mu}\epsilon_{r\phi} = \tilde{\mu}\left\{\frac{1}{r\sin\theta}\frac{\partial v_r}{\partial \phi} + r\frac{\partial}{\partial r}\left(\frac{v_\theta}{r}\right)\right\}$$

$$\sigma_{\theta\phi} = \sigma_{\phi\theta} = 2\tilde{\mu}\epsilon_{\theta\phi} = \tilde{\mu}\left\{\frac{\sin\theta}{r}\frac{\partial}{\partial \theta}\left(\frac{v_\phi}{\sin\theta}\right) + \frac{1}{r\sin\theta}\frac{\partial v_\theta}{\partial \phi}\right\} \tag{Eq 113}$$

PLASTICITY

Ideal Plastic Solids. Hooke's law applies to metals only in a certain range of small strain. For strain beyond an elastic limit, Hooke's law no longer applies, and behavior of metals beyond that limit becomes complex. The stress deviation σ'_{ij} has a second invariant J_2 defined as:

$$J_2 = \frac{1}{2}\sigma'_{ij}\sigma'_{ij} \tag{Eq 114}$$

Similarly, subtracting the mean strain from the strain tensor E_{ij} produces the strain deviation E'_{ij}:

$$E'_{ij} = E_{ij} - \frac{1}{3} E_{\alpha\alpha} \delta_{ij}$$

For isotropic material that obeys Hooke's law:

$$E'_{ij} = \frac{1}{2G} \sigma'_{ij} \qquad \text{(Eq 115)}$$

which no longer applies when the elastic limit is reached. In this case, the plastic strain deviation becomes the actual strain deviation minus the strain deviation that would be computed if Hooke's law still applied. The plastic strain deviation is denoted by:

$$E_{ij}^{(p)} = E'_{ij} - \frac{1}{2G} \sigma'_{ij} \qquad \text{(Eq 116)}$$

and total strain deviation by:

$$E'_{ij} = E_{ij}^{(p)} + \frac{1}{2G} \sigma'_{ij} \qquad \text{(Eq 117)}$$

If the instantaneous rate of plastic deformation is $\dot{E}_{ij}^{(p)}$, then the increment of plastic strain in the interval dt is $\dot{E}_{ij}^{(p)} dt$, and total plastic strain deviation in successive yielding increments will be the algebraic sum of the successive deformations:

$$E_{ij}^{(p)} = E_{ij}^{(p)}(0) + \int_0^t \dot{E}_{ij}^{(p)}(t)\, dt \qquad \text{(Eq 118)}$$

where $E_{ij}^{(p)}(0)$ is the value at time $t = 0$. For an ideal plastic solid obeying von Mises' yielding criterion and flow rule:

- Hooke's law holds at all time intervals for the mean stress and the mean strain; that is:

$$\sigma_{\alpha\alpha} = 3K E_{\alpha\alpha} \qquad \text{(Eq 119)}$$

- The material obeys Hooke's law when the second invariant J_2 is less than a constant k^2:

$$\dot{E}_{ij}^{(p)} = 0$$

when

$$J_2 < k^2 \qquad \text{(Eq 120)}$$

- Yielding occurs when $J_2 = k^2$. When the elastic limit is reached ($J_2 - k^2 = 0$), the rate of change of the plastic strain is proportional to the stress deviation:

$$\dot{E}_{ij}^{(p)} = \frac{1}{\tilde{\mu}} \sigma'_{ij} \qquad \text{(Eq 121)}$$

where $\tilde{\mu} > 0$ and $\tilde{\mu}$ is a positive factor of proportionality, which has the dimensions of the coefficient of viscosity of a fluid.

• Any stress state $J_2 > k^2$ cannot be realized in the material.

When only the total amount of plastic flow is of concern, Eq 121 may be replaced by:

$$\Delta E_{ij}^{(p)} = \lambda' \sigma_{ij}'$$

where $\lambda' > 0$, and λ' is an arbitrary factor of proportionality and not a characteristic constant of the material. The sign of λ' is determined by dissipation of energy involved in plastic flow.

Near the origin of the stress-strain diagrams of Fig. 2, the linear relationship remains in nearly all cases. For mild steel (Fig. 2a), the large, flat, yielding region A-B exhibits ideal plasticity. The slightly unstable region of the yield curve at peak A' is ignored by the ideal plasticity law. Beyond point B, the rise cannot be represented by the linear elasticity law or by the ideal plasticity law. These curved portions of stress-strain curves indicate strain hardening. Loading may be defined as a path in the stress space and the corresponding deformation history as a path in the strain space. There exists a scalar function, called a yield function or loading function, denoted by $f(\sigma_{ij}, E_{ij}^{(p)}, (\kappa))$, which depends on the state of stress and strain and the history of loading and characterizes the yielding of the material. The equation $f = 0$ represents a closed surface in the stress space. For $f < 0$, no change in plastic deformation occurs. For $f = 0$, change in plastic deformation occurs. No meaning is associated with $f > 0$. The parameter κ, called a work-hardening parameter, depends on the plastic deformation history of the material.

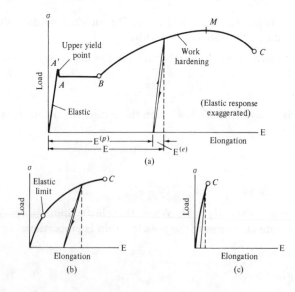

Figure 2 Typical load-elongation curves in simple tension tests

Yielding Condition of von Mises. The yielding condition of von Mises is defined by the yield function:

$$f(\sigma_{ij}) = J_2 - k^2 \qquad\qquad (\text{Eq } 122)$$

where J_2 is the second invariant of the stress deviation:

$$J_2 = \frac{1}{2}\sigma'_{ij}\,\sigma'_{ij} \qquad\qquad (\text{Eq } 123)$$

In Eq 120, k is a constant independent of strain history. The stress state is defined by $J_2 \leqq k^2$, with plastic flow occurring when $J_2 = k^2$; the condition $J_2 > k^2$ can never be realized. For a work-hardening material, k can change with strain history.

Example 1. A material obeying von Mises' yield condition is subjected to a simple shear σ_{12}. All other stress components vanish, a condition realizable in torsion of a thin-walled tube. Then $J_2 = \sigma_{12}{}^2$, and yielding should occur when:

$$\sigma_{12} = k \qquad\qquad (\text{Eq } 124)$$

with k the yield stress in simple shear. As shown in Eq 122, yielding occurs when the second invariant of the stress deviator, J_2, exceeds some critical value, and where (in terms of principal stress):

$$J_2 = \frac{1}{6}\left[(\sigma_1 - \sigma_2)^2 + (\sigma_2 - \sigma_3)^2 + (\sigma_3 - \sigma_1)^2\right]$$

To relate the constant k to yielding in the tension test, consider that at the yielding point in uniaxial tension:

$$\sigma_2 = \sigma_3 = 0 \qquad \sigma_1 = \sigma_0 \qquad \sigma_0{}^2 + \sigma_0{}^2 = 6k^2 \qquad \sigma_0 = \sqrt{3}k \qquad (\text{Eq } 125)$$

Substituting Eq 125 in the expression $J_2 = k^2$ results in the common form of the von Mises' yield criterion:

$$\sigma_0 = \frac{1}{\sqrt{2}}\left[(\sigma_1 - \sigma_2)^2 + (\sigma_2 - \sigma_3)^2 + (\sigma_3 - \sigma_1)^2\right]^{1/2} \qquad (\text{Eq } 126)$$

or in terms of stress components:

$$\sigma_0 = \frac{1}{\sqrt{2}}\left[(\sigma_{xx} - \sigma_{yy})^2 + (\sigma_{yy} - \sigma_{zz})^2 + (\sigma_{zz} - \sigma_{xx})^2 + 6(\sigma_{xy}{}^2 + \sigma_{yz}{}^2 + \sigma_{xx}{}^2)^2\right]^{1/2}$$

$$(\text{Eq } 127)$$

Equations 126 and 127 predict that yielding will occur when the stress differences on the right side of the equation exceed the yield stress in uniaxial tension σ_0.

To identify the constant k in the expression $J_2 = k^2$, consider the state of stress in pure shear, as produced in a torsion test, $\sigma_1 = -\sigma_3 = \tau$ and $\sigma_2 = 0$. At yielding:

$$\sigma_1{}^2 + \sigma_1{}^2 + 4\sigma_1{}^2 = 6k^2 \qquad \text{and} \qquad \therefore \sigma_1 = k,$$

where k represents the yield stress in pure shear. Therefore:

$$k = \frac{1}{\sqrt{3}} \sigma_0 = 0.577\sigma_0 \qquad \text{(Eq 128)}$$

The von Mises' yield criterion implies that yielding does not depend on any particular normal stress or shear stress, but on a function of three values of principal shearing stresses. For example, total strain energy can be separated into a term depending on change of volume and a term depending on distortion. In terms of principal stresses:

$$W = \frac{1}{2E} [\sigma_1{}^2 + \sigma_2{}^2 + \sigma_3{}^2 - 2v(\sigma_1\sigma_2 + \sigma_2\sigma_3 + \sigma_1\sigma_3)] \qquad \text{(Eq 129)}$$

or in terms of the invariants of the stress tensor:

$$W = \frac{1}{2E} [I_1{}^2 - 2I_2(1 + v)] \qquad \text{(Eq 130)}$$

which can be expressed in terms of the bulk modulus (volume change) and the shear modulus (distortion). Substituting $E = \dfrac{9GK}{3K + G}$ and $v = \dfrac{3K - 2G}{6K + 2G}$ into Eq 130 produces:

$$W = \frac{I_1{}^2}{18K} + \frac{1}{6G} (I_1{}^2 - 3I_2) \qquad \text{(Eq 131)}$$

which shows that total strain energy can be separated into a term depending on change of volume and a term depending on distortion, that is:

$$W_{\text{distortion}} = \frac{1}{6G} (\alpha_1{}^2 + \alpha_2{}^2 + \alpha_3{}^2 - \alpha_1\alpha_2 - \alpha_2\alpha_3 - \alpha_1\alpha_3)$$

$$W_{\text{distortion}} = \frac{1}{12G} [(\sigma_1 - \sigma_2)^2 + (\sigma_2 - \sigma_3)^2 + (\sigma_3 - \sigma_1)^2] \qquad \text{(Eq 132)}$$

For a uniaxial state of stress $\sigma_1 = \sigma_0$, $\sigma_2 = \sigma_3 = 0$, and:

$$W_{\text{distortion}} = \frac{1}{12G} 2\sigma_0{}^2$$

$$\sigma_0 = \frac{1}{\sqrt{2}} [(\sigma_1 - \sigma_2)^2 + (\sigma_2 - \sigma_3)^2 + (\sigma_3 - \sigma_1)^2] \qquad \text{(Eq 133)}$$

Yielding Condition of Tresca. According to Tresca's criterion, the maximum shear stress must have the constant value k during plastic flow. Expressed analytically, the principal stresses $\sigma_1, \sigma_2, \sigma_3$, are the simplest to use. If:

$$\sigma_1 \geqq \sigma_2 \geqq \sigma_3 \qquad \text{(Eq 134)}$$

then Tresca's yielding condition is expressed as:

$$f \equiv \sigma_1 - \sigma_3 - 2k = 0 \qquad \text{(Eq 135)}$$

According to Tresca's condition, during plastic flow one of the differences $|\sigma_1 - \sigma_2|, |\sigma_2 - \sigma_3|, |\sigma_3 - \sigma_1|$ has the value $2k$. Hence:

$$f \equiv [(\sigma_1 - \sigma_2)^2 - 4k^2][(\sigma_2 - \sigma_3)^2 - 4k^2][(\sigma_3 - \sigma_1)^2 - 4k^2] = 0 \qquad \text{(Eq 136)}$$

which is symmetrical with respect to the principal stresses and can be expressed in the invariant form:

$$4J_2{}^3 - 27J_3{}^2 - 36k^2J_2{}^2 + 96k^4J_2 - 64k^6 = 0 \qquad \text{(Eq 137)}$$

where J_2, J_3 are the second and third invariants of the stress deviation tensor.

Plastic Stress-Strain Relationships. In the plastic region, the strains in general are not determined by the stresses alone, but depend on the entire history of loading. Therefore, the differentials or increments of plastic strain must be determined throughout the loading path and the total strain obtained by integration or summation. For example, a rod 1 in. long is extended in tension to 1¼ in. and then compressed to original length. On the basis of total deformation:

$$E = \int_1^{1¼} \frac{dL}{L} + \int_{1¼}^1 \frac{dL}{L} = 0 \qquad \text{(Eq 138)}$$

On an incremental basis, however:

$$E = \int_1^{1¼} \frac{dL}{L} + \int_{1¼}^1 - \frac{dL}{L} = 2 \ln 1¼ = 0.445 \qquad \text{(Eq 139)}$$

For loading paths in which all the stresses increase in the same ratio, that is, proportional loading, where

$$\frac{d\sigma_1}{\sigma_1} = \frac{d\sigma_2}{\sigma_2} = \frac{d\sigma_3}{\sigma_3} \qquad \text{(Eq 140)}$$

the plastic strains depend only on the final state of stress.

Prandtl-Reuss Equations. General three-dimensional equations relating the increments of total strain to the stress deviations are known as the Lévy-Mises equations. These are:

$$\frac{dE_{xx}}{\sigma'_{xx}} = \frac{dE_{yy}}{\sigma'_{yy}} = \frac{dE_{zz}}{\sigma'_{zz}} = \frac{dE_{yz}}{\sigma_{yz}} = \frac{dE_{zx}}{\sigma_{zx}} = \frac{dE_{xy}}{\sigma_{xy}} = d\lambda' \qquad \text{(Eq 141)}$$

or $d\varepsilon_{ij} = \sigma'_{ij} d\lambda'$ where σ'_{ij} is the stress deviator tensor and $d\lambda'$ is a nonnegative constant that may vary. The total strain increments are assumed equal to the plastic strain increments. The elastic strains are ignored. Applications thus are limited to problems of large plastic flow. Equations that expand Eq 141 to include both elastic and plastic components of strain are known as the Prandtl-Reuss equations. The plastic strain increment is assumed at any instant of loading to be proportional to the instantaneous stress deviation; that is:

$$\frac{dE_{xx}{}^P}{\sigma'_{xx}} = \frac{dE_{yy}{}^P}{\sigma'_{yy}} = \frac{dE_{zz}{}^P}{\sigma'_{zz}} = \frac{dE_{xy}{}^P}{\sigma_{xy}} = \frac{dE_{yz}{}^P}{\sigma_{yz}} = \frac{dE_{zx}{}^P}{\sigma_{zx}} = d\lambda' \qquad \text{(Eq 142)}$$

or

$$dE_{ij}{}^P = \sigma'_{ij} d\lambda'$$

Because elastic strains are not considered in Eq 141, they apply only for an ideal (rigid) plastic solid for which the elastic strain is small compared with the plastic strain. Equation 141 can be written as:

$$\frac{dE_{xx} - dE_{yy}}{\sigma'_{xx} - \sigma'_{yy}} = \frac{dE_{yy} - dE_{zz}}{\sigma'_{yy} - \sigma'_{zz}} = \frac{dE_{zz} - dE_{xx}}{\sigma'_{zz} - \sigma'_{xx}} = \frac{dE_{yz}}{\sigma_{yz}} = \frac{dE_{xz}}{\sigma_{xz}} = \frac{dE_{xy}}{\sigma_{xy}} = d\lambda'$$

$$\text{(Eq 143)}$$

which can be written in terms of the actual stresses:

$$dE_x = \frac{2}{3} d\lambda \left[\sigma_x - \frac{1}{2} (\sigma_y + \sigma_z) \right]$$

$$dE_y = \frac{2}{3} d\lambda \left[\sigma_y - \frac{1}{2} (\sigma_z + \sigma_x) \right]$$

$$dE_z = \frac{2}{3} d\lambda \left[\sigma_z - \frac{1}{2} (\sigma_x + \sigma_y) \right]$$

$$dE_{yz} = d\lambda' \sigma_{yz} \qquad dE_{xz} = d\lambda' \sigma_{xz} \qquad dE_{xy} = d\lambda' \sigma_{xy} \qquad \text{(Eq 144)}$$

To evaluate the constant $d\lambda'$, the invariant plastic strain, the effective strain, $\bar{E}$, is used:

$$d\bar{E} = \frac{\sqrt{2}}{3} [(dE_x - dE_y)^2 + (dE_y - dE_z)^2 + (dE_z - dE_x)^2 + 6(dE_{xy})^2$$

$$+ 6(dE_{yz})^2 + 6(dE_{xz})^2]^{1/2} \qquad \text{(Eq 145)}$$

Substituting Eq 144 into Eq 145 gives:

$$d\bar{E} = \frac{2}{3} d\lambda' \left\{ \frac{1}{\sqrt{2}} [(\sigma_x - \sigma_y)^2 + (\sigma_y - \sigma_z)^2 + (\sigma_z - \sigma_x)^2 + 6(\tau_{xy}{}^2 + \tau_{yz}{}^2 \right.$$

$$\left. + \tau_{xz}{}^2)]^{1/2} \right\}$$

$$d\bar{E} = \frac{2}{3} d\lambda' \bar{\sigma}$$

From this:

$$dE_x = \frac{d\bar{E}}{\bar{\sigma}} [\sigma_x - \frac{1}{2} (\sigma_y + \sigma_z)] \qquad\qquad dE_{yz} = \frac{3}{2} \frac{d\bar{E}}{\bar{\sigma}} \sigma_{yz}$$

$$dE_y = \frac{d\bar{E}}{\bar{\sigma}} [\sigma_y - \frac{1}{2} (\sigma_z + \sigma_x)] \qquad\qquad dE_{xz} = \frac{3}{2} \frac{d\bar{E}}{\bar{\sigma}} \sigma_{xz}$$

$$dE_z = \frac{d\bar{E}}{\bar{\sigma}} [\sigma_z - \frac{1}{2} (\sigma_x + \sigma_y)] \qquad\qquad dE_{xy} = \frac{3}{2} \frac{d\bar{E}}{\bar{\sigma}} \sigma_{xy} \qquad \text{(Eq 146)}$$

The term $d\bar{E}/\bar{\sigma}$ can be evaluated from the effective stress-effective strain curve. Equations 146 resemble the equations for Hooke's law. Instead of a fixed Young's modulus, the equations have a variable plastic modulus $\bar{\sigma}/d\bar{E}$, and Poisson's ratio is ½.

If the principal directions are considered, Eq 142 can be written:

$$\frac{dE_1{}^P}{\sigma_1'} = \frac{dE_2{}^P}{\sigma_2'} = \frac{dE_3{}^P}{\sigma_3'} = d\lambda' \qquad \text{(Eq 147)}$$

Equation 142 can be written also in terms of the actual stresses as:

$$dE_x{}^P = \frac{2}{3} d\lambda' \left[\sigma_x - \frac{1}{2}(\sigma_y + \sigma_z) \right]$$

$$dE_y{}^P = \frac{2}{3} d\lambda' \left[\sigma_y - \frac{1}{2}(\sigma_z + \sigma_x) \right]$$

$$dE_z{}^P = \frac{2}{3} d\lambda' \left[\sigma_z - \frac{1}{2}(\sigma_x + \sigma_y) \right]$$

$$dE_{xy}{}^P = d\lambda \sigma_{xy} \qquad dE_{yz}{}^P = d\lambda \sigma_{yz} \qquad dE_{zx}{}^P = d\lambda \sigma_{zx} \qquad \text{(Eq 148)}$$

To determine $d\lambda'$, Eq 142 is used:

$$(dE_x{}^P - dE_y{}^P)^2 + (dE_y{}^P - dE_z{}^P)^2 + (dE_z{}^P - dE_x{}^P)^2 + 6(dE_{xy}{}^P)^2$$
$$+ 6(dE_{yz}{}^P)^2 + 6(dE_{zx}{}^P)^2 = (d\lambda')^2 [(\sigma_x - \sigma_y)^2 + (\sigma_y - \sigma_z)^2$$
$$+ (\sigma_z - \sigma_x)^2 + 6\sigma_{xy}{}^2 + 6\sigma_{yz}{}^2 + 6\sigma_{zx}{}^2] \qquad \text{(Eq 149)}$$

Loading and Unloading Criteria. For a material in a plastic state at which the yield function vanishes:

$$f(\sigma_{ij}, E_{ij}{}^{(p)}, \kappa) = 0 \qquad \text{(Eq 150)}$$

If the time rate of f is considered, that is:

$$\dot{f} = \frac{\partial f}{\partial \sigma_{ij}} \dot{\sigma}_{ij} + \frac{\partial f}{\partial E_{ij}{}^{(p)}} \dot{E}_{ij}{}^{(p)} + \frac{\partial f}{\partial \kappa} \dot{\kappa} \qquad \text{(Eq 151)}$$

then $f = 0$ and $\dot{f} < 0$ at a time t would imply $f < 0$ the next instant of time. The criteria for unloading and loading in a plastic state are:

$$\frac{\partial f}{\partial \sigma_{ij}} \dot{\sigma}_{ij} < 0, \quad f = 0 \qquad \text{(Eq 152)}$$

during unloading;

$$\frac{\partial f}{\partial \sigma_{ij}} \dot{\sigma}_{ij} = 0, \quad f = 0 \qquad \text{(Eq 153)}$$

during neutral loading; and:

$$\frac{\partial f}{\partial \sigma_{ij}} \dot{\sigma}_{ij} > 0, \quad f = 0 \qquad \text{(Eq 154)}$$

during loading.

Flow Rule for Work-Hardening Materials. For work-hardening stable materials, the yield surface and all subsequent loading surfaces must be convex. An increment of stress $d\sigma_{ij}$ can be seen as a vector $d\mathbf{S}$ in the nine-dimensional stress space, and the corresponding plastic strains $dE_{ij}^{(p)}$ as the components of a vector $d\mathbf{E}$ in the same space. Then:

$$d\mathbf{S} \cdot d\mathbf{E} = |d\mathbf{S}| \, |d\mathbf{E}| \cos \psi \geqq 0 \qquad \text{(Eq 155)}$$

which implies that:

$$-\frac{\pi}{2} \leq \psi \leq \frac{\pi}{2} \qquad \text{(Eq 156)}$$

which is an indication of an acute angle between $d\mathbf{S}$ and $d\mathbf{E}$. The plastic strain increment vector must be normal to the loading surface at a regular point, and the vector must lie between adjacent normals to the loading surface at a surface corner. The rate of change in plastic strain must be a linear function of the rate of stress change. For the plastic strain rate vector at a smooth point P in Fig. 3 of the loading surface:

$$\dot{E}_{ij}^{(p)} = d\lambda' \, \frac{\partial f}{\partial \sigma_{ij}} \qquad \text{(Eq 157)}$$

where $d\lambda'$ is a function that may depend on stress, stress rate, strain, and strain history. Because subsequent loading surfaces pass through the loading point:

$$f(\sigma_{ij}, E_{ij}^{(p)}, \kappa) = 0 \qquad \text{(Eq 158)}$$

which is called the consistency condition, where loading from one plastic state leads to another. With κ a function of $e_{ij}^{(p)}$, then during loading:

$$\dot{f} = \frac{\partial f}{\partial \sigma_{ij}} \, \dot{\sigma}_{ij} + \frac{\partial f}{\partial E_{ij}^{(p)}} \, \dot{E}_{ij}^{(p)} + \frac{\partial f}{\partial \kappa} \, \frac{\partial \kappa}{\partial E_{ij}^{(p)}} \, \dot{E}_{ij}^{(p)} = 0 \qquad \text{(Eq 159)}$$

Substituting Eq 157 into Eq 159 gives:

$$d\lambda' = -\frac{\dfrac{\partial f}{\partial \sigma_{kl}} \, \dot{\sigma}_{kl}}{\left(\dfrac{\partial f}{\partial E_{ij}^{(p)}} + \dfrac{\partial f}{\partial \kappa} \, \dfrac{\partial \kappa}{\partial E_{ij}^{(p)}} \right) \dfrac{\partial f}{\partial \sigma_{ij}}} \qquad \text{(Eq 160)}$$

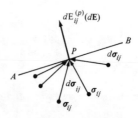

Figure 3   Possible stress increments corresponding to a plastic strain increment $d\mathbf{E}$.

and combining this result with Eq 157 yields:

$$\dot{E}_{ij}{}^{(p)} = \hat{G} \, \frac{\partial f}{\partial \sigma_{ij}} \frac{\partial f}{\partial \sigma_{kl}} \, \dot{\sigma}_{kl} \qquad \text{(Eq 161)}$$

where

$$\hat{G} = - \cfrac{1}{\left(\cfrac{\partial f}{\partial E_{mn}{}^{(p)}} + \cfrac{\partial f}{\partial \kappa} \cfrac{\partial \kappa}{\partial E_{mn}{}^{(p)}} \right) \cfrac{\partial f}{\partial \sigma_{mn}}}$$

For a surface composed of individual smooth loading surfaces f_p that meet to form corners, if loading surfaces described by $f_p = 0$ act independently, the total plastic deformation can be written as:

$$\dot{E}_{ij}{}^{(p)} = \sum_{p=1}^{n} C_p h_p \frac{\partial f_p}{\partial \sigma_{ij}} \frac{\partial f_p}{\partial \sigma_{kl}} \, \dot{\sigma}_{kl} \qquad \text{(Eq 162)}$$

where $C_p = 0$ if $f_p < 0$, or $(\partial f_p / \partial \sigma_{ij}) \dot{\sigma}_{ij} < 0$; $C_p = 1$ if $f_p = 0$, and $(\partial f_p / \partial \sigma_{ij}) \dot{\sigma}_{ij} \geq 0$; and h_p quantities are positive functions of stress, strain, and strain history.

Example 2. If $f = J_2 - \kappa$, where J_2 is the second invariant of the stress deviation and κ is a hardening parameter that depends on plastic deformation, then the flow rule at yielding is:

$$\dot{E}_{ij}{}^{(p)} = \hat{G} \, \frac{\partial f}{\partial \sigma_{ij}} \frac{\partial f}{\partial \sigma_{kl}} \, \dot{\sigma}_{kl} = \hat{G} \left(\frac{\partial f}{\partial J_2} \frac{\partial J_2}{\partial \sigma'_{ij}} \right) \left(\frac{\partial J_2}{\partial \sigma'_{kl}} \frac{d\sigma'_{kl}}{dt} \right)$$

$$= \hat{G} \sigma'_{ij} \dot{J}_2$$

for $\dot{J}_2 \geq 0$.

Subsequent Loading Surfaces. To determine subsequent loading surfaces as plastic flow proceeds, the manner in which plastic deformation $E_{ij}{}^{(p)}$ enters into the loading surface must be considered:

$$f(\sigma_{ij}, E_{ij}{}^{(p)}, \kappa) = 0 \qquad \text{(Eq 163)}$$

Laws describing this behavior are called hardening rules. If plastic deformation is assumed to be independent of hydrostatic pressure, the loading surfaces in the principal stress space can be seen as cylinders of infinite length perpendicular to the π-plane $\sigma_1 + \sigma_2 + \sigma_3 = 0$. Several proposed hardening rules are shown in Fig. 4. In Fig. 4(a) is Tresca's initial yield surface, a regular hexagon on the π-plane $\sigma_1 + \sigma_2 + \sigma_3 = 0$. Isotropic hardening, which assumes a uniform expansion of the initial yield surface, is shown in Fig. 4(b). The subsequent yield surfaces may be written as:

$$f = f(J_2, J_3) - \kappa = 0 \qquad \text{(Eq 164)}$$

where κ depends on the plastic strain history. Figure 4(c) illustrates Prager's kinematic hardening. The initial yield surface translates in the π-plane without rotation and without change in size. In general, the loading surface may be expressed as:

$$f(\sigma_{ij} - \alpha_{ij}) = 0 \qquad \text{(Eq 165)}$$

where α_{ij} represents translation of the center of the initial yield surface. If linear hardening is assumed, then:

$$\dot{\alpha}_{ij} = c\dot{E}_{ij}^{(p)} \qquad \text{(Eq 166)}$$

where c is a constant. From Eq 165 and Eq 166:

$$d\lambda' = \frac{1}{c}\frac{(\partial f/\partial \sigma_{ij})\dot{\sigma}_{ij}}{(\partial f/\partial \sigma_{kl})(\partial f/\partial \sigma_{kl})} \qquad \text{(Eq 167)}$$

Prager's kinematic hardening rule was modified by Ziegler by replacing Eq 166 with the relationship:

$$\dot{\alpha}_{ij} = \dot{\mu}(\sigma_{ij} - \alpha_{ij}) \qquad \text{(Eq 168)}$$

where $\dot{\mu} > 0$. The direction of motion of the center of the initial yield surface agrees with the radius vector that joins the instantaneous center α_{ij} with the load point σ_{ij}, as shown in Fig. 4(d).

VISCOELASTIC SOLIDS

Constitutive Equations. For viscoelastic media, the constitutive equations relating stress and deformation vary from one medium to another. In viscoelasticity, the predominating irreversibility is caused by the dissipation of energy by the stress tensor during nonequilibrium processes. The thermal effects are usually neglected. The stress tensor is related to the strain tensor through the following general differential equation, where the dots indicate time derivatives:

$$\ldots \tilde{\tilde{B}}_{ijkr}\ddot{\sigma}_{kr} + \tilde{B}_{ijkr}\dot{\sigma}_{kr} + \sigma_{ij} = C_{ij} + C_{ijkr}E_{kr} + \tilde{C}_{ijkr}\dot{E}_{kr} + \ldots \qquad \text{(Eq 169)}$$

where E_{kr} is the Lagrangian linear strain tensor and $C_{ij}, C_{ijkr} \ldots, \tilde{B}_{ijkr} \ldots$

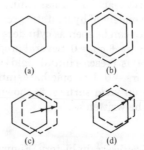

(a)   (b)

(c)   (d)

Figure 4   Hardening rules. (a) Initial yield condition, (b) isotropic hardening, (c) kinematic hardening, (d) modified kinematic hardening

are coefficients. When the coefficients are assumed to be constants and the displacement derivatives small, the governing theory is called linear visco-elasticity. The elastic-plastic results just described are typical of those obtained by slow application of the load in a testing machine. Under rapid loading, the material's intrinsic characteristics usually cause deviations from Eq 169. Also, if the strain is large, the characteristic stress-strain laws for metals are generally nonlinear.

Creep Behavior. The progressive deformation, or time-dependent plastic flow, of a material at constant stress is called creep. The engineering creep curve of a metal is determined by applying a constant load to a tensile specimen maintained at a constant temperature, and the strain (extension) of the specimen is determined as a function of time. General procedures for creep testing are described in ASTM E139-69.

A simple tension specimen of lead wire under a constant tension load produces a creep curve as illustrated in Fig. 5. After an initial extension, the rate of strain decreases gradually, remains nearly constant for a period, then accelerates until the specimen breaks. The three stages of creep are called, respectively, the primary, the secondary, and the tertiary creep. Curve A demonstrates an idealized creep curve. The slope ($d\mathrm{E}/dt$ or $\dot{\mathrm{E}}$) is the creep rate. The constant-stress creep curve represents the superposition of two separate creep processes that occur after the sudden strain. The first component is a transient creep with a creep rate decreasing with time, and the second is constant-rate viscous creep (Fig. 6). The creep curve can be approximated by:

$$\mathrm{E} = \mathrm{E}_0(1 + \beta t^{1/3})e^{(-K_4 t)} \tag{Eq 170}$$

where ε is the strain in time t, β and $-K_4$ are constants and β is the transient creep. The constant K_4 describes a constant-rate extension per unit length. The creep curve also can be approximated by:

$$\mathrm{E} = \mathrm{E}_0 + \mathrm{E}_t(1 - e^{-rt}) + \dot{\mathrm{E}}_s t \tag{Eq 171}$$

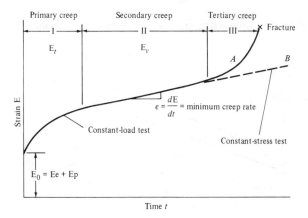

Figure 5 Typical creep curve

where

E_0 = the instantaneous strain on loading
E_t = the limit for transient creep
 r = the ratio of transient creep rate to the transient creep strain
$\dot{E}_s = E_s$ = the steady-state creep rate

If a creep test is performed at constant stress, the final stage of accelerated elongation generally does not appear. As shown in Fig. 5, the creep curve at constant load differs considerably from that at constant stress.

Empirical Equations for Creep Behavior. Equations developed to predict creep behavior in such problems as bending, torsion, internal pressure, and rotation are often a compromise between accuracy and simplicity. Justification must be sought through experimentation with problem models. The first three stages of a typical creep curve might require four terms to describe total strain:

$$E = E_e + E_p + E_t + E_v \tag{Eq 172}$$

where E_e, E_p, E_t and E_v are the elastic, plastic, transient creep, and quasi-viscous creep components (Fig. 7). Assuming constant temperature, E_e and E_p are functions of stress only, while E_t and E_v are functions of stress and time. As shown in Fig. 8(a), the values of E_e and E_p may be visualized from a static stress-strain diagram. From Hooke's law, $\sigma = E\text{E}$, the elastic strain is

$$E_e = \frac{\sigma_P}{E} \tag{Eq 173}$$

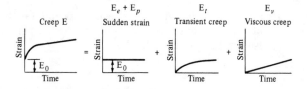

Figure 6   Competing processes determining a creep curve

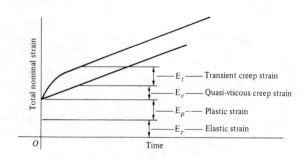

Figure 7

where σ_P is the proportional limit stress, and E is the strain produced. If $\sigma = \sigma_P + K_1 E_p^{K_2}$ represents the plastic portion of the curve, the initial plastic strain can be expressed by the power function:

$$E_p = \left(\frac{\sigma - \sigma_P}{K_1}\right)^{1/K_2} \qquad \text{(Eq 174)}$$

where K_1 and K_2 are constants found by experiment. If σ is less than σ_P, plastic strain does not exist, and the elastic strain is determined from Hooke's law. The first stage of the creep curve as shown in Fig. 8(b) also may be described by using a continuous function for the static stress-strain diagram given by:

$$\sigma = A E^n \qquad \text{(Eq 175)}$$

where E is the total initial strain, and A and n are constants. The sum of the first two terms of Eq 172 becomes:

$$E_e + E_p = E = \left(\frac{\sigma}{A}\right)^{1/n} \qquad \text{(Eq 176)}$$

The mathematical form of the last two terms of Eq 172 can be expressed in a manner similar to that of Eq 170, that is:

$$E_t = K_3(1 - e^{-K_4 t}) \qquad \text{(Eq 177)}$$

and

$$E_v = K_5 t \qquad \text{(Eq 178)}$$

where K_3, K_4, and K_5 are determined experimentally. Although K_4 may be assumed a constant, K_3 and K_5 are functions of stress. In evaluating K_5, consider the first derivative of Eq 172 with respect to time. Since E_e and E_p are independent of time:

$$\frac{dE}{dt} = \frac{dE_t}{dt} + \frac{dE_v}{dt} = K_3 K_4 e^{-K_4 t} + K_5$$

After a relatively short time under moderate temperature and stress, the first term essentially vanishes. Creep rate C becomes:

$$C = \frac{dE}{dt} = K_5 \qquad \text{(Eq 179)}$$

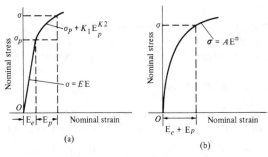

(a)

(b)

Figure 8

For a given temperature, a straight line equation may be written $\log C = \log K_6 + m \log \sigma$ where m (greater than unity) is the slope and K_6 is creep rate C when stress σ is unity. Using the antilog of this expression produces:

$$C = K_6 \sigma^m \qquad \text{(Eq 180)}$$

For many metals, this power function is a realistic evaluation of K_5 in Eq 179 where K_6 is an arbitrary constant. For the transient creep strain component E_t, there is experimental and mathematical justification for assuming the power function:

$$K_3 = K_7 \sigma^p \qquad \text{(Eq 181)}$$

where K_7 and p are constants and $p > 1$.

Creep at Lower Temperatures. High-temperature creep is predominantly steady-state or viscous creep, while below about one-half the melting point $(T_m/2)$, transient, or primary, creep predominates. A general equation for the time laws of creep is:

$$\dot{E} = At^{-n'} \qquad \text{(Eq 182)}$$

where A and n' are empirical constants. Different types of creep behavior can be described by Eq 182 depending on the value of n'. If $n' = 0$, the creep rate is constant. When $n' = 1$, Eq 182 becomes:

$$E = \alpha \ln t \qquad \text{(Eq 183)}$$

where α is a constant. Equation 183 describes logarithmic creep at low temperatures. When $n' = \dfrac{2}{3}$, Eq 182 becomes, for transient creep:

$$E = \beta t^{1/3} \qquad \text{(Eq 184)}$$

Logarithmic creep occurs at low temperatures and low stresses, where recovery cannot occur.

Temperature and Steady-State Creep. Steady-state or secondary creep predominates at temperatures above about $T_m/2$. If it is assumed that creep is a singly activated process, it can be expressed by:

$$\dot{E} = Ae^{-\Delta H/RT} \qquad \text{(Eq 185)}$$

where

ΔH = activation energy for the rate-controlling process
A = a constant containing the frequency of vibration of the flow unit, entropy change, and a factor that depends on the structure of the material
T = absolute temperature
R = universal gas constant, 1.987 cal/(mol)($^\circ$K)

Assuming that A remains constant with small temperature changes, and using a differential temperature change in the creep test, then:

$$\dot{E}_1 e^{\Delta H/RT_1} = A = \dot{E}_2 e^{\Delta H/RT_2} \qquad \Delta H = R\left(\ln \frac{\dot{E}_1}{\dot{E}_2}\right)\left(\frac{T_1 T_2}{T_1 - T_2}\right) \qquad \text{(Eq 186)}$$

High-Temperature Creep. When the recovery rate is fast enough and the strain-hardening rate slow enough so that a balance is reached, a steady-state creep condition referred to as recovery creep occurs. If the strain-hardening rate is $h = \partial\sigma/\partial E$ and the recovery rate is $r = -\partial\sigma/\partial t$, then for a steady-state creep rate E_s, the flow stress remains constant at $d\sigma = \dfrac{\partial\sigma}{\partial t}\,dt + \dfrac{\partial\sigma}{\partial E}\,dE = 0$ and:

$$\dot{E}_s = \frac{dE}{dt} = -\frac{\partial\sigma/\partial t}{\partial\sigma/\partial E} = \frac{r}{h} \tag{Eq 187}$$

Viscoelastic Models. Viscoelastic stress-strain laws can be illustrated by equivalent one-dimensional mechanical models. A linear elastic solid may be visualized as an elastic spring with a linear relationship between the applied force on the spring and the corresponding stretching of the spring:

$$P = Ky \tag{Eq 188}$$

where P = the applied force; y = the elongation or compression of the spring; K = the linear spring constant.

The corresponding elastic or generalized Hooke's law becomes:

$$\sigma_{ij} = C_{ijkr}E_{kr} \tag{Eq 189}$$

where σ_{ij} is substituted for P, C_{ijkr} for K, and E_{kr} for y, in Eq 188. A linear viscous medium may be illustrated by a linear dashpot, with a linear relationship existing between the applied force and the time rate of deformation of the dashpot; that is:

$$P = C\dot{y} \tag{Eq 190}$$

A series of mechanical models of viscoelastic materials is given in Table 3.

Examples of Creep Behavior. Two examples of creep behavior are described below.

Example 1. A typical creep equation for annealed 304 stainless steel is:

$$E = E_L + E_x(1 - e^{-st}) + E_t(1 - e^{-rt}) + \dot{E}_s t \tag{Eq 191}$$

where

$$E_L = \text{loading strain}$$

$$E_x = 0 \text{ for } \sigma \leqq 6000 \text{ psi}$$

$$= G + H\sigma \text{ for } \sigma > 6000 \text{ psi}$$

$$s = D\left[\sinh\left(\frac{\beta_r\sigma}{n^r}\right)\right]^{n_r}\exp\left(-\frac{Q}{RT}\right)$$

$$r = B\left[\sinh\left(\frac{\beta_r\sigma}{n_r}\right)\right]^{n_r}\exp\left(-\frac{Q}{RT}\right)$$

Table 3 Viscoelastic materials

Model	Name	Differential equation		Creep compliance, $J(t)$
			Inequalities	
	Elastic solid	$\sigma = C_0 E$		$1/C_0$
	Viscous fluid	$\sigma = C_1 \dot{E}$		t/C_1
	Maxwell fluid	$\dot{\sigma} + B_1 \sigma = C_1 \dot{E}$		$(B_1 + t)/C_1$
	Kelvin solid	$\sigma = C_0 E + C_1 \dot{E}$		$\dfrac{1}{C_0}(1 - E^{-\lambda t}), \lambda = \dfrac{C_0}{C_1}$
	3-parameter solid	$\sigma + B_1 \dot{\sigma} = C_0 E + C_1 \dot{E}$	$C_1 > B_1 C_0$	$\dfrac{B_1}{C_1}E^{-\lambda t} + \dfrac{1}{C_0}(1 - E^{-\lambda t})$, $\lambda = C_0/C_1$
	3-parameter fluid	$\sigma + B_1 \dot{\sigma} = C_1 \dot{E} + C_2 \ddot{E}$	$B_1 C_1 > C_2$	$\dfrac{t}{C_1} + \dfrac{B_1 C_1 - C_2}{C_1^2}(1 - E^{-\lambda t})$, $\lambda = C_1/C_2$
	4-parameter fluid	$\sigma + B_1 \dot{\sigma} + B_2 \ddot{\sigma} = C_1 \dot{E} + C_2 \ddot{E}$	$B_1 C_1 > C_2, B_1^2 > 4B_2$ $B_1 C_1 C_2 > B_2 C_1^2 + C_2^2$	$\dfrac{t}{C_1} + \dfrac{B_1 C_1 - C_2}{C_1^2}(1 - E^{-\lambda t})$ $+ \dfrac{B_2}{C_2}E^{-\lambda t}, \lambda = C_1/C_2$

Table 3 Viscoelastic materials (continued)

Model	Name	Differential equation		Creep compliance, $J(t)$
			Inequalities	
	4-parameter solid	$\sigma + B_1\dot{\sigma} = C_0 E + C_1\dot{E} + C_2\ddot{E}$ $C_1 > B_1C_0,\ C_1^2 > 4C_0C_2$ $C_1B_1 > C_0B_1^2 + C_2$		$\dfrac{1 + B_1\lambda_1}{C_2\lambda_1(\lambda_2 - \lambda_1)}(1 - \mathrm{E}^{-\lambda_1 t})$ $+ \dfrac{1 + B_1\lambda_2}{C_2\lambda_2(\lambda_1 - \lambda_2)}(1 - \mathrm{E}^{-\lambda_2 t})$ where λ_1, λ_2 are roots of $C_2\lambda^2 - C_1\lambda + C_0 = 0$

Name	Relaxation modulus, $Y(t)$	Complex compliance	
		Real part, $G_1(\omega)$	Imaginary part, $G_2(\omega)$
Elastic solid	C_0	$1/C_0$	0
Viscous fluid	$C_1\delta(t)$	0	$-1/C_1\omega$
Maxwell fluid	$\dfrac{C_1}{B_1}e^{-t/B_1}$	$\dfrac{B_1}{C_1}$	$-\dfrac{1}{C_1\omega}$
Kelvin solid	$C_0 + C_1\delta(t)$	$\dfrac{C_0}{C_0^2 + C_1^2\omega^2}$	$-\dfrac{C_1\omega}{C_0^2 + C_1^2\omega^2}$
3-parameter solid	$\dfrac{C_1}{B_1}e^{-t/B_1} + C_0(1 - e^{-t/B_1})$	$\dfrac{C_0 + B_1C_1\omega^2}{C_0^2 + C_1^2\omega^2}$	$-\dfrac{(C_1 - C_0B_1)\omega}{C_0^2 + C_1^2\omega^2}$

(continued)

Table 3 Viscoelastic materials (continued)

Model	Relaxation modulus, $Y(t)$	Complex compliance	
		Real part, $G_1(\omega)$	Imaginary part, $G_2(\omega)$
3-parameter fluid	$\dfrac{C_2}{B_1}\delta(t) + \dfrac{1}{B_1}\left(C_1 - \dfrac{C_2}{B_1}\right)e^{-t/B_1}$	$\dfrac{B_1C_1 - C_2}{C_1^2 + C_2^2\omega^2}$	$-\dfrac{C_1 + B_1C_2\omega^2}{(C_1^2 + C_2^2\omega^2)\,\omega}$
4-parameter fluid	$\dfrac{1}{\sqrt{B_1^2 - 4B_2}}\big[(C_1 - \alpha C_2)e^{-\alpha t}$ $- (C_1 - \beta C_2)e^{-\beta t}\big]$ $\left.\begin{array}{c}\alpha\\\beta\end{array}\right\} = \dfrac{1}{2B_2}\left(B_1 \pm \sqrt{B_1^2 - 4B_2}\right)$	$\dfrac{(B_1C_1 - C_2) + B_2C_2\omega^2}{C_1^2 + C_2^2\omega^2}$	$-\dfrac{C_1 + (C_2B_1 - B_2C_1)\omega^2}{(C_1^2 + C_2^2\omega^2)\,\omega}$
4-parameter solid	$\dfrac{C_2}{B_1}\delta(t) + \dfrac{C_1B_1 - C_2}{B_1^2}$ $- \dfrac{1}{B_1^2}(C_1B_1 - C_0B_1^2 - C_2)(1 - e^{-t/B_1})$	$\dfrac{C_0 + (B_1C_1 - C_2)\omega^2 + C_2^2\omega^4}{C_0^2 + (C_1^2 - 2C_0C_2)\omega^2 + C_2^2\omega^4}$	$-\dfrac{(C_1 - B_1C_0)\omega + C_2B_1\omega^3}{C_0^2 + (C_1^2 - 2C_0C_2)\omega^2 + C_2^2\omega^4}$

$$\dot{E}_m = A \left[\sinh \left(\frac{\beta_e \sigma}{n_e} \right) \right]^{n_e} \exp \left(-\frac{Q}{RT} \right) \qquad E_t = C \frac{\dot{E}_m}{r}$$

and referring to Eq 172:

$$E_L = E_e + E_p \qquad E_t = E_x(1 - e^{-st}) + E_t(1 - e^{-rt}) \qquad E_v = \dot{E}_s t$$

The expression for E is valid for stress values less than σ_{max} given below:

Temp, °C (°F) 427 (800) 482 (900) 538 (1000) 593 (1100) 649 (1200) 704 (1300)
σ_{max}, psi   25,000   25,000   25,000   25,000   22,000   18,000

Values for various parameters at varying temperatures are given in Table 4 for annealed 304 stainless steel.

Example 2. Two different types of creep behavior generally are exhibited by 2¼ Cr-1 Mo steel. Moreover, the material can display significant strength variations due to heat treatment and other effects. For both types of creep behavior, creep time, and strain can be related by:

$$E_c = \frac{Cpt}{1 + pt} + \dot{E}_s t \qquad\qquad \text{(Eq 192)}$$

where

E_c = creep strain, %; t = time, h.

The parameters C, p, and $\dot{E}_s$ have two sets of values corresponding to the two types of creep behavior. Parameters C, p, and $\dot{E}_s$ will be used with Type I creep, and C', p', and $\dot{E}_s'$ refer to Type II creep (see Fig. 9). For 2¼ Cr-1 Mo steel, the values of these parameters are given by the following equations where logarithms are common logs (base 10).

Type I creep

$$\log C = 1.0328 + \frac{168680}{TU} - 0.023772\, U + 0.0079141\, U \log \sigma$$

$$\log p = 7.6026 + 3.3396 \log \sigma - 12323/T$$

$$\log \dot{E}_s = 6.7475 + 0.011426\, \sigma + \frac{987.72}{U} \log \sigma - \frac{13494}{T}$$

Type II creep

$$\log C' = -0.051086 + \frac{140730}{TU} - 0.01\, U + 0.0037345\, U \log \sigma$$

$$\log p' = 8.1242 + 0.017678\, \sigma + \frac{404.63}{U} \log \sigma - 11659/T$$

$$\log \dot{E}_s' = 11.498 - 8.2226\, U/T - 20448/T + \frac{5862.4}{T} \log \sigma$$

Table 4 Parameter values for creep equation, annealed 304 stainless steel

Parameter	Value of parameter		
	At 427 to 453.9 °C (800 to 849.9 °F)	At 454 to 537.9 °C (850 to 999.9 °F)	At 538 to 592.9 °C (1000 to 1099.9 °F)
G, %	0	$2.24449 - 3.08457 \times 10^{-3} T(°K)$	-0.257143
H, %/psi	0	$-3.74081 \times 10^{-4} + 5.14244 \times 10^{-7} T(°K)$	4.28571×10^{-5}
D, hr^{-1}	2.266×10^{15}	$1.9155 \times 10^{29} \exp(-3.95522 \times 10^{-2} T)(°K)$	→
β_r, psi^{-1}	←	$-2.252 \times 10^{-4} + 5.401 \times 10^{-7} T(°K)$	→
n_r	←	3.5	→
C	$2.469 \times 10^{-3} \exp\left(\dfrac{6580.986}{T(°K)}\right)$	$56.2405 - 5.91691 \times 10^{-2} T(°K)$	→
B, hr^{-1}	←	2.518×10^{13}	→
A, %/hr	←	1.38×10^{13}	→
β_e, psi^{-1}	←	$-3.652 \times 10^{-4} + 7.518 \times 10^{-7} T(°K)$	→
n_e	←	6	→
Q, cal/mol	←	$67,000$	→
R, cal/mol − °K	←	1.987	→

Table 4 Parameter values for creep equation, annealed 304 stainless steel (continued)

Parameter	Value of parameter
	At 593 to 704 °C (1100 to 1300 °F)
G, %	-0.257143
H, %/psi	4.28571×10^{-5}
D, hr^{-1}	2.518×10^{14}
β_r, psi^{-1}	$-2.252 \times 10^{-4} + 5.401 \times 10^{-7} T(°K)$
n_r	3.5
C	5
B, hr^{-1}	2.518×10^{13}
A, %/hr	1.38×10^{13}
β_e, psi^{-1}	$-3.652 \times 10^{-4} + 7.518 \times 10^{-7} T(°K)$
n_e	6
Q, cal/mol	$67,000$
R, cal/mol·°K	1.987

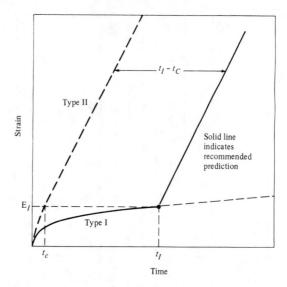

Figure 9 Method for predicting the transition from Type I to Type II creep

SELECTED REFERENCES

- Malvern, L. E., *Introduction to the Mechanics of a Continuous Medium,* Prentice-Hall, Englewood Cliffs, NJ, 1969
- Frederick, D. and Chung, T. S., *Continuum Mechanics,* Allyn and Bacon, Boston, 1965
- Fung, Y. C., *Foundations of Solid Mechanics,* Prentice-Hall, Englewood Cliffs, NJ, 1965
- Dieter, G. E., *Mechanical Metallurgy,* McGraw-Hill, New York, 1976
- Disa, F. A., *Mechanics of Metals,* Addison-Wesley, Reading, MA, 1968
- Yuan, S. W., *Foundations of Fluid Mechanics,* Prentice-Hall, Englewood Cliffs, NJ, 1967
- Sokolnikoff, I. S., *Mathematical Theory of Elasticity,* McGraw-Hill, New York, 1966
- Hughes, W. F. and Gaylord, E. W., *Basic Equations of Engineering Science,* Schaum Publishing Company, New York, 1964
- Ambartsumyan, S. A., Theory of Anisotrophic Shells, State Publishing House for Physical and Mathematical Literature, Moscow, 1961 (NASA Technical Translation Report No. NASA TT F-118)
- Flugge, Wilhelm, *Viscoelasticity,* Blaisdell Publishing Co., Waltham, MA, 1967
- Mendelson, Alexander, *Plasticity Theory and Application,* Macmillan, New York, 1970
- *Nuclear Systems Materials Handbook,* Hanford Engineering Development Laboratory, Richland, WA

20
Thermodynamics

By Richard J. Gross, Ph.D.
Department of Mechanical Engineering
University of Akron

Thermodynamics involves the study of energy. Classical thermodynamics deals with masses internally in equilibrium or masses that have a uniform temperature, a uniform pressure, and other uniform properties throughout the mass. A mass that has a uniform temperature is said to be in thermal equilibrium. Two bodies in thermal equilibrium with a third, that is, having the same temperature as the third, are in thermal equilibrium with each other. This condition is called the zeroth law of thermodynamics.

International Temperature Scale and Fixed Points. The International Temperature Scale, also called the International Practical Temperature Scale, establishes: (1) temperature values at selected fixed points, (2) equations for calculating temperatures at points between the fixed points, and (3) procedures to calibrate measuring instruments and to take measurements. The fixed point temperatures are:

Hydrogen triple point	−259.34 °C
Hydrogen boiling point at 33.33 kPa	−256.108 °C
Hydrogen boiling point at 101.325 kPa	−252.87 °C
Neon boiling point at 101.325 kPa	−246.048 °C
Oxygen triple point	−218.789 °C
Oxygen boiling point at 101.325 kPa	−182.962 °C
Water triple point	0.01 °C
Water boiling point at 101.325 kPa	100.00 °C
Zinc freezing point at 101.325 kPa	419.58 °C
Silver freezing point at 101.325 kPa	961.93 °C
Gold freezing point at 101.325 kPa	1064.43 °C

Temperatures are measured by the following instruments:

• Range 1 (−259.34 to 0 °C), platinum resistance thermometer
• Range 2 (0 to 630.74 °C), platinum resistance thermometer

- Range 3 (630.74 to 1064.43 °C), platinum versus rhodium-platinum thermo-couple
- Range 4 (above 1064.43 °C), optical thermometer

Significant fixed points have been calculated for the following temperature scales:

Temperature scale	Absolute zero	Ice point	Water triple point(a)	Water steam point
Celsius (°C)	−237.15	0.00	0.01	100.00
Fahrenheit (°F).......	−459.67	32.00	32.02	212.00
Kelvin (K)	0.00	273.15	273.16	373.15
Rankine (°R)	0.00	491.67	491.69	671.67

(a) The water triple point is the condition where ice, liquid water, and water vapor can exist in equilibrium.

Conservation of Mass. The principle of conservation of mass can be written for either a fixed amount of mass, called a closed system, or a fixed region of space, called a control volume. Mass can either enter or leave a control volume. In a closed system the formulation is mass = constant.

Control Volume Formulations. The differential form for a fixed control volume is:

$$\frac{\partial \rho}{\partial t} + \frac{\partial (\rho u)}{\partial x} + \frac{\partial (\rho v)}{\partial y} + \frac{\partial (\rho w)}{\partial z} = 0$$

where ρ = mass density; t = time; u, v, w = velocity in the x, y, and z directions, respectively (Fig. 1).

The integral form for a fixed control volume is:

$$\frac{\partial}{\partial t} \int_{\mathcal{V}} \rho d\mathcal{V} + \int_{A} \rho (\vec{u} \cdot \hat{n}) dA = 0 \qquad \text{(Eq 1)}$$

where
ρ = mass density
t = time
$\mathcal{V}$ = volume of control volume
A = surface area of control volume
$\vec{u}$ = velocity of fluid entering or leaving the control volume and measured relative to the control surface
$\hat{n}$ = unit vector facing outward from the control surface of the control volume and normal to the control surface at each point where mass flows into or out of the control volume

The integral form for a moving control volume (Fig. 2) is:

$$\frac{d}{dt}\int_{V}\rho\,dV + \int_{A}\rho(\vec{u}\cdot\hat{n})\,dA = 0$$

where ρ, t, V, A, $\vec{u}$, $\hat{n}$ are defined in the same way as for the control volume fixed with respect to the x, y, z coordinate system in Eq 1.

FIRST LAW OF THERMODYNAMICS CONSERVATION OF ENERGY

One of the fundamental laws of thermodynamics is that energy cannot be created or destroyed. Energy can only be converted from one form to another, for example from potential to kinetic energy, heat to work, internal energy to kinetic energy, or transferred from one mass to another as heat or work.

Closed System Formulation. The general energy equation is $Q - W = E_f = E_i$ where:

- Q = heat transfer across the system boundary as the system proceeds from state i to state f. Heat is an energy transfer across a system boundary due to a temperature difference. Heat transfer to the system is positive and heat transfer from the system is negative
- W = work transfer across the system boundary as the system proceeds from state i to state f. Work is an energy transfer across a system boundary due to a property difference other than a temperature difference. Work done by the system is positive and work done on the system is negative. The criterion for work being done by a system is that the system could pass through the same sequence of states as the system passes from state i to state f and the sole effect on the surroundings could be the raising of a weight. The criterion for work done on the system is obtained by interchanging the system and the surroundings and applying the criterion to the new system

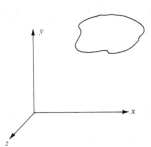

Figure 1   Control volume fixed with respect to x, y, z coordinate system

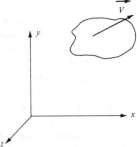

Figure 2   Moving control volume. Note: $\vec{V}$ = velocity of control volume with respect to x, y, z coordinate system

$E_f - E_i$ = energy change of the system and includes changes in internal, kinetic, potential, electrical, chemical, nuclear, or surface energies

The reduced energy equation is $Q - W' = U_f - U_i$ where:

W' = same as defined above except W' includes only work transfers due to a deformation of the control volume
$U_f - U_i$ = internal energy change of the system boundary

The reduced energy equation is a form of the principle of conservation of energy that is written by an observer on a coordinate system fixed on the center of mass of the closed system. This observer does not record any change in the kinetic and potential energies of the mass or any translation work on the mass.

Control Volume Formulation. The general energy equation for a control volume is:

$$Q - \dot{W} = \frac{d}{dt} \int_{\Psi} \rho \left(u + \frac{V^2}{2} + gz \right) d\Psi + \int_A \rho \left(h + \frac{V^2}{2} + gz \right) (\vec{u} \cdot \hat{n}) dA \quad \text{(Eq 2)}$$

where
$\dot{Q}$ = rate of heat transfer across the control surface (or open system boundary) without a mass transfer and due to a temperature difference. Heat transfer to the material inside the control volume is positive and heat transfer from the material inside the control volume is negative
$\dot{W}$ = rate of work (or power) transfer across the control surface without a mass transfer and due to a property difference other than a temperature difference. Power transfer from the material in the control volume is positive and power transfer to the material in the control volume is negative. The criterion for a power transfer by or on the material in the control volume is similar to the work criterion for a closed system (or systems). $\dot{W}$ would include the rate of work done on or by the material in the control volume also when the control volume changes size and shape
t = time
ρ = mass density
u = internal energy per unit mass. u could be interpreted as including surface energy and electromagnetic energies if involved in the process
V = velocity measured relative to a convenient frame of reference
g = local acceleration of gravity
z = elevation above some reference datum
Ψ = volume of control volume
h = enthalpy = $u + p/\rho$ where p is the absolute pressure
$\vec{u}$ = velocity of fluid leaving or entering the control volume and measured relative to the local control surface
$\hat{n}$ = unit outward normal vector at the local control surface
A = control volume surface area

The energy equation for uniform properties throughout the control volume and at each inlet and outlet is given by:

$$\dot{Q} - \dot{W} = \frac{d}{dt}\left[m_{CV}\left(u + \frac{V^2}{2} + gz\right)_{CV}\right] +$$

$$\sum_{out} \dot{m}\left(h + \frac{V^2}{2} + gz\right) - \sum_{in} \dot{m}\left(h + \frac{V^2}{2} + g\right) \qquad \text{(Eq 3)}$$

where
m_{CV} = mass in the control volume at any instant of time t
$\dot{m}$ = mass flow rate into or out of the control volume at each inlet or outlet

The time derivative d/dt in Eq 3 is used if the control volume is moving relative to the coordinate system and $\partial/\partial t$ is used if the control volume is fixed relative to the coordinate system. When a control volume is fixed relative to the coordinate system and steady state conditions and uniform properties exist:

$$\dot{Q} - \dot{W} = \sum_{out} \dot{m}\left(h + \frac{1}{2}V^2 + gz\right) - \sum_{in} \dot{m}\left(h + \frac{1}{2}V^2 + gz\right) \qquad \text{(Eq 4)}$$

The values $\dot{Q}$, $\dot{W}$, and $\dot{m}$ do not change with time.

Gibbs' equations may be applied to a process followed by a closed system or may be applied to a fixed amount of mass as it flows through a control volume. They may be applied regardless of whether the fixed amount of mass undergoes a reversible or irreversible process as long as the end points of such a process are true thermodynamic states; that is, properties are uniform throughout the fixed amount of mass. Gibbs' equations can be then applied between the inlet and outlet of a control volume for steady state conditions. Gibbs' equations are:

$$Tds = du + pdv \qquad Tds = dh - vdp$$

where T = absolute temperature; s = entropy per unit mass; p = absolute pressure; v = specific volume.

Thermodynamic Processes for a Control Volume. A steady-state process is characterized by the condition where the mass flow rates and all properties of each point in the control volume do not change with time, that is, $\partial/\partial t = 0$. Consider a control volume moving relative to one coordinate system (XYZ) and fixed relative to another (xyz) as shown in Fig. 3. The xyz observer may see a steady-state condition in his coordinate system but the XYZ observer may not. For steady state conditions seen by the xyz observer, use Eq 2 (with $d/dt = \partial/\partial t = 0$) if nonuniform properties exist throughout the control volume and at the inlet and outlet flow areas, and Eq 4 if uniform properties exist throughout the control volume and at the inlet and outlet flow areas.

A steady-flow process is characterized by the condition where $\dot{Q}$, $\dot{W}$ (Eq 2), the mass flow rate and all properties at each point of each inlet and outlet are constant in time. For example, consider an air compressor with constant

$\dot{Q}$ and $\dot{W}$. An observer on the compressor casing does not observe a steady-flow condition as there are flow-rate pulsations at the inlet and outlet. If the control surface is sufficiently far from the compressor so that flow and property fluctuations have been damped out, the process is considered a steady-flow process.

Many authors consider the terms "steady-flow" and "steady-state" as being equivalent and the same as a "steady-state, steady-flow" process described below. Use Eq 2 if properties are nonuniform and Eq 3 if properties are uniform. The steady-state, steady-flow process is characterized by:

- A control volume that is fixed relative to the coordinate system
- A condition where mass flow rate as well as all properties at each point of each inlet and outlet flow area are constant in time
- A condition where mass flow rate and all properties at each point inside the control volume are constant in time
- A condition where $\dot{Q}$ and $\dot{W}$ are constant in time

Equation 2 (with $\partial/\partial t = 0$) is used if properties are nonuniform and Eq 4 is used if properties are uniform.

The uniform state, uniform flow process is characterized by:

- A control volume that is fixed relative to the coordinate system
- A condition where properties of the mass flow rate are uniform over each inlet and outlet flow area and are constant in time, that is, the mass flow rates may change with time but the properties will not
- A condition where properties of the mass inside the control volume are uniform throughout the control volume at each instant of time, but may change with time

Equation 3 is used under these conditions.

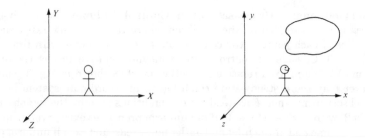

Figure 3 Relative control-volume movement. Control volume fixed relative to xyz which moves with velocity $\vec{V}$ relative to XYZ

WORK EQUATIONS

Closed System—Work of Deformation. The general equation for the work of deformation W' for a reversible process is given by:

$$W' = \int_i^f p\,d\Psi$$

where the system proceeds from the initial state i to the final state f. The work of deformation w' per unit mass is:

$$w' = \int_i^f p\,dv$$

where p is the absolute pressure used to calculate the work done by the system or the gage pressure used to calculate the net useful work, that is, system work minus work done on the atmosphere (Fig. 4).

The following equations in Cases 1 through 6 are used to calculate the work of deformation for specific reversible processes.

Case 1. Constant pressure (isobaric), reversible process:

$$W' = p(\Psi_f - \Psi_i) \qquad w' = p(v_f - v_i)$$

where p is absolute pressure or gage pressure, depending on whether system work or net work is being calculated.

Case 2. Constant pressure (isobaric), reversible process for an ideal gas:

$$W' = mR)T_f - T_i) \qquad w' = R(T_f - T_i)$$

Case 3. Constant volume (isometric), reversible process:

$$W' = 0 \qquad w' = 0$$

Case 4. Constant temperature (isothermal), reversible process for an ideal gas:

$$W' = mRT_i \ln \frac{v_f}{v_i}$$

$$W' = mRT_i \ln \frac{\Psi_f}{\Psi_i}$$

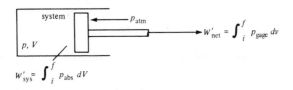

Figure 4 Work by closed system.
$W'_{net} = \int_i^f p_{gage}\,d\Psi$
$W'_{sys} = \int_i^f p_{abs}\,d\Psi$

$$W' = mRT_i \ln \frac{p_i}{p_f}$$

$$w' = \frac{W'}{m}$$

Case 5. Adiabatic or adiabatic and reversible process (isentropic process):

$$W' = m(u_i - u_f) \qquad w' = (u_i - u_f)$$

An adiabatic and reversible process is isentropic, but an isentropic process need not necessarily be both adiabatic and reversible.

Case 6. Polytropic, reversible process:

$$W' = \frac{(p_f \Psi_f - p_i \Psi_i)}{1 - n} \qquad w' = \frac{p_f v_f - p_i v_i}{1 - n}$$

Control Volume, Steady-State Conditions (Constant g). The general equations for work for a reversible process under steady-state conditions are:

$$w = - \left[\int_1^2 v \, dp + \frac{V_2{}^2 - V_1{}^2}{2} + g(z_2 - z_1) \right]$$

$$\dot{W} = \dot{m}w$$

where p = absolute pressure. Point 1 represents the inlet state and point 2 the outlet state.

The following equations in Cases 1 through 7 are used to calculate the control volume work or power for specific reversible processes.

Case 1. Constant pressure (isobaric), reversible process:

$$w = \frac{V_1{}^2 - V_2{}^2}{2} + g(z_1 - z_2)$$

$$\dot{W} = \dot{m}w$$

Case 2. Constant specific volume (isometric), reversible process:

$$w = v(p_1 - p_2) + \frac{V_1{}^2 - V_2{}^2}{2} + g(z_1 - z_2)$$

$$\dot{W} = \dot{m}w$$

Case 3. Constant specific volume (isometric), reversible process for an ideal gas:

$$w = R(T_1 - T_2) + \frac{V_1{}^2 - V_2{}^2}{2} + g(z_1 - z_2)$$

$$\dot{W} = \dot{m}w$$

Case 4. Constant temperature (isothermal), reversible process for an ideal gas:

$$w = RT_1 \ln \frac{p_1}{p_2} + \frac{V_1{}^2 - V_2{}^2}{2} + g(z_1 - z_2)$$

$$w = RT_1 \ln \frac{v_2}{v_1} + \frac{V_1{}^2 - V_2{}^2}{2} + g(z_1 - z_2)$$

$$\dot{W} = \dot{m}w$$

Case 5. Adiabatic or adiabatic and reversible process (isentropic process):

$$\dot{W} = -\dot{m}\left[(h_2 - h_1) + \frac{V_2{}^2 - V_1{}^2}{2} + g(z_2 - z_1)\right]$$

$$w = -\left[(h_2 - h_1) + \frac{V_2{}^2 - V_1{}^2}{2} + g(z_2 - z_1)\right]$$

Case 6. Polytropic, reversible process:

$$w = \frac{-n}{n-1}(p_2 v_2 - p_1 v_1) + \frac{V_1{}^2 - V_2{}^2}{2} + g(z_1 - z_2)$$

$$\dot{W} = \dot{m}w$$

Case 7. Adiabatic, reversible process for an ideal gas with constant specific heat:

$$w = \frac{kRT_1}{k-1}\left[1 - \left(\frac{p_2}{p_1}\right)^{\frac{k-1}{k}}\right] + \frac{V_1{}^2 - V_2{}^2}{2} + g(z_1 - z_2)$$

HEAT TRANSFER EQUATIONS

Closed System. The general equation for the heat transfer, Q, for a reversible process is given by:

$$Q = \int_i^f T\,dS$$

where Q is the total heat transfer as the system proceeds from the initial state i to the final state f, T is the absolute temperature (K or °R) and S is the total entropy of the mass m. The heat transfer per unit mass q is:

$$q = \int_i^f T\,ds$$

Also:

$$Q = mq = m\int_i^f T\,ds$$

where s is the entropy per unit mass.

The following equations in Cases 1 through 7 are used to calculate the heat transfer for specific reversible processes.

Case 1.   Constant pressure (isobaric), reversible process:

$$Q = m(h_f - h_i) \qquad q = h_f - h_i$$

Case 2.   Constant pressure (isobaric), reversible process for an ideal gas with constant specific heat:

$$Q = m\,C_p \ln\frac{T_f}{T_i} \qquad q = C_p \ln\frac{T_f}{T_i}$$

Case 3.   Constant volume (isometric), reversible process:

$$Q = m(u_f - u_i) \qquad q = u_f - u_i$$

Case 4.   Constant volume (isometric), reversible process for an ideal gas with constant specific heat:

$$Q = mC_v \ln\frac{T_f}{T_i} \qquad q = C_v \ln\frac{T_f}{T_i}$$

Case 5.   Constant temperature (isothermal), reversible process for an ideal gas:

$$Q = T_i(S_f - S_i) = W$$

$$Q = mR\,T_i \ln\frac{v_f}{v_i}$$

$$Q = mR\,T_i \ln\frac{V_f}{V_i}$$

$$Q = mR\,T_i \ln\frac{p_i}{p_f}$$

$$q = \frac{Q}{m} = w$$

Case 6.   Adiabatic or adiabatic and reversible process (isentropic process):

$$Q = 0 \qquad q = 0$$

Case 7.   Polytropic, reversible process:

$$q = h_f - h_i - \frac{n}{n-1}(p_f v_f - p_i v_i)$$

$$q = u_f - u_i - \frac{1}{n-1}(p_f v_f - p_i v_i)$$

$$Q = mq$$

Control Volume, Steady-State Conditions (constant *g*). The general equations for heat transfer for a reversible process are given by:

$$q = \int_1^2 T \, ds \qquad \dot{Q} = \dot{m}q$$

The following equations in Cases 1 through 7 are used to calculate the heat transfer for specific reversible processes.

Case 1. *Constant pressure (isobaric), reversible process:*

$$q = (h_2 - h_1) \qquad \dot{Q} = \dot{m}q$$

Case 2. *Constant specific volume (isometric), reversible process:*

$$q = (u_2 - u_1) \qquad \dot{Q} = \dot{m}q$$

Case 3. *Constant specific volume (isometric), reversible process for an ideal gas with constant specific heat:*

$$q = C_v(T_2 - T_1) \qquad \dot{Q} = \dot{m}q$$

Case 4. *Constant temperature (isothermal), reversible process for an ideal gas:*

$$q = h_2 - h_1 - RT_1 \ln \frac{p_1}{p_2}$$

$$q = h_2 - h_1 - RT_1 \ln \frac{v_2}{v_1}$$

$$q = T_1(s_2 - s_1)$$

$$\dot{Q} = \dot{m}q$$

Case 5. *Constant temperature (isothermal), reversible process for an ideal gas with constant specific heat:*

$$q = C_p(T_2 - T_1) - RT_1 \ln \frac{p_1}{p_2}$$

$$q = C_p(T_2 - T_1) - RT_1 \ln \frac{v_2}{v_1}$$

$$q = T_1(s_2 - s_1)$$

$$\dot{Q} = \dot{m}q$$

Case 6. *Adiabatic or adiabatic and reversible process (isentropic process):*

$$q = 0 \qquad \dot{Q} = 0$$

Case 7. *Polytropic, reversible process:*

$$q = (h_2 - h_1) - \frac{n}{n - 1}(p_2 v_2 - p_1 v_1)$$

$$\dot{Q} = \dot{m}q$$

PROPERTY RELATIONS

Entropy Change Equations—Closed System or Control Volume, Steady-State Conditions. For a reversible process, the general equations for the entropy change of a pure substance are given by:

$$s_2 - s_1 = \int_1^2 \frac{du}{T} + \int_1^2 \frac{p}{T}\, dv$$

$$s_2 - s_1 = \int_1^2 \frac{dh}{T} - \int_1^2 \frac{v}{T}\, dp$$

$$s_2 - s_1 = \int_1^2 C_v \frac{dT}{T} + \int_1^2 \left(\frac{\partial p}{\partial T}\right)_v dv$$

$$s_2 - s_1 = \int_1^2 C_p \frac{dT}{T} - \int_1^2 \left(\frac{\partial v}{\partial T}\right)_p dp$$

where T = absolute temperature; v = specific volume; C_v = specific heat at constant volume; C_p = specific heat at constant pressure.

For a closed system, 1 represents the initial state and 2 the final state. For a control volume, 1 represents the inlet and 2 the outlet.

The following equations in Cases 1 through 9 are used to calculate the entropy change of a pure substance for specific reversible processes.

Case 1. Reversible process for an ideal gas:

$$s_2 - s_1 = \int_1^2 C_v \frac{dT}{T} + R \ln \frac{v_2}{v_1}$$

$$s_2 - s_1 = \int_1^2 C_p \frac{dT}{T} - R \ln \frac{p_2}{p_1}$$

where R = specific gas constant.

Case 2. Reversible process for an ideal gas with constant specific heats:

$$s_2 - s_1 = C_v \ln \frac{T_2}{T_1} + R \ln \frac{v_2}{v_1}$$

$$s_2 - s_1 = C_p \ln \frac{T_2}{T_1} - R \ln \frac{p_2}{p_1}$$

$$s_2 - s_1 = C_p \ln \frac{v_2}{v_1} + C_v \ln \frac{p_2}{p_1}$$

Case 3. Constant pressure (isobaric), reversible process:

$$s_2 - s_1 = \int_1^2 \frac{dh}{T}$$

Case 4. Constant pressure, reversible process for an ideal gas:

$$s_2 - s_1 = \int_1^2 C_p \frac{dT}{T}$$

Case 5. Constant specific volume (isometric), reversible process:

$$s_2 - s_1 = \int_1^2 \frac{du}{T}$$

Case 6. Constant specific volume, reversible process for an ideal gas:

$$s_2 - s_1 = \int_1^2 C_v \frac{dT}{T}$$

Case 7. Adiabatic, reversible process:

$$s_2 - s_1 = 0$$

Case 8. Isentropic process:

$$s_2 - s_1 = 0$$

Case 9. Mixing of ideal gases at constant temperature and constant total pressure, p:

$$\Delta S = \sum_{\ell=1}^{N} n_i \bar{R} \ln \frac{p_i}{p}$$

where
p_i = partial pressure of component i
p = total pressure of mixture

$$= \sum_{\ell=1}^{N} X_i p_i$$

= initial pressure of each component before mixing
N = number of components
n_i = moles of component i
X_i = mole fraction of component i

Process Equations. The following equations in Cases 1 through 6 relate the properties of a pure substance during specific reversible processes.

Case 1. Constant pressure (isobaric), reversible process for an ideal gas:

$$\frac{v}{T} = \text{Constant} = \frac{R}{p}$$

Case 2. Constant specific volume (isometric), reversible process for an ideal gas:

$$\frac{p}{T} = \text{Constant} = \frac{R}{v}$$

Case 3. *Constant temperature (isothermal), reversible process for an ideal gas:*

$$pv = \text{Constant} = RT_1$$

Case 4. *Polytropic, reversible process:*

$$pv^n = \text{Constant} \qquad n = \text{Constant} = \frac{\ln\left(\dfrac{p_2}{p_1}\right)}{\ln\left(\dfrac{v_1}{v_2}\right)}$$

Case 5. *Polytropic, reversible process for an ideal gas:*

$$pv^n = \text{Constant}$$

$$Tp^{\frac{1-n}{n}} = \text{Constant}$$

$$Tv^{n-1} = \text{Constant}$$

$$n = \text{Constant} = \frac{\ln\left(\dfrac{p_2}{p_1}\right)}{\ln\left(\dfrac{v_1}{v_2}\right)}$$

Case 6. *Isentropic process for an ideal gas with constant specific heats:*

$$pv^k = \text{constant}$$

$$Tp^{\frac{1-k}{k}} = \text{Constant}$$

$$Tv^{k-1} = \text{Constant}$$

$$k = \frac{C_p}{C_v} = \text{Constant}$$

Equations of State. The following equations relate the properties of a pure substance (Tables 1 and 2). In all equations:

T = absolute temperature T_c = critical point temperature
p = absolute pressure p_c = critical point pressure
v = mass specific volume v_c = critical point specific volume
$\bar{v}$ = molar specific volume

R = specific gas constant = $\dfrac{\bar{R}}{M}$ M = molecular weight

$\bar{R}$ = universal gas constant = $0.08205 \dfrac{\ell \cdot \text{atm}}{\text{gmol} \cdot \text{K}} = 8.315 \dfrac{\text{J}}{\text{gmol} \cdot \text{K}}$

$\bar{R} = 0.08315 \dfrac{\text{bar} \cdot \text{m}^3}{\text{kgmol} \cdot \text{K}} = 1545 \dfrac{\text{ft} \cdot \text{lbf}}{\text{lbmol} \cdot °\text{R}} = 1.986 \dfrac{\text{kcal}}{\text{kmol} \cdot \text{K}}$

$\bar{R} = 0.730 \dfrac{\text{atm} \cdot \text{ft}^3}{\text{lbmol} \cdot °\text{R}} = 10.73 \dfrac{\text{psia} \cdot \text{ft}^3}{\text{kmol} \cdot \text{K}}$

Table 1 Critical properties and van der Waals constants, SI units

Substance	T_c, K	p_c, bar	$\bar{v}_c$, $\dfrac{\text{m}^3}{\text{kmol}}$	$Z_c = \dfrac{P_c v_c}{RT_c}$	van der Waals a, $\text{bar}\left(\dfrac{\text{m}^3}{\text{kmol}}\right)^2$	b, $\dfrac{\text{m}^3}{\text{kmol}}$
Acetylene (C_2H_2)	309	62.8	0.112	0.274	4.410	0.0510
Air (equivalent)	133	37.7	0.0829	0.284	1.358	0.0364
Ammonia (NH_3)........	406	112.8	0.0723	0.242	4.233	0.0373
Benzene (C_6H_6)........	562	49.3	0.256	0.274	18.63	0.1181
n-Butane (C_4H_{10})	425.2	38.0	0.257	0.274	13.80	0.1196
Carbon dioxide (CO_2)...	304.2	73.9	0.0941	0.276	3.643	0.0427
Carbon monoxide (CO)..	133	35.0	0.0928	0.294	1.463	0.0394
Refrigerant 12 (CCl_2F_2)	385	40.1	0.214	0.270	10.78	0.0998
Ethane (C_2H_6).........	305.4	48.8	0.221	0.273	5.575	0.0650
Ethylene (C_2H_4)	283	51.2	0.143	0.284	4.563	0.0574
Helium (He)	5.2	2.3	0.0579	0.300	0.0341	0.0234
Hydrogen (H_2)	33.2	13.0	0.0648	0.304	0.247	0.0265
Methane (CH_4)........	190.7	46.4	0.0991	0.290	2.285	0.0427
Nitrogen (N_2).........	126.2	33.9	0.0897	0.291	1.361	0.0385
Oxygen (O_2)	154.4	50.5	0.0741	0.290	1.369	0.0315
Propane (C_3H_8)........	370	42.7	0.195	0.276	9.315	0.0900
Sulfur dioxide (SO_2)....	431	78.7	0.124	0.268	6.837	0.0568
Water (H_2O)...........	647.3	220.9	0.0558	0.230	5.507	0.0304

The ideal gas law (perfect gas law) is expressed as:

$$pv = RT$$
$$p\bar{v} = \bar{R}T$$

The van der Waals equation is:

$$\left(p + \frac{a}{v^2}\right)(v - b) = RT$$

where

$$a = \frac{27}{64}\frac{R^2 T_c^2}{p_c}$$

$$b = \frac{RT_c}{8p_c}$$

$$v_c = \frac{3RT_c}{8p_c}$$

Table 2 Critical properties and van der Waals constants, English engineering units

Substance	T_c, °R	p_c, atm	$\bar{v}_c$, ft³/(lbmol)	$Z_c = \dfrac{p_c v_c}{R T_c}$	van der Waals a, atm [ft³/(lbmol)]²	van der Waals b, ft³/(lbmol)
Acetylene (C_2H_2)	556	62	1.80	0.274	1121	0.818
Air (equivalent)	239	37.2	1.33	0.284	345.2	0.585
Ammonia (NH_3)	730	111.3	1.16	0.242	1076	0.598
Benzene (C_6H_6)	1013	48.7	4.11	0.274	4736	1.896
n-Butane (C_4H_{10})	765	37.5	4.13	0.274	3508	1.919
Carbon dioxide (CO_2)	548	72.9	1.51	0.276	926	0.686
Carbon monoxide (CO)	239	34.5	1.49	0.294	372	0.632
Refrgerant 12 (CCl_2F_2)	693	39.6	3.43	0.270	2718	1.595
Ethane (C_2H_6)	549	48.2	3.55	0.273	1410	1.041
Ethylene (C_2H_4)	510	50.5	2.29	0.284	1158	0.922
Helium (He)	9.33	2.26	0.93	0.300	8.66	0.376
n-Heptane (C_7H_{16})	972	27	6.86	0.26	7866	3.298
Hydrogen (H_2)	59.8	12.8	1.04	0.304	62.8	0.426
Methane (CH_4)	344	45.8	1.59	0.290	581	0.685
Methyl chloride (CH_3Cl)	749	65.8	2.29	0.276	1917	1.040
Nitrogen (N_2)	227	33.5	1.44	0.291	346	0.618
Nonane (C_9H_{20})	1071	22.86	8.86	0.250		
n-Octane (C_8H_{18})	1025	24.6	7.82	0.258	9601	3.76
Oxygen (O_2)	278	49.8	1.19	0.290	348	0.506
Propane (C_3H_8)	666	42.1	3.13	0.276	2368	1.445
Sulfur dioxide (SO_2)	775	77.7	1.99	0.268	1738	0.911
Water (H_2O)	1165	218.2	0.896	0.230	1400	0.488

The constants a and b are found in Tables 1 and 2. The compressibility factor equation is expressed as:

$$Z = \frac{pv}{RT}$$

where Z = compressibility factor; p_R = reduced pressure = $\frac{p}{p_c}$; T_R = reduced temperature = $\frac{T}{T_c}$; v_R = reduced specific volume = $\frac{vp_c}{RT_c}$.

Modified critical temperature T_c' and pressure p_c' are defined by:

$$p_c' = p_c + 8 \qquad T_c' = T_c + 8$$

and are used for hydrogen and helium where T_c is in K and p_c is in atmospheres. Figure 5 shows the generalized compressibility factor in graphic form.

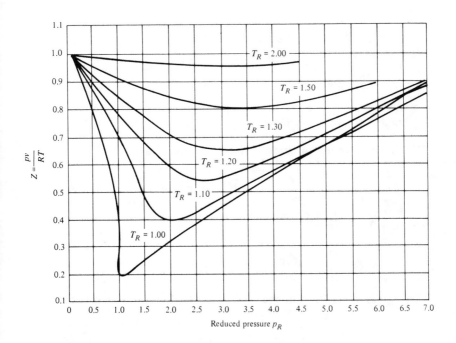

Figure 5 Generalized compressibility factor, Z

The virial equations of state are expressed as:

$$pv = a + bp + cp^2 + dp^3 + \cdots$$

$$pv = a\left(1 + \frac{b}{v} + \frac{c}{v^2} + \frac{d}{v^3} + \cdots\right)$$

where $a = a(T)$
  $b = b(T)$
  $c = c(T)$ and so on

All sets of coefficients $(a, b, c, d, \ldots)$ are virial coefficients and can be found from experimental data or statistical mechanics.

The Berthelot equation of state is expressed as:

$$p = \frac{RT}{v - b} - \frac{a}{Tv^2}$$

The constants a and b must be found from experimental data for a particular fluid.

The Dieterici equation of state is expressed as:

$$p = \frac{RT}{v - b} e^{-a/RTv}$$

The constants a and b must be found from experimental data for a particular fluid.

The Clausius equation of state is expressed as:

$$p(\mathbb{V} - b') = mRT$$

where $b' = \frac{16}{3} N \pi r^3$

r = one half the center to center distance of two colliding molecules
N = number of molecules in volume V

The Redlich-Kwong equation of state is expressed as:

$$p = \frac{RT}{v - b} - \frac{a}{T^{1/2} v(v + b)}$$

where $a = 0.4275 \dfrac{R^2 T_c^{2.5}}{p_c}$

  $b = 0.0867 \dfrac{RT_c}{p_c} = 0.26\, v_c$

Table 3 gives numerical values of Redlich-Kwong constants for selected gases.

Table 3 Redlich-Kwong constants

Substance	Constants for p in bar (s), v in m^3/(kmol), and T in K		Constants for p in atm, v in ft^3/(lbmol), and T in °R	
	a	b	a	b
Carbon dioxide, CO_2.........	64.64	0.02969	21,970	0.4757
Carbon monoxide, CO........	17.26	0.02743	5,870	0.4395
Methane, CH_4..............	32.19	0.02969	10,930	0.4757
Nitrogen, N_2...............	15.59	0.02681	5,300	0.4294
Oxygen, O_2	17.38	0.02199	5,900	0.3522
Propane, C_3H_8.............	183.07	0.06269	62,190	1.0040
Refrigerant 12, CCl_2F_2	214.03	0.06913	72,710	1.1080
Sulfur dioxide, SO_2..........	144.49	0.03939		
Water, H_2O................	142.64	0.02110	48,460	0.3381

The Benedict-Webb-Rubin equation of state, which is especially applicable to hydrocarbons, is expressed as:

$$p = \frac{RT}{v}\left(B_0 RT - A_0 - \frac{C_0}{T^2}\right)\frac{1}{v^2}$$
$$+ \frac{bRT - a}{v^3} + \frac{a\alpha}{v^6} + \frac{c}{v^3 T^2}\left(1 + \frac{\gamma}{v^2}\right)e^{(-\gamma/v^2)}$$

The constants in the equation are defined in Table 4 for various gases.

Specific Internal Energy Change—Closed System or Steady-State Control Volume. The following equations are used to calculate the internal energy change of a pure substance. The term "specific" refers to the property per unit mass or per unit mole. For a closed system, 1 represents the initial state and 2 the final state. For a control volume, 1 represents the inlet and 2 the outlet.

For a reversible process:

$$u_2 - u_1 = \int_1^2 C_v dT + \int_1^2 \left[T\left(\frac{\partial p}{\partial T}\right)_v - p\right]dv$$

For a constant volume (isometric) reversible process:

$$u_2 - u_1 = \int_1^2 C_v dT$$

For a reversible process for an ideal gas:

Table 4   Benedict-Webb-Rubin

		p in bar(s), v in m^3/(kmol), T in K			
Con-stants	n-Butane, C_4H_{10}	Carbon dioxide, CO_2	Carbon monoxide, CO	Methane, CH_4	Nitrogen, N_2
a	1.9068	0.1386	0.0371	0.0500	0.0254
A_0	10.216	2.7730	1.3587	1.8791	1.0673
b	0.039998	0.007210	0.002632	0.003380	0.002328
B_0	0.12436	0.04991	0.05454	0.04260	0.04074
c	3.205×10^5	1.511×10^4	1.054×10^3	2.578×10^3	7.379×10^2
C_0	1.006×10^6	1.404×10^5	8.673×10^3	2.286×10^4	8.164×10^3
α	1.101×10^{-3}	8.470×10^{-5}	1.350×10^{-4}	1.244×10^{-4}	1.272×10^{-4}
γ	0.0340	0.00539	0.0060	0.0060	0.0053

		p in atm, v in ft^3/(lb mol), T in °R			
Con-stants	n-Butane, C_4H_{10}	Carbon dioxide, CO_2	Carbon monoxide, CO	Methane, CH_4	Nitrogen, N_2
a	7747	563.1	150.7	203.1	103.2
A_0	2590	703.0	344.5	476.4	270.6
b	10.27	1.852	0.676	0.868 ،	0.598
B_0	1.993	0.7998	0.8740	0.6827	0.6529
c	4.219×10^9	1.989×10^8	1.387×10^7	3.393×10^7	9.713×10^6
C_0	8.263×10^8	1.153×10^8	7.124×10^6	1.878×10^7	6.706×10^6
α	4.531	0.3486	0.5556	0.5120	0.5235
γ	8.732	1.384	1.541	1.541	1.361

$$u_2 - u_1 = \int_1^2 C_v dT$$

where $C_v = C_v(T)$.

Specific Enthalpy Change—Closed System or Steady-State Control Volume. The following equations are used to calculate the enthalpy change of a pure substance. The term "specific" refers to the property per unit mass or per unit mole. For a closed system, 1 represents the initial state and 2 the final state. For a control volume, 1 represents the inlet and 2 the outlet.

For a reversible process:

$$h_2 - h_1 = \int_1^2 C_p dT + \left[v - T\left(\frac{\partial v}{\partial T}\right)_p \right] dp$$

For a constant pressure (isobaric), reversible process:

$$h_2 - h_1 = \int_1^2 C_p\, dT$$

For a reversible process for an ideal gas:

$$h_2 - h_1 = \int_1^2 C_p\, dT$$

where $C_p = C_p(T)$.

SECOND LAW OF THERMODYNAMICS

The second law states that it is not possible to construct a device whose sole effect is the extraction of heat from a heat source and the conversion of this heat completely into mechanical work. The second law means that some energy is always "lost"; no heat engine is 100% efficient. The following equations give the cycle thermodynamic efficiency for various devices operating under steady-state conditions.

Cycle Thermodynamic Efficiency and Coefficient of Performance. The efficiency, η, of a Carnot heat engine, shown schematically in Fig. 6, is given by:

$$\eta = \frac{W}{Q_H} = 1 - \frac{T_L}{T_H} \qquad \frac{Q_L}{Q_H} = \frac{T_L}{T_H}$$

The coefficient of performance (COP) of a Carnot refrigerator, shown schematically in Fig. 7, is given by:

$$(COP)_{\text{Heating}} = \frac{Q_H}{W} = \frac{T_H}{T_H - T_L}$$

$$(COP)_{\text{Cooling}} = \frac{Q_L}{W} = \frac{T_L}{T_H - T_L}$$

$$\frac{Q_L}{Q_H} = \frac{T_L}{T_H}$$

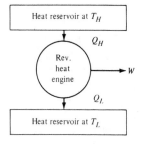

Figure 6   Carnot heat engine

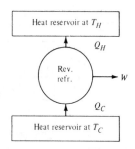

Figure 7   Carnot refrigeration

where

T_H = absolute temperature of high-temperature reservoir
Q_H = heat transfer from high-temperature reservoir
W = work done by engine
Q_L = heat transfer to low-temperature reservoir
T_L = absolute temperature of low-temperature reservoir

The efficiency, η, of an air standard Carnot cycle (Fig. 8) is given by:

$$\eta = 1 - \frac{1}{(CR)^{k-1}} = 1 - \frac{T_1}{T_3} = 1 - \frac{T_4}{T_2}$$

where for all air standard cycles

CR = compression ratio
 $k = C_p/C_v$, constant C_p and C_v
 T = absolute temperature
 p = absolute pressure

The efficiency, η, of an air standard Otto cycle (Fig. 9) is given by:

$$\eta = 1 - \frac{1}{(CR)^{k-1}} = 1 - \frac{T_1}{T_2}$$

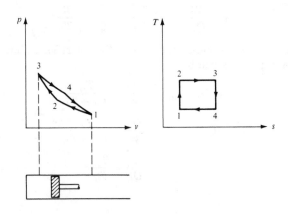

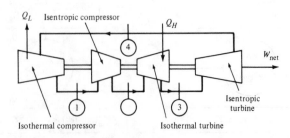

Figure 8   Air standard Carnot cycle

The efficiency, η, of an air standard Diesel cycle (Fig. 10) is given by:

$$\eta = 1 - \frac{(T_4 - T_1)}{k(T_3 - T_2)} = 1 - \frac{1}{k(CR)^{k-1}} \left[\frac{\left(\dfrac{v_3}{v_2}\right)^k - 1}{\left(\dfrac{v_3}{v_2}\right) - 1} \right]$$

The efficiency, η, of an air standard Stirling cycle (Fig. 11) is given by:

$$\eta = 1 - \frac{T_2}{T_3} = 1 - \frac{T_1}{T_4}$$

The efficiency, η, of an air standard Ericsson cycle (Fig. 12) is given by:

$$\eta = 1 - \frac{T_2}{T_3} = 1 - \frac{T_1}{T_4}$$

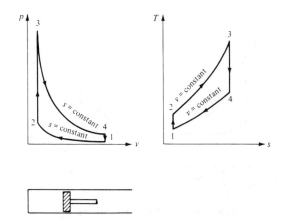

Figure 9   Air standard Otto cycle

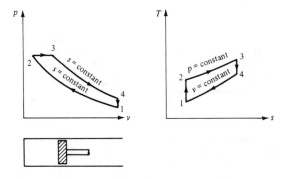

Figure 10   Air standard Diesel cycle

The efficiency, η, of an air standard Atkinson cycle (Fig. 13) is given by:

$$\eta = 1 - \frac{k}{(CR)^{k-1}} \left[\frac{\left(\frac{p_3}{p_2}\right)^{1/k} - 1}{\left(\frac{p_3}{p_2}\right) - 1} \right]$$

The efficiency, η, of an air standard closed Brayton cycle (Fig. 14) is given by:

$$\eta = 1 - \frac{1}{\left(\dfrac{p_2}{p_1}\right)^{\frac{k-1}{k}}}$$

The efficiency, η, of an air standard open Brayton cycle (Fig. 15) is given by:

$$\eta = 1 - \frac{T_4 - T_1}{T_3 - T_2}$$

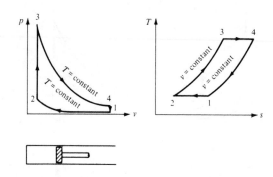

Figure 11   Air standard Stirling cycle

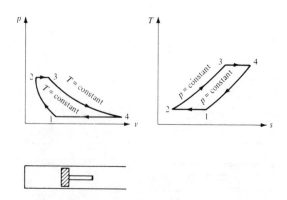

Figure 12   Air standard Ericsson cycle

The efficiency, η, of an air standard open Brayton cycle with regeneration (Fig. 16) is given by:

$$\eta = \frac{(T_3 - T_2) - (T_4 - T_1)}{T_3 - T_5}$$

Process Efficiency. The following equations give the efficiencies of various processes for steady-state conditions. Nozzle efficiency, η, is given by:

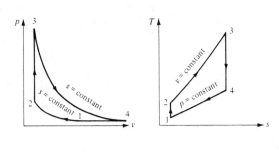

Figure 13   Air standard Atkinson cycle

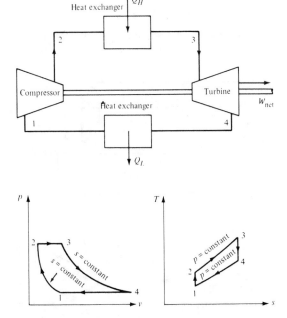

Figure 14   Air standard closed Brayton cycle

$$\eta_{\text{nozzle}} = \frac{V_2^2}{V_2'^2}$$

for a system shown in Fig. 17, where V_2' = ideal outlet velocity for the condition where the outlet entropy s_2 equals the inlet entropy s_1 and the actual exit (or outlet) pressure is p_2.

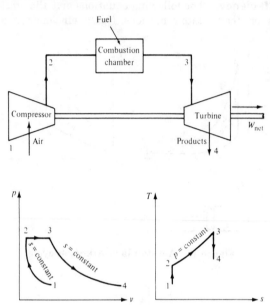

Figure 15 Air standard Brayton cycle

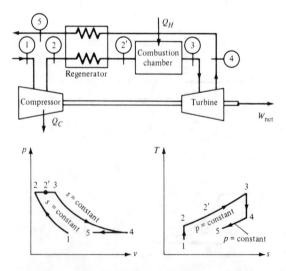

Figure 16 Air standard open Brayton cycle

Turbine isentropic efficiency, η, is given by:

$$\eta_{\text{turbine}} = \frac{\text{(actual work per unit mass)}}{\left(\begin{array}{l}\text{isentropic work per unit}\\\text{mass for actual inlet}\\\text{conditions and actual}\\\text{exit pressure}\end{array}\right)}$$

Compressor isentropic efficiency, η, is given by:

$$\eta_{\text{compressor}} = \frac{\left(\begin{array}{l}\text{isentropic work per unit}\\\text{mass for actual inlet con-}\\\text{ditions and actual exit}\\\text{pressure}\end{array}\right)}{\text{(actual work per unit mass)}}$$

Compressor isothermal efficiency, η, is given by:

$$\eta_{\text{compressor}} = \frac{\left(\begin{array}{l}\text{isothermal work per unit}\\\text{mass for actual inlet con-}\\\text{ditions and actual exit}\\\text{pressure}\end{array}\right)}{\text{(actual work per unit mass)}}$$

Boiler or burner combustion efficiency, η, is given by:

$$\eta_{\text{boiler}} = \frac{\left(\begin{array}{l}\text{rate of heat transferred}\\\text{to working fluid(s)}\end{array}\right)}{\left(\begin{array}{l}\text{fuel mass flow rate times}\\\text{fuel heating value}\end{array}\right)} \qquad \text{(Eq 5)}$$

In Eq 5, either the higher heating value or the lower heating value could be used; by common practice, the higher heating value is normally used.

Increase of entropy principle. Unlike energy, entropy is not conserved. For example, the entropy of an adiabatic, closed system, if left to itself, could increase in time as the system approached equilibrium. Mathematically, the entropy of this system would attain its maximum possible value when equi-

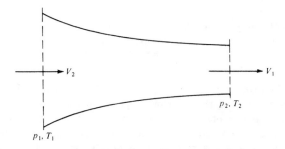

Figure 17 Nozzle schematic

librium is reached. One interpretation of entropy is that it represents the degree of "disorder" of the molecules of a system. The system is in disorder if the various molecules of a multicomponent system are uniformly distributed throughout the system. The system is most ordered if each type of molecule is separated from the others. Another interpretation of entropy is that it is a measure of the fraction of the system energy that cannot be converted into work. The larger entropy means that less work can be obtained from the energy of the system.

In the following equations, the inequality (>0) applies to an irreversible process while the equality ($=0$) applies to a reversible process. The subscript i refers to the initial state and f to the final state. S represents the entropy of either a system or its surroundings.

For a closed system and its surroundings:

$$dS_{\text{SYSTEM}} + dS_{\text{SURR}} \geq 0$$

$$S_{f,\text{SYSTEM}} - S_{i,\text{SYSTEM}} + S_{f,\text{SURR}} - S_{i,\text{SURR}} \geq 0$$

For an adiabatic, closed system:

$$dS \geq 0$$

$$S_f - S_i \geq 0$$

For an isolated system:

$$dS > 0$$

$$S_f - S_i \geq 0$$

For a control volume:

$$\frac{dS_{cv}}{dt} + \sum_{\text{out}} \dot{m}s - \sum_{\text{in}} \dot{m}s \geq \int_{A_{\text{control surface}}} \frac{\dot{q}}{T} \, dA$$

where

T = absolute temperature
$\dot{q}$ = heat transfer rate per unit area of the control surface and added to or lost from the control volume
cv = control volume

For a control volume and its surroundings:

$$\frac{dS_{cv}}{dt} + \frac{dS_{\text{SURR}}}{dt} \geq 0$$

Reversible Power, Irreversibility, and Availability. Irreversibility is the difference between the maximum power obtainable (reversible power) and the actual power obtainable from the control volume; availability is a mathematical definition and represents the reversible work per unit mass when a unit mass proceeds from the state of interest to a state of zero velocity, ambient temperature and ambient pressure.

Point i represents the initial state, f the final state, 1 the inlet state and 2 the outlet state. Uniform properties are assumed over each flow area and throughout the control volume. Equations 6 through 11 apply to a control volume. The corresponding equations applicable to a closed system are obtained by setting each mass flow rate equal to zero.

Reversible power for a steady state control volume is given by:

$$\dot{W}_{rev} = \sum_{inlet} \dot{m}_1 \left(h_1 - T_0 s_1 + \frac{V_1^2}{2} + g z_1 \right)$$
$$- \sum_{outlet} \dot{m}_2 \left(h_2 - T_0 s_2 + \frac{V_2^2}{2} + g z_2 \right)$$
$$+ m_i \left(u_i - T_0 s_i + \frac{V_i^2}{2} + g z_i \right) - m_f \left(u_f - T_0 s_f + \frac{V_f^2}{2} + g z_f \right) \quad \text{(Eq 6)}$$

Irreversibility for a steady state process is given by:

$$\dot{I} = \dot{W}_{rev} - \dot{W}_{actual} \quad \text{(Eq 7)}$$

where $\dot{W}_{actual}$ is obtained from the first law of thermodynamics applied to the actual control volume; also by:

$$\dot{I} = T_0 \left(\sum_{outlet} \dot{m}_2 s_2 - \sum_{inlet} \dot{m}_1 s_1 + m_f s_f - m_i s_i \right) - \dot{Q}_{cv} \quad \text{(Eq 8)}$$

where $\dot{Q}_{cv}$ = rate of heat transfer into the control volume of interest; also by:

$$\dot{I} = T_0 \left(\frac{dS_{control\ volume}}{dt} + \frac{dS_{surroundings}}{dt} \right) \quad \text{(Eq 9)}$$

and by:

$$\dot{I} = T_0 \left(\frac{dS_{control\ volume}}{dt} + \sum \dot{m}_2 s_2 - \sum \dot{m}_1 s_1 - \frac{Q_{cv}}{T_0} \right) \quad \text{(Eq 10)}$$

where T_0 = ambient absolute temperature.

Availability for a steady-state control volume is given by:

$$\psi = \left(h - T_0 s + \frac{V^2}{2} + g z \right) - (h_0 - T_0 s_0 + g z_0) \quad \text{(Eq 11)}$$

where the zero subscript represents the state in which the fluid is in equilibrium with the surroundings (at ambient temperature T_0 and pressure P_0).

MIXTURES AND SOLUTIONS

The following equations apply to a system consisting of several homogeneous phases.

Chemical Reactions. For chemical reactions of ideal gas mixtures at temperature T and total pressure p, the reaction equation is:

$$\nu_A A + \nu_B B \leftrightarrows \nu_C C + \nu_D D$$

$$\text{(Reactants)} \qquad \text{(Products)}$$

The law of mass action is expressed as:

$$K = \frac{p_C{}^{\nu_C} p_D{}^{\nu_D}}{p_A{}^{\nu_A} p_B{}^{\nu_B}} = \frac{x_C{}^{\nu_C} x_D{}^{\nu_D}}{x_A{}^{\nu_A} x_D{}^{\nu_D}} p^{\nu_C + \nu_D - \nu_A - \nu_B}$$

$$= \frac{\nu_A \bar{g}_A{}^0 + \nu_B \bar{g}_B{}^0 - \nu_C \bar{g}_C{}^0 - \nu_D \bar{g}_D{}^0}{\bar{R} T}$$

where

K = equilibrium constant
$\bar{g}_i{}^0$ = Gibbs function per unit mole of component i at absolute temperature T and 1.0 atm pressure
p = absolute pressure of mixture in atmospheres
x_i = mole fraction of component i
ν_i = coefficient in reaction equation (i = A, B, C, or D)
$\bar{R}$ = universal gas constant
T = absolute temperature

Table 5 gives equilibrium constants for various simple reactions.

The van't Hoff equation is given as:

$$\frac{d(\ln K)}{d(1/T)} = \frac{\nu_A \bar{h}_A{}^0 + \nu_B \bar{h}_B{}^0 - \nu_C \bar{h}_C{}^0 - \nu_D \bar{h}_D{}^0}{\bar{R}}$$

where

$\bar{h}_i{}^0$ = enthalpy per unit mole of component i at temperature T and superscript zero means 1 atm pressure.

Equilibrium of a heterogeneous system is expressed by the Gibbs-Duhem equation:

$$S \, dT + \Psi \, dp = \sum_{i=1}^{N} n_i d\bar{\mu}_i$$

where

$\bar{\mu}_i$ = chemical potential of component i at the partial pressure p_i of component i and the temperature T of the mixture
S = entropy of mixture
T = absolute temperature
Ψ = volume of mixture
p = total pressure of mixture
n_i = moles of component i
x_i = mole fraction of component i
N = number of components

Ideal Gas Equations. For all equations:
N = number of components
x_i = mole fraction of component i
n_i = moles of component i
n = total moles of mixture

Table 5 Natural logarithms of the equilibrium constant K (for 1.0 atm pressure)

Temp, K	$H_2 \rightleftharpoons 2H$	$O_2 \rightleftharpoons 2O$	$N_2 \rightleftharpoons 2N$	$2H_2O \rightleftharpoons 2H_2 + O_2$
298	-164.005	-186.975	-367.480	-184.416
500	-92.827	-105.630	-213.372	-105.382
1000	-39.803	-45.150	-99.127	-46.326
1200	-30.874	-35.005	-80.011	-36.364
1400	-24.463	-27.742	-66.329	-29.218
1600	-19.637	-22.285	-56.055	-23.842
1800	-15.866	-18.030	-48.051	-19.652
2000	-12.840	-14.622	-41.645	-16.290
2200	-10.353	-11.827	-36.391	-13.536
2400	-8.276	-9.497	-32.011	-11.238
2600	-6.517	-7.521	-28.304	-9.296
2800	-5.002	-5.826	-25.117	-7.624
3000	-3.685	-4.357	-22.359	-6.172
3200	-2.534	-3.072	-19.937	-4.902
3400	-1.516	-1.935	-17.800	-3.782
3600	-0.609	-0.926	-15.898	-2.784
3800	0.202	-0.019	-14.199	-1.890
4000	0.934	0.796	-12.660	-1.084
4500	2.486	2.513	-9.414	0.624
5000	3.725	3.895	-6.807	1.992
5500	4.743	5.023	-4.666	3.120
6000	5.590	5.963	-2.865	4.064

Temp, K	$2H_2O \rightleftharpoons H_2 + 2OH$	$2CO_2 \rightleftharpoons 2CO + O_2$	$N_2 + O_2 \rightleftharpoons 2NO$
298	-212.416	-207.524	-70.104
500	-120.562	-115.232	-40.590
1000	-52.068	-47.058	-18.776
1200	-40.566	-35.742	-15.138
1400	-32.198	-27.684	-12.540
1600	-26.132	-21.660	-10.588
1800	-21.314	-16.994	-9.072
2000	-17.456	-13.270	-7.862
2200	-14.296	-10.240	-6.866
2400	-11.664	-7.720	-6.038
2600	-9.438	-5.602	-5.342
2800	-7.526	-3.788	-4.742
3000	-5.874	-2.222	-4.228
3200	-4.424	-0.858	-3.776
3400	-3.152	0.338	-3.380
3600	-2.176	1.402	-3.026
3800	-1.002	2.352	-2.712
4000	-0.088	3.198	-2.432
4500	1.840	4.980	-1.842
5000	3.378	6.394	-1.372
5500	4.636	7.542	-0.994
6000	5.686	8.490	-0.682

y_i = mass fraction of component i
m_i = mass of component i
m = mass of mixture
M_i = molecular weight of component i
M = mixture molecular weight
$\bar{R}$ = universal gas constant
R = average specific gas constant
R_i = specific gas constant of component i
V_i = partial volume of component i
V = volume of mixture
p_i = partial pressure of component i
p = total pressure of mixture

Dalton's law of partial pressures is expressed as:

$$p = \sum_{i=1}^{N} p_i$$

Amagat's law of partial volumes is expressed as:

$$V = \sum_{i=1}^{N} V_i$$

Mixture molecular weight is found by:

$$M = \frac{\sum_{i=1}^{N} m_i}{\sum_{i=1}^{N} n_i} = \sum_{i=1}^{N} x_i M_i$$

Mixture average specific gas constant is found by:

$$R = \sum_{i=1}^{N} y_i R_i$$

Mixture average specific heat (either C_P or C_v) is found by:

$$C_{ave} = \sum_{i=1}^{N} y_i C_i \qquad \bar{C}_{ave} = \sum_{i=1}^{N} x_i \bar{C}_i$$

where C has dimensions of energy/(mass · temp) and $\bar{C}$ has dimensions of energy/(mole · temp) (Table 6).

Mixture average internal energy is found by:

$$u_{ave} = \sum_{i=1}^{N} y_i u_i \qquad \bar{u}_{ave} = \sum_{i=1}^{N} x_i \bar{u}_i$$

and the mixture average enthalpy is found by:

$$h_{ave} = \sum_{i=1}^{N} y_i h_i \qquad \bar{h}_{ave} = \sum_{i=1}^{N} x_i \bar{h}_i$$

Table 6 Constant pressure specific heats at zero pressure

The equations in Table 6 are used to calculate the specific heats, $\overline{C}_p$, of ideal gases. The specific heat at constant volume, $\overline{C}_v$, is calculated by $\overline{C}_v = \overline{C}_p - \overline{R}$, where $\overline{R}$ is the universal gas constant.

Gas	$\overline{C}_p, \dfrac{\text{kcal}}{\text{kmol} \cdot \text{K}}, \dfrac{\text{Btu}}{\text{lb mol} \cdot {}^{\circ}\text{R}}$	Range, ${}^{\circ}\text{R}$	Max error, %
N_2	$9.3355 - 122.56\,\theta^{-1.5} + 256.38\,\theta^{-2} - 196.08\,\theta^{-3}$	540–6300	0.43
O_2	$8.9465 + 4.8044 \times 10^{-3}\,\theta^{1.5} - 42.679\,\theta^{-1.5} + 56.615\,\theta^{-2}$	540–6300	0.30
H_2	$13.505 - 167.96\,\theta^{-0.75} + 278.44\,\theta^{-1} - 134.01\,\theta^{-1.5}$	540–6300	0.60
CO	$16.526 - 0.16841\,\theta^{0.75} - 47.985\,\theta^{-0.5} + 42.246\,\theta^{-0.75}$	540–6300	0.42
OH	$19.490 - 14.185\,\theta^{0.25} + 4.1418\,\theta^{0.75} - 1.0196\,\theta$	540–6300	0.43
NO	$14.169 - 0.40861\,\theta^{0.5} - 16.877\,\theta^{-0.5} + 17.899\,\theta^{-1.5}$	540–6300	0.34
H_2O	$34.190 - 43.868\,\theta^{0.25} + 19.778\,\theta^{0.5} - 0.88407\,\theta$	540–6300	0.43
CO_2	$-0.89286 + 7.2967\,\theta^{0.5} - 0.98074\,\theta + 5.7835 \times 10^{-3}\,\theta^2$	540–6300	0.19
NO_2	$11.005 + 51.650\,\theta^{-0.5} - 86.916\,\theta^{-0.75} + 55.580\,\theta^{-2}$	540–6300	0.26
CH_4	$-160.82 + 105.10\,\theta^{0.25} - 5.9452\,\theta^{0.75} + 77.408\,\theta^{-0.5}$	540–3600	0.15
C_2H_4	$-22.800 + 29.433\,\theta^{0.5} - 8.5185\,\theta^{0.75} + 43.683\,\theta^{-3}$	540–3600	0.07
C_2H_6	$1.648 + 4.124\,\theta - 0.153\,\theta^2 + 1.74 \times 10^{-3}\,\theta^3$	540–2700	0.83
C_3H_8	$-0.966 + 7.279\,\theta - 0.3755\,\theta^2 + 7.58 \times 10^{-3}\,\theta^3$	540–2700	0.40
C_4H_{10}	$0.945 + 8.873\,\theta - 0.438\,\theta^2 + 8.36 \times 10^{-3}\,\theta^3$	540–2700	0.54

$$\theta = \frac{T(\text{Kelvin})}{100} = \frac{T(\text{Rankine})}{180}$$

Gas	$\overline{C}_p, \dfrac{\text{kJ}}{\text{kmol} \cdot \text{K}}$	Range, K	Max error, %
N_2	$39.060 - 512.79\,\theta^{-1.5} + 1072.7\,\theta^{-2} - 820.40\,\theta^{-3}$	300–3500	0.43
O_2	$37.432 + 0.020102\,\theta^{1.5} - 178.57\,\theta^{-1.5} + 236.88\,\theta^{-2}$	300–3500	0.30
H_2	$56.505 - 702.74\,\theta^{-0.75} + 1165.0\,\theta^{-1} - 560.70\,\theta^{-1.5}$	300–3500	0.60
CO	$69.145 - 0.70463\,\theta^{0.75} - 200.77\,\theta^{-0.5} + 176.76\,\theta^{-0.75}$	300–3500	0.42
OH	$81.546 - 59.350\,\theta^{0.25} + 17.329\,\theta^{0.75} - 4.2660\,\theta$	300–3500	0.43
NO	$59.283 - 1.7096\,\theta^{0.5} - 70.613\,\theta^{-0.5} + 74.889\,\theta^{-1.5}$	300–3500	0.34
H_2O	$143.05 - 183.54\,\theta^{0.25} + 82.751\,\theta^{0.5} - 3.6989\,\theta$	300–3500	0.43
CO_2	$-3.7357 + 30.529\,\theta^{0.5} - 4.1034\,\theta + 0.024198\,\theta^2$	300–3500	0.19
NO_2	$46.045 + 216.10\,\theta^{-0.5} - 363.66\,\theta^{-0.75} + 232.550\,\theta^{-2}$	300–3500	0.26
CH_4	$-672.87 + 439.74\,\theta^{0.25} - 24.875\,\theta^{0.75} + 323.88\,\theta^{-0.5}$	300–2000	0.15
C_2H_4	$-95.395 + 123.15\,\theta^{0.5} - 35.641\,\theta^{0.75} + 182.77\,\theta^{-3}$	300–2000	0.07
C_2H_6	$6.895 + 17.26\,\theta - 0.6402\,\theta^2 + 0.00728\,\theta^3$	300–1500	0.83
C_3H_8	$-4.042 + 30.46\,\theta - 1.571\,\theta^2 + 0.03171\,\theta^3$	300–1500	0.40
C_4H_{10}	$3.954 + 37.12\,\theta - 1.833\,\theta^2 + 0.03498\,\theta^3$	300–1500	0.54

$$\theta = T(\text{Kelvin})/100$$

where u and h have dimensions of energy/mass and $\bar{u}$ and $\bar{h}$ have dimensions of energy/mole. Mixture average entropy is found by:

$$s_{ave} = \sum_{i=1}^{N} y_i s_i \qquad \bar{s}_{ave} = \sum_{i=1}^{N} x_i \bar{s}_i$$

where s has dimensions of energy/(mass · temp) and $\bar{s}$ has dimensions of energy/(mole · temp).

The Clausius-Clapeyron equation applies to a pure substance with one phase in equilibrium with another. Absolute temperature and pressure are denoted by T and p. The general form for the Clausius-Clapeyron equation is:

$$\left(\frac{dp}{dT}\right)_{sat} = \frac{s'' - s'}{v'' - v'} = \frac{h'' - h'}{T(v'' - v')}$$

The integrated form for the solid-vapor region, which assumes ideal gas vapor and h_{ig} = constant, is:

$$\ln\frac{p_B}{p_A} = \frac{h_{ig}}{R}\left(\frac{1}{T_A} - \frac{1}{T_B}\right)$$

The integrated form for the liquid-vapor region, which assumes ideal gas vapor and h_{fg} = constant, is:

$$\ln\frac{p_B}{p_A} = \frac{h_{fg}}{R}\left(\frac{1}{T_A} - \frac{1}{T_B}\right)$$

The integrated form for the solid-vapor region, which assumes constant h_{if} and v_{if}, is:

$$p_B - p_A = \frac{h_{if}}{v_{if}}\ln\frac{T_B}{T_A}$$

where

p = absolute pressure
T = absolute temperature
h = enthalpy (per unit mass)
$h_{if} = h_f - h_i$
$h_{ig} = h_g - h_i$
$h_{fg} = h_g - h_f$
R = specific gas constant
v = specific volume
$v_{if} = v_f - v_i$
s = entropy (per unit mass)
Subscripts: i = ice
$\qquad\qquad f$ = liquid
$\qquad\qquad g$ = vapor (gas)

Psychrometrics—Dry Air and Water Vapor Considered Ideal Gases. Psychrometrics is the study of the thermodynamic properties of moist air and the analysis of conditions and processes involving moist air.

Humidity ratio, W, is expressed as:

$$W = \frac{\text{mass of water vapor in air sample}}{\text{mass of dry air in same air sample}} = 0.622\frac{p_w}{p - p_w}$$

where p = total absolute pressure, and p_W = partial absolute pressure of water vapor.

Relative humidity, ϕ, is expressed as:

$$\phi = \frac{\text{partial pressure of water vapor in air}}{\left(\begin{array}{l}\text{saturation pressure of water vapor}\\ \text{at dry bulb temperature}\end{array}\right)} = \frac{p_w}{(p_{w,\,sat})_{dbt}}$$

where $(p_{w,\,sat})_{dbt}$ = saturation pressure of water vapor at the dry bulb temperature.

Specific humidity, q, is expressed as:

$$q = \frac{\text{mass of water vapor in air sample}}{\text{total mass of same air sample}} = \frac{W}{1 + W}$$

Degree of saturation, μ, is expressed as:

$$\mu = \frac{\text{humidity ratio}}{\left(\begin{array}{l}\text{humidity ratio of saturated}\\ \text{air at the dry bulb temper-}\\ \text{ature}\end{array}\right)} = \left[\frac{p_w}{p - p_w}\right]\left[\frac{p - (p_{w,\,sat})_{dbt}}{(p_{w,\,sat})_{dbt}}\right]$$

Specific volume is expressed by:

$$v = \frac{\text{volume of sample}}{\text{mass of dry air in sample}} = \frac{R_{da}T}{p}(1 + 1.608\,W)$$

where R_{da} = specific gas constant for dry air.

Enthalpy is expressed as:

$$h = h_{da} + W\,h_g$$

where

W = humidity ratio (lbm water/lbm dry air)
h_{da} = enthalpy of dry air per unit mass of dry air
h_{da} = 0 at 0 °F
h_{da} = $0.240T$ (Btu/lbm dry air with T in °F)
h_g = enthalpy of saturated water vapor at the dry bulb temperature (Btu/lbm water)
h_g = 0 for liquid water at 32.0 °F and 14.696 psia
$h_g \cong 1061 + 0.444T$ (Btu/lbm water with T in °F)

The relationship of humidity ratio and dry-bulb temperature T and wet bulb temperature T':

$$W = \frac{(1093 - 0.556T')\,W' - 0.240\,(T - T')}{1093 + 0.444T - T'}$$

with T and T' in °F, W and W' in lbm water/lbm dry air, and W' = humidity ratio of saturated air at T'.

SELECTED REFERENCES

- Crawford, F. H., and van Vorst, W. D., *Thermodynamics for Engineers*, Harcourt, Brace, and World, Inc., New York, 1968.
- Huang, F. F., *Engineering Thermodynamics*, Macmillan, New York, 1976.
- Lee, J. F., Sears, F. W., and Turcotte, D. L., *Statistical Thermodynamics*, Addison-Wesley, Reading, MA, 1963.
- Reynolds, W. C., *Thermodynamics*, McGraw-Hill, New York, 1968.
- Saad, M. A., *Thermodynamics for Engineers*, Prentice Hall, Englewood Cliffs, NJ, 1966.
- Sonntag, R. E. and Van Wylen, G. J., *Introduction to Thermodynamics: Classical and Statistical*, John Wiley & Sons, New York, 1982, Second Edition.
- Van Wylen, G. J., and Sonntag, R. E., *Fundamentals of Classical Thermodynamics*, John Wiley & Sons, New York, 1973, Second Edition.
- Wark, K., *Thermodynamics*, McGraw-Hill, New York, 1977.
- Wood, B. D., *Applications of Thermodynamics*, Addison-Wesley, Reading, MA, 1982, Second Edition.

21
Heat Transfer

By Benjamin T. F. Chung, Ph.D.
Department of Mechanical Engineering
University of Akron

Heat transfer is energy in transit as a result of temperature difference. Whenever a temperature difference exists in a medium or between media, heat transfer must take place. Mechanical engineers deal with problems of heat transfer in the fields of internal combustion engines, power generation, refrigeration, heating, and ventilation. Metallurgical and ceramic engineers must control temperatures accurately during the heat treatment of various metals and ceramics to achieve the desired properties of the heat treated material. In all fields of engineering, problems are confronted concerning the most effective transmission of heat or the protection of a construction most effectively against heat losses or gains.

Three recognized modes of heat transfer are conduction, convection, and thermal radiation. They differ entirely in physical mechanism and governing laws. In conduction, heat flows from a high-temperature region to a region of lower temperature within a medium or between different media in direct physical contact. Conduction is the only mechanism by which heat can flow in opaque solids. Convective heat transfer occurs when a fluid is mixed due to gross movement of fluid mass. Energy transfer from one fluid particle to another remains a process of conduction, but the energy may be transferred from one point in space to another by the fluid displacement. Therefore, convection is the most important mechanism of energy transfer between a solid and a liquid or a gas. Thermal radiation is a process of heat transfer from one body to another by electromagnetic wave motion. The transmission of radiant energy does not require a carrying medium.

The basic law of heat conduction, proposed by Fourier, states that the rate of heat flow in a material is proportional to the area perpendicular to heat flow and the temperature gradient at that section. The proportion constant is called thermal conductivity of the material. In general, the thermal conductivity varies with temperature. Some industrial problems involving heat conduction are the annealing of castings, the vulcanizing of rubber, and the heating or cooling of the walls of buildings, furnaces, and ovens.

The prediction of the rates at which heat is transferred by convection from a solid surface by an ambient fluid involves a thorough understanding of principles of heat conduction, fluid dynamics, and boundary layer theory. The complexities involved in an analytical approach may be combined in terms of a single parameter by introduction of Newton's law of cooling, which states that the heat flux due to convection is the product of film coefficient (or heat transfer coefficient) and the temperature difference between the surface and ambient fluid. The heat transfer coefficient is not a material property but a complex function of system geometry, fluid flow, and fluid properties. Heat transfer by convection occurs on walls of rooms, on the outside of cold and warm pipes, and between surfaces and fluid of all types of heat exchangers. Boiling and condensation are also classified as convection heat transfer.

All bodies emit radiant energy. An ideal radiator, called a black body, emits radiant energy at a rate proportional to the fourth power of the absolute temperature of the body. This is known as Stefan-Boltzmann law of thermal radiation. Other surfaces, such as a glossy painted surface, do not radiate as much energy as the black body. To describe the gray nature of such a surface, the term emissivity is introduced. Emissivity is the ratio of radiation of the gray surface to an ideal black surface. The importance of radiation becomes intensified at high temperature levels. Consequently, radiation contributes substantially to heat transfer in boilers, furnaces, combustion chambers, nuclear power plants, and rocket nozzles. Solar radiation plays an important part in the design of heating and ventilating systems. Radiation can also be of importance in some instances when free convection is present even though the temperature levels are not elevated.

Most industrial problems dealing with heat exchange do not involve a single mechanism of heat transfer, but include a combination of two or more. In a steam condenser, heat transfer occurs through a series of conduction and convection processes between the condensing steam and the cooling water. In a furnace of large steam generators, heat is transferred simultaneously by radiation, convection, and conduction.

HEAT CONDUCTION

Conduction heat transfer involves energy transfer by physical interaction between adjacent molecules of substances at different temperatures. Heat flow within a homogeneous material is analogous to the flow of electricity in a conductor. The quantity flowing per unit of time is proportional to the:

- Conductivity of the material
- Area of the conductor perpendicular to the path
- Potential temperature gradient

If the heat flowing into a body is exactly equal to the heat flowing out, a steady-state condition exists. This condition refers only to cases where the temperature at any given point within the body is independent of the time.

If the inflow and outflow of heat are not equal, and the temperature at a given point and the heat content of the body vary with time, then heat is said to be flowing in an unsteady state.

FOURIER LAW, HEAT CONDUCTION EQUATIONS, AND BOUNDARY CONDITIONS

The basic law of heat conduction was first presented by a French physicist, Fourier, and is referred to as Fourier's law of heat conduction. Table 1 presents the general form related to various coordinate systems. From Fourier's law and the first law of thermodynamics, the differential equations for heat conduction in solids can be derived (see Table 2). To determine temperature distribution due to heat conduction, boundary conditions must be known. Frequently encountered boundary conditions in conduction are summarized in Table 3.

Table 1   Fourier's law of heat conduction

General form	$\mathbf{q}(\mathbf{v}, \theta) = -k \, \nabla(\mathbf{r}, \theta)$
Cartesian system	$q_x = -k \dfrac{\partial T}{\partial x}$ $q_y = -k \dfrac{\partial T}{\partial y}$ $q_z = -k \dfrac{\partial T}{\partial z}$
Cylindrical system $x = r \cos \phi$ $y = r \sin \phi$ $z = z$	$q_r = -k \dfrac{\partial T}{\partial r}$ $q_\phi = -k \dfrac{1}{r} \dfrac{\partial T}{\partial \phi}$ $q_z = -k \dfrac{\partial T}{\partial z}$
Spherical system $x = r \sin \psi \sin \phi$ $y = r \sin \psi \cos \phi$ $z = r \cos \psi$	$q_r = -k \dfrac{\partial T}{\partial r}$ $q_\phi = -k \dfrac{1}{r} \dfrac{\partial T}{\partial \phi}$ $q_\psi = -k \dfrac{1}{r \sin \phi} \dfrac{\partial T}{\partial \psi}$

Table 2 Differential equations for heat conduction in solids

General form with variable thermal properties	$\rho c_p \dfrac{\partial T(\mathbf{r}, \theta)}{\partial \theta} = \nabla \cdot [k \nabla T(\mathbf{r}, \theta)] + g(\mathbf{r}, \theta)$
General form with constant thermal properties	$\dfrac{1}{a} \dfrac{\partial T(\mathbf{r}, \theta)}{\partial \theta} = \nabla^2 T(\mathbf{r}, \theta) + \dfrac{g(\mathbf{r}, \theta)}{k}$
General form, constant properties, without heat source	$\dfrac{1}{a} \dfrac{\partial T(\mathbf{r}, \theta)}{\partial \theta} = \nabla^2 T(\mathbf{r}, \theta)$ (Fourier equation)
General form, constant properties, steady state	$\nabla^2 T(\mathbf{r}) + \dfrac{g\mathbf{r}}{k} = 0$ (Poisson equation)
General form, constant properties, steady state without heat source	$\nabla^2 T(\mathbf{r}) = 0$ (Laplace equation)
Cartesian system, constant properties	$\dfrac{\partial^2 T}{\partial x^2} + \dfrac{\partial^2 T}{\partial y^2} + \dfrac{\partial^2 T}{\partial z^2} + \dfrac{g(x, y, z, \theta)}{k} = \dfrac{1}{a} \dfrac{\partial T}{\partial \theta}$
Cylindrical system, constant properties	$\dfrac{1}{r} \dfrac{\partial}{\partial r}\left(r \dfrac{\partial T}{\partial r}\right) + \dfrac{1}{r^2} \dfrac{\partial^2 T}{\partial \phi^2} + \dfrac{\partial^2 T}{\partial z^2} + \dfrac{g(r, \phi, z, \theta)}{k}$ $= \dfrac{1}{a} \dfrac{\partial T}{\partial \theta}$
Spherical system, constant properties	$\dfrac{1}{r^2} \dfrac{\partial}{\partial r}\left(r^2 \dfrac{\partial T}{\partial r}\right) + \dfrac{1}{r^2 \sin \psi} \dfrac{\partial}{\partial \psi}\left(\sin \psi \dfrac{\partial T}{\partial \psi}\right) +$ $\dfrac{1}{r^2 \sin^2 \psi} \dfrac{\partial^2 T}{\partial \phi^2} + \dfrac{g(r, \phi, \psi, \theta)}{k} = \dfrac{1}{a} \dfrac{\partial T}{\partial \theta}$

THERMAL CONDUCTIVITY OF SUBSTANCES

Thermal conductivity is a thermophysical property of the conducting medium which represents the rate of conduction heat transfer per unit area for a unit temperature gradient. Table 4 lists thermal conductivity values for several materials. In general, thermal conductivity is strongly temperature dependent. Variations in thermal conductivity are shown in Fig. 1 for several representative substances. Values of thermal conductivity, k, for a substance depend also on chemical composition, on the physical state and texture, and on pressure.

ONE-DIMENSIONAL STEADY-STATE HEAT CONDUCTION

Neither the heat flow rate nor the temperature distribution in a one-dimensional system varies with time. Furthermore, heat flow is in one direction. Certain practical problems, such as heat conduction through a slab, or through the wall of a pipe or a spherical vessel, fall into this category. The

Table 3 Boundary conditions of heat conduction in solids

Description of system	Schematic diagram	Boundary condition
Prescribed surface temperature		$T = T_s$ at $n = s$
Prescribed heat flux at the surface		(a) $-k\left(\dfrac{\partial T}{\partial n}\right) = +q''$ at $n = s$ (b) $-k\left(\dfrac{\partial T}{\partial n}\right) = -q''$ at $n = s$
Insulation at the surface		$\dfrac{\partial T}{\partial n} = 0$ at $n = s$
Heat transfer to the ambient with temperature T_∞ by convection		$-k\dfrac{\partial T}{\partial n} = h(T - T_\infty)$ at $n = s$
Heat transfer to environment at temperature T_e by radiation		$-k\dfrac{\partial T}{\partial n} = \sigma\varepsilon(T^4 - T_e^4)$ at $n = s$

(continued)

Table 3 Boundary conditions of heat conduction in solids (continued)

Description of system	Schematic diagram	Boundary condition
Transfer heat to the ambient by convection while receiving heat flux from a distance		$-k\dfrac{\partial T}{\partial n} + q'' =$ $h(T - T_\infty)$ at $n = s$
Interface of two continua of different conductivities at perfect contact		$-k_1\dfrac{\partial T_1}{\partial n} =$ $-k_2\dfrac{\partial T_2}{\partial n}$ at $n = s$ $T_1 = T_2$ at $n = s$
Two solid continua in relative motion with pressure on interface p, the coefficient of dry friction, μ, and the relative velocity, V		$-k_1\dfrac{\partial T_1}{\partial n} + \mu pV =$ $-k_2\left(\dfrac{\partial T_2}{\partial n}\right)$ at $n = s$
Ablation or sublimation of solid with melted material removed upon its formation	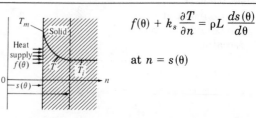	$f(\theta) + k_s\dfrac{\partial T}{\partial n} = \rho L\dfrac{ds(\theta)}{d\theta}$ at $n = s(\theta)$

(continued)

Table 3   Boundary conditions of heat conduction in solids (continued)

Description of system	Schematic diagram	Boundary condition
Solid-liquid interface for one-dimensional solidification and melting problems	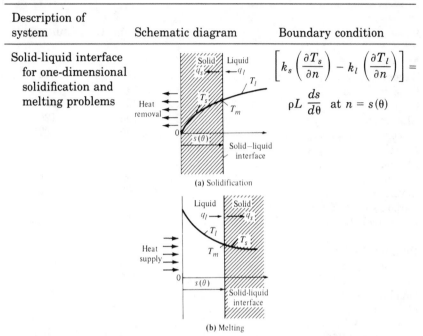	$$\left[k_s \left(\frac{\partial T_s}{\partial n} \right) - k_l \left(\frac{\partial T_l}{\partial n} \right) \right] = $$ $$\rho L \frac{ds}{d\theta} \quad \text{at } n = s(\theta)$$

L = Latent heat of fusion; s = melting, solidification or surface recession distance, or interface; $ds/d\theta$ = melting, solidification or ablation rate, $f(\theta)$ = time dependent surface heat flux; subscript s = solid phase; subscript l = liquid phase, ρ = density.

Fourier law and the differential equation of heat conduction for this case are reduced to:

$$Q = -kA \frac{dT}{dx} \quad \text{or} \quad Q = -kA \frac{dT}{dr}$$

and

$$\frac{1}{r^n} \frac{d}{dr} \left(r^n \frac{dT}{dr} \right) = 0$$

with r replacing x for $n = 0$, and with $n = 0, 1, 2$ representing slab, cylinder, and sphere, respectively. Table 5 presents temperature distribution and heat transfer rate for some simple systems in one-dimensional steady state conduction.

ONE-DIMENSIONAL COMPOSITE STRUCTURE AT STEADY STATE

Heat transfer in composite regions consisting of several layers has practical applications, such as rocket thrust chamber liners, fuel elements of nuclear reactors, and space re-entry bodies. Consider N layers of material

Table 4 Thermal conductivity of various substances at room temperature

Substance	k	
	W/(m °C)	Btu/(h ft °F)
Metals		
Silver..	420	240
Copper...	390	230
Gold	320	180
Aluminum	200	120
Silicon	150	87
Nickel	91	53
Chromium......................................	90	52
Iron (pure)	80	46
Germanium	60	35
Carbon steel (1% C)...........................	54	31
Alloy steel (18% Cr, 8% Ni)...................	16	9.2
Nonmetal solids		
Diamond, type 2A	2300	1300
Diamond, type 1...............................	900	520
Sapphire (Al_2O_3)	46	27
Limestone......................................	1.5	0.87
Glass (Pyrex 7740).............................	1.0	0.58
Teflon (Duroid 5600)	0.40	0.23
Brick (B & W K-28)............................	0.25	0.14
Plaster...	0.13	0.075
Cork	0.040	0.023
Liquids		
Mercury..	8.7	5.0
Water..	0.6	0.35
Freon F-12	0.08	0.046
Gases		
Hydrogen.......................................	0.18	0.10
Air...	0.026	0.015
Nitrogen	0.026	0.015
Steam..	0.018	0.01
Freon F-12	0.0097	0.0056

Note: (1 W/(m-°C) = 0.5778 Btu/(h-ft-°F)
From Ref 62.

having different thicknesses and thermal conductivities (Fig. 2). The contact resistance between layers is negligible. To determine the heat flow rate, Q, and temperature profile, T, of the structure, assuming one-dimensional heat conduction, the analogy between the diffusion and electric current can be extended to obtain:

$$\frac{1}{U_i A_i} = \frac{1}{U_0 A_0} = R_i + \sum_{n=1}^{N} R_n + R_0 = \frac{T_i - T_0}{Q}$$

where R_i, R_0 and R_n are the thermal resistances at the internal surface, external surface and the nth layer, respectively; U_i and U_0 are the overall

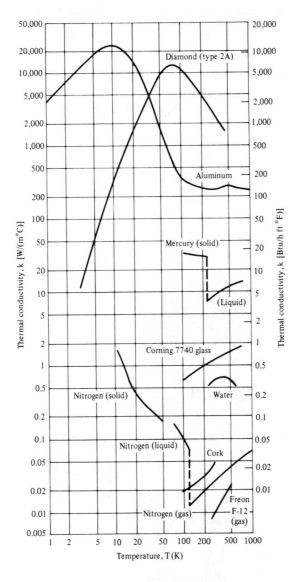

Figure 1 Variation of thermal conductivity k with temperature T for representative substances

Table 5 Temperature distribution and heat transfer rate through slab, hollow cylinder and hollow sphere

Conducting body	Schematic diagram	Temperature distribution, $\dfrac{T - T_2}{T_1 - T_2}$	Thermal conductance, $\dfrac{Q}{T_1 - T_2}$
Slab		$\left(1 + \dfrac{x}{d}\right)$	$\dfrac{kA}{L}$
Circular cylinder	Length of cylinder = l	$\dfrac{\ln(r - r_2)}{\ln(r_1 - r_2)}$	$\dfrac{2\pi k l}{\ln(r_2/r_1)}$
Hollow sphere		$\dfrac{\left(\dfrac{1}{r} - \dfrac{1}{r_2}\right)}{\left(\dfrac{1}{r_1} - \dfrac{1}{r_2}\right)}$	$\dfrac{4\pi k}{\left(\dfrac{1}{r_1} - \dfrac{1}{r_2}\right)}$

heat transfer coefficients at the internal and external surfaces, respectively; and A_i and A_0 are the cross section areas perpendicular to heat flow at the internal and the external surfaces. The explicit forms for the inverse of overall heat transfer coefficient at the external surface, $1/U$, for various geometries are presented in Table 6.

To obtain the temperature distribution in the structure, Q is expressed in terms of the temperature difference $T - T_0$ and associated resistances (from the series $R_n, R_{n+1}, R_{n+2}, \ldots, R_N$). The result is:

$$Q = \frac{T - T_0}{(1/k_n)\int_s^{s_{n+1}} ds/A(s) + \sum_{m=n+1}^{N} (1/k_m)\int_{s_m}^{s_{m+1}} ds/A(s) + 1/h_0 A(s_{N+1})}$$

where T represents the temperature of the location s (Fig. 2). The dimen-

Table 6 Inverse of overall heat transfer coefficient on the external surface, $1/U_0$, of one-dimensional composites

General formula	$\dfrac{A(s_{N+1})/A(s_1)}{h_i} + A(s_{N+1})\displaystyle\sum_{n=1}^{N}\frac{1}{k_n}\int_{s_n}^{s_{n+1}}\frac{ds}{A(s)} + \frac{1}{h_0}$
Cartesian system	$\dfrac{1}{h_i} + \displaystyle\sum_{n=1}^{N}\frac{L_n}{k_n} + \frac{1}{h_0}$
Cylindrical system	$\dfrac{(r_{N+1}/r_1)}{h_i} + r_{N+1}\displaystyle\sum_{n=1}^{N}\frac{1}{k_n}\ln\left(\frac{r_{n+1}}{r_n}\right) + \frac{1}{h_0}$
Spherical system	$\dfrac{(r_{N+1}/r_1)^2}{h_i} + r_{N+1}^2\displaystyle\sum_{n=1}^{N}\frac{1}{k_n}\left(\frac{1}{r_n} - \frac{1}{r_{n+1}}\right) + \frac{1}{h_0}$

Note: $A(s_n)$ = cross sectional area of nth layer composite at the location s_n; L_n = thickness of nth layer; see Fig. 2 for other notations.

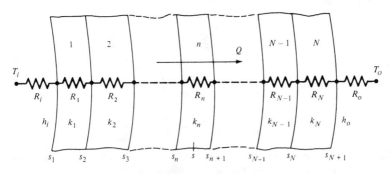

Figure 2 One-dimensional composite structure

sionless temperature profile can be expressed in terms of U_0 for various geometric systems (see Table 7). These formulations are restricted to the steady-state one-dimensional heat conduction. In practice, the combination of series- and parallel-connected structures is also important, especially in Cartesian geometry. Figure 3(a) illustrates a parallel-series composite wall that is represented by the thermal circuit shown in Fig. 3(b). The corresponding overall heat transfer coefficient is given by:

$$U = \frac{1}{(b_1 + b_2)(R_1 + R_2 + R_3)} = \frac{1}{\dfrac{L_1}{k_1} + \dfrac{b_1 + b_2}{(k_1 b_2/L_2) + (k_2 b_1/L_2)} + \dfrac{L_3}{k_3}}$$

CRITICAL RADIUS FOR INSULATED PIPES AND SPHERES

An application of one-dimensional composite structure formulas having practical significance involves insulation of small pipes, electrical wires, and spheres. Given a pipe or sphere of fixed outside radius, as shown in Fig. 4, the insulation thickness that yields the optimum insulating effect must be determined. As insulation is added, the outer surface temperature decreases, but the surface area for convective heat dissipation increases. Some optimum thickness of insulation may exist due to these opposing

Table 7 Dimensionless temperature profile in one-dimensional composites, $\dfrac{T - T_0}{T_i - T_0}$

General formula	$U_0 \left[\dfrac{A(s_{N+1})}{k_n} \displaystyle\int_s^{s_{n+1}} \dfrac{ds}{A(s)} + A(s_{N+1}) \times \right.$ $\left. \displaystyle\sum_{m=n+1}^{N} \dfrac{1}{k_m} \int_{s_m}^{s_{m+1}} \dfrac{ds}{A(s)} + \dfrac{1}{h_0} \right]$
Cartesian system	$U_0 \left[\dfrac{x_{n+1} - x}{k_n} + \displaystyle\sum_{m=n+1}^{N} \dfrac{x_{m+1} - x_m}{k_m} + \dfrac{1}{h_0} \right]$
Cylindrical system	$U_0 \left[\dfrac{r_{N+1}}{k_n} \ln\left(\dfrac{r_{n+1}}{r}\right) + r_{N+1} \times \right.$ $\left. \displaystyle\sum_{m=n+1}^{N} \dfrac{1}{k_m} \ln\left(\dfrac{r_{m+1}}{r_m}\right) + \dfrac{1}{h_0} \right]$
Spherical system	$U_0 \left[\dfrac{r_{N+1}}{k_n} \left(\dfrac{r_{N+1}}{r} - \dfrac{r_{N+1}}{r_{n+1}}\right) + r_{N+1}^2 \times \right.$ $\left. \displaystyle\sum_{m=n+1}^{N} \dfrac{1}{k_m} \left(\dfrac{1}{r_m} - \dfrac{1}{r_{m+1}}\right) + \dfrac{1}{h_0} \right]$

Note: x_n = distance of inner surface of nth composite layer; r_n = inner radius of nth composite layer; see Fig. 2 for other notations.

effects. At a certain radius of insulation, the heat loss is maximum instead of minimum, which is known as critical radius, r_0^*. Table 8 lists governing equations for determining the critical radius of insulated pipe and sphere for these cases of constant heat transfer coefficients and variable heat transfer coefficients with and without the effect of thermal radiation. When the surface radiation is included, the determination of the critical radius requires the solutions of nonlinear systems of equations because both surface temperature, T_0, and critical radius, r_0^*, are unknown under this condition.

STEADY-STATE HEAT TRANSFER FROM EXTENDED SURFACES

One of the important applications of heat transfer is the thermal analysis of extended surfaces or fins to increase the heat transfer between the struc-

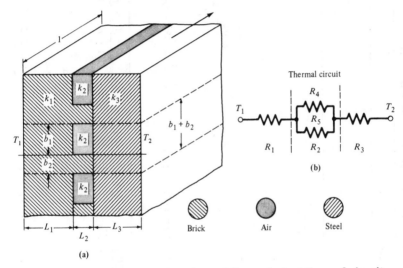

Figure 3 Parallel-series composite and its equivalent thermal circuit

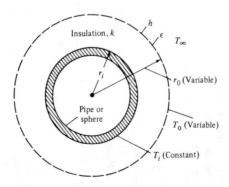

Figure 4 Critical thickness of pipe or sphere insulation

Table 8 Equations for critical radius, r_0^*, in radial conduction

Boundary condition	Cylindrical system	Spherical system
Constant heat transfer coefficient without radiation	$r_0^* = \dfrac{k}{h}$	$r_0^* = \dfrac{2k}{h}$
Variable heat transfer coefficient with $h = \dfrac{(T_0 - T_\infty)^n}{r_0^m}$ and without radiation	$r_0^* = \dfrac{k(1 - m)}{h(1 + n)}$	$r_0^* = \dfrac{k(2 - m)}{h(1 + n)}$
Constant heat transfer coefficient but with radiation	$r_0^* = \dfrac{k}{h + 4\varepsilon\sigma T_0^3}$ $\dfrac{k(T_i - T_0)}{\ln \dfrac{r_0^*}{r_i}} = hr_0^*(T_0 - T_\infty) + r_0^*\sigma\varepsilon(T_0^4 - T_\infty^4)$	$r_0^* = \dfrac{2k}{h + 4\sigma\varepsilon T_0^3}$ $\dfrac{kr_i(T_i - T_0)}{r_0^* - r_i} = hr_0^*(T_0 - T_\infty) + \sigma\varepsilon r_0^*(T_0^4 - T_\infty^4)$
Variable heat transfer coefficient with $h = (T_0 - T_\infty)^n / r_0^m$ and with radiation	$r_0^* = \dfrac{k[h(1 - m)(T_0 - T_\infty) + \varepsilon\sigma(T_0^4 - T_\infty^4)]}{[(1 + n)h + 4\varepsilon\sigma T_0^3][h(T_0 - T_\infty) + \sigma\varepsilon(T_0^4 - T_\infty^4)]}$ and $\dfrac{k(T_i - T_0)}{\ln \dfrac{r_0^*}{r_i}} = hr_0^*(T_0 - T_\infty) + r_0^*\sigma\varepsilon(T_0^4 - T_\infty^4)$	$r_0^* = \dfrac{k[(2 - m)h(T_0 - T_m) + 2\sigma\varepsilon(T_0^4 - T_\infty^4)]}{[(1 + n)h + 4\varepsilon\sigma T_0^3][h(T_0 - T_\infty) + \sigma\varepsilon(T_0^4 - T_\infty^4)]}$ and $\dfrac{kr_i(T_i - T_0)}{r_0^* - r_i} = hr_0^*(T_0 - T_\infty) + \sigma\varepsilon r_0^*(T_0^4 - T_\infty^4)$

ture and an ambient fluid. Fins on one side of a wall separating two heat exchanging fluids are most effective when made part of the face on which the thermal surface resistivity is greatest. Among considerations in fin design and placement are (a) maximum cooling efficiency; (b) minimum material for cost, weight, and space; (c) minimum resistance to the flow of ambient cooling medium; (d) adequate strength; and (e) ease of manufacture. Table 9 presents formulas for temperature profiles, total heat transfer rate, and fin efficiencies for nine different fin types. The results are based on the assumptions that thermal properties are constant; radiation is not considered; heat transfer at fin tip is negligibly small, and heat conduction is one dimensional. The fin efficiency is defined as the ratio of the actual heat transfer to the maximum possible heat transfer from the fin. Figures 5 and 6 show the comparisons of fin efficiencies of four longitudinal fins and four spines or pin fins, respectively. Table 10 gives optimum dimensions of some common longitudinal and pin fins in terms of fin profile area, or fin volume, heat transfer coefficient, and thermal conductivity.

MULTIDIMENSIONAL STEADY-STATE HEAT CONDUCTION

The problems of steady-state heat conduction in more than one dimension can be solved by analytical, graphical, experimental-analogic, and numerical means. The analytical approach is recommended in dealing with systems that are simple in geometry and boundary conditions. When geometry or

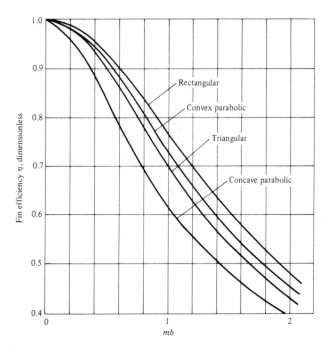

Figure 5 Comparison of fin efficiencies of four longitudinal fins

Table 9a   Heat transfer characteristics of various types of fin

Type of fin	Schematic diagram
Longitudinal fin of rectangular profile	
Longitudinal fin of triangular profile	
Longitudinal fin of concave parabolic profile	
Longitudinal fin of convex parabolic profile	

(continued)

Table 9a Heat transfer characteristics of various types of fin (continued)

Type of fin	Schematic diagram
Radial fin of rectangular profile	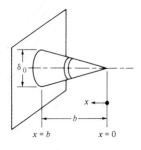
Radial fin of hyperbolic profile	
Cylindrical spine	
Conical spine	

(continued)

Table 9a Heat transfer characteristics of various types of fin (continued)

Type of fin	Schematic diagram
Spine of concave parabolic profile	
Spine of convex parabolic profile	

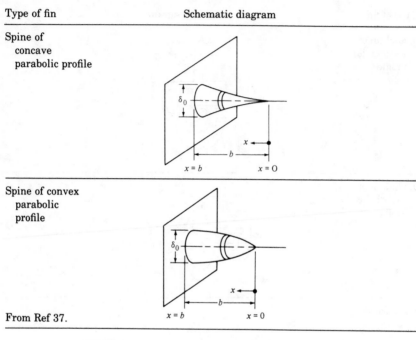

From Ref 37.

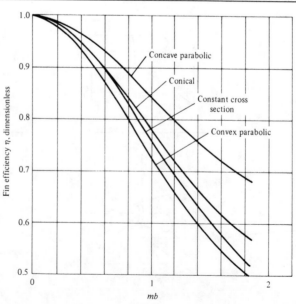

Figure 6 Comparison of fin efficiencies of four spines

Table 9b Heat transfer characteristics of various types of fins

Type of fin	Temperature profile, $\dfrac{T - T_\infty}{T_b - T_\infty} = \dfrac{\Theta}{\Theta_b}$	Rate of total heat dissipation, Q
Longitudinal fin of rectangular profile	$\dfrac{\cosh mx}{\cosh mb}$	$k\delta_o m\Theta_b \tanh mb$
Longitudinal fin of triangular profile	$\dfrac{I_0(2m\sqrt{bx})}{I_0(2mb)}$	$\dfrac{2h\Theta_b I_1(2mb)}{mI_0(2mb)}$
Longitudinal fin of concave parabolic profile	$\left(\dfrac{x}{b}\right)^{P_1}$	$\dfrac{k\delta_o\Theta_b}{2b}\left[-1 + \sqrt{1 + (2mb)^2}\right]$
Longitudinal fin of convex parabolic profile	$\left(\dfrac{x}{b}\right)^{1/4} \dfrac{I_{-1/3}\left(\frac{4}{3}mb^{1/4}x^{3/4}\right)}{I_{-1/3}\left(\frac{4}{3}mb\right)}$	$k\delta_o\Theta_b m\,\dfrac{I_{2/3}\left(\frac{4}{3}mb\right)}{I_{-1/3}\left(\frac{4}{3}mb\right)}$
Radial fin of rectangular profile	$\dfrac{[K_1(mr_e)I_0(mr) + I_1(mr_e)K_0(mr)]}{I_0(mr_o)K_1(mr_e) + I_1(mr_e)K_0(mr_o)}$	$2\pi r_o\delta_o km\Theta_b\left[\dfrac{I_1(mr_e)K_1(mr_o) - K_1(mr_e)I_1(mr_o)}{I_0(mr_o)K_1(mr_e) + I_1(mr_e)K_0(mr_o)}\right]$
Radial fin of hyperbolic profile	$\left(\dfrac{r}{r_o}\right)^{1/2}\left\{\dfrac{I_{2/3}\left(\frac{2}{3}Mr_e^{3/2}\right)I_{1/3}\left(\frac{2}{3}Mr^{3/2}\right) - I_{-2/3}\left(\frac{2}{3}Mr_e^{3/2}\right)I_{-1/3}\left(\frac{2}{3}Mr^{3/2}\right)}{I_{2/3}\left(\frac{2}{3}Mr_e^{3/2}\right)I_{1/3}\left(\frac{2}{3}Mr_o^{3/2}\right) - I_{-2/3}\left(\frac{2}{3}Mr_e^{3/2}\right)I_{-1/3}\left(\frac{2}{3}Mr_o^{3/2}\right)}\right\}$	$2\pi kr_o\delta_o\Theta_b M\sqrt{r_o}\,\psi$

(continued)

Table 9b   Heat transfer characteristics of various types of fins (continued)

Type of fin	Temperature profile, $\dfrac{T - T_x}{T_b - T_x} = \dfrac{\Theta}{\Theta_b}$	Rate of total heat dissipation, Q
Cylindrical spine	$\dfrac{\cosh mx}{\cosh mb}$	$\dfrac{\pi}{4}\, kd^2 m\Theta_b \tanh mb$
Conical spine	$\left(\dfrac{b}{x}\right)^{1/2}\dfrac{I_1(2M\sqrt{x})}{I_1(2M\sqrt{b})}$	$\dfrac{\pi k\delta_o{}^2\Theta_b M}{4\sqrt{b}}\left[\dfrac{I_2(2M\sqrt{b})}{I_1(2M\sqrt{b})}\right]$
Spine of concave parabolic profile	$\left(\dfrac{x}{b}\right)^{P_1}$	$\dfrac{\pi k\delta_o{}^2\Theta_b[-3 + (9 + 4M^2)^{1/2}]}{8b}$
Spine of convex parabolic profile	$\dfrac{I_0\left(\frac{4}{3}\sqrt{2}\,mb^{1/4}x^{3/4}\right)}{I_0\left(\frac{4}{3}\sqrt{2}\,mb\right)}$	$\dfrac{\sqrt{2}}{4}\,k\pi\delta_o{}^2\Theta_b m\,\dfrac{I_1\left(\frac{4}{3}\sqrt{2}\,mb\right)}{I_0\left(\frac{4}{3}\sqrt{2}\,mb\right)}$

Table 9b Heat transfer characteristics of various types of fins (continued)

Type of fin	Fin efficiency, $\eta = \dfrac{Q}{Q_{\text{ideal}}}$	Definition of key parameter
Longitudinal fin of rectangular profile	$\dfrac{\tanh mb}{mb}$	$m = (2h/k\delta_o)^{1/2}$
Longitudinal fin of triangular profile	$\dfrac{I_1(2mb)}{mbI_0(2mb)}$	$m = (2h/k\delta_o)^{1/2}$
Longitudinal fin of concave parabolic profile	$\dfrac{2}{1+\sqrt{1+(2mb)^2}}$	$P_1 = -\tfrac{1}{2} + \tfrac{1}{2}(1 + 4m^2b^2)^{1/2}$
Longitudinal fin of convex parabolic profile	$\dfrac{1}{mb}\dfrac{I_{2/3}\left(\tfrac{4}{3}mb\right)}{I_{-1/3}\left(\tfrac{4}{3}mb\right)}$	$m = \left(\dfrac{2h}{k\delta_o}\right)^{1/2}$
Radial fin of rectangular profile	$\dfrac{2r_o}{m(r_e^2 - r_o^2)}\left[\dfrac{I_1(mr_e)K_1(mr_o) - K_1(mr_e)I_1(mr_o)}{I_0(mr_o)K_1(mr_e) + I_1(mr_e)K_0(mr_o)}\right]$	$m = \left(\dfrac{2h}{k\delta_o}\right)^{1/2}$

(continued)

Table 9b   Heat transfer characteristics of various types of fins (continued)

Type of fin	Fin efficiency, $\eta = \dfrac{Q}{Q_{\text{ideal}}}$	Definition of key parameter
Radial fin of hyperbolic profile	$\dfrac{2r_o\psi}{m(r_e^2 - r_o^2)}$	$\psi = \dfrac{\left[I_{2/3}\left(\frac{2}{3}Mr_e^{3/2}\right)I_{-2/3}\left(\frac{2}{3}Mr_o^{3/2}\right) - I_{-2/3}\left(\frac{2}{3}Mr_e^{3/2}\right)I_{2/3}\left(\frac{2}{3}Mr_o^{3/2}\right)\right]}{\left[I_{-2/3}\left(\frac{2}{3}Mr_e^{3/2}\right)I_{-1/3}\left(\frac{2}{3}Mr_o^{3/2}\right) - I_{2/3}\left(\frac{2}{3}Mr_e^{3/2}\right)I_{1/3}\left(\frac{2}{3}Mr_o^{3/2}\right)\right]}$ $M^2 = m^2/r_o = \dfrac{2h}{k\delta_o r_o}$
Cylindrical spine	$\dfrac{\tanh mb}{mb}$	$m = (4h/kd)^{1/2}$
Conical spine	$\dfrac{\sqrt{2}\,I_2(2\sqrt{2}mb)}{(mb)I_1(2\sqrt{2}mb)}$	$M = (2m^2 b)^{1/2}$ and $m = (2h/k\delta_o)^{1/2}$
Spine of concave parabolic profile	$\dfrac{2}{1 + (1 + \frac{8}{9}m^2 b^2)^{1/2}}$	$M = \sqrt{2}\,mb$ and $m = (2h/k\delta_o)^{1/2}$ $P_1 = -\frac{3}{2} + \frac{1}{2}\sqrt{9 + 4M^2}$
Spine of convex parabolic profile	$\dfrac{1}{(2\sqrt{2}/3)\,mb}\dfrac{I_1\left(\frac{4}{3}\sqrt{2}mb\right)}{I_0\left(\frac{4}{3}\sqrt{2}mb\right)}$	$m = (2h/k\delta_o)^{1/2}$

From Ref 37.

boundary conditions involve heat transfer through surface conductance, volved to be practical.

Systems of complex geometry, but with isothermal and insulated boundaries, are readily solved by graphical or analogical methods. When the boundary conditions involve heat transfer through surface conductance, these methods become less useful and the numerical approach is recommended. This method has sufficient flexibility for problems with variable physical properties and nonuniform boundary conditions. Numerical solutions can be conveniently obtained by a digital computer.

In a two-dimensional system where only two temperature limits are involved, a conduction shape factor, S, may be defined in such a way that $Q = kS \Delta T_{\text{overall}}$. The values of S for several geometries are summarized in Table 11.

Table 10   Optimum dimensions of some longitudinal fins and spines

Fin profile / Dimension	Fin width, δ_0	Fin height, b
Longitudinal fin of rectangular profile	$0.791 \left[A_p^{\,2} \left(\dfrac{2h}{k} \right) \right]^{1/3}$	$1.262 \left(\dfrac{kA_p}{2h} \right)^{1/3}$
Longitudinal fin of triangular profile	$1.328 \left[A_p^{\,2} \left(\dfrac{2h}{k} \right) \right]^{1/3}$	$1.506 \left(\dfrac{A_p k}{2h} \right)^{1/3}$
Longitudinal fin of concave parabolic profile	$1.651 \left[A_p^{\,2} \left(\dfrac{2h}{k} \right) \right]^{1/3}$	$1.817 \left(\dfrac{A_p k}{2h} \right)^{1/3}$
Longitudinal fin of convex parabolic profile	$1.071 \left[A_p^{\,2} \left(\dfrac{2h}{k} \right) \right]^{1/3}$	$1.401 \left(\dfrac{kA_p}{2h} \right)^{1/3}$
Cylindrical spine	$1.308 \left[V^2 \left(\dfrac{2h}{k} \right) \right]^{1/5}$	$0.744 \left[V \left(\dfrac{k}{2h} \right)^2 \right]^{1/5}$
Conical spine	$1.701 \left[V^2 \left(\dfrac{2h}{k} \right) \right]^{1/5}$	$1.320 \left[V \left(\dfrac{k}{2h} \right)^2 \right]^{1/5}$
Spine of concave parabolic profile	$1.825 \left[V^2 \left(\dfrac{2h}{k} \right) \right]^{1/5}$	$1.911 \left[V \left(\dfrac{k}{2h} \right)^2 \right]^{1/5}$
Spine of convex parabolic profile	$1.564 \left[V^2 \left(\dfrac{2h}{k} \right) \right]^{1/5}$	$1.041 \left[V \left(\dfrac{k}{2h} \right)^2 \right]^{1/5}$

From Ref 3 and 7.

Table 11   Shape factor, S, for various systems in steady-state heat conduction, $S = \dfrac{Q}{k(T_1 - T_2)}$

Schematic diagram	Shape factor	Restrictions

Isothermal cylinder of radius r buried in semi-infinite medium having isothermal surface

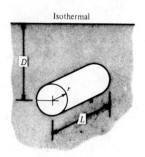

$$\dfrac{2\pi L}{\cosh^{-1}(D/r)}$$ 　　$L \gg r$

$$\dfrac{2\pi L}{\ln(2D/r)}$$ 　　$\begin{array}{l} L \gg r \\ D > 3r \end{array}$

$$\dfrac{2\pi L}{\ln\dfrac{L}{r}\left\{ 1 - \dfrac{\ln L/(2D)}{\ln(L/r)} \right\}}$$ 　　$\begin{array}{l} D \gg r \\ L \gg D \end{array}$

Isothermal sphere of radius r buried in infinite medium

$$4\pi r$$

Isothermal sphere of radius r buried in semi-infinite medium having isothermal surface

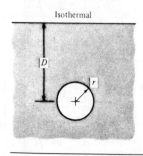

$$\dfrac{4\pi r}{1 - r/2D}$$

(continued)

Table 11 Shape factor, S, for various systems in steady-state heat conduction, $S = \dfrac{Q}{k(T_1 - T_2)}$ (continued)

Schematic diagram	Shape factor	Restrictions

Conduction between two isothermal cylinders buried in infinite medium

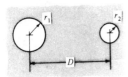

$$\dfrac{2\pi L}{\cosh^{-1}\left(\dfrac{D^2 - r_1^2 - r_2^2}{2 r_1 r_2}\right)}$$

$L \gg r$

$L \gg D$

Isothermal cylinder of radius r placed in semi-infinite medium as shown

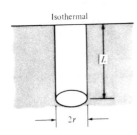

$$\dfrac{2\pi L}{\ln(2L/r)}$$

$L \gg 2r$

Isothermal rectangular parallelepiped buried in semi-infinite medium having isothermal surface

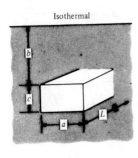

$$1.685 L \left[\log\left(1 + \dfrac{b}{a}\right)\right]^{-0.59}\left(\dfrac{b}{c}\right)^{-0.078}$$

(continued)

Table 11 Shape factor, S, for various systems in steady-state heat conduction, $S = \dfrac{Q}{k(T_1 - T_2)}$ (continued)

Schematic diagram	Shape factor	Restrictions
Thin horizontal disk buried in semi-infinite medium with isothermal surface		

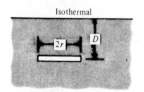

	$4r$	$D = 0$
	$8r$	$D \gg 2r$

Hemisphere buried in semi-infinite medium

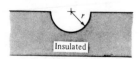

$$2\pi r$$

Isothermal sphere buried in semi-infinite medium with insulated surface

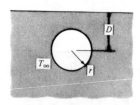

$$\frac{4\pi r}{1 + r/2D}$$

Two isothermal spheres buried in infinite medium

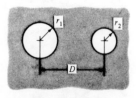

$$\frac{4\pi}{\dfrac{r_2}{r_1}\left[1 - \dfrac{(r_1/D)^4}{1 - (r_2/D)^2}\right] - \dfrac{2r_2}{D}} \qquad D > 5r$$

(continued)

Table 11 Shape factor, S, for various systems in steady-state heat conduction, $S = \dfrac{Q}{k(T_1 - T_2)}$ (continued)

Schematic diagram	Shape factor	Restrictions

Thin rectangular plate of length L buried in semi-infinite medium having isothermal surface

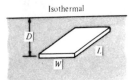

$$\frac{\pi W}{\ln(4W/L)} \qquad\qquad D = 0$$

$$\frac{2\pi W}{\ln(4W/L)} \qquad\qquad D \gg W$$

Parallel disks buried in infinite medium

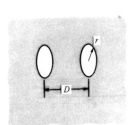

$$\frac{4\pi}{2\left[\dfrac{\pi}{2} - \tan^{-1}(r/D)\right]} \qquad\qquad D > 5r$$

Eccentric cylinders of length L

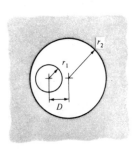

$$\frac{2\pi L}{\cosh^{-1}\left(\dfrac{r_1^{\,2} + r_2^{\,2} - D^2}{2r_1 r_2}\right)} \qquad\qquad L \gg r_2$$

(continued)

Table 11 **Shape factor, S, for various systems in steady-state heat conduction, $S = \dfrac{Q}{k(T_1 - T_2)}$ (continued)**

Schematic diagram	Shape factor	Restrictions

Cylinder centered in a square of length L

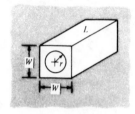

$$\frac{2\pi L}{\ln(0.54W/r)}$$

$L \gg W$

Pipe in a triangular body

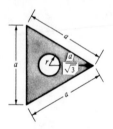

$$\frac{2\pi L}{\ln\left(\dfrac{0.327a}{r}\right)}$$

Square pipe

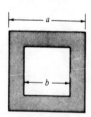

$$\frac{6.791L}{\ln\left(\dfrac{a}{b}\right) - 0.054}$$

Pipe in a pentagonal body

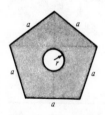

$$\frac{2\pi L}{\ln\left(\dfrac{0.724a}{r}\right)}$$

(continued)

Table 11 Shape factor, S, for various systems in steady-state heat conduction, $S = \dfrac{Q}{k(T_1 - T_2)}$ (continued)

Schematic diagram	Shape factor	Restrictions

Pipe in a hexagonal body

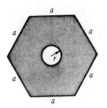

$$\frac{2\pi L}{\ln\left(\dfrac{0.898a}{r}\right)}$$

Confocal ellipses

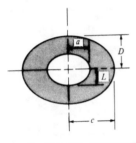

$$\frac{2\pi L}{\ln\left(\dfrac{c + D}{a + D}\right)}$$

Strip in an elliptical body

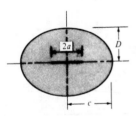

$$\frac{2\pi L}{\ln\left(\dfrac{D + c}{a}\right)}$$

Rectangular duct buried in a solid

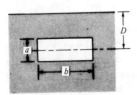

$$\frac{\left(5.7 + \dfrac{6}{2a}\right) L}{\ln\left(\dfrac{3.5D}{b^{1/4}a^{3/4}}\right)}$$

(continued)

Table 11 Shape factor, S, for various systems in steady-state heat conduction, $S = \dfrac{Q}{k(T_1 - T_2)}$ (continued)

Schematic diagram	Shape factor	Restrictions

Row of pipes buried in a solid (for any one pipe)

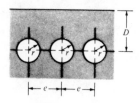

$$\frac{2\pi L}{\ln\left[\dfrac{e}{\pi r}\sinh\left(\dfrac{2\pi D}{e}\right)\right]}$$

Pipes in semi-infinite solid

$$\frac{2\pi L}{\ln\left[\dfrac{e}{\pi r}\sinh\left(\dfrac{\pi D}{e}\right)\right]}$$

Pipes in midplane of solid

Toroidal body buried in a soil

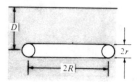

$$4\pi^2 R/\ln\left[8\frac{R}{r}\left(\frac{\ln(4R/D)}{\ln(8R/r)}\right)+1\right] \qquad r \ll D \ll R$$

$$4\pi^2 R/\ln(8R/r) \qquad\qquad D \gg R$$

Strip buried in a solid

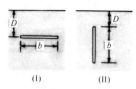

(I) $\quad\dfrac{2.94L}{(D/b)^{0.32}}$

(II) $\quad\dfrac{2.38L}{(D/b)^{0.24}}$

T_1 and T_2 are two isothermal surface temperatures of the body summarized from Ref 27 and 66.

UNSTEADY-STATE HEAT CONDUCTION

If a solid body is rapidly subjected to a change in environment, some time must elapse before temperature equilibrium or steady-state prevails. Analyses must be modified to account for the change in internal energy of the body with time, and boundary conditions must be adjusted to match the physical situation in the unsteady-state heat transfer problem. Unsteady heat flow problems also include periodic variations of temperature and heat flow, such as found in internal combustion engines, air conditioning, instrumentation, and process control.

System with Negligible Internal Thermal Resistance. Although no materials possess an infinite thermal conductivity, many transient heat flow problems may be solved with acceptable accuracy by assuming that the internal conductive resistance is so small that the system temperature is substantially uniform at any instant. This assumption is justified when the external thermal resistance between the surface and the surrounding medium is so large compared to the internal thermal resistance that it controls the heat transfer process. Analysis based on this assumption is called lumped heat capacity analysis. A measure of the thermal resistance within a solid body is the ratio of the internal to the external resistance. This ratio can be written in dimensionless form as hL/k, the Biot number, where h is the average unit-surface conductance, L is a significant length dimension obtained by dividing the volume of the body by its surface area, and k is the thermal conductivity of the solid body. When the Biot number is less than 0.1, the lumped capacity type of analysis is expected to yield a reasonable estimate. For a solid with a uniform initial temperature T_i suddenly placed in an environment with a uniform temperature T_∞, if the heat transfer coefficient and specific heat are constant, the lumped capacity analysis leads to the following expression for temperature history of the solid:

$$\frac{T - T_\infty}{T_i - T_\infty} = \exp(-kA\theta/\rho\, cV)$$

$$= \exp(-F_0 B_i)$$

where B_i and F_0 are the Biot number and Fourier number respectively $(F_0 = a\theta/L^2)$. The instantaneous transfer rate at any time, θ, is:

$$q = \rho\, cV \frac{dT}{d\theta} = kA\,(T_\infty - T_i)\exp(-B_i \cdot F_0)$$

The amount of heat transfer in time interval, θ, which equals the change of internal energy of the lumped system becomes:

$$Q = \int_0^\theta q\, d\theta = (T_\infty - T_i)\rho\, cV[1 - \exp(B_i \cdot F_0)]$$

A summary of temperature histories of some simple systems on the basis of lumped capacity analysis is presented in Table 12.

System with Negligible Surface Thermal Resistance. When the internal thermal resistance of a solid is substantially higher than the surface resistance, the heat transfer coefficient may be considered infinite $(h \to \infty)$ so that the initial body surface temperature T_0, is suddenly changed to and maintained at a constant ambient temperature T_∞ (i.e., $T_0 = T_\infty$). For this case, the determination of temperature distribution requires the solution of partial differential equations. Analytical solutions are available for simple geometries with constant thermal properties k, ρ and c (Table 13). The corresponding graphical representations are shown in Fig. 7 through 10.

System with Finite Surface and Internal Thermal Resistance. In most practical conduction heat transfer problems, both the thermal conductivity of the solid and the surface heat transfer coefficient are finite.

508/ENGINEERING MATHEMATICS

Table 12 Temperature history of simple systems of negligible internal thermal resistance ($k \to \infty$)

System	Temperature history, $\dfrac{T - T_\infty}{T_i - T_\infty}$
Infinite plate of thickness L	$e^{-(2h/L\rho c)\theta}$
Infinite cylinder of radius r_0	$e^{-(2h/r_0\rho c)\theta}$
Sphere of radius r_0	$e^{-(3h/r_0\rho c)\theta}$
Infinite square rod of side a	$e^{-(4h/a\rho c)\theta}$
Cube of side a	$e^{-(6h/a\rho c)\theta}$
A thin plate submerged in a fluid with temperature that varies linearly with time, i.e., $T_\infty = a + b\theta$	$\theta = (a + b\theta) - \dfrac{\rho c V b}{hA} +$ $\left(T_i - a + \dfrac{\rho c V b}{hA}\right) e^{-(hA/\rho c V)\theta}$

Note: ρ = density; c = specific heat; V = volume of the body; A = surface area.

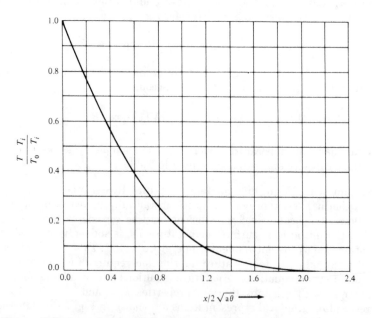

$x/2\sqrt{a\theta} \longrightarrow$

Figure 7 Temperature response, temperature gradient, and heating rate in a semi-infinite solid, $x \geq 0$, after sudden change in surface temperature from T_i when $\theta < 0$ to T_0 for $\theta \geq 0$, ($T_0 = T_\infty$)

Therefore, the convective boundary conditions must be employed in the solution of Fourier differential equations. A large number of analytical solutions are available in the literature. Table 14 illustrates a few simple systems encountered frequently in engineering practice, with corresponding temperature charts presented in Fig. 11 through 20 (Heisler and Gröber charts).

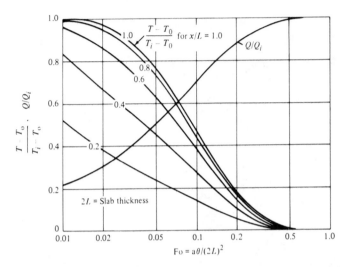

Figure 8 The temperature distribution and heat flow in an infinite slab of thickness 2L at a temperature T_i which has its surface temperature suddenly changed to T_0. (x is measured from the surface)

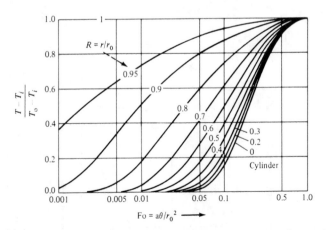

Figure 9 Temperature response of a cylinder, $0 \leq r \leq r_0$, after sudden change in external surface temperature at $r = r_0$ from T_i when $\theta < 0$ to T_0 for $\theta \geq 0$

Table 13 Temperature distribution and heat transfer in time interval θ

Schematic diagram	Temperature distribution, $\dfrac{T - T_0}{T_i - T_0}$	Initial energy storage, Q_i	Heat transfer in time interval θ, $\dfrac{Q}{Q_i}$
Semi-infinite solid 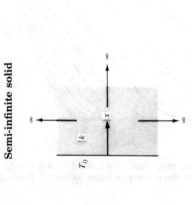	$\mathrm{erf}\left(\dfrac{x}{2\sqrt{\alpha\theta}}\right)$	$\rho c A(T_i - T_0)$	$-\dfrac{2}{\sqrt{\pi}}\sqrt{\alpha\theta}$
Infinite cylinder of radius r_0	$\displaystyle\sum_{n=1}^{\infty}\frac{1}{\beta_n}\exp(-\beta_n^2\alpha\theta/r_0^2)$ $\dfrac{J_0[\beta_n r/r_0]}{J_1(\beta_n)}$ β_n are the roots of $J_0(\beta) = 0$	$\rho c \pi r_0^2(T_i - T_0)$	$\displaystyle\sum_{n=1}^{\infty}\frac{-1}{\beta_n^2}\left\{1 - \exp[-\beta_n^2\alpha\theta/r_0^2]\right\}$

(continued)

Table 13 Temperature distribution and heat transfer in time interval θ (continued)

Schematic diagram	Temperature distribution, $\dfrac{T-T_0}{T_i-T_0}$	Initial energy storage, Q_i	Heat transfer in time interval θ, $\dfrac{Q}{Q_i}$

Infinite plate of thickness 2L

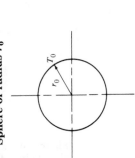

$T_0 = T_\infty$

Temperature distribution:
$$\frac{2}{\pi}\sum_{n=0}^{\infty}\exp\left\{-\left[\left(n+\frac{1}{2}\right)\pi\right]^2\frac{\alpha\theta}{L^2}\right\}\frac{(-1)^n}{n+\frac{1}{2}}\cos\left(n+\frac{1}{2}\right)\frac{\pi x}{L}$$

Initial energy storage:
$$\rho c A L(T_i - T_0)$$

Heat transfer:
$$\frac{2}{\pi^2}\sum_{n=0}^{\infty}\frac{-1}{\left(n+\frac{1}{2}\right)^2}\left[1-\exp\left\{-\left[\left(n+\frac{1}{2}\right)\pi\right]^2\frac{\alpha\theta}{L^2}\right\}\right]$$

Sphere of radius r_0

Temperature distribution:
$$\frac{2r_0}{\pi r}\sum_{n=1}^{\infty}\frac{(-1)^{n+1}}{n}\exp\left[-\frac{n^2\pi^2\alpha\theta}{r_0^2}\right]\sin\left(\frac{n\pi r}{r_0}\right)$$

Initial energy storage:
$$\frac{4}{3}\pi r_0^{\,3}\rho c(T_i - T_0)$$

Heat transfer:
$$\frac{6}{\pi^2}\sum_{n=1}^{\infty}\frac{-1}{n^2}\left[1-\exp\left(-\frac{n^2\pi^2\alpha\theta}{r_0^2}\right)\right]$$

Note: T_i = initial temperature, $T_0 = T_\infty$, surface temperature; J_0 = Bessel function of the first kind with zero order; J_1 = Bessel function of the first kind with first order; erf = error function

Two- and Three-Dimensional Transient Systems. Many practical problems involve two- and three-dimensional heat flow. The solution of such problems is often achieved from a product solution. Several one-dimensional transient solutions may be combined to obtain the solution to a two- or three-dimensional transient problem. Figure 21 shows the required product solution for the geometries indicated. In such cases, the body is initially at a uniform temperature equal to T_i and is instantaneously placed in a convective environment at temperature T_∞. The following notations are employed in Fig. 21:

$$C(r, \theta) = \frac{T(r, \theta) - T_\infty}{T_i - T_\infty}$$

$$P(x, \theta) = \frac{T(x, \theta) - T_\infty}{T_i - T_\infty}$$

$$S(x, \theta) = \frac{T(x, \theta) - T_\infty}{T_i - T_\infty}$$

where

$C(r, \theta)$ represents a transient solution for a cylindrical geometry
$P(x, \theta)$ represents a transient solution for a plane wall
$S(x, \theta)$ represents a transient solution for a semi-infinite body

CONVECTION HEAT TRANSFER

Convection heat transfer occurs between a fluid and a solid surface in contact with the fluid. When fluids are everywhere at rest, the problem becomes one of either simple heat conduction or simple diffusion. If fluid motion is induced by such means as a pump, blower, wind or vehicle motion,

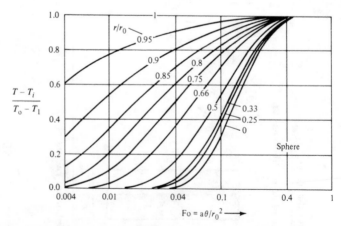

Figure 10 Temperature response of a sphere, $0 \leq r \leq r_0$, after sudden change in external surface temperature at $r = r_0$ from T_i when $\theta < 0$ to T_0 for $\theta \geq 0$

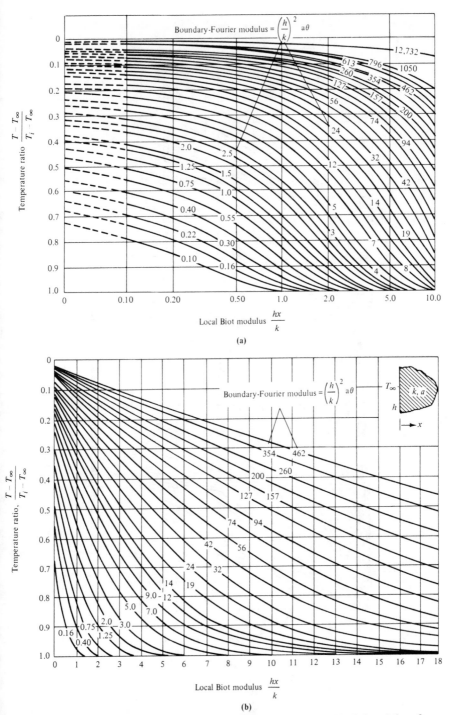

Figure 11 Dimensionless temperature distribution in a semi-infinite slab subjected to a sudden change in environmental temperature

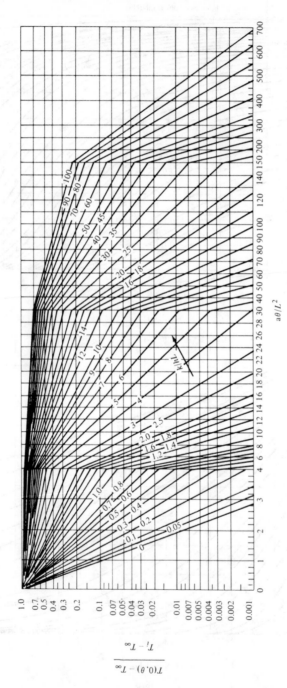

Figure 12 Midplane temperature for an infinite plate of thickness 2L

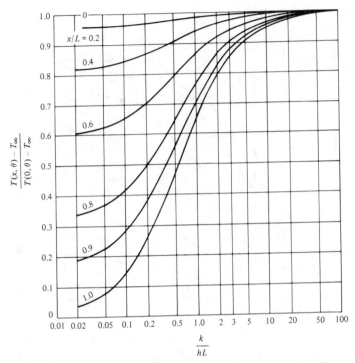

Figure 13 Temperature as a function of center temperature in an infinite plate of thickness 2L

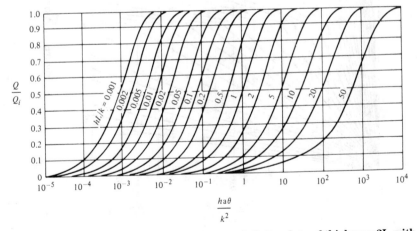

Figure 14 Dimensionless heat loss Q/Q_i of an infinite plate of thickness 2L with time

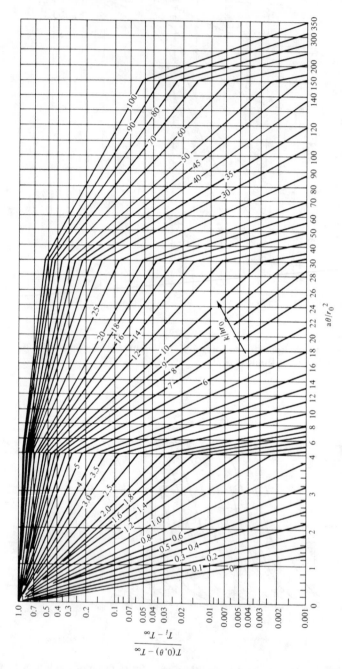

Figure 15 Axis temperature for an infinite cylinder of radius r_0

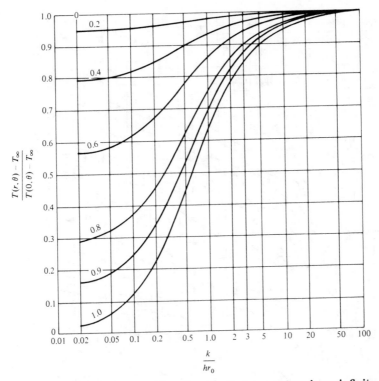

Figure 16 Temperature as a function of axis temperature in an infinite cylinder of radius r_0

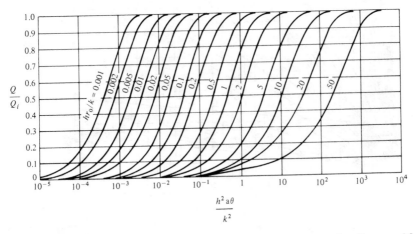

Figure 17 Dimensionless heat loss Q/Q_i of an infinite cylinder of radius r_0 with time

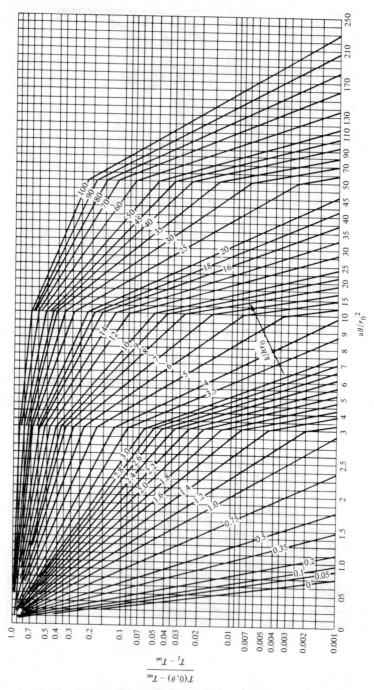

Figure 18 Center temperature for a sphere of radius r_0

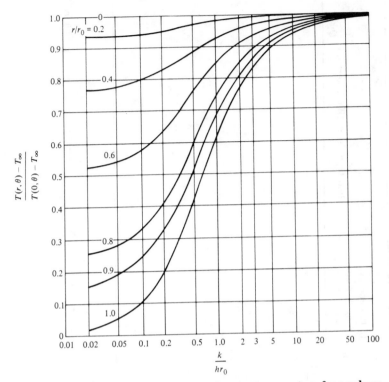

Figure 19 Temperature as a function of center temperature for a sphere of radius r_0

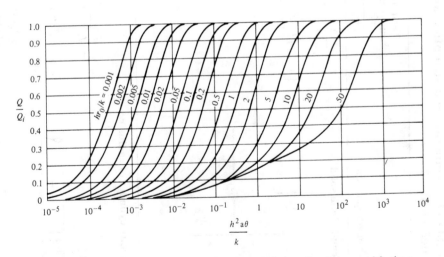

Figure 20 Dimensionless heat loss Q/Q_i of a sphere of radius r_0 with time

Table 14 Temperature distribution and heat transfer in solids with finite conductivity and transfer coefficient

Schematic diagram	Temperature distribution, $\dfrac{T - T_\infty}{T_i - T_\infty}$	Initial energy storage per unit area, Q_i	Heat transfer in time interval θ, $\dfrac{Q}{Q_i}$
Semi-infinite solid 	$\operatorname{erf}\left(\dfrac{x}{2\sqrt{a\theta}}\right) + \exp\left[\dfrac{hx}{k} + \dfrac{h^2 a\theta}{k^2}\right]$ $\left[1 - \operatorname{erf}\left(\dfrac{x}{2\sqrt{a\theta}} + \dfrac{h}{k}\sqrt{a\theta}\right)\right]$		
Infinite cylinder of radius r_0 	$2\sum_{n=1}^{\infty} \dfrac{J_1(\beta_n) J_0(\beta_n r/r_0)}{J_0^2(\beta_n) + J_1^2(\beta_n)}$ $\exp(-\beta_n^2 a\theta/r_0^2)$ where β_n are the roots of $\beta = \dfrac{h r_0 J_0(\beta)}{k J_1(\beta)}$	$\rho c \pi r_0^2 (T_i - T_\infty)$	$4\sum_{n=1}^{\infty} \dfrac{1}{\beta_n^2} \dfrac{-J_1^2(\beta_n)}{\beta_n^2 J_0^2(\beta_n) + J_1^2(\beta_n)} [1 - \exp(-\beta_n^2 a\theta/r_0^2)]$

Table 14 Temperature distribution and heat transfer in solids with finite conductivity and transfer coefficient (continued)

Schematic diagram	Temperature distribution, $\dfrac{T - T_\infty}{T_i - T_\infty}$	Initial energy storage per unit area, Q_i	Heat transfer in time interval θ, $\dfrac{Q}{Q_i}$
Infinite plate of thickness $2L$	$4\displaystyle\sum_{n=1}^{\infty} \left(\dfrac{\sin \beta_n}{2\beta_n + \sin 2\beta_n} \right) e^{-\beta_n^2 \alpha\theta/L^2}$ $\cos\left(\dfrac{\beta_n x}{L} \right)$ where β_n are the roots of $\beta \tan \beta = hL/k$	$\rho c_p L (T_i - T_\infty)$	$4\displaystyle\sum_{n=1}^{\infty} \dfrac{-\sin^2 \beta_n}{2\beta_n^2 + \beta_n \sin 2\beta_n}[1 - \exp(-\beta_n^2 \alpha\theta/L^2)]$
Sphere of radius r_0	$4\displaystyle\sum_{n=1}^{\infty} \dfrac{\sin \beta_n - \beta_n \cos \beta_n}{2\beta_n - \sin 2\beta_n}$ $\exp[-\beta_n^2 \alpha\theta/r_0^2]$ $\dfrac{\sin(\beta_n r/r_0)}{(\beta_n r/r_0)}$ where β_n are the roots of $\beta \cot \beta = 1 - \dfrac{hr_0}{k}$	$\dfrac{4}{3}\pi r_0^3 \rho c (T_i - T_\infty)$	$12\displaystyle\sum_{n=1}^{\infty} \dfrac{-(\sin \beta_n - \beta_n \cos \beta_n)^2}{\beta_n^3 (2\beta_n - \sin 2\beta_n)}$ $[1 - \exp(-\beta_n^2 \alpha\theta/r_0^2)]$

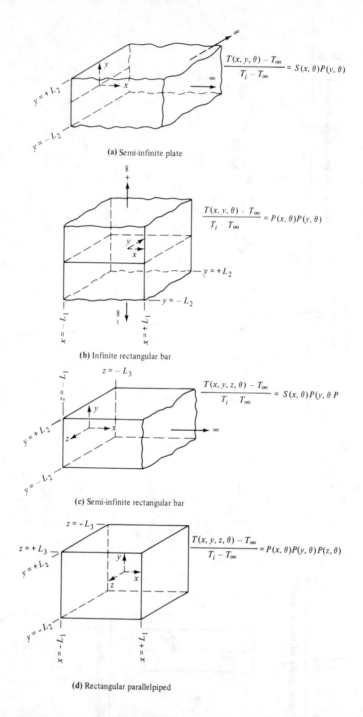

(a) Semi-infinite plate

$$\frac{T(x, y, \theta) - T_\infty}{T_i - T_\infty} = S(x, \theta)P(y, \theta)$$

(b) Infinite rectangular bar

$$\frac{T(x, y, \theta) - T_\infty}{T_i - T_\infty} = P(x, \theta)P(y, \theta)$$

(c) Semi-infinite rectangular bar

$$\frac{T(x, y, z, \theta) - T_\infty}{T_i - T_\infty} = S(x, \theta)P(y, \theta)P$$

(d) Rectangular parallelpiped

$$\frac{T(x, y, z, \theta) - T_\infty}{T_i - T_\infty} = P(x, \theta)P(y, \theta)P(z, \theta)$$

Figure 21 Product solutions for temperatures in multidimensional systems

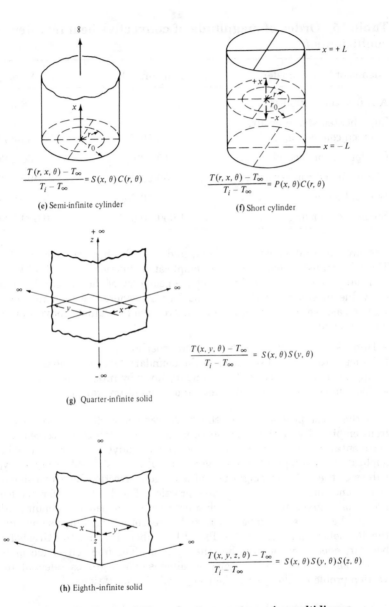

$$\frac{T(r, x, \theta) - T_\infty}{T_i - T_\infty} = S(x, \theta)C(r, \theta)$$

(e) Semi-infinite cylinder

$$\frac{T(r, x, \theta) - T_\infty}{T_i - T_\infty} = P(x, \theta)C(r, \theta)$$

(f) Short cylinder

$$\frac{T(x, y, \theta) - T_\infty}{T_i - T_\infty} = S(x, \theta)S(y, \theta)$$

(g) Quarter-infinite solid

$$\frac{T(x, y, z, \theta) - T_\infty}{T_i - T_\infty} = S(x, \theta)S(y, \theta)S(z, \theta)$$

(h) Eighth-infinite solid

Figure 21 Product solutions for temperatures in multidimensional systems (continued)

the process is generally called forced convection. If the fluid motion arises from external force fields such as gravity, acting on a density gradient induced by the transport process itself, the process is referred to as free convection. The rate of heat transfer by convection between a solid and fluid is evaluated by Newton's law of cooling, $Q = hA(T_s - T_\infty)$, where A is the sur-

Table 15   Order of magnitude of convective heat transfer coefficients h

Means of heat transfer	Btu/h-ft^2-°F	W/m^2-K
Air, free convection 1-5		6-30
Superheated steam or air, forced convection..................... 5-50		30-300
Oil, forced convection.................. 10-300		60-1,800
Water, forced convection.............. 50-2,000		300-6,000
Water, boiling 500-10,000		3,000-60,000
Steam, condensing 1,000-20,000		6,000-120,000

face area in contact with the fluid, and h is the heat transfer coefficient. The heat transfer coefficient is a complicated function of the fluid flow, the thermal properties of the fluid, and the geometry of the system. Its numerical value in general depends on the location where the fluid temperature, T_∞ is measured. Four general methods are used to evaluate convection transfer coefficients:

• Dimensional analysis combined with experiments
• Exact mathematical solutions of the boundary-layer equations
• Approximate analyses of the boundary layer by integral methods
• The analogy between heat, mass, and momentum transfer

In the most practical case, the heat transfer coefficients are evaluated from empirical equations. These equations are obtained by correlating experimental results coupling with dimensional analysis. For most engineering applications, average values are generally of interest. Table 15 gives typical values of the order of magnitude of average convection heat transfer coefficients encountered in engineering practice. The heat transfer coefficients are usually given by a relationship between one dependent nondimensional group, the Nusselt number, Nu, and three other nondimensional groups, the Reynolds number, Re; the Prandtl number, Pr; and the Grashof number, Gr, depending on whether the case involves free convection or forced convection. Table 16 gives some of dimensionless groups relevant to convection problems along with their physical interpretations.

Exact mathematical analyses of convective heat transfer requires the simultaneous solution of the equations describing the fluid motion and the energy transfer in the moving fluid. Hence, the knowledge of fluid flow is essential to the fundamental study of the convective heat transfer processes.

Table 16 Physical interpretation of some dimensionless groups

Name of the dimensionless group	Group	Physical interpretation
Biot (Bi)	$\dfrac{hL_c}{k}$	$\dfrac{\text{internal resistance to heat conduction}}{\text{external resistance to heat conduction}}$
Eckert (E)........	$\dfrac{u_\infty^2}{c_p(T_W - T_\infty)}$	$\dfrac{\text{kinetic energy}}{\text{thermal energy}}$
Euler (Eu)	$\dfrac{p}{\rho u_\infty^2}$	$\dfrac{\text{pressure forces}}{\text{inertia forces}}$
Fourier (Fo)......	$\dfrac{k\theta}{\rho c_p L_c^2}$	$\dfrac{\text{dimensionless time for transient}}{\text{conduction}}$
Froude (Fr)	$\dfrac{u_\infty^2}{L_c g}$	$\dfrac{\text{inertia forces}}{\text{gravity forces}}$
Grashof (Gr)	$\dfrac{gL_c^3 \beta(T_W - T_\infty)}{v^2}$	$\dfrac{\text{(buoyancy forces) (inertia forces)}}{\text{(viscous forces)}^2}$
Lewis (Le)	$\dfrac{D\rho_{cp}}{k}$	$\dfrac{\text{mass diffusivity}}{\text{thermal diffusivity}}$
Mach (M)	$\dfrac{u_\infty}{u_c}$	$\dfrac{\text{velocity}}{\text{sonic velocity}}$
Nusselt (Nu)	$\dfrac{hL_c}{k}$	ratio of temperature gradients
Peclet (Pe)	$\dfrac{c_p \rho u_\infty L_c}{k}$	$\dfrac{\text{convective heat transfer}}{\text{conductive heat transfer}}$
Prandtl (Pr).......	$\dfrac{\mu c_p}{k}$	$\dfrac{\text{momentum diffusivity}}{\text{thermal diffusivity}}$
Rayleigh (Ra)	$\dfrac{gL_c^3 \beta(T_W - T_\infty)}{v\alpha}$	$\dfrac{\text{forces due to buoyancy and inertia}}{\text{forces due to viscosity and thermal diffusion}}$
Reynolds (Re)	$\dfrac{\rho u_\infty L_c}{\mu}$	$\dfrac{\text{inertia forces}}{\text{viscous forces}}$
Schmidt (Sc)	$\dfrac{\mu}{\rho D}$	$\dfrac{\text{momentum diffusivity}}{\text{mass diffusivity}}$
Sherwood (Sh).....	$\dfrac{h_D L_c}{\mathscr{D}}$	ratio of concentration gradients
Stanton (St)	$\dfrac{h}{c_p \rho u_\infty}$	$\dfrac{\text{heat transfer at wall}}{\text{convective heat transfer}}$

Table 17   Key differential equations of fluid flow

Continuity equation	$\nabla \cdot \mathbf{V} = 0$

Equation of motion

Free convection. . . . . $\rho \dfrac{d\mathbf{V}}{d\theta} = \mu \nabla^2 \mathbf{V} - \rho g \beta (T - T_\infty)$

Forced convection. . . . . $\rho \dfrac{d\mathbf{V}}{d\theta} = -\nabla p + \mu \nabla^2 \mathbf{V} + \rho g$

Energy equation. . . . . $\rho c_p \dfrac{dT}{d\theta} = k \nabla^2 T + \mu \overline{\Phi}$

$\dfrac{d}{d\theta}$ = substantial time derivative, $\dfrac{d}{d\theta} = \dfrac{\partial}{\partial\theta} + \mathbf{V} \cdot \nabla$

$\mathbf{V} = \mathbf{u_i} + \mathbf{v_j} + \mathbf{w_k}$, velocity field

$\overline{\Phi}$ = dissipation function, e.g., $\overline{\Phi} = 2\left[\left(\dfrac{\partial u}{\partial x}\right)^2 + \left(\dfrac{\partial v}{\partial y}\right)^2 + \left(\dfrac{\partial w}{\partial z}\right)^2 \right] + \left(\dfrac{\partial v}{\partial x} + \dfrac{\partial u}{\partial y}\right)^2 +$

$\left(\dfrac{\partial w}{\partial y} + \dfrac{\partial v}{\partial z}\right)^2 + \left(\dfrac{\partial u}{\partial z} + \dfrac{\partial w}{\partial x}\right)^2 - \dfrac{2}{3}\left(\dfrac{\partial u}{\partial x} + \dfrac{\partial v}{\partial y} + \dfrac{\partial w}{\partial z}\right)^2$ for Cartesian coordinates

μ = dynamic viscosity
β = coefficient of volumetric thermal expansion

Differential Equations of Fluid Flow. Table 17 summarizes these equations for laminar flow with constant thermal properties. The important differential equations of fluid flow are the:

- Continuity equation, based on the law of conservation of mass
- Momentum equation, based on Newton's second law of motion
- Energy equations, based on the law of conservation of energy

ANALOGY BETWEEN HEAT TRANSFER AND MOMENTUM TRANSFER

In hydrodynamic analysis of both forced and free convection, it is important to establish whether the flow is laminar or turbulent. Laminar forced or natural convection flows exist when individual elements of fluid follow a smooth streamline path. The flow is turbulent when the movement of elements of fluid is unsteady and random. The dimensionless group known as Reynolds number is the criterion for determining whether laminar or turbulent flow is the stable form under given conditions. Complete mathematical equations describing the fluid flow and heat transfer mechanism can be written for laminar flow, although the equations can be solved analytically only for a number of simple systems, such as flow over a flat plate or through a circular tube. Our knowledge of turbulent exchange mechanism is not sufficient to write equations describing the temperature distribution directly. A useful tool for analyzing the turbulent heat transfer process is the concept of analogy between heat and momentum, that is, the heat transfer coefficient is expressed in terms of friction coefficient, f, which is available from experiments. Table 18 presents a few well known analogy formulas for turbulent pipe flow of gases and liquids. The Reynolds analogy is satisfactory for gases only ($\mathrm{Pr} \approx 1$), but the Colburn analogy can be used

Table 18 Analogy formula for Stanton number of tube flow

Type of analogy	Stanton No., $St = \dfrac{Nu}{RePr}$
Reynolds	$\dfrac{f}{8}$
Prandtl	$\dfrac{\dfrac{f}{8}}{1 + 5\sqrt{\dfrac{f}{8}}\,(Pr - 1)}$
Von Karman	$\dfrac{\dfrac{f}{8}}{1 + 5\sqrt{\dfrac{f}{8}}\left\{ Pr - 1 + \ln\left[1 + \dfrac{5}{6}(Pr - 1)\right]\right\}}$
Colburn's	$\dfrac{f}{8}\,Pr^{-2/3}$
Deissler and Webb	$\dfrac{\dfrac{f}{8}}{1.07 + 9\sqrt{\dfrac{f}{8}}\,(Pr - 1)\,Pr^{-1/4}}$
Petukhov and Popov	$\dfrac{\dfrac{f}{8}}{1.07 + 12.7\sqrt{\dfrac{f}{8}}\,(Pr^{2/3} - 1)}$

The friction factor here is defined as $f = \tau_w/(\tfrac{1}{2}\rho u_b^{\,2})$. Another form of friction factor known as Faning friction factor is encountered frequently in engineering. It is one quarter of the present value.

for a fluid having Prandtl numbers ranging from 0.6 to 50.

To apply the analogy between heat and momentum transfers, it is necessary to know the friction factor. Table 19 summarizes the equations available for the prediction of friction factors for both laminar and turbulent flows in various geometries. Nomenclature for flow across tube banks is shown in Fig. 22. In addition, the friction factor chart for pipe flow is shown in Fig. 23, which is known as the Moody Chart.

FORCED CONVECTION OF EXTERNAL FLOW

External flow includes (a) flow along a flat plate; (b) flow over a bluff body such as a sphere, wire, or tube; and (c) flow normal to tube bundles. The important difference between flows over a plate and over a bluff body lies

Table 19 Equations for friction coefficient at various flow and geometri conditions

Flow and geometry	Friction coefficient equation	Restriction and rem
Laminar flow in either smooth or rough pipe	$f = \dfrac{64}{\text{Re}}$	Re < 2,000
Turbulent flow in smooth pipe and parallel planes	$\dfrac{1}{\sqrt{\dfrac{f}{4}}} = 4.0 \log\left(\text{Re}\,\sqrt{\dfrac{f}{4}}\right) - 0.4$	Re > 3,000
Turbulent flow in rectangular, triangular and trapezoidal conduit	$\dfrac{f}{4} = 0.079\,\text{Re}^{-0.25}$	Re < 100,000
Fully turbulent flow in rough pipe	$\dfrac{1}{\sqrt{\dfrac{f}{4}}} = 4 \log\dfrac{D}{e} + 2.28$	$\dfrac{D/e}{\text{Re}\sqrt{\dfrac{f}{4}}} > 0.01$
Transition flow in rough pipe	$\dfrac{1}{\sqrt{\dfrac{f}{4}}} = 4 \log\dfrac{D}{e} + 2.28 - 4 \log$ $\left(1 + 4.67\,\dfrac{D/e}{\text{Re}\sqrt{\dfrac{f}{4}}}\right)$	
Laminar flow over flat plate	$f_x = 0.664\,\text{Re}_x^{-0.5}$	$\text{Re}_x < 5 \times 10^5$
Turbulent flow over flat plate	$f_x = 0.0592\,\text{Re}_x^{-0.2}$	$5 \times 10^5 < \text{Re}_x < 10$
Flow across tube banks in line arrangement	$f =$ $4\left[0.044 + \dfrac{0.08\,(S_l/D)}{[(S_t - D)/D]^{[0.43 + (1.13D/S_l)]}}\right]\text{Re}_{\max}^{-0.15}$	2,000 < Re < 40,0 (a)
Flow across tube bank in staggered arrangement	$f =$ $4\left[0.25 + \dfrac{0.1175}{\left(\dfrac{S_t - D}{D}\right)^{1.08}}\right]\text{Re}_{\max}^{-0.16}$	2,000 < Re < 40,0 (a)

Note: $\text{Re}_{\max}$ = maximum Reynolds number = $\dfrac{\rho u_{\max} D}{\mu}$

(a) See Fig. 22 for notations

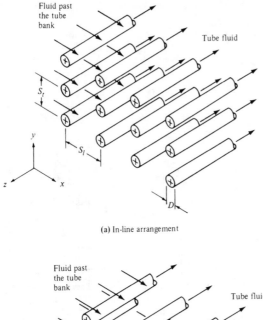

(a) In-line arrangement

(b) Staggered arrangement

Figure 22 Nomenclature for flow across tube banks

in the behavior of the boundary layer. On a streamlined body, the flow separation, if it takes place at all, occurs near the rear. On a bluff body, the point of separation of the boundary layer often lies not far from the leading edge.

The flat plate is the simplest geometry to analyze. It has been thoroughly studied and the results are very useful. For several geometries, Table 20 shows a summary of the dimensionless mean heat transfer coefficient, Nu, for external flow. Heat transfer in flow across tube banks is of particular importance in the design of heat exchangers. The correlations for the average Nusselt numbers for this situation have the following form:

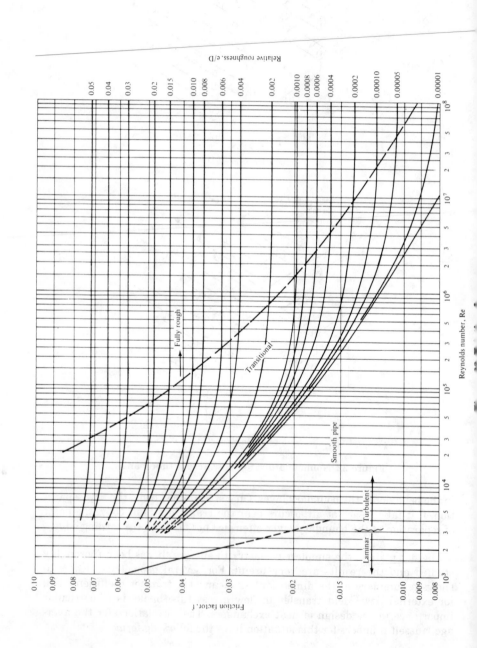

Table 20 Correlations for forced convection from external flow

Geometry	Correlation for Nu	Restrictions
Flow over flat plate	$0.664 \, Re_L^{1/2} Pr^{1/3}$	Laminar $Re < 5 \times 10^5$
	$(0.036 \, Re_L^{4/5} - 836) Pr^{1/3}$	$Re > 5 \times 10^5$
	$0.036 \, (Re_L^{0.8} Pr^{0.43} - 17{,}400) + 297 Pr^{1/3}$	$10^5 < Re_L < 5.5 \times 10^6$ $0.7 < Pr < 380$
	$0.036 \, Pr^{0.42} (Re_L^{0.8} - 9{,}200)(\mu_\infty/\mu_w)^{0.14}$	$0.26 < \mu_\infty/\mu_w < 3.5$
Inclined plate	$0.86 \, Re^{1/2} Pr^{1/3}$	
Flow across cylinder	$[0.8327 - 0.4 \ln (RePr)]^{-1}$	$RePr < 0.2$
	$0.3 + 0.62\phi[1 + 3.92 \times 10^{-4} Re^{5/8}]^{4/5}$ $\phi = Re^{1/2} Pr^{1/3} [1 + (0.4/Pr)^{2/3}]^{-1/4}$	$0.2 < RePr$
	$0.989 \, Re^{0.33} Pr^{1/3}$	$0.4 < Re < 4$
	$0.911 \, Re^{0.385} Pr^{1/3}$	$4 < Re < 40$
	$0.683 \, Re^{0.466} Pr^{1/3}$	$40 < Re < 4000$
	$0.193 \, Re^{0.618} Pr^{1/3}$	$4000 < Re < 40{,}000$
	$0.0266 \, Re^{0.805} Pr^{1/3}$	$40{,}000 < Re < 400{,}000$
	$(0.35 + 0.56 \, Re^{0.52}) Pr^{0.3}$	$0.1 < Re < 100{,}000$
	$(0.4 \, Re^{1/2} + 0.06 \, Re^{2/3}) Pr^{0.4} (\mu_b/\mu_w)^{1/4}$	$10 < Re < 100{,}000$
Flow across square tube	$0.246 \, Re^{0.58} Pr^{1/3}$	$5000 < Re < 100{,}000$
	$0.102 \, Re^{0.675} Pr^{1/3}$	$5000 < Re < 100{,}000$

(continued)

Note: All fluid properties are evaluated at the film temperature, $T_f = (T_w + T_\infty)/2$. The Reynolds number and the Prandtl number are evaluated at film temperature.
From Ref 33.

532/ENGINEERING MATHEMATICS

Table 20 Correlations for forced convection from external flow (continued)

Geometry	Correlation for Nu	Restrictions
Flow across hexagonal tube	$0.153\,\mathrm{Re}^{0.638}\mathrm{Pr}^{1/3}$	$5000 < \mathrm{Re} < 100{,}000$
	$0.16\,\mathrm{Re}^{0.638}\mathrm{Pr}^{1/3}$	$\begin{cases} 5000 < \mathrm{Re} < 19{,}500 \end{cases}$
	$0.0385\,\mathrm{Re}^{0.782}\mathrm{Pr}^{1/3}$	$\begin{cases} 19{,}000 < \mathrm{Re} < 100{,}000 \end{cases}$

Flow across vertical plate	$0.228\,\mathrm{Re}^{0.731}\mathrm{Pr}^{1/3}$	$4000 < \mathrm{Re} < 15{,}000$

Flow across sphere ($L_c = D$)	$0.37\,\mathrm{Re}^{0.6}$	$17 < \mathrm{Re} < 70{,}000$
	$(0.97 + 0.68\,\mathrm{Re}^{0.5})\mathrm{Pr}^{0.3}$	$1 < \mathrm{Re} < 2000$
	$(1.2 + 0.53\,\mathrm{Re}^{0.54})\mathrm{Pr}^{0.3}[\mu_f/\mu_w]^{0.25}$	$1 < \mathrm{Re} < 200{,}000$
	$2 + (0.4\,\mathrm{Re}^{1/2} + 0.06\,\mathrm{Re}^{2/3})\,\mathrm{Pr}^{0.4}(\mu_b/\mu_w)^{1/4}$	$3.5 < \mathrm{Re} < 76{,}000$

Note: All fluid properties are evaluated at the film temperature, $T_f = (T_w + T_\infty)/2$. The Reynolds number and the Prandtl number are evaluated at film temperature. From Ref 33.

$$\mathrm{Nu} = C\,\mathrm{Re}_{max}\,\mathrm{Pr}^{1/3}$$

where Re_{max} is the Reynolds number based on the largest velocity. All fluid properties in the various dimensionless groups are evaluated at the film temperature. The values of C and n are presented in Table 21 for tube banks

Table 21 Values of C and n in the correlation for heat transfer in flow across tube banks of 10 rows or more

$$Nu = C\,Re^n\,Pr^{1/3} \quad (2000 < Re_{max} < 40{,}000)$$

S_t/D		S_l/D							
		1.25		1.5		2.0		3.0	
		C	n	C	n	C	n	C	n
In-line:	1.250	0.348	0.592	0.275	0.608	0.100	0.704	0.0633	0.752
	1.500	0.367	0.586	0.250	0.620	0.101	0.702	0.0678	0.744
	2.000	0.418	0.570	0.299	0.602	0.229	0.632	0.198	0.648
	3.000	0.290	0.601	0.357	0.584	0.374	0.581	0.286	0.608
Staggered:	0.600	—	—	—	—	—	—	0.213	0.636
	0.900	—	—	—	—	0.446	0.571	0.401	0.581
	1.000	—	—	0.497	0.558	—	—	—	—
	1.125	—	—	—	—	0.478	0.565	0.518	0.560
	1.250	0.518	0.556	0.505	0.554	0.519	0.556	0.522	0.562
	1.500	0.451	0.568	0.460	0.562	0.452	0.568	0.488	0.568
	2.000	0.404	0.572	0.416	0.568	0.482	0.556	0.449	0.570
	3.000	0.310	0.592	0.356	0.580	0.440	0.562	0.421	0.574

Note: See Fig. 22 for geometry and notations.

Table 22 Ratio of (Nu) for N rows deep to (Nu) for 10 rows deep

N	1	2	3	4	5	6	7	8	9	10
Ratio for in-line tubes .	0.64	0.80	0.87	0.90	0.92	0.94	0.96	0.98	0.99	1.0
Ratio for staggered tubes	0.68	0.75	0.83	0.89	0.92	0.95	0.97	0.98	0.99	1.0

of 10 rows or more. If the number of rows is less than 10, the Nu value obtained from Table 21 should be multiplied by an appropriate factor from Table 22.

FORCED CONVECTION OF INTERNAL FLOW

The heating and cooling of fluids flowing in conduits are important heat transfer processes in engineering. In convective heat transfer problems of pipe flow, two types of boundary conditions encountered most frequently are uniform wall temperature (UWT) and uniform wall heat flux (UHF). In either case, the Nusselt number is expressed in terms of the Reynolds number and Prandtl number. Table 23 summarizes the correlations for forced convection of internal flow under fully developed conditions.

When the fluid enters the pipe, a certain distance, called entrance length, is required for the velocity to be fully developed. After the entrance length, the velocity is independent of axial position. Similarly, the thermal entrance length is the distance required for the temperature profile to become fully developed. The heat transfer coefficient decreases as fluid moves farther from the entrance. Table 24 provides the values of local Nusselt numbers for laminar flow through a circular tube subject to constant wall temperature and constant wall flux conditions. For the case of turbulent flow, the local Nusselt numbers in the combined thermal and hydrodynamic entry length of circular tubes with UHF and UWT are shown in Fig. 24 and 25, respectively.

FREE CONVECTION

Free convection currents transfer internal energy stored in the fluid in essentially the same manner as forced convection currents. However, the intensity of the mixing motion is generally less in free convection; consequently, the heat transfer coefficients are lower than that of forced convection. Free convection is the dominant heat-flow mechanism from steam

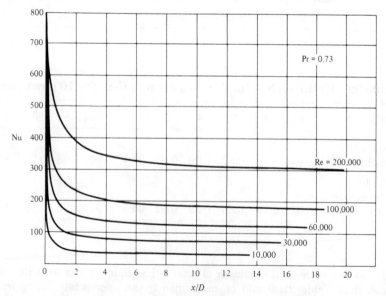

Figure 24 Nusselt number in the combined thermal and hydrodynamic entry length of a circular tube with uniform heat flux at wall

Table 23 Correlations for forced convection from internal flow

Flow geometry	Correlation for Nu	Restrictions
Flow through a smooth circular tube	UWT: $1.86(\text{RePr})^{1/3}(D/C)^{1/3}(\mu/\mu_w)^{0.14}$	Laminar flow $\text{RePr}(D/L) > 10$
$\text{Re}_{\text{cr}} = 2300$	UWT: $3.66 + \dfrac{0.0668(D/L)\,\text{RePr}}{1 + 0.04[(D/L)\,\text{RePr}]^{2/3}}$	Laminar flow
	Fully developed	
	UWT: $\text{Nu} = 3.658$ UHF: $\text{Nu} = 4.364$	Laminar flow
	UWT: $0.021\text{Re}^{0.8}\text{Pr}^{0.6}$ UHF: $0.022\text{Re}^{0.8}\text{Pr}^{0.6}$	Turbulent flow $0.5 < \text{Pr} < 1.0$
	UHF: $\dfrac{\left(\dfrac{f}{8}\right)\text{RePr}(\mu/\mu_w)^n}{1.07 + 12.7\sqrt{\dfrac{f}{8}}\,(\text{Pr}^{2/3} - 1)}$	Turbulent flow $2 < \text{Pr} < 140$
	$f = [1.82\log_{10}\text{Re} - 1.64]^{-2}$	$5 \times 10^3 < \text{Re} < 1.25 \times 10^5$ $0.08 < (\mu/\mu_w) < 40$
	$n = 0.11$ for heating; 0.25 for cooling	
	UWT: $5.0 + 0.025(\text{RePr})^{0.8}$ UHF: $4.82 + 0.0185(\text{RePr})^{0.827}$	Liquid metal $1000 < \text{RePr}$
		Liquid metal $10^2 < \text{RePr} < 10^4$ $3.6 \times 10^3 < \text{Re} < 9.05 \times 10^5$ (continued)

Note: UHF = uniform heat flux at the boundary; UWT = uniform wall temperature; thermal properties are evaluated at bulk temperature except μ_w, which is evaluated at the wall temperature; f = friction factor for a smooth tube; ε/D = relative roughness of wall. From Ref 33.

Table 23 Correlations for forced convection from internal flow (continued)

Flow geometry	Correlation for Nu	Restrictions
Flow through a rough circular tube	UWT: $\dfrac{\left(\frac{f}{8}\right)\mathrm{Re\,Pr}}{1 + 1.5\mathrm{Re}^{-1/8}\mathrm{Pr}^{-1/6}[(f/f_s)\mathrm{Pr} - 1]}$	$\mathrm{Pr} < 1$ $500 < \mathrm{Re} < 8 \times 10^4$
	UHF: $\left(\dfrac{f}{8}\right)\mathrm{Re\,Pr}\left\{1 + \left[5.19\mathrm{Pr}^{0.44}(e^*)^{0.2} - 8.48\right]\sqrt{\dfrac{f}{8}}\right\}$	$1.2 < \mathrm{Pr} < 5.9$
	$e^* = \mathrm{Re}\sqrt{\dfrac{f}{8}} \times \dfrac{\varepsilon}{D}$	$6 \times 10^4 < \mathrm{Re} < 5 \times 10^5$ $0.0024 < \dfrac{\varepsilon}{D} < 0.049$
Flow between plates	UWT: $12 + 0.03\mathrm{Re}^m\mathrm{Pr}^n$	
	$m = 0.88 - \dfrac{0.24}{3.6 + \mathrm{Pr}}$	$0.1 < \mathrm{Pr} < 10^4$
	$n = 0.33 + 0.5e^{-0.6\mathrm{Pr}}$	$10^4 < \mathrm{Re} < 10^6$
	$8.3 + 0.02\mathrm{Re}^{0.82}\mathrm{Pr}^n$	$0.004 < \mathrm{Pr} < 0.1$
	$n = 0.52 + \dfrac{0.0096}{0.02 + \mathrm{Pr}}$	$10^4 < \mathrm{Re} < 10^6$
Helically coiled tube, coil dia. D, tube dia. d	UWT: $\dfrac{0.32 + 3(d/D)}{0.86 - 0.8(d/D)}$	Laminar flow $20 < \mathrm{Re}(d/D)^{1/2} < 830$ $30 < \mathrm{Pr} < 450$ $0.01 < (d/D) < 0.08$
	$\mathrm{Re}^{0.5}\mathrm{Pr}^{0.33}(d/L)^{(0.14 + 0.8(d/D))}$	
	UHF: $1.268\mathrm{Re}^{0.26}\mathrm{Pr}^{1/6}$	

Note: UHF = uniform heat flux at the boundary; UWT = uniform wall temperature; thermal properties are evaluated at bulk temperature except μ_w, which is evaluated at the wall temperature; f = friction factor; f_s = friction factor for a smooth tube; ε/D = relative roughness of wall. From Ref. 33.

radiators, walls of a building, the human body, transmission lines, transformers, and electrically heated wires to a quiescent atmosphere. The determination of heat load on air conditioning or refrigeration equipment requires a knowledge of free convection heat transfer coefficients. Gravity is not the only body force which can produce free convection. Centrifugal forces and coriolis forces also influence free convective heat transfer, particularly in rotating systems. The Nusselt number associated with free convection from an isothermal wall is related to the Grashof number and Prandtl number by the expression $Nu = C(GrPr)^n R$, in which a correction function, R, is introduced to account for counteracting effects and to cover a wider range of parameters. Results of free convective heat transfer coefficients of various geometrical systems are presented in Table 25. The rate of free convection heat transfer between the solid surface and the surrounding fluid, apart from other factors, depends on whether the flow is laminar or turbulent. For an isothermal wall, laminar free convection occurs when $10^4 < PrGr < 10^9$, and turbulent free convection occurs when $PrGr > 10^9$. The free convection effect can be neglected when $PrGr < 10^3$.

Another interesting phenomenon of complex systems involving free convection is heat transfer inside an enclosed space such as heat transfer in two isothermal vertical plates with two different temperatures. For this case, the heat flux is conveniently expressed in terms of effective or apparent thermal conductivity, k_e, that is:

$$\frac{Q}{A} = k_e \frac{\Delta T_w}{\delta}$$

Table 24   Local laminar Nusselt number, for circular tube with uniform wall heat flux and wall temperature

$x^* = \dfrac{x}{r} \dfrac{1}{RePr}$	Nu_{x^*} for UHF	Nu_{x^*} for UWT
0.001	. . .	12.86
0.002	12.0	. . .
0.004	9.93	7.91
0.010	7.49	5.99
0.020	6.14	. . .
0.040	5.19	4.18
0.080	. . .	3.79
0.100	4.51	3.71
0.200	. . .	3.66
∞	4.36	3.66

From Ref 34.

where ΔT_w is the temperature difference of two surfaces, and δ is the distance between the two isothermal surfaces. The apparent conductivity which takes into account the free convection effect is expressed in a general form:

$$\frac{k_e}{k} = C(\mathrm{Gr}_\delta \mathrm{Pr})^n \left(\frac{L}{\delta}\right)^m$$

Table 26 lists values of C, n, and m for a number of physical systems.

MIXED CONVECTION AND CONVECTION FROM ROTATING BODIES

In some forced convection situations, velocities of forced flow are comparable with the velocities of natural convective currents, for example, when the air velocity is of the order 1 ft/sec. Under such conditions, a superposition of forced and natural convection, called mixed convection, must be considered. If the forced convection effects are very large, the influence of natural-convection current may be negligible, and similarly when the natural-convection forces are very strong, the forced convection effect may be neglected. The ratio of $\mathrm{Gr}/\mathrm{Re}^2$ gives a qualitative indication of the influence of buoyancy on forced convection. When $0.1 < \mathrm{Gr}/\mathrm{Re}^2 < 10$, mixed convection becomes significant. Regimes of free, forced, and mixed convection for flows through horizontal or vertical tubes are graphically shown in Fig. 26 and 27, respectively.

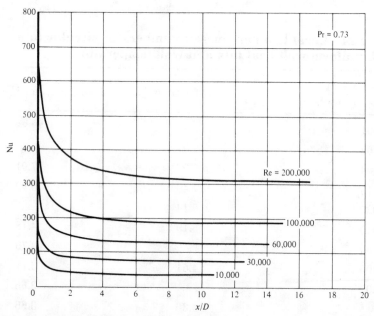

Figure 25 Nusselt number in the combined thermal and hydrodynamic entry length of a circular tube with constant wall temperature

Table 25 Free convection heat transfer coefficient for various systems, $Nu = C(GrPr)^n R$

System	Schematic diagram	C	n	R	Operating conditions
Exposed surfaces					
Horizontal cylinder	 $X = D$	0.53	$\frac{1}{4}$	1	Laminar flow
		0.13	$\frac{1}{3}$	1	Turbulent flow
Vertical plate and vertical cylinder with large diameter	 $X = L$	0.8	$\frac{1}{4}$	$\left[1 + \left(1 + \dfrac{1}{\sqrt{\mathrm{Pr}}}\right)^2\right]^{-1/4}$	Laminar flow; to obtain local Nu, use $C = 0.6$, $X = x$; formula applicable to vertical cylinder when $\dfrac{D}{L} \geq 38(\mathrm{Gr})^{-1/4}$
		0.0246	$\frac{2}{5}$	$[\mathrm{Pr}^{1/6}/(1 + 0.494\mathrm{Pr}^{2/3})]^{2/5}$	Turbulent flow; to obtain local Nu use $C = 0.0296$ and $X = x$
Heated horizontal plate facing upward	 $X = l$	0.54	$\frac{1}{4}$	1	Laminar flow; for circular disc of diameter D, use $X = 0.9D$
		0.14	$\frac{1}{3}$	1	Turbulent flow

(continued)

Table 25 Free convection heat transfer coefficient for various systems, $Nu = C(GrPr)^n R$ (continued)

System	Schematic diagram	C	n	R	Operating conditions
Vertical cylinder with small diameter		0.686	$\frac{1}{4}$	$[Pr/(1 + 1.05Pr)]^{1/4}$	Laminar flow; $Nu_{total} = Nu + 0.52\frac{L}{D}$
Heated horizontal plate facing downward		0.27	$\frac{1}{4}$	1	Laminar flow only

(continued)

HEAT TRANSFER/541

Table 25 Free convection heat transfer coefficient for various systems, $Nu = C(GrPr)^n R$ (continued)

System	Schematic diagram	C	n	R	Operating conditions
Moderately inclined plate		0.8	$\frac{1}{4}$	$\left[\dfrac{\cos\phi}{1 + \left(1 + \dfrac{1}{\sqrt{Pr}}\right)} \right]^{1/4}$	Laminar flow (multiply Gr by cos φ in the formula for inclined plate)
Sphere		0.49	$\frac{1}{4}$	1	Laminar flow (air)
Enclosed spaces					
Two horizontal parallel plates cold plate uppermost		0.195 0.068	$\frac{1}{4}$ $\frac{1}{3}$	$Pr^{-1/4}$ $Pr^{-1/3}$	Laminar (air) $10^4 < Gr$ $< 4 \times 10^5$ Turbulent (air) $Gr > 4 \times 10^5$

(continued)

Table 25 Free convection heat transfer coefficient for various systems, $\mathrm{Nu} = C(\mathrm{GrPr})^n \mathrm{R}$ (continued)

System	Schematic diagram	C	n	R	Operating conditions
Two vertical parallel plates at the same temperature		0.04	1	$(d/L)^3$	Air layer
Hollow vertical cylinder with open ends		0.01	1	$(d/L)^3$	Air column

(continued)

Table 25 Free convection heat transfer coefficient for various systems, $\mathrm{Nu} = C(\mathrm{GrPr})^n \mathrm{R}$ (continued)

System	Schematic diagram	C	n	R	Operating conditions
Two vertical parallel plates at different temperatures (h for both surfaces)	$\Delta T = T_h - T_c$	0.18	$\frac{1}{4}$	$(L/d)^{-1/9}(\mathrm{Pr})^{-1/4}$	Laminar (air) $2 \times 10^4 < \mathrm{Gr}$ $< 2 \times 10^5$
		0.065	$\frac{1}{3}$	$(L/d)^{-1/9}(\mathrm{Pr})^{-1/3}$	Turbulent (air) $2 \times 10^5 < \mathrm{Gr}$ $< 10^7$
Two inclined parallel plates	$\mathrm{Nu} = \frac{1}{2}\left[\mathrm{Nu}_{\mathrm{vert}} \cos \phi + \mathrm{Nu}_{\mathrm{horiz}} \sin \phi\right]$				
Two horizontal parallel plates hot plate uppermost	$\Delta T = T_h - T_c$	...	...	...	Pure conduction $q = k\dfrac{(T_h - T_c)}{d}$
		0.27	$\frac{1}{4}$	1	Laminar (air) 3×10^5 $< \mathrm{Gr} \cdot \mathrm{Pr}$ $< 3 \times 10^{10}$

(continued)

Table 25 Free convection heat transfer coefficient for various systems, Nu $= C(\mathrm{GrPr})^n \mathrm{R}$ (continued)

System	Schematic diagram	C	n	R	Operating conditions
Rectangular solid with uniform temperature		0.55	$\frac{1}{4}$	1	Laminar flow $$\frac{1}{X} = \frac{1}{c} + \frac{1}{(a+b)/2}$$

Note: X = characteristic length of the system; $\Delta T = T_w - T_\infty$, T_h = temperature of the hot surface, T_c = temperature of the cold surface; β = coefficient of volumetric thermal expansion for fluids; all properties are evaluated at film temperature except β which is computed from T_∞ or T_b.
From Ref 62 and 66.

$$k_e/k = C(\text{Gr}_\delta\text{Pr})^n(L/\delta)^m$$

Fluid	Geometry	$\text{Gr}_\delta\text{Pr}$	Pr	L/δ	C	n	m
Gas	Vertical plate, isothermal	<2000	$k_e/k = 1.0$				
		6000–200,000	0.5–2	11–42	0.197	$\frac{1}{4}$	$-\frac{1}{9}$
		200,000–1.1×10^7	0.5–2	11–42	0.073	$\frac{1}{3}$	$-\frac{1}{9}$
	Horizontal plate, isothermal, heated from below	<1700	$k_e/k = 1.0$				
		1700–7000	0.5–2	...	0.059	0.4	0
		7000–3.2×10^5	0.5–2	...	0.212	$\frac{1}{4}$	0
		>3.2×10^5	0.5–2	...	0.061	$\frac{1}{3}$	0
Liquid	Vertical plate, constant heat flux or isothermal	10^4–10^7	1–20,000	10–40	0.42(Pr^0.012)	$\frac{1}{4}$	−0.3
		10^6–10^9	1–20	1–40	0.046	$\frac{1}{3}$	0
	Horizontal plate, isothermal, heated from below	<1700	$k_e/k = 1.0$				
		1700–6000	1–5000	...	0.012	0.6	0
		6000–37,000	1–5000	...	0.375	0.2	0
		37,000–10^8	1–20	...	0.13	0.3	0
		>10^8	1–20	...	0.057	$\frac{1}{3}$	0
Gas or liquid	Vertical annulus	Same as vertical plates					
	Horizontal annulus, isothermal	6000–10^6	1–5000	...	0.11	0.29	0
		10^6–10^8	1–5000	...	0.40	0.20	0
	Spherical annulus	120–1.1×10^9	0.7–4000	...	0.228	0.226	0

From Ref 2.

Heat transfer in a rotating system provides typical examples of mixed convection. When the rotational speed is low or when the difference between the surface temperature and fluid bulk temperature is large, free convection may dominate. When rotational speed is sufficiently large, the influence of free convection becomes relatively small, and the predominant mode of heat transfer is by forced convection. When Gr is of the same order of magnitude as Re^2, the combined effects of free and forced convection must be taken into account. Table 27 gives the formulas for determining the heat transfer of various rotating systems.

THERMAL RADIATION

The emission of thermal radiation is governed by the temperature of the emitting body. Although the physical mechanism of radiation is not completely understood, radiant energy is sometimes visualized as transported by electromagnetic waves or by photons. Neither viewpoint completely describes the nature of all observed phenomena.

Electromagnetic phenomena encompass many types of radiation, from short-wavelength cosmic and γ rays to long-wavelength radio waves (see Fig. 28). Thermal radiation is the portion of the spectrum between wavelengths 10^{-7} and 10^{-4} m. The visible spectrum runs from 3.9×10^{-7} to $7.8 \times$

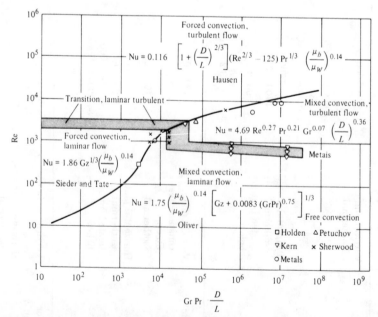

Figure 26 Regimes of free, forced, and mixed convection for flow through horizontal tubes

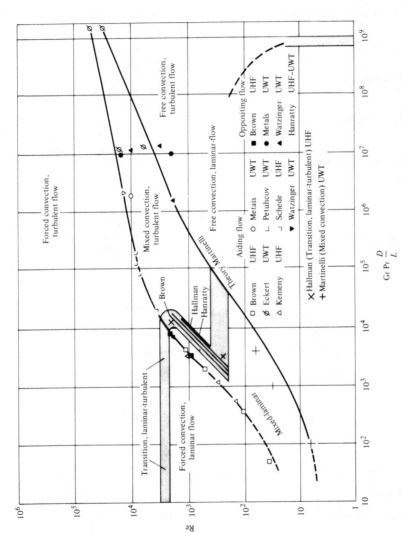

Figure 27 Regimes of free, forced, and mixed convection for flow through vertical tubes

Table 27 Heat transfer coefficient of rotating bodies

Formula	Conditions
Rotating disc	
$\mathrm{Nu} = (0.277 + 0.105\,\mathrm{Pr})\,\mathrm{Re}^{0.5}$	Laminar flow, $\mathrm{Re} < 2.5 \times 10^5$, $0.7 < \mathrm{Pr} < 5.0$
$\mathrm{Nu} = 1.1\,\mathrm{Re}^{0.5}$	Laminar flow, $\mathrm{Re} < 2.5 \times 10^5$, $\mathrm{Pr} = 10$
$\mathrm{Nu} = 0.015\,\mathrm{Re}^{0.8}$	Turbulent flow, $\mathrm{Re} > 2.5 \times 10^5$, $\mathrm{Pr} = 0.72$
$\mathrm{Nu} = 0.015\,\mathrm{Re}^{0.8} - 100\left(\dfrac{r_c}{R}\right)^2$	Laminar flow between $r = 0$ and $r = r_c$, turbulent flow between $r = r_c$ and $r = R$ where $r_c = (2.5 \times 10^5\,\nu/\omega)^{1/2}$, $\mathrm{Pr} = 0.72$
$\mathrm{Nu} = 0.4\,(\mathrm{Re}^2 + \mathrm{Gr})^{0.25}$ where	
$\mathrm{Nu} = \dfrac{hR}{k}$, $\mathrm{Re} = \dfrac{\omega R^2}{\nu}$, $\mathrm{Gr} = \dfrac{\beta g R^3 \pi^{3/2} \Delta T}{\nu^2}$	Combined effects of free convection and rotation in laminar flow (axis horizontal)

Rotating cone	
$\mathrm{Nu} = 0.515\,(\mathrm{Gr})^{0.25}$	Laminar free convection, $\mathrm{Pr} = 0.72$, $\mathrm{Gr}/\mathrm{Re}^2 > 2.0$
$\mathrm{Nu} = 0.33\,\mathrm{Re}^{0.5}$	Forced convection, $\mathrm{Pr} = 0.72$, $\mathrm{Gr}/\mathrm{Re}^2 < 0.05$
$\mathrm{Nu} = \mathrm{Re}^{0.5}[0.331 + 0.412\,(\mathrm{Gr}/\mathrm{Re}^2) + \cdots]$	Combined free and forced convection, $\mathrm{Pr} = 0.72$, $0.2 < \mathrm{Gr}/\mathrm{Re}^2 < 1.0$

(continued)

Table 27 Heat transfer coefficient of rotating bodies (continued)

Formula	Conditions

Rotating cone (continued)

where

$$\text{Nu} = \frac{hL}{k}, \ \text{Re} = \frac{\omega L^2 \sin \alpha}{\nu},$$

$$\text{Gr} = \frac{\beta g L^3 \cos \alpha \, \Delta T}{\nu^2}$$

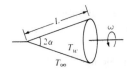

Rotating cylinder

$\text{Nu} = 0.456 \, (\text{GrPr})^{0.25}$
    Free convection, $\text{Re} <$ $(\text{Gr}/\text{Pr})^{0.5}$

$\text{Nu} = 0.18[(0.5 \, \text{Re}^2 + \text{Gr})\text{Pr}]^{0.315}$
    Combined free and forced convection, $\text{Re} \le 5 \times 10^4$

$$\text{Nu} = \frac{\text{Re} \cdot \text{Pr} \sqrt{C_D/2}}{5\text{Pr} + 5 \ln (3\text{Pr} + 1)} + \sqrt{2/C_D} - 12$$
    Forced convection, $\text{Re} > 10^5$

C_D from:

$$\frac{\text{Re}}{\text{B}} = -1.828 + 1.77 \ln \text{B}$$

for $\text{B} > 950$

$$\frac{\text{Re}}{\text{B}} = -3.68 + 2.04 \ln \text{B}$$

for $\text{B} < 950$

where $\text{B} = \text{Re} \sqrt{C_D}$

$\text{Nu} = 0.135[(0.5 \, \text{Re}^2 + \text{Re}_f^2 + \text{Gr})\text{Pr}]^{0.33}$
    Combined effects of rotation, free convection and crossflow, $\text{Re}_f < 1.5 \times 10^4$, $0.6 < \text{Pr} < 15$, $10^3 < \text{Re} < 5 \times 10^4$, value in square bracket [ ] $< 10^9$

where

$$\text{Nu} = \frac{hD}{k}, \ \text{Re} = \frac{\omega D^2}{\nu},$$

$$\text{Re}_f = \frac{v_\infty D}{\nu}, \ \text{Gr} = \frac{\beta g D^3 \Delta T}{\nu^2}$$

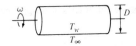

(continued)

Table 27   Heat transfer coefficient of rotating bodies (continued)

Formula	Conditions
Rotating sphere	
$\mathrm{Nu} = 0.43\ \mathrm{Re}^{0.5}\mathrm{Pr}^{0.4}$	Laminar flow, $\mathrm{Gr/Re}^2 <$ 0.1, $\mathrm{Re} < 5 \times 10^4$, $0.7 < \mathrm{Pr} < 217$
$\mathrm{Nu} = 0.066\ \mathrm{Re}^{0.67}\mathrm{Pr}^{0.4}$	Turbulent flow, $\mathrm{Gr/Re}^2$ 0.1, $5 \times 10^4 < \mathrm{Re} < 7 \times 10^5$, $0.7 < \mathrm{Pr} < 7$
$\mathrm{Nu} = 2\,(\mathrm{Re}^2 + \mathrm{Gr})^{0.164}$	Combined free and forced convection, $\mathrm{Gr/Re}^2 > 0.1$, $10^3 < \mathrm{Re} < 2 \times 10^4$, $4 \times 10^6 < \mathrm{Gr} < 2 \times 10^7$

where

$$\mathrm{Nu} = \frac{hD}{k},\ \mathrm{Re} = \frac{\omega D^2}{\nu}$$

$$\mathrm{Gr} = \frac{\beta g D^3 \Delta T}{\nu^2}$$

Note: The fluid properties are taken at the film temperature; ω = angular velocity of rotation; X = characteristic length; $\Delta T = T_w - T_\infty$, C_D = surface drag coefficient From Ref 66.

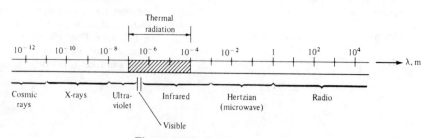

Figure 28 Radiation spectrum

10^{-7} m. The propagation velocity for all types of electromagnetic radiation in a vacuum is $c = \lambda \nu = 3 \times 10^8$ m/s, where λ is the wavelength and ν is the frequency of the radiation. Radiation heat transfer differs in two important respects from the conductive and convective modes: (a) no transfer medium is required, and (b) the energy transferred is proportional to the fourth or fifth power of the temperatures of the emitting bodies.

BLACKBODY AND THE BASIC LAWS OF THERMAL RADIATION

When radiant energy falls on a body, part may be absorbed, part reflected, and the remainder transmitted through the body. In mathematical form $\alpha + \rho + \tau = 1$, where α, ρ and τ are absorptance, reflectance, and transmittance, respectively. They represent the fraction of total energy absorbed, reflected, and transmitted, respectively. For the majority of opaque solid materials encountered in engineering, except for extremely thin layers, practically none of the radiant energy is transmitted through the body. Under this condition, $\alpha + \rho = 1$. An arrangement that absorbs all radiant energy at all wavelengths and reflects none is called a blackbody. Although no material with $\alpha = 1$ and $\rho = 0$ exists, it is used as a standard of comparison for a real body absorbing and emitting radiation.

For a blackbody, total emissive power is described by Stefan-Boltzmann's law, and its directional distribution of radiation intensity is described by Lambert's cosine law. The spectral distribution of radiation intensity is given by Planck's distribution law and the wavelength for the maximum spectral radiation intensity by Wien's displacement law. Thermal radiation emitted from a black surface flows uniformly into the whole hemispherical space as depicted in Fig. 29. A blackbody of surface area A, with uniform temperature T_1, loses heat to its surroundings (assumed black) with uniform temperature T_2, at a rate given by the equation $Q = A\sigma(T_1^4 - T_2^4)$.

The blackbody hemispherical emissive power is π times the directional emissive power, which is normal to the surface and equal to the radiation intensity. A summary of the blackbody thermal properties is given in Table 28. Some basic laws of thermal radiation are briefly presented below.

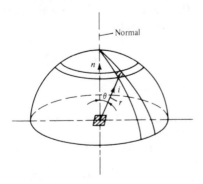

Figure 29 Diffuse radiation

Kirchhoff's Law. The ratio of the emissive power of a body in thermal equilibrium to that of a blackbody at the same temperature is equal to its absorptivity, expressed as:

$$\frac{e}{e_b} = \alpha \quad \text{or} \quad \varepsilon = \alpha$$

At a given temperature, the amount of incident radiation a body can absorb equals the amount it can emit. This law applies only to a few types of surfaces bearing gray surface characteristics.

Lambert's Cosine Law. Radiation intensity in a given direction is proportional to the cosine of the angle formed with the normal of the surface of emission:

$$i_{b\theta} = i_{bn} \cos \theta$$

When the surface radiation intensity follows the same cosine law of a blackbody radiation, the normal emissivity is independent of the angle θ, and it is identical with the hemispherical emissivity, $\varepsilon_n = \varepsilon$.

Planck's Distribution Law. Spectral distribution of the radiation intensity of a blackbody is given by the equation:

$$i_{\lambda b} = \frac{2C_1}{\lambda^5 (e^{C_2/\lambda T} - 1)}$$

which gives the magnitude of the emitted energy at each wavelength in the radiation spectrum. This equation can be rewritten as:

$$\frac{i_{\lambda b}}{T^5} = \frac{2C_1}{(\lambda T)^5 (e^{C_2/\lambda T} - 1)}$$

which states that for a given value of (λT), the ratio of $i_{\lambda b}/T^5$ is the same at all temperatures, and their relationship can be represented by a single curve.

Stefan-Boltzmann's Law. Total emissive power of a blackbody is proportional to the fourth power of the absolute temperature of the surface. The hemispherical total emissive power is given by:

$$e_b = \int_0^\infty e_{\lambda b} d\lambda = \int_0^\infty \pi i_{\lambda b} d\lambda = \sigma T^4$$

where σ is the Stefan-Boltzmann constant.

Wien's Displacement Law. As temperature increases, the maximum blackbody radiation intensity shifts in the direction of the shorter wavelengths. The wavelength for the maximum radiation intensity for temperature T can be calculated from the equation $\lambda_{\max} T = C_3$. The numerical values for the various radiation constants mentioned above are given in Table 29.

Table 28 Blackbody thermal properties

Symbol	Name	Definition	Geometry	Formula
$i'_{\lambda b}(\lambda, T)$	Spectral intensity	Emission in any direction per unit of projected area normal to that direction, and per unit time, wavelength interval about λ, and solid angle		$\dfrac{2C_1}{\lambda^5(e^{C_2/\lambda T} - 1)}$ Planck's law
$i'_b(T)$	Total intensity	Emission, including all wavelengths, in any direction per unit of projected area normal to that direction, and per unit time and solid angle		$\dfrac{\sigma T^4}{\pi}$
$e_{\lambda b}(\lambda, \theta, T)$	Directional spectral emissive power	Emission per unit solid angle in direction θ per unit surface area, wavelength interval, and time		$i'_{\lambda b} \cos\theta$ Lambert's cosine law

Note: Spectral denotes dependence on wavelength for any radiation quantity; superscript prime (') implies the directional quantity; $F_{0-\lambda}$ represents fraction of total blackbody intensity or emissive power lying in spectral region $0-\lambda$, that is, $F_{0-\lambda} = \int_0^\lambda \dfrac{e_{\lambda b}(\lambda)\,d\lambda}{\sigma T^4}$.

From Ref 59.

(continued)

Table 28 Blackbody thermal properties (continued)

Symbol	Name	Definition	Geometry	Formula
$e'_b(\theta, T)$	Directional total emissive power	Emission, including all wavelengths, in direction θ per unit surface area, solid angle, and time		$\dfrac{\sigma T^4}{\pi} \cos\theta$ Lambert's cosine law
$e_{\lambda b}(\lambda, \theta_1 - \theta_2, \varphi_1 - \varphi_2, T)$	Finite solid-angle spectral emissive power	Emission in solid angle $\theta_1 \le \theta \le \theta_2, \varphi_1 \le \varphi \le \varphi_2$ per unit surface area, wavelength interval, and time		$i'_{\lambda b} \dfrac{\sin^2\theta_2 - \sin^2\theta_1}{2}(\varphi_2 - \varphi_1)$
$e(\theta_1 - \theta_2, \varphi_1 - \varphi_2, T)$	Finite solid-angle total emissive power	Emission, including all wavelengths, in solid angle $\theta_1 \le \theta \le \theta_2, \varphi_1 \le \varphi \le \varphi_2$ per unit surface area and time		$\dfrac{\sigma T^4}{\pi}(\varphi_2 - \varphi_1) \dfrac{\sin^2\theta_2 - \sin^2\theta_1}{2}$

Note: Spectral denotes dependence on wavelength for any radiation quantity; superscript prime (') implies the directional quantity; $F_{0-\lambda}$ represents fraction of total blackbody intensity or emissive power lying in spectral region $0 - \lambda$, that is, $F_{0-\lambda} = \int_0^\lambda \dfrac{e_{\lambda b}(\lambda)d\lambda}{\sigma T^4}$.

From Ref 59.

(continued)

Table 28 Blackbody thermal properties (continued)

Symbol	Name	Definition	Geometry	Formula
$e_{\lambda b}(\lambda_1 - \lambda_2, \theta_1 - \theta_2, \varphi_1 - \varphi_2, T)$	Finite solid-angle band emissive power	Emission in solid angle $\theta_1 \leq \theta \leq \theta_2, \varphi_1 \leq \varphi \leq \varphi_2$ and wavelength band $\lambda_1 - \lambda_2$ per unit surface area and time		$\dfrac{\sigma T^4}{\pi}(\varphi_2 - \varphi_1)\dfrac{\sin^2\theta_2 - \sin^2\theta_1}{2}$ $\times (F_{0-\lambda_2} - F_{0-\lambda_1})$
$e_{\lambda b}(\lambda, T)$	Hemispherical spectral emissive power	Emission into hemispherical solid angle per unit surface area, wavelength interval, and time		$\pi i'_{\lambda b}$
$e_{\lambda b}(\lambda_1 - \lambda_2, T)$	Hemispherical band emissive power	Emission in wavelength band $\lambda_1 - \lambda_2$ into hemispherical solid angle per unit surface area and time		$(F_{0-\lambda_2} - F_{0-\lambda_1})\sigma T^4$

Note: Spectral denotes dependence on wavelength for any radiation quantity; superscript prime (') implies the directional quantity; $F_{0-\lambda}$ represents fraction of total blackbody intensity or emissive power lying in spectral region $0 - \lambda$, that is, $F_{0-\lambda} = \int_0^\lambda \dfrac{e_{\lambda b}(\lambda)\, d\lambda}{\sigma T^4}$.

From Ref 59.

(continued)

Table 28 Blackbody thermal properties (continued)

Symbol	Name	Definition	Geometry	Formula
$e_b(T)$	Hemispherical total emissive power	Emission, including all wavelengths, into hemispherical solid angle per unit surface area and time	All λ	σT^4 Stefan-Boltzmann's law

Note: Spectral denotes dependence on wavelength for any radiation quantity; superscript prime (′) implies the directional quantity; $F_{0-\lambda}$ represents fraction of total blackbody intensity or emissive power lying in spectral region $0-\lambda$, that is, $F_{0-\lambda} = \int_0^\lambda \dfrac{e_{\lambda b}(\lambda)d\lambda}{\sigma T^4}$.

From Ref 59.

Table 29 Radiation constants in Planck's, Stefan-Boltzmann's, and Wien's equations

Constant	Definition	Value
C_1	Planck's spectral energy distribution first constant	0.595×10^{-8} W-m^2
C_2	Planck's spectral energy distribution second constant	1.438×10^{-2} m-K
C_3	Wien's displacement law	0.289×10^{-2} m-K
σ	Stefan-Boltzmann's constant	5.669×10^{-8} W/m^2-K^4

RADIATION SHAPE FACTOR

In most practical problems involving radiation, the intensity of thermal radiation moving between surfaces is not greatly affected by intervening media. Unless the temperature is sufficient to cause ionization or dissociation, monatomic and most diatomic gases as well as air are transparent. Most industrial surfaces can be considered diffuse emitters and radiation reflectors in a heat transfer analysis. Thus, a key problem in calculating radiation heat transfer is to determine the fraction of the total diffuse radiation leaving one surface and intercepted by another. The fraction of diffusely distributed radiation leaving a surface A_i and reaching surface A_j is the radiation shape factor F_{i-j}. The first subscript denotes the emitting surface while the second subscript denotes the receiving surface.

For two black surfaces A_1 and A_2, as shown in Fig. 30, the net rate of transfer between A_1 and A_2 can be written as:

$$Q_{1-2} = \sigma(T_1{}^4 - T_2{}^4)A_1 F_{1-2}$$
$$= \sigma(T_1{}^4 - T_2{}^4)A_2 F_{2-1}$$

where

$$F_{1-2} = \frac{1}{\pi A_1} \int_{A_1} \int_{A_2} \frac{\cos\theta_1 \cos\theta_2}{S^2} dA_1 dA_2$$

$$F_{2-1} = \frac{1}{\pi A_2} \int_{A_1} \int_{A_2} \frac{\cos\theta_1 \cos\theta_2}{S^2} dA_1 dA_2$$

The shape factor F_{i-j} for diffuse radiation is a geometric property of two surfaces involved. One of the important properties of the shape factor is known as the reciprocal relationship, $A_1 F_{1-2} = A_2 F_{2-1}$. A summary of view factor and energy exchange relationships is presented in Table 30.

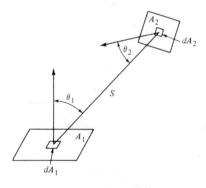

Figure 30 Geometrical shape-factor notation

Table 30 Summary of configuration-factor and energy-exchange relations

Net energy transfer	Configuration factor	Reciprocity
Elemental area to elemental area		
$d^2Q_{d1 \rightleftarrows d2} =$ $\sigma(T_1{}^4 - T_2{}^4)dA_1\,dF_{d1-d2}$	$dF_{d1-d2} =$ $\dfrac{\cos\theta_1\cos\theta_2}{\pi S^2}\,dA_2$	$dA_1\,dF_{d1-d2} =$ $dA_2\,dF_{d2-d1}$
Elemental area to finite area		
$dQ_{d1 \rightleftarrows 2} =$ $\sigma(T_1{}^4 - T_2{}^4)dA_1 F_{d1-2}$	$F_{d1-2} =$ $\displaystyle\int_{A_2} \dfrac{\cos\theta_1\cos\theta_2}{\pi S^2}\,dA_2$	$dA_1 F_{d1-2} =$ $A_2\,dF_{2-d1}$
Finite area to finite area		
$Q_{1 \rightleftarrows 2} =$ $\sigma(T_1{}^4 - T_2{}^4)A_1 F_{1-2}$	$F_{1-2} = \dfrac{1}{A_1}\displaystyle\int_{A_1}\int_{A_2}$ $\dfrac{\cos\theta_1\cos\theta_2}{\pi S^2}\,dA_2\,dA_1$	$A_1 F_{1-2} =$ $A_2 F_{2-1}$

RADIATION VIEW FACTORS FROM ELEMENTARY AREA dA₁ IMPINGING ON ANOTHER DIFFERENTIAL AREA dA₂

Area dA_1 of differential width and any length, to infinitely long strip dA_2 of differential width and with parallel generating line to dA_1

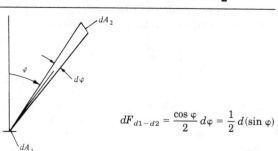

$$dF_{d1-d2} = \frac{\cos\varphi}{2}\,d\varphi = \frac{1}{2}\,d(\sin\varphi)$$

Strip of finite length b and of differential width, to differential strip of same length on parallel generating line

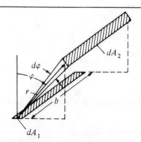

$$dF_{d1-d2} = \frac{\cos\varphi}{\pi}\,d\varphi \tan^{-1}\frac{b}{r}$$

Two ring elements on the interior of a right circular cylinder

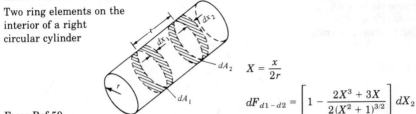

From Ref 59.

$$X = \frac{x}{2r}$$

$$dF_{d1-d2} = \left[1 - \frac{2X^3 + 3X}{2(X^2 + 1)^{3/2}} \right] dX_2$$

RADIATION VIEW FACTORS FROM DIFFERENTIAL AREA dA_1 TO FINITE AREA A_2

Area dA_1 of differential width and any length to any cylindrical surface A_2 generated by a line of infinite length moving parallel to itself and parallel to the plane of dA_1

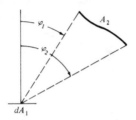

$$F_{d1-2} = \frac{1}{2} (\sin \varphi_2 - \sin \varphi_1)$$

Plane element dA_1 to plane parallel rectangle; normal to element passes through corner of rectangle

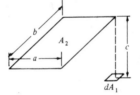

$$X = \frac{a}{c} \qquad Y = \frac{b}{c}$$

$$F_{d1-2} = \frac{1}{2\pi} \left(\frac{X}{\sqrt{1 + X^2}} \tan^{-1} \frac{Y}{\sqrt{1 + X^2}} + \frac{Y}{\sqrt{1 + Y^2}} \tan^{-1} \frac{X}{\sqrt{1 + Y^2}} \right)$$

Strip element to rectangle in plane parallel to strip; strip is opposite one edge of rectangle

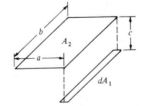

$$X = \frac{a}{c} \qquad Y = \frac{b}{c}$$

$$F_{d1-2} = \frac{1}{\pi Y} \left(\sqrt{1 + Y^2} \tan^{-1} \frac{X}{\sqrt{1 + Y^2}} - \tan^{-1} X + \frac{XY}{\sqrt{1 + X^2}} \tan^{-1} \frac{Y}{\sqrt{1 + X^2}} \right)$$

Plane element dA_1 to rectangle in plane 90° to plane of element

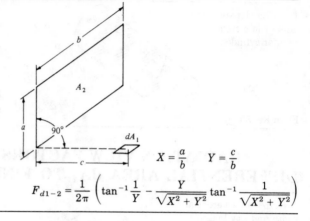

$$X = \frac{a}{b} \qquad Y = \frac{c}{b}$$

$$F_{d1-2} = \frac{1}{2\pi} \left(\tan^{-1} \frac{1}{Y} - \frac{Y}{\sqrt{X^2 + Y^2}} \tan^{-1} \frac{1}{\sqrt{X^2 + Y^2}} \right)$$

Plane element dA_1 to parallel isosceles triangle of height h and sides r; normal to element passes through vertex of triangle

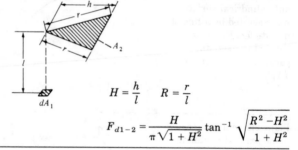

$$H = \frac{h}{l} \qquad R = \frac{r}{l}$$

$$F_{d1-2} = \frac{H}{\pi \sqrt{1 + H^2}} \tan^{-1} \sqrt{\frac{R^2 - H^2}{1 + H^2}}$$

Plane element dA_1 to parallel polygon having n equal sides; normal to element passes through center of polygon

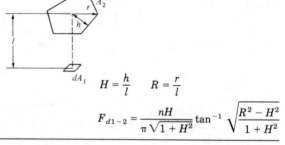

$$H = \frac{h}{l} \qquad R = \frac{r}{l}$$

$$F_{d1-2} = \frac{nH}{\pi \sqrt{1 + H^2}} \tan^{-1} \sqrt{\frac{R^2 - H^2}{1 + H^2}}$$

Strip element dA_1 to rectangle in plane 90° to plane of strip

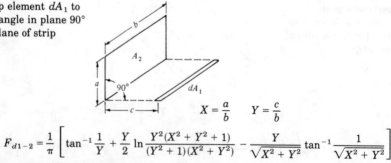

$$X = \frac{a}{b} \qquad Y = \frac{c}{b}$$

$$F_{d1-2} = \frac{1}{\pi} \left[\tan^{-1} \frac{1}{Y} + \frac{Y}{2} \ln \frac{Y^2(X^2 + Y^2 + 1)}{(Y^2 + 1)(X^2 + Y^2)} - \frac{Y}{\sqrt{X^2 + Y^2}} \tan^{-1} \frac{1}{\sqrt{X^2 + Y^2}} \right]$$

Plane element dA_1 to circular disk in plane parallel to element; normal to element passes through center of disk

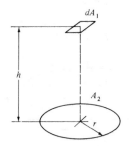

$$F_{d1-2} = \frac{r^2}{h^2 + r^2}$$

Plane element dA_1 to circular disk in plane parallel to element

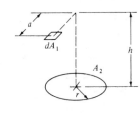

$$H = \frac{h}{a} \qquad R = \frac{r}{a}$$

$$Z = 1 + H^2 + R^2$$

$$F_{d1-2} = \frac{1}{2} \left(1 - \frac{1 + H^2 - R^2}{\sqrt{Z^2 - 4R^2}} \right)$$

Plane element dA_1 to circular disk; planes containing element and disk intersect at 90°; $l \geq r$

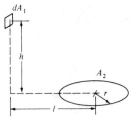

$$H = \frac{h}{l} \qquad R = \frac{r}{l}$$

$$Z = 1 + H^2 + R^2$$

$$F_{d1-2} = \frac{H}{2} \left(\frac{Z}{\sqrt{Z^2 - 4R^2}} - 1 \right)$$

Plane element dA_1 to parallel circular segment; normal to element passes through center of disk containing segment

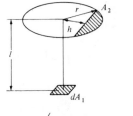

$$H = \frac{h}{l} \qquad R = \frac{r}{l}$$

$$F_{d1-2} = \frac{1}{\pi} \left(\frac{R^2}{1 + R^2} \cos^{-1} \frac{H}{R} - \frac{H}{\sqrt{1 + H^2}} \tan^{-1} \sqrt{\frac{R^2 - H^2}{1 + H^2}} \right)$$

Plane element dA_1 to elliptical plate in plane parallel to element; normal to element passes through center of plate

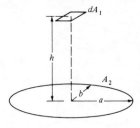

$$F_{d1-2} = \frac{ab}{\sqrt{(h^2 + a^2)(h^2 + b^2)}}$$

Strip element dA_2 of any length to infinitely long cylinder; $y \geq r$

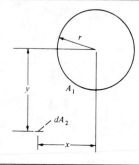

$$X = \frac{x}{r} \qquad Y = \frac{y}{r}$$

$$F_{d2-1} = \frac{Y}{X^2 + Y^2} \qquad (Y \geq 1)$$

Element of any length on cylinder to plane of infinite length and width

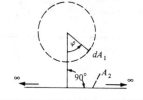

$$F_{d1-2} = \frac{1}{2}(1 + \cos \varphi)$$

Plane element dA_1 to right circular cylinder of finite length l and radius r; normal to element passes through one end of cylinder and is perpendicular to cylinder axis

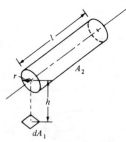

$$L = \frac{l}{r} \qquad H = \frac{h}{r}$$

$$X = (1 + H)^2 + L^2$$

$$Y = (1 - H)^2 + L^2$$

$$F_{d1-2} = \frac{1}{\pi H} \tan^{-1} \frac{1}{\sqrt{H^2 - 1}} + \frac{L}{\pi}\left[\frac{X - 2H}{H\sqrt{XY}} \tan^{-1} \sqrt{\frac{X(H-1)}{Y(H+1)}} - \frac{1}{H} \tan^{-1} \sqrt{\frac{H-1}{H+1}} \right]$$

Ring element dA_1 on interior of right circular cylinder to circular disk A_2 at end of cylinder

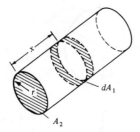

$$X = \frac{x}{2r}$$

$$F_{d1-2} = \frac{X^2 + \frac{1}{2}}{\sqrt{X^2 + 1}} - X$$

Spherical point source to a sphere of radius r

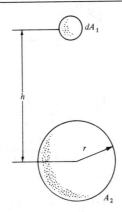

$$R = \frac{r}{h}$$

$$F_{d1-2} = \frac{1}{2}\left(1 - \sqrt{1 - R^2}\right)$$

Plane element dA_1 to sphere of radius r; normal to center of element passes through center of sphere

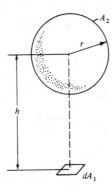

$$F_{d1-2} = \left(\frac{r}{h}\right)^2$$

Plane element dA_1 to sphere of radius r; tangent to element passes through center of sphere

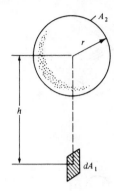

$$H = \frac{h}{r}$$

$$F_{d1-2} =$$

$$\frac{1}{\pi}\left(\tan^{-1}\frac{1}{\sqrt{H^2-1}} - \frac{\sqrt{H^2-1}}{H^2}\right)$$

Differential element dA_1 to an arbitrary disk

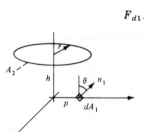

$$F_{d1-2} = \frac{1}{2}\left[\left(\frac{r^2 - p^2 - h^2}{\sqrt{(r^2 + p^2 + h^2)^2 - 4p^2r^2}} + 1\right)\cos\theta + \right.$$

$$\left. \frac{h}{p}\left(1 - \frac{r^2 + p^2 + h^2}{\sqrt{(r^2 + p^2 + h^2)^2 - 4p^2r^2}}\right)\sin\theta\right]$$

when

$$\tan^{-1}\frac{h}{p-r} \le \theta \le \tan^{-1}\frac{h}{p+r}$$

$$F_{d1-2} = \frac{(r^2 - p^2 - h^2)\cos\theta - (r^2 + p^2 + h^2)\dfrac{h\sin\theta}{p}}{\pi\sqrt{(r^2 + p^2 + h^2)^2 - 4p^2r^2}} \cdot$$

$$\tan^{-1}\left\{\sqrt{\frac{(r^2 + p^2 + h^2 + 2pr)(r - p + h\cot\theta)}{(r^2 + p^2 + h^2 - 2pr)(r + p - h\cot\theta)}}\right\} +$$

$$\frac{1}{2\pi}\left(\cos\theta + \frac{h}{p}\sin\theta\right)\left[\pi - \cos^{-1}\left(\frac{h\cot\theta - p}{r}\right)\right] +$$

$$\frac{1}{\pi}\tan^{-1}\left(\frac{\sin\theta}{h}\sqrt{r^2 - (h\cot\theta - p)^2}\right)$$

when

$$\tan^{-1}\frac{h}{p+r} \le \theta \le \tan^{-1}\frac{h}{p-r}$$

Differential element dA_1 to an arbitrary sphere

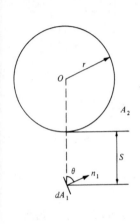

$$F_{d1-2} = \frac{\cos \theta}{(1 + S)^2}$$

when $\tan^{-1}(-A) \leq \theta \leq \tan^{-1}(A)$ and $-\frac{\pi}{2} \leq \theta \leq \frac{\pi}{2}$

$$F_{d1-2} = -\frac{\sqrt{(S + 1)^2 - 1} \sin \theta}{\pi (S + 1)^2} \sqrt{1 - [(S + 1)^2 - 1] \cot^2 \theta} +$$

$$\frac{1}{\pi} \tan^{-1} \left(\frac{\sin \theta \sqrt{1 - [(S + 1)^2 - 1] \cot^2 \theta}}{\sqrt{(S + 1)^2 - 1}} \right) +$$

$$\frac{\cos \theta}{\pi (S + 1)^2} \cos^{-1}(-\sqrt{(S + 1)^2 - 1} \cot \theta)$$

when

$$\tan^{-1}(-A) \geq \theta \geq \tan^{-1}(A) \text{ and } 0 \leq \theta \leq \pi$$

$$S = s/r \text{ and } A = \sqrt{(S + 1)^2 - 1}$$

dA_1 and a rectangular plane intersection at an angle ϕ

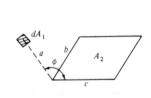

$$F_{d1-2} = \frac{1}{2\pi} \left[\tan^{-1}B + \frac{1}{X} (C \cos \phi - 1) \tan^{-1}\frac{B}{X} + \right.$$

$$\left. \frac{B \cos \phi}{Y} \left\{ \tan^{-1} \left(\frac{C - \cos \phi}{Y} \right) + \tan^{-1} \left(\frac{\cos \phi}{Y} \right) \right\} \right]$$

$$B = \frac{b}{a} \quad C = \frac{c}{a} \quad X = \sqrt{1 + C^2 - 2C \cos \phi}$$

$$Y = \sqrt{B^2 + \sin^2 \phi}$$

A spherical point source dA_1 to a rectangular plane intersecting at an angle ϕ

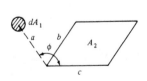

$$F_{d1-2} = \frac{1}{4\pi} \left\{ \tan^{-1} \left[\frac{B(C - \cos \phi)}{\sqrt{B^2 + C^2 + 1 - 2C \cos \phi}} \right] + \right.$$

$$\left. \tan^{-1} \left(\frac{B \cos \phi}{\sqrt{1 + B^2}} \right) \right\}$$

$$B = \frac{b}{a} \quad C = \frac{c}{a}$$

A line source dA_1 and a rectangular plane intersecting at an angle ϕ

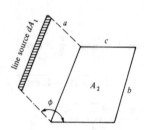

$$F_{d1-2} = \frac{1}{\pi} \left\{ \tan^{-1}B + \frac{\sin^2\phi}{2B} \ln\left[\frac{B^2 + X^2}{(1 + B^2)X^2}\right] - \right.$$

$$\frac{\sin 2\phi}{4B}\left[\frac{\pi}{2} - \phi + \tan^{-1}\left(\frac{C - \cos\phi}{\sin\phi}\right)\right] +$$

$$\frac{Y}{B}\left[\tan^{-1}\left(\frac{C - \cos\phi}{Y}\right) + \tan^{-1}\left(\frac{\cos\phi}{Y}\right)\right] \times$$

$$\left. \cos\phi + \frac{C\cos\phi - 1}{X}\tan^{-1}\left(\frac{B}{X}\right)\right\}$$

$$B = \frac{b}{a} \qquad C = \frac{c}{a} \qquad X = \sqrt{C^2 - 2C\cos\phi + 1}$$

From Ref 10, 50, 59, and 66. $\qquad Y = \sqrt{B^2 + \sin^2\phi}$

RADIATION VIEW FACTOR FROM FINITE AREA A_1 TO FINITE AREA A_2

Two infinitely long, directly opposed parallel plates of the same finite width

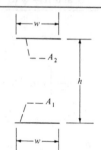

$$F_{1-2} = F_{2-1} = \sqrt{1 + H^2} - H$$

$$H = \frac{h}{w}$$

Identical, parallel, directly opposed rectangles

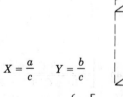

$$X = \frac{a}{c} \qquad Y = \frac{b}{c}$$

$$F_{1-2} = \frac{2}{\pi XY}\left\{\ln\left[\frac{(1 + X^2)(1 + Y^2)}{1 + X^2 + Y^2}\right]^{1/2} + X\sqrt{1 + Y^2}\tan^{-1}\frac{X}{\sqrt{1 + Y^2}} + \right.$$

$$\left. Y\sqrt{1 + X^2}\tan^{-1}\frac{Y}{\sqrt{1 + X^2}} - X\tan^{-1}X - Y\tan^{-1}Y\right\}$$

Two infinitely long plates of equal finite width w, having one common edge, and at an included angle α to each other

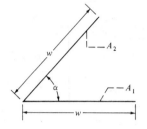

$$F_{1-2} = F_{2-1} = 1 - \sin\frac{\alpha}{2}$$

Two infinitely long plates of unequal widths h and w, having one common edge, and at an angle of 90° to each other

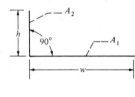

$$F_{1-2} = \tfrac{1}{2}(1 + H - \sqrt{1 + H^2})$$

$$H = \frac{h}{w}$$

Two finite rectangles of same length, having one common edge, and at an angle of 90° to each other

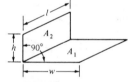

$$H = \frac{h}{l} \qquad W = \frac{w}{l}$$

$$F_{1-2} = \frac{1}{\pi W} \left(W \tan^{-1}\frac{1}{W} + H \tan^{-1}\frac{1}{H} - \sqrt{H^2 + W^2}\ \tan^{-1}\frac{1}{\sqrt{H^2 + W^2}} \right.$$

$$\left. + \tfrac{1}{4}\ln\left\{ \frac{(1 + W^2)(1 + H^2)}{1 + W^2 + H^2} \left[\frac{W^2(1 + W^2 + H^2)}{(1 + W^2)(W^2 + H^2)} \right]^{w^2} \left[\frac{H^2(1 + H^2 + W^2)}{(1 + H^2)(H^2 + W^2)} \right]^{H^2} \right\} \right)$$

Infinitely long enclosure formed by three plane areas

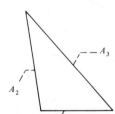

$$F_{1-2} = \frac{A_1 + A_2 - A_3}{2A_1}$$

Parallel circular disks with centers along the same normal

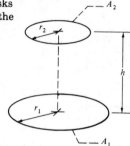

$$R_1 = \frac{r_1}{h} \qquad R_2 = \frac{r_2}{h}$$

$$X = 1 + \frac{1 + R_2{}^2}{R_1{}^2}$$

$$F_{1-2} = \frac{1}{2}\left[X - \sqrt{X^2 - 4\left(\frac{R_2}{R_1}\right)^2} \right]$$

Infinitely long plane of finite width to parallel infinitely long cylinder

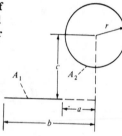

$$F_{1-2} = \frac{r}{b-a}\left(\tan^{-1}\frac{b}{c} - \tan^{-1}\frac{a}{c} \right)$$

Infinitely long parallel cylinders of the same diameter

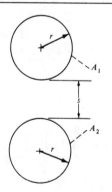

$$X = 1 + \frac{s}{2r}$$

$$F_{1-2} = F_{2-1} = \frac{1}{\pi}\left(\sqrt{X^2 - 1} + \sin^{-1}\frac{1}{X} - X \right)$$

Concentric cylinders of infinite length

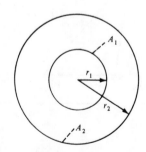

$$F_{1-2} = 1$$

$$F_{2-1} = \frac{r_1}{r_2}$$

$$F_{2-2} = 1 - \frac{r_1}{r_2}$$

Two concentric cylinders
of same finite length

$$R = \frac{r_2}{r_1} \qquad L = \frac{l}{r_1}$$

$$A = L^2 + R^2 - 1$$

$$B = L^2 - R^2 + 1$$

$$F_{2-1} = \frac{1}{R} - \frac{1}{\pi R}\left\{ \cos^{-1}\frac{B}{A} - \frac{1}{2L}\left[\sqrt{(A+2)^2 - (2R)^2}\cos^{-1}\frac{B}{RA} + \right.\right.$$

$$\left.\left. B\sin^{-1}\frac{1}{R} - \frac{\pi A}{2} \right] \right\}$$

$$F_{2-2} = 1 - \frac{1}{R} + \frac{2}{\pi R}\tan^{-1}\frac{2\sqrt{R^2-1}}{L} - \frac{L}{2\pi R}\left[\frac{\sqrt{4R^2+L^2}}{L} \right.$$

$$\sin^{-1}\frac{4(R^2-1)+(L^2/R^2)(R^2-2)}{L^2+4(R^2-1)} -$$

$$\left. \sin^{-1}\frac{R^2-2}{R^2} + \frac{\pi}{2}\left(\frac{\sqrt{4R^2+L^2}}{L} - 1 \right) \right]$$

Sphere of radius r_1 to
disk of radius r_2; normal
to center of disk passes
through center of sphere

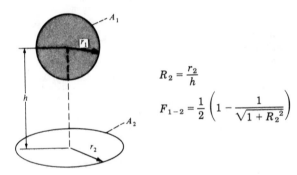

$$R_2 = \frac{r_2}{h}$$

$$F_{1-2} = \frac{1}{2}\left(1 - \frac{1}{\sqrt{1+R_2^2}} \right)$$

Sphere to sector of disk;
normal to center of disk
passes through center of
sphere

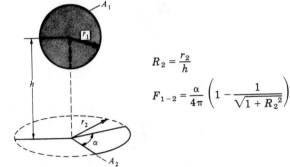

$$R_2 = \frac{r_2}{h}$$

$$F_{1-2} = \frac{\alpha}{4\pi}\left(1 - \frac{1}{\sqrt{1+R_2^2}} \right)$$

Sphere to segment of disk

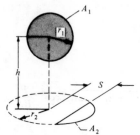

$$R_2 = \frac{r_2}{h} \qquad S = \frac{s}{h}$$

$$F_{1-2} = \frac{1}{8} - \frac{\cos^{-1}(S/R_2)}{2\pi\sqrt{1 + R_2{}^2}} + \frac{1}{4\pi}\sin^{-1}\frac{(1 - S^2)R_2{}^2 - 2S^2}{(1 + S^2)R_2{}^2}$$

Concentric spheres

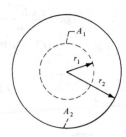

$$F_{1-2} = 1$$

$$F_{2-1} = \left(\frac{r_1}{r_2}\right)^2$$

$$F_{2-2} = 1 - \left(\frac{r_1}{r_2}\right)^2$$

Differential or finite area on the inside of a spherical cavity

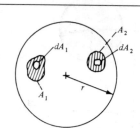

$$dF_{d1-d2} = dF_{1-d2} = \frac{dA_2}{4\pi r^2}$$

$$F_{d1-2} = F_{1-2} = \frac{A_2}{4\pi r^2}$$

Inner surface of circular cylinder to base

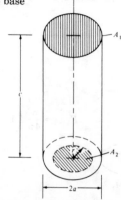

$$F_{1-2} = \frac{1}{4C}\left[\sqrt{C^4 + 2C^2(1 + R^2) + (1 - R^2)^2} - (1 - R^2 + C^2)\right]$$

$$C = \frac{c}{a} \qquad R = \frac{r}{a}$$

Inner surface of cylinder
between C_1 and C_2 to base
ring between r_2 and r_1

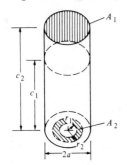

$$F_{1-2} = \frac{1}{4(C_2 - C_1)} \left[\sqrt{C_2^4 + 2C_2^2(1 + R_1^2) + (1 - R_1^2)^2} - \right.$$
$$\sqrt{C_2^4 + 2C_2^2(1 + R_2^2) + (1 - R_2^2)^2} +$$
$$\sqrt{C_1^4 + 2C_1^2(1 + R_2^2) + (1 - R_2^2)^2} -$$
$$\left. \sqrt{C_1^4 + 2C_1^2(1 + R_1^2) + (1 - R_1^2)^2} \right]$$

$$C_1 = \frac{c_1}{a} \qquad C_2 = \frac{c_2}{a} \qquad R_1 = \frac{r_1}{a} \qquad R_2 = \frac{r_2}{a}$$

Spherical surface to base
in equatorial plane

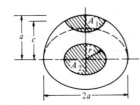

$$F_{1-2} = \frac{1}{4(1 - C)} \left[\sqrt{4R^2 + (1 - R^2)^2} - \right.$$
$$\left. \sqrt{4R^2C^2 + (1 - R^2)^2} \right]$$

$$C = \frac{c}{a} \qquad R = \frac{r}{a}$$

Ring on hemispherical
surface to ring on the
base

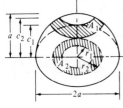

$$F_{1-2} = \frac{1}{4(C_2 - C_1)} \left[\sqrt{4R_2^2C_2^2 + (1 - R_2^2)^2} - \right.$$
$$\sqrt{4R_1^2C_2^2 + (1 - R_1^2)^2} + \sqrt{4R_1^2C_1^2 + (1 - R_1^2)^2} -$$
$$\left. \sqrt{4R_2^2C_1^2 + (1 - R_2^2)^2} \right]$$

$$C_1 = \frac{c_1}{a} \qquad C_2 = \frac{c_2}{a} \qquad R_1 = \frac{r_1}{a} \qquad R_2 = \frac{r_2}{a}$$

Nonconcentric infinitely
long cylinders

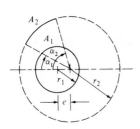

$$F_{1-2} = \frac{1}{2\pi} \left[\frac{\alpha_2 - \alpha_1}{2} + \tan^{-1}\left(\frac{r_2 + e}{r_2 - e} \tan\frac{\alpha_2}{2} \right) \right.$$
$$\left. - \tan^{-1}\left(\frac{r_2 + e}{r_2 - e} \tan^{-1}\frac{\alpha_1}{2} \right) \right]$$

Infinite plane to a row
of pipes

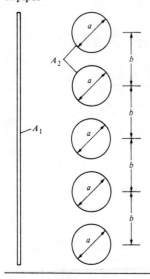

$$F_{1-2} = 1 - \sqrt{1 - (a/b)^2} + \frac{a}{b} \tan^{-1} \sqrt{(b/a)^2 - 1}$$

$$F_{2-1} = \frac{1}{\pi} \left[\frac{b}{a} - \sqrt{\left(\frac{b}{a}\right)^2 - 1} + \tan^{-1} \sqrt{\left(\frac{b}{a}\right)^2 - 1} \right]$$

$F_{1-(2)n} = 1 - (1 - F_{1-(2)1})^n$ for n rows of in-line
pipes.
The radiation areas per unit length may be taken as

$$A_1 = b \qquad A_2 = \pi a$$

$F_{1-(2)1}$ is the configuration factor for one row of pipes.

Sphere to the external
surface of a coaxial
(circular cylinder)

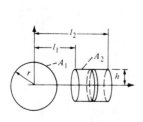

$$F_{1-2} = \frac{H}{2\pi} \left(L_2 \tan^{-1} \sqrt{\frac{1 - H^2}{L_2{}^2 + H^2 - 1}} - \right.$$

$$L_1 \tan^{-1} \sqrt{\frac{1 - H^2}{L_1{}^2 + H^2 - 1}} -$$

$$\frac{L_2}{H\sqrt{L_2{}^2 + H^2}} \cos^{-1} \frac{H\sqrt{L_2{}^2 + H^2 - 1}}{L_2} +$$

$$\left. \frac{L_1}{H\sqrt{L_1{}^2 + H^2}} \cos^{-1} \frac{H\sqrt{L_1{}^2 + H^2 - 1}}{L_1} \right)$$

$$H = \frac{h}{r} \qquad L_1 = \frac{l_1}{r} \qquad L_2 = \frac{l_2}{r}$$

One side of an annular
ring to a coaxial
hemisphere

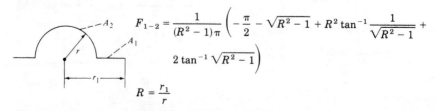

$$F_{1-2} = \frac{1}{(R^2 - 1)\pi} \left(-\frac{\pi}{2} - \sqrt{R^2 - 1} + R^2 \tan^{-1} \frac{1}{\sqrt{R^2 - 1}} + \right.$$

$$\left. 2 \tan^{-1} \sqrt{R^2 - 1} \right)$$

$$R = \frac{r_1}{r}$$

Sphere to one side of the intersecting coaxial annular ring or disk

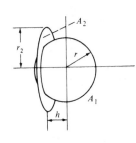

$$F_{1-2} = \frac{1}{2\pi}\left[-\frac{\sqrt{(1-H^2)(R^2+H^2-1)}}{2} + \right.$$

$$\frac{R^2}{2}\tan^{-1}\sqrt{\frac{1-H^2}{R^2+H^2-1}} - \frac{(1+2H-H^2)\pi}{4} +$$

$$\frac{H}{\sqrt{R^2+H^2}}\cos^{-1}\frac{H\sqrt{R^2+H^2-1}}{R} +$$

$$\left. \tan^{-1}\sqrt{\frac{R^2+H^2-1}{1-H^2}}\right] \qquad -1 \le H \le 1$$

$$H = \frac{h}{r} \qquad R = \frac{r_2}{r}$$

Sphere to one side of a coaxial disk

$$F_{1-2} = \frac{1}{2\pi}\left[\frac{\sqrt{1-H^2}}{2}\left(-\sqrt{R_2^2+H^2-1} + \sqrt{R_1^2+H^2-1}\right) + \right.$$

$$\frac{R_2^2}{2}\tan^{-1}\sqrt{\frac{1-H^2}{R_2^2+H^2-1}} - \frac{R_1^2}{2}\tan^{-1}\sqrt{\frac{1-H^2}{R_1^2+H^2-1}} +$$

$$\frac{H}{\sqrt{R_2^2+H^2}}\cos^{-1}\frac{H\sqrt{R_2^2+H^2-1}}{R_2} -$$

$$\frac{H}{\sqrt{R_1^2+H^2}}\cos^{-1}\frac{H\sqrt{R_1^2+H^2-1}}{R_1} +$$

$$\left. \tan^{-1}\sqrt{\frac{R_2^2+H^2-1}{1-H^2}} - \tan^{-1}\sqrt{\frac{R_1^2+H^2-1}{1-H^2}}\right]$$

$$H = \frac{h}{r} \qquad R = \frac{r_2}{r}$$

Annular ring to a coaxial cylinder or cylindrical rod

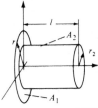

$$F_{1-2} = \frac{1}{\pi(1-R^2)}\left[(1-R^2)\tan^{-1}\sqrt{\frac{1+R}{1-R}} - \sqrt{(1+R^2+L^2)^2-4R^2}\ \cdot \right.$$

$$\tan^{-1}\left(\sqrt{\frac{(1+R^2+L^2+2R)(1-R)}{(1+R^2+L^2-2R)(1+R)}}\right) + \tfrac{1}{2}L^2\cos^{-1}(R) + 2RL\tan^{-1}\left(\frac{\sqrt{1-R^2}}{L}\right) \right]$$

$$R = \frac{r_2}{r} \qquad L = \frac{l}{r}$$

Disk to a coaxial convergent cone

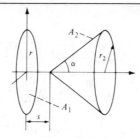

$$F_{1-2} = \tfrac{1}{2}[R^2 + (S + R \cot \alpha)^2 + 1 - \sqrt{[1 + R^2 + (S + R \cot \alpha)^2]^2 - 4R^2}]$$

If $\alpha \geq \tan^{-1} \dfrac{r}{s}$

$$F_{1-2} = \frac{1}{\pi} \left\{ -AB \tan^{-1}\left(\frac{AC}{BD}\right) + (1 + S^2) \tan^{-1}\frac{C}{D} + \frac{\sin \alpha}{\cos^2 \alpha} \left[EF \tan^{-1}\frac{CD}{E} + \right. \right.$$

$$S^2 \tan^{-1}\frac{CD}{S} + (CD)^2$$

$$\left. \left(\tan^{-1}\frac{E}{CD} - \tan^{-1}\frac{S}{CD}\right) \right] + \left[\frac{R(E + S)}{\sin 2\alpha} - SR \tan \alpha \right] \cdot \cos^{-1}(-S \tan \alpha) \right\}$$

If $\alpha \leq \tan^{-1} \dfrac{r}{s}$

where

$$A = \sqrt{(S + R \cot \alpha)^2 + (1 + R)^2} \qquad B = \sqrt{(S + R \cot \alpha)^2 + (1 - R)^2}$$
$$C = \sqrt{\cos \alpha + S \sin \alpha}$$

$$D = \sqrt{\cos \alpha - S \sin \alpha}, \ E = R \cot \alpha + S, \ F = R \cot \alpha - S, \ S = \frac{s}{r}, \ R = \frac{r_2}{r}$$

Annular ring to a coaxial intersecting convergent truncated cone

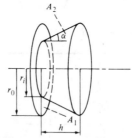

$$F_{1-2} = \frac{1}{\pi(1 - R_i^2)} \left\{ -A'B' \tan^{-1}\frac{A'C'}{B'D'} + C'^2D'^2 \tan^{-1}\frac{D'}{C'} + \frac{\sin \alpha}{\cos^2 \alpha} \right.$$

$$\left[\left(H^2 + \frac{2HR_i}{\tan \alpha}\right) \tan^{-1}\frac{\sqrt{E'}}{H} + E' \tan^{-1}\frac{H}{\sqrt{E'}} \right] +$$

$$\left. \left(\frac{H^2}{2\cos^2\alpha} + HR_i \tan \alpha\right) \cos^{-1}(R_i) \right\} \quad \text{where}$$

$$A' = \sqrt{H^2 + [1 + H \tan \alpha + R_i]^2} \qquad B' = \sqrt{H^2 + [1 - H \tan \alpha - R_i]^2}$$
$$C' = \sqrt{1 - R_i}, \ D = \sqrt{1 + R_i}, \ E' = \cos^2\alpha(1 - R_i^2), \ R_i = \frac{r_i}{r_0}$$

Summarized from Ref 9, 10, 11, 50, 59, and 66.

RADIATION EXCHANGE IN BLACK ENCLOSURE

Consider the energy transfer within an enclosure composed of N black surfaces that are individually isothermal (Fig. 31). The net energy loss due to radiation at the kth surface or the energy required from an external source through conduction, convection, or internal generation to maintain the kth surface at T_k is:

$$Q_k = \sigma A_k \sum_{j=1}^{N} (T_k^4 - T_j^4) F_{k-j}$$

which is the net energy transferred from A_k to each surface.

RADIATION EXCHANGE IN GRAY ENCLOSURE

An enclosure with N discrete surface areas is shown in Fig. 32. A complex radiative exchange occurs inside the enclosure when radiation leaves a surface, is partially reflected by other surfaces and is then re-reflected many times within the enclosure with partial absorption at each surface contact. An analysis can be formulated with the net-radiation method. Based on this method, the relationships between energy flux at temperature in diffuse gray enclosures are obtained. They are summarized in Table 31 under various boundary conditions.

As can be seen from Table 31, the desired quantities (a) the external heat input, Q_k; (b) the radiosity, J_k; and (c) the surface temperature T_k at a particular surface k are obtained from the solution of N systems of equations. Table 32 gives some formulas for diffuse radiant heat exchange for systems commonly encountered in engineering applications.

RADIATION SHIELDS

Radiation heat transfer can be substantially reduced by means of radiation shields, usually consisting of a surface opaque to radiant transmission

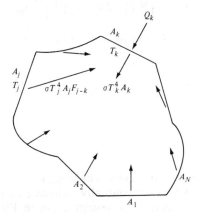

Figure 31 Enclosure composed of N black isothermal surfaces

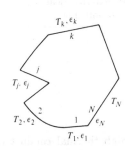

Figure 32 Enclosure composed of N discrete gray surface areas with typical surfaces j and k

Table 31 Relationship between energy flux and temperature in diffuse gray enclosures

Known boundary conditions	Desired quantities	Relationship
T_k on all surfaces $1 \le k \le N$	Q_k J_k	$\displaystyle\sum_{j=1}^{N} \left(\frac{\delta_{kj}}{\varepsilon_j} - F_{k-j} \frac{1-\varepsilon_j}{\varepsilon_j} \right) \frac{Q_j}{A_j} = \sum_{j=1}^{N} (\delta_{kj} - F_{k-j})\sigma$
		$\delta_{kj} = \begin{cases} 1 \text{ when } k = j \\ 0 \text{ when } k \ne j \end{cases}$
		$\displaystyle\sum_{j=1}^{N} [\delta_{kj} - (1-\varepsilon_k)F_{k-j}]J_j = \varepsilon_k \sigma T_k^4$ $k = 1, 2, \dots N$
Q_k on all surfaces $1 \le k \le N$	T_k J_k	$\displaystyle\sum_{j=1}^{N} (\delta_{kj} - F_{k-j})\sigma T_j^4 = \sum_{j=1}^{N} \left(\frac{\delta_{kj}}{\varepsilon_j} - F_{k-j} \frac{1-\varepsilon_j}{\varepsilon_j} \right)$ $\left(J_k - \displaystyle\sum_{j=1}^{N} F_{k-j}J_j \right) = \dfrac{Q_k}{A_k}$
T_k for $1 \le k \le m$ Q_k for $m+1 \le k \le N$	Q_k for $1 \le k \le m$ T_k for $m+1 \le k \le N$ J_k for $1 \le k \le N$	$\displaystyle\sum_{j=1}^{N} [\delta_{kj} - (1-\varepsilon_k)F_{k-j}]J_j = \varepsilon_k \sigma T_k^4 \quad 1 \le k \le m$ $\displaystyle\sum_{j=1}^{N} (\delta_{kj} - F_{k-j}) J_j = \dfrac{Q_k}{A_k} \quad m+1 \le k \le N$ Solve for J_j from above N system equations first then: $Q_k = \dfrac{A_k \varepsilon_k}{1-\varepsilon_k}(\sigma T_k^4 - J_k) \quad 1 \le k \le m$ $T_k = \left[\left(\dfrac{Q_k(1-\varepsilon_k)}{A\varepsilon_k} + J_k \right) \dfrac{1}{\sigma} \right]^{1/4} \quad m+1 \le k \le$

Note: Q_k equals external heat input to kth surface; J_k is radiosity, or energy leaving kth surfa per unit area and unit time.

with high thermal conductivity and low emissivity. Shielding effectiveness is increased if the shields are placed between mutually radiating surfaces or over a surface against radiation heating. The configuration in Fig. 33 shows two large parallel walls separated by N radiation shields. The heat flow rate by radiation per unit area, q, at steady state is given by:

$$q = \frac{\sigma(T_1^4 - T_2^4)}{1/\varepsilon_1 + 1/\varepsilon_2 - 1 + \sum_{n=1}^{N} (1/\varepsilon_{n1} + 1/\varepsilon_{n2} - 1)}$$

where ε_{n1} and ε_{n2} are the emissivities on both sides of a typical shield, n. In most instances, the ε is the same on both sides of each shield, and all the shields have the same ε. If all the shield emissivities are represented as ε_s, then q becomes:

$$q = \frac{\sigma(T_1^4 - T_2^4)}{1/\varepsilon_1 + 1/\varepsilon_2 - 1 + N(2/\varepsilon_s - 1)}$$

If wall emissivities are the same as the shield emissivities, that is, $\varepsilon_1 = \varepsilon_2 = \varepsilon_s$, then the above expression reduces to:

$$q = \frac{\sigma(T_1^4 - T_2^4)}{(N + 1)(2/\varepsilon_s - 1)}$$

where q decreases as $1/(N + 1)$ as the number of shields increases. The expression for heat flow through a series of concentric cylindrical or spherical radiation shields is similar to that for flat plates, as shown in Fig. 34. Thus:

$$Q = \frac{A_1\sigma(T_1^4 - T_2^4)}{1/\varepsilon_1 + (A_1/A_2)(1/\varepsilon_2 - 1) + \sum_{n=1}^{N} (A_1/A_{sn})(1/\varepsilon_{n1} + 1/\varepsilon_{n2} - 1)}$$

where the walls A_1 and A_2 and all the shields A_{sn} are diffuse. If all the shield emissivities are the same and equal to ε_s, then:

$$Q = \frac{A_1\sigma(T_1^4 - T_2^4)}{1/\varepsilon_1 + 1/\varepsilon_s - 1 + \sum_{n=1}^{N-1} (A_1/A_{sn})(2/\varepsilon_s - 1) + (A_1/A_{sN})(1/\varepsilon_s + 1/\varepsilon_2 - 1)}$$

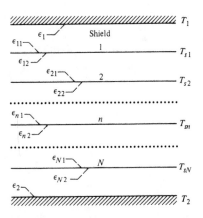

Figure 33 Parallel walls separated by N radiation shields

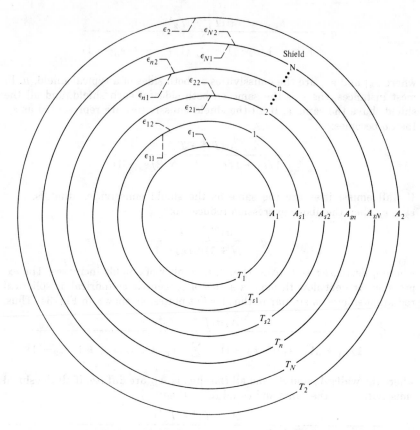

Figure 34 Radiation shields between concentric cylinders or spheres

Table 32 Rate of radiant energy exchange between diffuse surfaces

Schematic diagram	Radiation heat exchange rate

Gray surface to blackbody surroundings

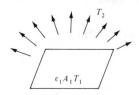

$$Q_{1-2} = \varepsilon_1 \sigma (T_1^4 - T_2^4) A_1$$

Two arbitrary surfaces

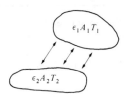

$$Q_{1-2} = \frac{\sigma \varepsilon_1 \varepsilon_2 A_1 F_{1-2}(T_1^4 - T_2^4)}{\varepsilon_1 \varepsilon_2 + \varepsilon_2 F_{1-2}(1 - \varepsilon_1) + \varepsilon_1 F_{2-1}(1 - \varepsilon_2)}$$

Two infinitely large parallel planes

$$Q_{1-2} = \frac{1}{\dfrac{1}{\varepsilon_1} + \dfrac{1}{\varepsilon_2} - 1} \sigma (T_1^4 - T_2^4) A_1$$

A small enclosed body and the enclosure

$$Q_{1-2} = \varepsilon_1 A_1 \sigma (T_1^4 - T_2^4)$$

Infinitely long concentric cylinders, concentric spheres or an arbitrary enclosed body and its enclosure

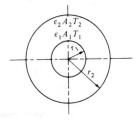

$$Q_{1-2} = \frac{1}{\dfrac{1}{\varepsilon_1} + \dfrac{A_1}{A_2}\left(\dfrac{1}{\varepsilon_2} - 1\right)} \sigma (T_1^4 - T_2^4) A_1$$

(continued)

Table 32   Rate of radiant energy exchange between diffuse surfaces (continued)

Schematic diagram	Radiation heat exchange rate

Two black surfaces in the presence of reradiating surfaces

$$Q_{\underset{r}{1-2}} = r(T_1^4 - T_2^4)A_1 F_{1r2}$$

where

$$F_{\underset{r}{1-2}} = F_{1-2} + \cfrac{1}{\cfrac{1}{F_{1-r}} + \cfrac{A_1}{A_2 F_{2-r}}}$$

Two black surfaces which do not "see" themselves in the presence of reradiating surfaces

$$Q_{\underset{r}{1-2}} = \sigma(T_1^4 - T_2^4)A_1 F_{1-2}$$

where

$$F_{1-2} = \frac{A_2 - A_1 F_{1-2}^2}{A_1 + A_2 - 2A_1 F_{1-2}}$$

Two arbitrary gray surfaces in the presence of reradiating surfaces

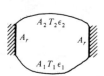

$$Q_{\underset{r}{1-2}} = \sigma A_1 F_{1-2}(T_1^4 - T_2^4)$$

where

$$F_{1-2} = \cfrac{1}{\cfrac{1}{F_{1r2}} + \cfrac{1}{\varepsilon_1} - 1 + \cfrac{A_1}{A_2}\left(\cfrac{1}{\varepsilon_2} - 1\right)}$$

and

$$F_{\underset{r}{1-2}} = F_{1-2} + \cfrac{1}{\cfrac{1}{F_{1-r}} + \cfrac{A_1}{A_2 F_{2-r}}}$$

A gas and a black bounding surface

$$Q_{A-g} = \sigma A_1(\varepsilon_g T_g^4 - \alpha_g T_w^4)$$

(continued)

Table 32 Rate of radiant energy exchange between diffuse surfaces (continued)

Schematic diagram	Radiation heat exchange rate

A gas and a black bounding surface in the presence of a reradiating bounding surface

$$Q_{A-g} = \bar{\varepsilon}_g A_1 (T_g^4 - T_w^4)$$

where

$$\bar{\varepsilon}_g = \left[1 + \frac{A_r/A_1}{1 + \dfrac{\varepsilon_g}{(1-\varepsilon_g)F_{r-1}}} \right] \varepsilon_g$$

= equivalent emissivity

A gas and a gray bounding surface in the presence of a reradiating bounding surface

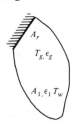

$$Q_{A_{r}-c} = \frac{\sigma A_1 (T_g^4 - T_w^4)}{\dfrac{1}{\bar{\varepsilon}_g} + \dfrac{1}{\varepsilon_1} - 1}$$

where

$$\bar{\varepsilon}_g = \left[1 + \frac{A_r/A_1}{1 + \dfrac{\varepsilon_g}{(1-\varepsilon_g)F_{r-1}}} \right] \varepsilon_g$$

REFERENCES

1. Anderson, J.T. and Saunders, O.A., Convection from an Isolated Heated Horizontal Cylinder Rotating about its Axis, *Proc. Roy. Soc.*, 217A, 1953, 555
2. Andrews, R.V., Solving Conductive Heat Transfer Problems with Electrical-Analogue Shape Factors, *Chemical Engineering Progress*, 5, No.2 , 1955, 67
3. Arpaci, V.S., *Conduction Heat Transfer*, Addison-Wesley, Reading, MA, 1966
4. Brown, C.K. and Gauvin, W.H., Combined Free and Forced Convection, Parts I & II, *Canadian Journal of Chemical Engineering*, 43, 1965, 306 and 313
5. Buschman, A.J. and Pittmann, C.M., Configuration Factors for Exchange of Radiant Energy between Axisymmetric Sections of Cylinders, Cones and Hemispheres and Their Base, *NASA TN D-944*, 1961
6. Chapman, A.J., *Heat Transfer*, 3rd ed., MacMillan, New York, 1974
7. Chung, B.T.F., *Heat Transfer Processes Notes*, University of Akron, unpublished work
8. Chung, B.T.F. and Sumitra, P.S., Radiation Shape Factor from Plane Point Sources, *Journal of Heat Transfer*, 94, 1972, 328

9. Chung, B.T.F. and Naraghi, M.H.N., Some Exact Solutions for Radiation View Factors for Spheres, *AIAA Journal*, 19, 1981, 1077

10. Chung, B.T.F. and Naraghi, M.H.N., A Simpler Formulation for Radiative View Factors from Spheres to a Class of Axisymmetric Bodies, *Journal of Heat Transfer*, 104, 1982, 201

11. Chung, B.T.F., Kermani, M.M. and Naraghi, M.H.N., A Formulation of Radiation View Factors from Conical Surfaces, *AIAA Paper No. 83-0156*, 1983

12. Cobb, E.C. and Saunders, O.A., Heat Transfer from a Rotating Disc, *Proc. Roy. Soc.*, 236A, 1956, 343

13. Deissler, R.G., Analysis of Turbulent Heat Transfer, Mass Transfer and Friction in Smooth Tubes at High Prandtl Numbers, *NASA TR 1210*, 1955

14. Dipprey, D.F. and Sabersky, R.H., Heat and Momentum Transfer in Smooth and Rough Tubes at Various Prandtl Numbers, *International Journal of Heat Mass Transfer*, 6, 1963, 329

15. Eckert, E. and Jackson, T., Analysis of Turbulent Free Convection Boundary Layer on Flat Plate, *NASA TN 2207*, 1950

16. Eckert, E.R.G. and Drake, R.M., *Heat and Mass Transfer*, 2nd ed., McGraw Hill Book Co., New York, 1959

17. Ede, A.J., Advances in Free Convection, *Advances in Heat Transfer*, 4, Academic Press, 1967

18. Fand, R.M., Heat Transfer by Forced Convection from a Cylinder to Water in Crossflow, *International Journal of Heat Mass Transfer*, 8, 1965, 995

19. Feingold, A. and Gupta, K.G., New Analytical Approach to the Evaluation of Configuration Factors in Radiation from Spheres and Infinitely Long Cylinders, *Journal of Heat Transfer*, 92, 1970, 67

20. Fishenden, M. and Saunders, O.A., *An Introduction to Heat Transfer*, Oxford University Press, 1950

21. Grimson, E.D., Correlation and Utilization of New Data on Flow Resistance and Heat Transfer for Cross Flow of Gases over Tube Banks, *Trans. ASME*, 59, 1937, 583

22. Grober, H., Erk, S., and Grigull, U., *Fundamentals of Heat Transfer*, McGraw-Hill, New York, 1961

23. Hahne, E. and Grigull, U., Formfakter and Formweider stand der Stationaun Mehrdimensionalen Warmeleitung, *International Journal of Heat Mass Transfer*, 18, 1975, 251

24. Hamilton, D.C. and Morgan, W.R., Radiant Interchange Configuration Factors, *NASA TN 2836*, 1952

25. Heisler, M.P., Temperature Charts for Induction and Constant Temperature Heating, *Trans. ASME*, 69, 1947, 227

26. Hering, R.G. and Grosh, R.J., Laminar Combined Convection from a Rotating Cone, *Journal of Heat Transfer*, 85, 1963, 29

27. Holman, J.P., *Heat Transfer*, 5th ed., McGraw-Hill, St. Louis, 1981

28. Hottel, H.C., Radiant Heat Transmis Between Surfaces Separated by Non-absorbing Media, *Trans. ASME*, 53, 1931, 265

29. Incropera, F.P. and Dewitt, D.P., *Fundamentals of Heat Transfer*, John Wiley & Sons, New York, 1981

30. Jakob, M., *Heat Transfer*, Vol 1, John Wiley & Sons, New York, 1957
31. Jakob, M., *Heat Transfer*, Vol 2, John Wiley & Sons, New York, 1957
32. Jakob, M., Heat Transfer and Flow Resistance in Cross Flow of Gases over Tube Banks, *Trans. ASME*, 60, 1938, 384
33. Karlekar, B.V. and Desmond, R.M., *Engineering Heat Transfer*, West Publishing, New York, 1977
34. Kays, M.W., and Crawford, M.E., *Convective Heat and Mass Transfer*, 2nd ed., McGraw-Hill, New York, 1980
35. Kays, W.M. and Lo, R.K., Basic Heat Transfer and Flow Friction Data for Gas Flow Normal to Banks of Staggered Tubes: Use of a Transient Technique, Stanford University, *Tech. Rep. 15, Navy Contract N6-ONR 251 T.O.6*, 1952
36. Kays, W.M. and Bjorklund, I.S., Heat Transfer from a Rotating Cylinder with and without Cross Flow, *Trans. ASME*, 80, 1958, 70
37. Kern, D.Q. and Kraus, A.D., *Extended Surface Heat Transfer*, 2nd ed., McGraw-Hill, New York, 1972
38. Knudsen, J.G. and Katz, D.L., *Fluid Dynamics and Heat Transfer*, McGraw-Hill, St. Louis, 1958
39. Kramers, H., Heat Transfer from Spheres to Flowing Media, *Physica*, 12, 1946, 61
40. Kreith, F., Roberts, L.R., Sullivan, J.A. and Sinha, S.N., Convection Heat Transfer and Flow Phenomena of Rotating Spheres, *International Journal of Heat Transfer*, 6, 1963, 881
41. Kreith, F., Convective Heat Transfer in Rotating Systems, *Advances in Heat Transfer*, 5, Academic Press, 1968
42. Kreith F., *Principles of Heat Transfer*, 3rd ed., Harper & Row, New York, 1973
43. Kutateladze, S.S. and Borishanskii, V.M., *A Concise Encyclopedia of Heat Transfer*, Pergamon Press, 1966
44. LeFevre, E.J. and Ede, A.J., Laminar Free Convection from the Outer Surface of a Vertical Circular Cylinder, *Proc. 9th Congress, Applied Mech. Paper 1167*, 1956
45. Leuenberger, H. and Person, R.A., Compilation of Radiation Shape Factors for Cylindrical Assemblies, *ASME Paper No. 56-A-144*, 1956
46. Lienhard, J.H., *A Heat Transfer Textbook*, Prentice Hall, Englewood Cliffs, NJ, 1981
47. McAdams, W.H., *Heat Transmission*, 3rd ed., McGraw-Hill, New York, 1954
48. Metais, B. and Eckert, E.R.G., Forced, Mixed and Free Convection Regimes, *ASME Journal of Heat Transfer*, 86, 1964, 295
49. Morgan, V.T., The Overall Convective Heat Transfer from Smooth Circular Cylinders, *Advances in Heat Transfer*, 11, Academic Press, 1975
50. Naraghi, M.H.N. and Chung, B.T.F., Radiation Configuration Factor Between Disks and a Class of Axisymmetric Bodies, *Journal of Heat Transfer*, 104, 1982, 426
51. Ozisik, M.N., *Boundary Value Problems of Heat Conduction*, International Textbook Co., Scranton, PA, 1968

52. Ostrach, S., An Analysis of Laminar Free Convective Flow and Heat Transfer about a Flat Plate Parallel to the Direction of the Generating Body Force, *NASA TN 2635*, 1952

53. Petukhov, B.S. and Popov, V.N., Theoretical Calculation of Heat Exchange and Frictional Resistance in Turbulent Flow in Tubes of an Incompressible Fluid with Variable Physical Properties, *Trans. in High Temperature*, 1, No. 1, 1963

54. Powell, R.W., Ho, C.Y., and Lidey, P.E., *Thermal Conductivity of Selected Materials, NSRDS-NBS* 8, Washington, DC, U.S. Department of Commerce, 1966

55. Rohsenow, W.M. and Hartnett, J.P., *Handbook of Heat Transfer*, McGraw-Hill, New York, 1973

56. Rudenberg, R., Die Ausbreitung der Luft-und Erdfelder um Hochapannungaleitungen besonders bei Erd und Kurzschterssen, *Electrotech. Z.*, 46, 1945, 1342

57. Schneider, P.J., *Conduction Heat Transfer*, Addison-Wesley, Reading, MA, 1955

58. Schneider, P.J., *Temperature Response Charts*, John Wiley & Sons, New York, 1963

59. Siegel, R., and Howell, J.R., *Thermal Radiation Heat Transfer*, 2nd ed., McGraw-Hill, New York, 1980

60. Sparrow, E.M., Hallman, T.M., and Seigel, R., Turbulent Heat Transfer in the Thermal Entrance Region of a Pipe with Uniform Heat Flux, *Applied Sci. Res.*, A7, 1957, 37

61. Sparrow, E.M. and Cess, R.D., *Radiation Heat Transfer*, Wadsworth Publishing Co., Englewood Cliffs, NJ, 1966

62. Thomas, L.C., *Fundamentals of Heat Transfer*, Prentice Hall, Englewood Cliffs, NJ, 1980

63. Touloukian, Y.S., Powell, R.W., Ho, C.Y., and Klemens, P.G., *Thermophysical Properties of Matter*, Vol 1-3, IFI/Plenum Data Corporation, New York, 1970

64. Webb, R.L., A Critical Evaluation of Analytical Solutions and Reynolds Analogy Equations for Turbulent Heat and Mass Transfer in Smooth Tubes, *Warme-und Stoffubertragung*, Bd. 4, 1971, 197

65. Whitaker, S., Forced Convection Heat Transfer Correlation for Flow in Pipes, Past Flat Plate, Single Cylinders, Single Spheres and Flow in Packed Beds and Tube Bundles, *AICHE Journal*, 18, 1972, 361

66. Wong, H.Y., *Handbook of Essential Formulas and Data on Heat Transfer for Engineers*, Longman Group Ltd., London, 1977

22
Fluid Dynamics

A fluid cannot resist shear stress by static deformation in the manner of a solid. Any shear stress applied to a fluid results in motion of that fluid, which continues as long as the shear stress is applied. A fluid at rest must be in a state of zero shear stress, a state known as the hydrostatic stress condition. A liquid, which is composed of relatively close-packed molecules with strong cohesive forces, retains its volume and forms a free surface in a gravitational field if the upper surface is not confined. Gases, with widely spaced molecules and negligible cohesive forces, are free to expand until encountering confining walls.

PROPERTIES OF FLUIDS

THE CONTINUUM

Certain properties are defined on the basis of fluid particles being considered as a continuous medium. A fluid particle is composed of many finite-sized molecules with finite distance between the molecules. For air under standard conditions, there are 2×10^{19} molecules in 1 cm^3, with a mean distance travelled between each molecular collision of 6.35×10^{-6} cm. Therefore, the overall motion of the fluid is of interest, not the motion of individual molecules, and the fluid can be treated as a continuous medium, also called a continuum.

PRESSURE

Pressure is defined at a point in a continuum as:

$$p = \lim_{A \to A'} \frac{F}{A} \qquad \text{(Eq 1)}$$

where F is the force normal to the surface A and A' is the smallest area surrounding the point that is consistent with continuum approach. The mean pressure over a plane area in a fluid is the ratio of the normal force acting on an area to the area. The pressure at a point is the limit approached by the mean pressure as the area is reduced to a very small size around the point. When pressure is measured relative to zero pressure, it is called absolute pressure. When pressure is measured relative to surrounding atmospheric pressure, it is called gage pressure.

DENSITY

Density at a point in a continuum is defined as:

$$\rho = \lim_{V \to V'} \frac{M}{V} \qquad \text{(Eq 2)}$$

where M is the mass in volume V and V' is the smallest volume surrounding the point that is consistent with the continuum approach. Mean density is the ratio of the fluid mass to the volume. Density at a point is the limit approached by the mean density as the volume is reduced to a very small size around the point.

COEFFICIENT OF COMPRESSIBILITY

This property describes the change of volume with applied pressure at a given temperature:

$$\beta = -\frac{1}{V} \left(\frac{\partial V}{\partial p} \right)_T \qquad \text{(Eq 3)}$$

Its reciprocal, the isothermal bulk modulus κ, is defined as:

$$\kappa = -V \left(\frac{\partial p}{\partial V} \right)_T \qquad \text{(Eq 4)}$$

VISCOSITY

In a solid, shear stress is generally proportional to shear strain, and the material ceases to deform when equilibrium is reached. In a viscous fluid, however, shear stress is proportional to the time rate of strain. The proportionality factor for the viscous fluid is the dynamic, or absolute, viscosity:

$$\tau = \mu \frac{du}{dy} \qquad \text{(Eq 5)}$$

where τ is the shear stress, μ is the dynamic viscosity, and du/dy is the time rate of strain or velocity gradient (Fig. 1). This linear variation of shear

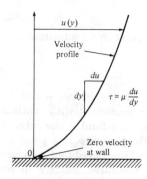

Figure 1

stress with rate of strain describes the behavior of a large class of fluids called Newtonian fluids. The velocity gradient at the boundary must be finite since the shear stress cannot be infinite. When the velocity profile is such that the gradient becomes smaller farther away from the boundary, the shear stress will reach a maximum at the boundary and will decrease with distance from the wall. Another form of the coefficient of viscosity is the kinematic viscosity, defined as:

$$\nu = \frac{\mu}{\rho}$$

Variation of Viscosity with Temperature. Temperature has a strong effect on viscosity while pressure exerts a moderate effect. The viscosity of gases and most liquids increases slowly with increases in pressure. Gas viscosity increases with temperature, the functional relationship being approximated by the two common equations listed below:

$$\frac{\mu}{\mu_0} \approx \begin{cases} \left(\dfrac{T}{T_0}\right)^n & \text{power law} \\[2ex] \dfrac{(T/T_0)^{3/2}(T_0 + S)}{T + S} & \text{Sutherland law} \end{cases} \qquad \text{(Eq 6)}$$

where μ_0 is a known viscosity at a known absolute temperature T_0 and n and S are constants. For air, $n \approx 0.67$ and $S \approx 110$ K.

Liquid viscosity decreases with temperature in a manner roughly described by the exponential function, $\mu \approx ae^{-bT}$. Preferred, however, is the empirical result:

$$\ln \frac{\mu}{\mu_0} \approx a + b\left(\frac{T_0}{T}\right) + c\left(\frac{T_0}{T}\right)^2 \qquad \text{(Eq 7)}$$

For water, with $T_0 = 273.16$ K and $\mu_0 = 0.001792$ kg/(m $\cdot$ s), acceptable values are $a = -1.94$, $b = -4.80$, and $c = 6.74$, with accuracy of about $\pm 1\%$.

Non-Newtonian Fluids. Fluids that do not follow the linear law of Eq 5 are called non-Newtonian and are analyzed as problems in rheology. Figure 2 shows how the shear stress varies with respect to the strain rate for some different types of fluids as compared to Newtonian fluids.

SURFACE TENSION

Liquid surfaces exert a tension on portions of surfaces and objects that are in contact with the liquid even in the absence of motion. This tension acts in the plane of the surface and the magnitude of the force per unit length is defined as the surface tension, σ.

VAPOR PRESSURE

Molecules escape from a liquid surface until the pressure of the space in contact with the surface reaches a value such that there is no net exchange of molecules between the liquid and vapor. This pressure is called the saturated vapor pressure, p_v. The vapor pressure is a function of the temperature of the liquid.

FLUID STATICS

PRESSURE

The pressure intensity, or pressure, is a scalar quantity and was previously defined in Eq 1. Figure 3 shows a free body diagram of forces on a fluid element in a static fluid. Analysis of these forces shows that pressure at a point in a static fluid acts with the same magnitude in all directions:

$$p_n = p_x = p_y = p_z \qquad (Eq\ 8)$$

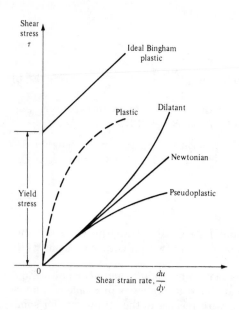

Figure 2 Rheological behavior of viscous materials. Stress versus strain rate

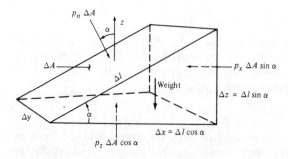

Figure 3 Pressure forces on a fluid element

VARIATION OF PRESSURE WITH ELEVATION

Considering the forces on the element in Fig. 4, it can be shown that by applying the equations of equilibrium the pressure variation becomes:

$$\frac{dp}{dl} = -\gamma \sin \alpha$$

Noting that $\sin \alpha = dz/dl$:

$$\frac{dp}{dl} = -\gamma \frac{dz}{dl} \qquad \text{(Eq 9)}$$

or

$$\frac{dp}{dz} = -\gamma \qquad \text{(Eq 10)}$$

where $\gamma = pg$ (specific weight). This is the basic equation for the variation of hydrostatic pressure with elevation. For a fluid with a uniform density, this pressure variation becomes:

$$\frac{p_1}{\gamma} + z_1 = \frac{p_2}{\gamma} + z_2 \qquad \text{(Eq 11)}$$

or

$$\Delta p = -\gamma \, \Delta z \qquad \text{(Eq 12)}$$

The sum shown in Eq 11, $p/\gamma + z$, is called the piezometric head.

The static pressure variation in a compressible fluid can be determined using the ideal gas equation of state:

$$\rho = \frac{p}{RT} = \frac{1}{v} \qquad \text{(Eq 13)}$$

where $v \equiv$ specific volume. This can be expressed in the form:

$$\gamma = \frac{pg}{RT} \qquad \text{(Eq 14)}$$

where R = gas constant, T = absolute temperature, p = absolute pressure. The temperature variation in the troposphere, is given by:

$$T = T_0 - \alpha (z - z_0) \qquad \text{(Eq 15)}$$

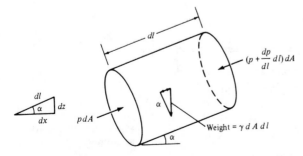

Figure 4 Pressure variation with elevation

T_0 is the temperature at a reference level where the pressure is known and α is the lapse rate. Using Eq 14, the pressure relation becomes:

$$\frac{dp}{dz} = -\frac{pg}{RT}$$

(Eq 16)

For the stratosphere, the temperature is assumed to be constant. Therefore:

$$\ln p = -\frac{zg}{RT} + C$$

(Eq 17)

At $z = z_0$, $p = p_0$ and: $p = p_0 e^{-(z-z_0)g/RT}$

(Eq 18)

MANOMETERS

The basic law governing manometers is Pascal's Law: Any two points at the same elevation in a continuous mass of the same static fluid will be at the same pressure. For an open manometer (Fig. 5) the pressures are related by:

$$p_A = p_a - \rho_1 g(z_A - z_1) - \rho_2 g(z_1 - z_2)$$

(Eq 19)

where p_a is the atmospheric pressure.

For differential manometers, with a gas flowing, the pressure difference between points 1 and 2 is given by $\Delta p = \gamma_m \Delta h$, where γ_m is the specific weight of the manometer liquid and Δh is the deflection of this liquid (Fig. 6). For a more dense fluid in the pipe:

$$\Delta p = (\gamma_m - \gamma_f)\Delta h$$

(Eq 20)

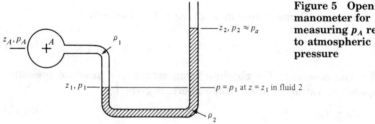

Figure 5   Open manometer for measuring p_A relative to atmospheric pressure

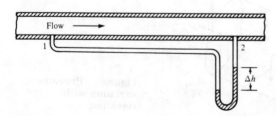

Figure 6   Differential manometer

where γ_f = specific weight of fluid in pipe; γ_m = specific weight of manometer fluid.

FORCES ON SUBMERGED SURFACES

Plane (Flat) Surfaces. For the flat plate shown in Fig. 7, the differential force on the differential area, dA, is:

$$dF = p \, dA \qquad \text{or} \qquad dF = \gamma y \sin \alpha \, dA$$

Total force on the area becomes:

$$F = \int_A p \, dA = \int_A \gamma y \sin \alpha \, dA \qquad \text{(Eq 21)}$$

For constant γ and $\sin \alpha$, Eq 21 is integrated to give:

$$F = (\gamma y \sin \alpha) A \qquad \text{(Eq 22)}$$

Therefore, the resultant hydrostatic force on a plane surface is the product of the pressure at the centroid of the surface and the area of the surface:

$$F = \bar{p} A \qquad \text{(Eq 23)}$$

The position of the center of pressure (Fig. 7) is given by:

$$y_{cp} = \bar{y} + \frac{\bar{I}}{\bar{y} A} \qquad \text{(Eq 24)}$$

where $\bar{y}$ is the centroid of the flat area; $\bar{I}$ = moment of inertia about the axis through the centroid and parallel to the surface of the fluid.

The location of the x-coordinate of the center of pressure is:

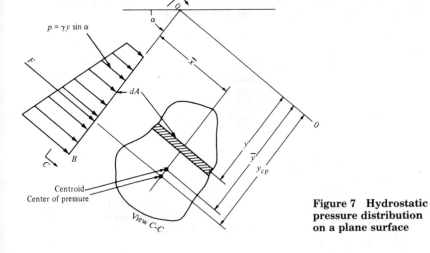

Figure 7 Hydrostatic pressure distribution on a plane surface

$$x_{cp} = \frac{I_{xy}}{\bar{y}A} + \bar{x} \qquad \text{(Eq 25)}$$

where I_{xy} = product of inertia of the plate about the centroidal axes; $x_{cp} = \bar{x}$ if plate is symmetric about one of the centroidal axes.

Curved Surfaces. Vertical forces on a fluid volume in contact with a curved surface (Fig. 8) are given by:

$$F_{Ry} = F_V + F_W \qquad \text{(Eq 26)}$$

where F_v is due to the pressure of the fluid along OB, F_w is due to the weight of the fluid in the volume AOB and F_{Ry} is the vertical reaction of surface AB. The reaction F_{Rx} serves to balance the pressure force caused by the fluid along OA. Forces on the curved surface can therefore be analyzed by applying the equations of equilibrium to the fluid volume (AOB) supported by the surface.

Buoyancy. The two basic laws concerning buoyancy are:
1. A body immersed in a fluid experiences a vertical buoyant force equal to the weight of the fluid it displaces;

   The net vertical force on a submerged body is:

$$F_B = (\rho g) \text{ (body volume)} \qquad \text{(Eq 27)}$$

2. A floating body displaces its own weight in the fluid in which it floats.

   The net vertical force on a floating body is given by:

$$F_B = (\rho g) \text{ (displaced volume)} \qquad \text{(Eq 28)}$$

FLUID MOTION

KINEMATIC RELATIONSHIPS—VELOCITY AND ACCELERATION

Velocity is a vector function of position and time with three components u, v, and w, each of which is a scalar field in itself:

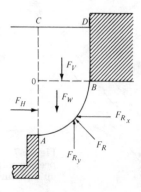

Figure 8 Analysis of hydrostatic force on a curved surface

$$\mathbf{V}(x, y, z, t) = u(x, y, z, t)\mathbf{i} + v(x, y, z, t)\mathbf{j} + w(x, y, z, t)\mathbf{k} \tag{Eq 29}$$

By mathematically manipulating the velocity-field function, kinematic properties such as the acceleration vector, the local angular-velocity vector, and the volume flux through a surface can be derived.

The acceleration vector is found from the time derivative of the velocity vector, that is:

$$\mathbf{a} = \frac{d\mathbf{V}}{dt} = \frac{\partial \mathbf{V}}{\partial t} + \frac{\partial \mathbf{V}}{\partial x}\frac{dx}{dt} + \frac{\partial \mathbf{V}}{\partial y}\frac{dy}{dt} + \frac{\partial \mathbf{V}}{\partial z}\frac{dz}{dt} \tag{Eq 30}$$

where $dx = u\,dt$; $dy = v\,dt$; $dz = w\,dt$.
Therefore:

$$\frac{d\mathbf{V}}{dt} = \frac{\partial \mathbf{V}}{\partial t} + \left(u\frac{\partial \mathbf{V}}{\partial x} + v\frac{\partial \mathbf{V}}{\partial y} + w\frac{\partial \mathbf{V}}{\partial z} \right) \tag{Eq 31}$$

where the first term on the right-hand side is called the local acceleration, and the three terms in the parentheses are called the convective acceleration. The total acceleration (Eq 31) of a particle can also be written:

$$\mathbf{a} = \frac{d\mathbf{V}}{dt} = \frac{\partial \mathbf{V}}{\partial t} + (\mathbf{V} \cdot \boldsymbol{\nabla})\mathbf{V} \tag{Eq 32}$$

where $\boldsymbol{\nabla} = \mathbf{i}\dfrac{\partial}{\partial x} + \mathbf{j}\dfrac{\partial}{\partial y} + \mathbf{k}\dfrac{\partial}{\partial z}$.

The operator, $\dfrac{d}{dt} = \dfrac{\partial}{\partial t} + (\mathbf{V} \cdot \boldsymbol{\nabla})$, may be applied to any fluid property, either scalar or vector, and is given the name substantial or material derivative.

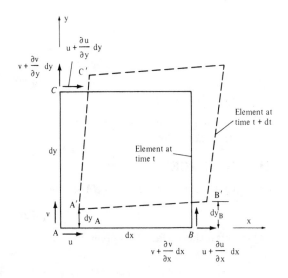

Figure 9 Deformation of fluid element

ROTATION OF FLUID AND VORTICITY

Considering rotation about the z axis in Fig. 9, the angular velocity is given by:

$$\omega_z = \frac{\omega_{AB} + \omega_{AC}}{2} \tag{Eq 33}$$

where $\omega_{AB} = \dfrac{\partial v}{\partial x}$; $\omega_{AC} = -\dfrac{\partial u}{\partial y}$.

Therefore:

$$\omega_z = \frac{1}{2}\left(\frac{\partial v}{\partial x} - \frac{\partial u}{\partial y}\right) \tag{Eq 34}$$

The rate of rotations about the x and y axes are:

$$\omega_x = \frac{1}{2}\left(\frac{\partial w}{\partial y} - \frac{\partial v}{\partial z}\right) \tag{Eq 35}$$

$$\omega_y = \frac{1}{2}\left(\frac{\partial u}{\partial z} - \frac{\partial w}{\partial x}\right) \tag{Eq 36}$$

The vorticity vector for cartesian coordinates is:

$$\boldsymbol{\Omega} = \left(\frac{\partial w}{\partial y} - \frac{\partial v}{\partial z}\right)\mathbf{i} + \left(\frac{\partial u}{\partial z} - \frac{\partial w}{\partial x}\right)\mathbf{j} + \left(\frac{\partial v}{\partial x} - \frac{\partial u}{\partial y}\right)\mathbf{k}$$

$$= 2 \cdot \boldsymbol{\omega} = 2(\boldsymbol{\nabla} \times \mathbf{V}) \tag{Eq 37}$$

For incompressible flow:

$$\boldsymbol{\nabla} \cdot \mathbf{V} = 0 \tag{Eq 38}$$

Flow with negligible local angular velocity or vorticity is called irrotational, and:

$$\boldsymbol{\nabla} \times \mathbf{V} = \begin{vmatrix} \mathbf{i} & \mathbf{j} & \mathbf{k} \\ \dfrac{\partial}{\partial x} & \dfrac{\partial}{\partial y} & \dfrac{\partial}{\partial z} \\ u & v & w \end{vmatrix} = 0 \tag{Eq 39}$$

Equation 39 implies that for irrotational flow:

$$\frac{\partial w}{\partial y} = \frac{\partial v}{\partial z} \qquad \frac{\partial u}{\partial z} = \frac{\partial w}{\partial x} \qquad \frac{\partial v}{\partial x} = \frac{\partial u}{\partial y}$$

FLOW RATE THROUGH A SURFACE

As shown in Fig. 10, the volume that leaves through area dA in time dt is:

$$dV = V\,dt\,dA\cos\theta = (\mathbf{V} \cdot \mathbf{n})\,dA\,dt \tag{Eq 40}$$

The total volume rate of flow Q through the surface S is given by:

$$Q = \int_S (\mathbf{V} \cdot \mathbf{n})\,dA = \int_S V_n\,dA \qquad \text{(Eq 41)}$$

where V_n is the component of $\mathbf{V}$ normal to dA and $\mathbf{n}$ is the outward normal unit vector. The mass flow is expressed as:

$$\dot{m} = \int_S \rho(\mathbf{V} \cdot \mathbf{n})\,dA = \int_S \rho V_n\,dA \qquad \text{(Eq 42)}$$

For constant density it becomes:

$$\dot{m} = \rho Q \qquad \text{(Eq 43)}$$

The average velocity passing through the surface can be computed from Q by:

$$V_{\text{avg}} = \frac{Q}{A} = \frac{\displaystyle\int_S V_n\,dA}{\displaystyle\int_S dA} \qquad \text{(Eq 44)}$$

STREAMLINES

Streamlines are used to visualize the flow patterns in a fluid. For any given instant, they represent lines in the flow field across which no fluid passes. The velocity of every fluid particle on the streamline is in the direction tangent to the line, and when a sufficient number of such streamlines in the flow field are known, the flow pattern is determined, as shown in Fig. 11.

Mathematically, this means that every vector arc length $d\mathbf{r}$ along a streamline must be tangent to $\mathbf{V}$ and their respective components must be in exact proportion. Therefore:

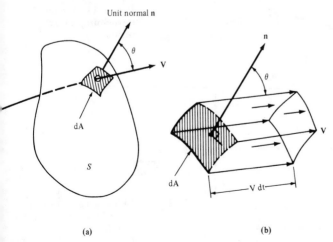

Figure 10 Volume rate of flow through an arbitrary surface. (a) An elemental area dA on the surface. (b) The incremental volume moving through dA equals VdtdA cos θ

$$\frac{dx}{u} = \frac{dy}{v} = \frac{dz}{w} = \frac{dr}{V} \qquad \text{(Eq 45)}$$

and

$$\frac{dx}{ds} = u \qquad \frac{dy}{ds} = v \qquad \frac{dz}{ds} = w \qquad \text{(Eq 46)}$$

where ds is a parameter equal to the ratios in Eq 45. These equations can be integrated to find streamline equations.

VARIATION OF PRESSURE DUE TO RIGID BODY MOTION

For a tank (Fig. 12) undergoing uniform acceleration, the angle of the liquid surface is:

$$\tan \alpha = \frac{a_x}{g} \qquad \text{(Eq 47)}$$

Pressure can be easily determined using this angle to find the fluid depth.

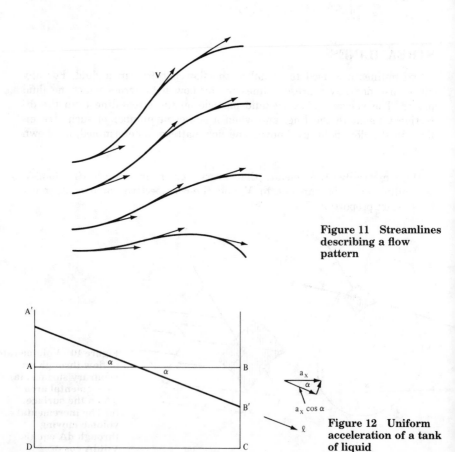

Figure 11 Streamlines describing a flow pattern

Figure 12 Uniform acceleration of a tank of liquid

For a tank (Fig. 13) undergoing rotation, the pressure variation becomes:

$$\frac{d}{dr}(p + \gamma z) = \rho r \omega^2 \qquad\qquad\qquad\qquad \text{(Eq 48)}$$

Integration produces:

$$p + \gamma z = \frac{\rho r^2 \omega^2}{2} + \text{constant}$$

or

$$\frac{p}{\gamma} + z - \frac{V^2}{2g} = \text{constant} \qquad\qquad\qquad\qquad \text{(Eq 49)}$$

CONCEPT OF THE CONTROL VOLUME

EULERIAN AND LAGRANGIAN VIEWS

In analyzing problems in mechanics, two approaches, have evolved. In the Lagrangian method, equations of motion are written for a moving particle. Variations in a fluid property are monitored for each individual particle as it moves through the flow field and the property, say pressure, is considered a function of time, $p = p(t)$.

The Eulerian approach requires analysis of the fluid particles as they pass given locations in the flow field. The fluid property is considered a function of the spatial coordinates as well as time and $p = p(x, y, z, t)$. This is often called the control volume viewpoint and is the one most often used in fluid mechanics.

CONTROL VOLUME TRANSPORT EQUATION

The symbol B is used to represent a general extensive property, and β is used for the corresponding intensive property. The volume rate of flow past a given area A can be written as: $\quad Q = \mathbf{V} \cdot \mathbf{A}$

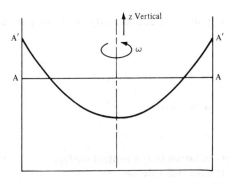

Figure 13 Rigid body rotation of a liquid in a tank

if the velocity vector $\mathbf{V}$ is considered uniform over the vector area $\mathbf{A}$. For the control volume of Fig. 14, the net volumetric flow rate out of the control volume is:

$$Q_{\text{out}} - Q_{\text{in}} = \mathbf{V}_2 \cdot \mathbf{A}_2 + \mathbf{V}_1 \cdot \mathbf{A}_1 \qquad \text{(Eq 50)}$$

The net mass flow rate then becomes:

$$\dot{m} = \sum_{cs} \rho \mathbf{V} \cdot \mathbf{A} \qquad \text{(Eq 51)}$$

where the summation indicates that several inflow and outflow areas can be considered. This is similar to Eq 42.

For the rate of flow of an extensive property B out of the control volume, the mass rate is multiplied by the intensive property β:

$$\dot{B} = \sum_{cs} \beta \rho \mathbf{V} \cdot \mathbf{A} \qquad \text{(Eq 52)}$$

Generally, this equation is used in integral form:

$$\dot{B} = \int_{cs} \beta \rho \mathbf{V} \cdot d\mathbf{A} \qquad \text{(Eq 53)}$$

The transport equation relates the rate of change of property B for a fixed amount of mass (system) to the change in the property as it relates to the control volume. The equation is:

$$\frac{dB_{\text{sys}}}{dt} = \frac{\partial}{\partial t} \int_{cv} \beta \rho \, dV + \int_{cs} \beta \rho \mathbf{V} \cdot d\mathbf{A} \qquad \text{(Eq 54)}$$

where the left-hand side is the rate of change of the extensive property of the system. The right-hand side refers to accumulation of the property in the control volume and flow of the property across the control surface. For steady flow, the equation becomes:

$$\frac{dB_{\text{sys}}}{dt} = \int_{cs} \beta \rho \mathbf{V} \cdot d\mathbf{A} \qquad \text{(Eq 55)}$$

Note that B can be either a scalar or vector quantity.

For a control volume moving at constant velocity with respect to an inertial frame:

$$\mathbf{V}_r = \mathbf{V} - \mathbf{V}_s \qquad \text{(Eq 56)}$$

and

$$\frac{d}{dt}(B_{\text{sys}}) = \int_{cv} \frac{\partial}{\partial t}(\beta \rho) dV + \int_{cs} \beta \rho (\mathbf{V}_r \cdot \mathbf{n}) dA \qquad \text{(Eq 57)}$$

where

$\qquad \mathbf{V}_r$ = fluid velocity relative to the control surface
$\qquad \mathbf{V}_s$ = velocity of the control volume
$\qquad \mathbf{V}$ = absolute fluid velocity

For the most general situation, the control volume is both moving and deforming arbitrarily. The control surface has a deformation, its velocity $\mathbf{V}_s = \mathbf{V}_s(\mathbf{r}, t)$, so that the relative velocity becomes $\mathbf{V}_r = \mathbf{V}(\mathbf{r}, t) - \mathbf{V}_s(\mathbf{r}, t)$. This may be a complicated function. The volume integral in Eq 57 must allow the volume elements to distort with time, and therefore the time derivative must be applied after integration. The transport theorem becomes:

$$\frac{d}{dt}(B_{sys}) = \frac{\partial}{\partial t}\left(\int_{cv} \beta\rho\, dV\right) + \int_{cs} \beta\rho\,(\mathbf{V}_r \cdot \mathbf{n})\, dA \qquad \text{(Eq 58)}$$

LAWS TO WHICH THE CONTROL VOLUME CONCEPT IS APPLIED

The time rate of change of total mass M of a system of particles (conservation of mass) is:

$$\frac{dM}{dt} = 0 \qquad \text{(Eq 59)}$$

The time rate of change of momentum of a system of particles is equal to the sum of the externally applied forces (Newton's second law):

$$\sum \mathbf{F} = \frac{d(M\mathbf{V})}{dt} \qquad \text{(Eq 60)}$$

The rate of change of total energy of a system of particles is equal to the rate of addition of heat less the rate of work done by the system (conservation of energy):

$$\frac{dE}{dt} = \frac{d\hat{Q}}{dt} - \frac{dW}{dt} \qquad \text{(Eq 61)}$$

These laws express the time rate of change of fluid quantities for a system of particles and must now be applied to the control volume.

CONTINUITY EQUATION

INTEGRAL FORMULATION

The general form of the continuity equation (conservation of mass) is:

$$\int_{cs} \rho\mathbf{V} \cdot d\mathbf{A} = -\frac{\partial}{\partial t}\int_{cv} \rho\, dV \qquad \text{(Eq 62)}$$

This states that the net rate of mass outflow from the control volume equals the rate of decrease of mass within the control volume. For steady flow:

$$\int_{cs} \rho \mathbf{V} \cdot d\mathbf{A} = 0 \tag{Eq 63}$$

If the flow is steady and the velocity is constant across several inflow and outflow sections:

$$\sum \rho \mathbf{V} \cdot \mathbf{A} = 0$$

For one inflow and one outflow such as seen in Fig. 14:

$$\rho_1 V_1 A_1 = \rho_2 V_2 A_2 \tag{Eq 64}$$

If ρ is constant, then:

$$V_1 A_1 = V_2 A_2 \tag{Eq 65}$$

DIFFERENTIAL FORMULATION

The differential formulation may be derived by applying the transport equation to a differential control volume. For cartesian coordinates, the continuity equation is:

$$\frac{\partial}{\partial x}(\rho u) + \frac{\partial}{\partial y}(\rho v) + \frac{\partial}{\partial z}(\rho w) = -\frac{\partial \rho}{\partial t} \tag{Eq 66}$$

If the flow is steady this becomes:

$$\frac{\partial}{\partial x}(\rho u) + \frac{\partial}{\partial y}(\rho v) + \frac{\partial}{\partial z}(\rho w) = 0 \tag{Eq 67}$$

For an incompressible fluid, then:

$$\frac{\partial u}{\partial x} + \frac{\partial v}{\partial y} + \frac{\partial w}{\partial z} = 0 \tag{Eq 68}$$

for both steady and unsteady flow. In vector notation, Eq 68 becomes:

$$\nabla \cdot \mathbf{V} = 0 \tag{Eq 69}$$

MOMENTUM EQUATION

INTEGRAL FORM—LINEAR MOMENTUM

From Newton's second law, it can be shown that the summation of all external forces on a system equals the net rate at which momentum crosses

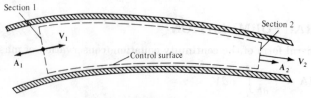

Figure 14

the control surface plus the rate at which momentum is accumulated inside
the control volume:

$$\sum \mathbf{F} = \int_{cs} \mathbf{V}\rho\mathbf{V} \cdot d\mathbf{A} + \frac{\partial}{\partial t}\int_{cv} \mathbf{V}\rho dV \qquad \text{(Eq 70)}$$

The two types of forces usually considered are surface forces and body
forces:

$$\sum \mathbf{F} = \sum \mathbf{F}_S + \sum \mathbf{F}_B \qquad \text{(Eq 71)}$$

In cartesian coordinates, the momentum equation for each direction is given
as follows:

x-direction:

$$\sum F_x = \sum_{cs} u(\rho\mathbf{V} \cdot \mathbf{A}) + \frac{\partial}{\partial t}\int_{cv} u\rho \, dV \qquad \text{(Eq 72)}$$

y-direction:

$$\sum F_y = \sum_{cs} v(\rho\mathbf{V} \cdot \mathbf{A}) + \frac{\partial}{\partial t}\int_{cv} v\rho \, dV \qquad \text{(Eq 73)}$$

z-direction:

$$\sum F_z = \sum_{cs} w(\rho\mathbf{V} \cdot \mathbf{A}) + \frac{\partial}{\partial t}\int_{cv} w\rho \, dV \qquad \text{(Eq 74)}$$

The $\sum\limits_{cs}$ term used in Eq 72 through 74 indicates that the velocities are
uniformly distributed across the areas.

The use of an average (uniform) velocity across a surface results in an
error. The simple one-dimensional momentum flux calculation,

$$\int_{cs} \mathbf{V}(\rho\mathbf{V} \cdot \mathbf{n}) dA = \int \rho V^2 dA = \rho A \bar{V}^2,$$

where $\bar{V}$ represents the average velocity, should be modified using the term
$\alpha\rho A\bar{V}^2$. The factor α is the dimensionless momentum flux correction factor,
$\alpha \geq 1$, defined as

$$\alpha = \int \left(\frac{V}{\bar{V}}\right)^2 dA \qquad \text{(Eq 75)}$$

where V is the actual velocity (spatially varying).

INTEGRAL FORM—ANGULAR MOMENTUM (MOMENT OF MOMENTUM)

The extensive property describing angular momentum for the system is:

$$B_{\text{sys}} = \int (\mathbf{r} \times \mathbf{V})\rho \, dV = \text{angular momentum of the system} \qquad \text{(Eq 76)}$$

The general form of the angular momentum equation becomes:

$$\sum \mathbf{M} = \int_{cs} (\mathbf{r} \times \mathbf{V}) \rho \mathbf{V} \cdot d\mathbf{A} + \frac{\partial}{\partial t} \int_{cv} (\mathbf{r} \times \mathbf{V}) \rho \, dV \tag{Eq 77}$$

For uniform velocity across the inlet and outlet areas:

$$\sum \mathbf{M} = \sum_{cs} (\mathbf{r} \times \mathbf{V}) \rho \mathbf{V} \cdot \mathbf{A} + \frac{\partial}{\partial t} \int_{cv} (\mathbf{r} \times \mathbf{V}) \rho \, dV \tag{Eq 78}$$

DIFFERENTIAL FORM—LINEAR MOMENTUM

As previously stated, the forces in a linear momentum system are of two types, body forces and surface forces. Body forces are due to external fields (gravity, magnetism, electric potential) which act upon the entire mass within the element. The only body force considered here is gravity. The surface forces are caused by stresses on a fluid element, the general state of stress for an element being shown in Fig. 15. The stress tensor is defined as:

$$\tau_{ij} = \begin{vmatrix} -p + \tau'_{xx} & \tau_{yx} & \tau_{zx} \\ \tau_{xy} & -p + \tau'_{yy} & \tau_{zy} \\ \tau_{xz} & \tau_{yz} & -p + \tau'_{zz} \end{vmatrix} \tag{Eq 79}$$

The basic differential momentum equation for an infinitesimal element now becomes:

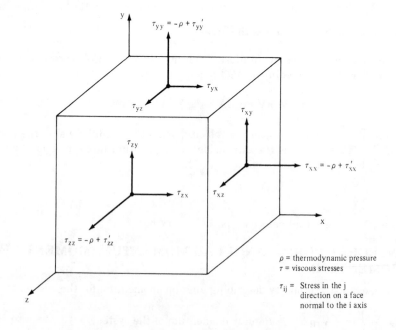

ρ = thermodynamic pressure
τ = viscous stresses

τ_{ij} = Stress in the j direction on a face normal to the i axis

Figure 15   Notation for stresses on a fluid element

$$\rho \mathbf{g} - \nabla p + \nabla \cdot \tau'_{ij} = \rho \frac{d\mathbf{V}}{dt} \qquad \text{(Eq 80)}$$

where

$$\frac{d\mathbf{V}}{dt} = \frac{\partial \mathbf{V}}{\partial t} + u \frac{\partial \mathbf{V}}{\partial x} + v \frac{\partial \mathbf{V}}{\partial y} + w \frac{\partial \mathbf{V}}{\partial z}$$

and

$$\tau'_{ij} = \begin{vmatrix} \tau'_{xx} & \tau_{yx} & \tau_{zx} \\ \tau_{xy} & \tau'_{yy} & \tau_{zy} \\ \tau_{xz} & \tau_{yz} & \tau'_{zz} \end{vmatrix}$$

This last tensor is called the viscous stress tensor and results from removing the thermodynamic pressure from Eq 79. The third term in Eq 80 represents the viscous force per unit volume exerted on the fluid element.

In cartesian coordinates, the three components of the momentum equation are:

$$\rho g_x - \frac{\partial p}{\partial x} + \frac{\partial \tau'_{xx}}{\partial x} + \frac{\partial \tau_{yx}}{\partial y} + \frac{\partial \tau_{zx}}{\partial z} = \rho \left(\frac{\partial u}{\partial t} + u \frac{\partial u}{\partial x} + v \frac{\partial u}{\partial y} + w \frac{\partial u}{\partial z} \right)$$

$$\rho g_y - \frac{\partial p}{\partial y} + \frac{\partial \tau_{xy}}{\partial x} + \frac{\partial \tau'_{yy}}{\partial y} + \frac{\partial \tau_{zy}}{\partial z} = \rho \left(\frac{\partial v}{\partial t} + u \frac{\partial v}{\partial x} + v \frac{\partial v}{\partial y} + w \frac{\partial v}{\partial z} \right)$$

$$\rho g_z - \frac{\partial p}{\partial z} + \frac{\partial \tau_{xz}}{\partial x} + \frac{\partial \tau_{yz}}{\partial y} + \frac{\partial \tau'_{zz}}{\partial z} = \rho \left(\frac{\partial w}{\partial t} + u \frac{\partial w}{\partial x} + v \frac{\partial w}{\partial y} + w \frac{\partial w}{\partial z} \right) \qquad \text{(Eq 81)}$$

For frictionless flow, $\tau'_{ij} = 0$, and the equation becomes:

$$\rho \mathbf{g} - \nabla p = \rho \frac{d\mathbf{V}}{dt} \qquad \text{(Eq 82)}$$

This is Euler's equation for inviscid flow. It can be integrated along a streamline to get the Bernoulli equation.

For a Newtonian fluid, the viscous stresses are proportional to the strain rates of the fluid element and the coefficient of viscosity. If the fluid is considered to be both isotropic and incompressible, the terms of the stress tensor become:

$$\tau'_{xx} = 2\mu \frac{\partial u}{\partial x} \qquad \tau'_{yy} = 2\mu \frac{\partial v}{\partial y} \qquad \tau'_{zz} = 2\mu \frac{\partial w}{\partial z}$$

$$\tau_{xy} = \tau_{yx} = \mu \left(\frac{\partial u}{\partial y} + \frac{\partial v}{\partial x} \right) \qquad \tau_{xz} = \tau_{zx} = \mu \left(\frac{\partial w}{\partial x} + \frac{\partial u}{\partial z} \right)$$

$$\tau_{yz} = \tau_{zy} = \mu \left(\frac{\partial v}{\partial z} + \frac{\partial w}{\partial y} \right) \qquad \text{(Eq 83)}$$

where μ is the viscosity coefficient. The momentum equation for a Newtonian fluid with constant density and viscosity is now written as:

$$\rho g_x - \frac{\partial p}{\partial x} + \mu \left(\frac{\partial^2 u}{\partial x^2} + \frac{\partial^2 u}{\partial y^2} + \frac{\partial^2 u}{\partial z^2} \right) = \rho \frac{du}{dt}$$

$$\rho g_y - \frac{\partial p}{\partial y} + \mu \left(\frac{\partial^2 v}{\partial x^2} + \frac{\partial^2 v}{\partial y^2} + \frac{\partial^2 v}{\partial z^2} \right) = \rho \frac{dv}{dt}$$

$$\rho g_z - \frac{\partial p}{\partial z} + \mu \left(\frac{\partial^2 w}{\partial x^2} + \frac{\partial^2 w}{\partial y^2} + \frac{\partial^2 w}{\partial z^2} \right) = \rho \frac{dw}{dt} \qquad \text{(Eq 84)}$$

These are referred to as the Navier-Stokes equations. In vector form, this set has the form:

$$\rho \frac{d\mathbf{V}}{dt} = \rho \mathbf{g} - \nabla p + \mu \nabla^2 \mathbf{V} \qquad \text{(Eq 85)}$$

The $\frac{d}{dt}$ terms in Eq 80, 84 and 85 refer to the substantial derivative.

ENERGY EQUATION

INTEGRAL FORM

The symbol E refers to the total energy of the system and e is the energy per unit mass. From the first law of thermodynamics, $dE/dt = \dot{Q} - \dot{W}$ and the energy equation becomes:

$$\dot{Q} - \dot{W} = \frac{\partial}{\partial t} \int_{cv} e\rho \, dV + \sum_{cs} e\rho \mathbf{V} \cdot \mathbf{A} \qquad \text{(Eq 86)}$$

where the velocity and the energy crossing the control surface are considered constant over a flow area. The $\dot{Q}$ and $\dot{W}$ indicate rates for heat transfer and work, respectively.

The term e can be replaced by its equivalent, $e = \hat{u} + \frac{V^2}{2} + zg$. These terms represent the internal energy, kinetic energy, and potential energy per unit mass. The energy equation becomes:

$$\dot{Q} - \dot{W} = \frac{\partial}{\partial t} \int_{cv} \left(\frac{V^2}{2} + gz + \hat{u} \right) \rho \, dV + \sum_{cs} \left(\frac{V^2}{2} + gz + \hat{u} \right) \rho \mathbf{V} \cdot \mathbf{A} \qquad \text{(Eq 87)}$$

Work is the sum of the shaft work and the flow work.

Flow work is the work done by pressure forces as the system moves through space. This is expressed for all streams passing through the control surface as:

$$\dot{W}_f = \sum_{cs} p\mathbf{V} \cdot \mathbf{A} \qquad \text{(Eq 88)}$$

where area vector $\mathbf{A}$ is considered to be directed outward. Shaft work is defined as any work other than flow work.

Using flow work and shaft work, the energy equation takes the form:

$$\dot{\tilde{Q}} - \dot{W}_s = \frac{\partial}{\partial t} \int_{cv} \left(\frac{V^2}{2} + gz + \hat{u} \right) \rho \, dV +$$

$$\sum_{cs} \left(\frac{p}{\rho} + \frac{V^2}{2} + gz + \hat{u} \right) \rho \mathbf{V} \cdot \mathbf{A} \qquad \text{(Eq 89)}$$

If the velocity or the other properties are not uniform across the section, then:

$$\dot{\tilde{Q}} - \dot{W}_s = \frac{\partial}{\partial t} \int_{cv} \left(\frac{V^2}{2} + gz + \hat{u} \right) \rho \, dV +$$

$$\int_{cs} \left(\frac{p}{\rho} + \frac{V^2}{2} + gz + \hat{u} \right) \rho \mathbf{V} \cdot d\mathbf{A} \qquad \text{(Eq 90)}$$

For steady flow:

$$\dot{\tilde{Q}} - \dot{W}_s = \sum_{cs} \left(\frac{V^2}{2} + gz + h \right) \rho \mathbf{V} \cdot \mathbf{A} \qquad \text{(Eq 91)}$$

where the property of enthalpy, $h = \frac{p}{\rho} + \hat{u}$, has been employed. With a single inflow and outflow, this equation reduces to:

$$\frac{1}{\dot{m}} (\dot{\tilde{Q}} - \dot{W}_s) + gz_1 + h_1 + \frac{V_1^2}{2} = gz_2 + h_2 + \frac{V_2^2}{2} \qquad \text{(Eq 92)}$$

The kinetic energy terms in Eq 92 are not exact since V_1 and V_2 are assumed to be constant across the input and output areas. If we consider for the moment that $\bar{V}_1$ and $\bar{V}_2$ represent these average (uniform) velocities, then the proper kinetic energy terms are $\lambda_1 \frac{\bar{V}_1^2}{2}$ and $\lambda_2 \frac{\bar{V}_2^2}{2}$, where λ_1 and λ_2 are the kinetic energy correction factors. The term λ is defined by:

$$\lambda = \frac{1}{A} \int \left(\frac{V}{\bar{V}} \right)^3 dA \qquad \text{(Eq 93)}$$

where V is the actual velocity (spatially varying) at the control surface. Some common values for λ are (a) 1.0, constant velocity over the section; (b) 2.0, parabolic laminar flow; and (c) 1.05, turbulent flow. The momentum correction factors of Eq 75 do not vary from 1.0 as much as the values of λ. The use of the correction factors do not account for the rather remote possibility that enthalpy varies across the section.

Eq 92 may be rewritten in the following form:

$$\frac{p_1}{\gamma} + \frac{V_1^2}{2g} + z_1 = \frac{p_2}{\gamma} + \frac{V_2^2}{2g} + z_2 + \frac{\dot{W}}{mg} + h_L \qquad \text{(Eq 94)}$$

This arrangement assigns units of length (feet, meters) to each term. The symbol h_L represents losses between points 1 and 2 (head loss) and includes heat transfer from the control volume resulting from viscous dissipation and any loss of mechanical energy in general.

For a stream tube (a filament of fluid of infinitesimal cross section bounded by streamlines) containing an inviscid fluid and without any shaft work, Eq 94 leads to Bernoulli's equation:

$$\frac{p_1}{\gamma} + \frac{V_1^2}{2g} + z_1 = \frac{p_2}{\gamma} + \frac{V_2^2}{2g} + z_2 \qquad \text{(Eq 95)}$$

Equation 95 can be derived either from the energy equation, as above, or by integrating Euler's equation (Eq 82) along a streamline. It is thus considered valid if applied along a streamline in a frictionless, incompressible, steady flow with no shaft work, and also may be shown to apply between any two points in an incompressible, irrotational, steady flow field.

DIFFERENTIAL FORMULATION

The heat transfer across the control surface is considered here to be by conduction only. Expressed in vector form, Fourier's law shows that:

$$\dot{Q} = \nabla \cdot (k \, \nabla T) \, dx \, dy \, dz \qquad \text{(Eq 96)}$$

where k is the thermal conductivity. The net viscous-work rate can be shown to be:

$$\dot{W}_v = - \left[\frac{\partial}{\partial x} (u\tau'_{xx} + v\tau_{xy} + w\tau_{xz}) + \frac{\partial}{\partial y} (u\tau_{yx} + v\tau'_{yy} + w\tau_{yz}) \right.$$

$$\left. + \frac{\partial}{\partial z} (u\tau_{zx} + v\tau_{zy} + w\tau'_{zz}) \right] dx \, dy \, dz$$

$$= -\nabla \cdot (\mathbf{V} \cdot \tau'_{ij}) \, dx \, dy \, dz \qquad \text{(Eq 97)}$$

The resulting form of the differential energy equation is:

$$\rho \frac{de}{dt} + \mathbf{V} \cdot \nabla p = \nabla \cdot (k \, \nabla T) + \nabla \cdot (\mathbf{V} \cdot \tau'_{ij}) \qquad \text{(Eq 98)}$$

where $e = \hat{u} + \frac{1}{2}V^2 + gz$. The viscous-work term can be separated as follows:

$$\nabla \cdot (\mathbf{V} \cdot \tau'_{ij}) \equiv \mathbf{V} \cdot (\nabla \cdot \tau'_{ij}) + \Phi \qquad \text{(Eq 99)}$$

where Φ is the viscous dissipation function. For an incompressible Newtonian fluid:

$$\Phi = \mu \left[2 \left(\frac{\partial u}{\partial x} \right)^2 + 2 \left(\frac{\partial v}{\partial y} \right)^2 + 2 \left(\frac{\partial w}{\partial z} \right)^2 + \left(\frac{\partial v}{\partial x} + \frac{\partial u}{\partial y} \right)^2 \right.$$

$$\left. + \left(\frac{\partial w}{\partial y} + \frac{\partial v}{\partial z} \right)^2 + \left(\frac{\partial u}{\partial z} + \frac{\partial w}{\partial x} \right)^2 \right] \qquad \text{(Eq 100)}$$

The viscous dissipation is always positive.

The usual vector form of the general differential energy equation that can be obtained using Eq 98, 99 and 100 is:

$$\rho \frac{\partial \hat{u}}{\partial t} + p(\mathbf{\nabla} \cdot \mathbf{V}) = \mathbf{\nabla} \cdot (k\,\mathbf{\nabla}T) + \Phi \qquad \text{(Eq 101)}$$

This form neglects radiation and internal energy generation. Using the approximation:

$$d\hat{u} \approx c_v dT$$

where c_v (constant volume specific heat), μ, k and ρ are constants, the energy equation takes the form:

$$\rho c_v \frac{dT}{dt} = k \nabla^2 T + \Phi \qquad \text{(Eq 102)}$$

where $\dfrac{dT}{dt} = \dfrac{\partial T}{\partial t} + u\,\dfrac{\partial T}{\partial x} + v\,\dfrac{\partial T}{\partial y} + w\,\dfrac{\partial T}{\partial z}$

BOUNDARY CONDITIONS FOR THE DIFFERENTIAL EQUATIONS

Typical boundary conditions are shown in Fig. 16 and described below.

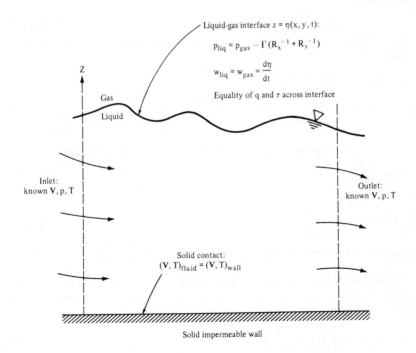

Figure 16 Typical boundary conditions in viscous heat-conducting fluid-flow. From White (Ref 2) with permission

Initial Condition. For unsteady flow, there must be an initial condition or a known initial spatial distribution for each variable: ρ, $\mathbf{V}$, p, $\hat{u}$, and T.

Solid Wall. For a solid, impermeable wall, there is no velocity slip and no temperature jump in a viscous heat-conducting fluid:

$$\mathbf{V}_{\text{fluid}} = \mathbf{V}_{\text{wall}} \qquad T_{\text{fluid}} = T_{\text{wall}} \tag{Eq 103}$$

An exception to Eq 103 exists in an extremely rarefied gas flow, where slippage can occur.

Inlet or Outlet of Control Volume. At any inlet or outlet section of the flow, complete distribution of velocity, pressure, and temperature must be known for all times.

Liquid/Gas Interface. The interface is denoted by $z = \eta(x, y, t)$. There is equality of vertical velocity across the interface, so that no holes appear between liquid and gas and:

$$w_{\text{liq}} = w_{\text{gas}} = \frac{d\eta}{dt} = \frac{\partial \eta}{\partial t} + u\frac{\partial \eta}{\partial x} + v\frac{\partial \eta}{\partial y} \tag{Eq 104}$$

This is the kinematic boundary condition. The viscous-shear stresses must also balance:

$$(\tau_{zy})_{\text{liq}} = (\tau_{zy})_{\text{gas}} \qquad (\tau_{zx})_{\text{liq}} = (\tau_{zx})_{\text{gas}} \tag{Eq 105}$$

The pressures must balance at the interface except for surface-tension effects:

$$p_{\text{liq}} = p_{\text{gas}} - \Gamma(R_x^{-1} + R_y^{-1}) \tag{Eq 106}$$

where $R_x^{-1} + R_y^{-1} = \dfrac{\partial^2\eta/\partial x^2 + \partial^2\eta/\partial y^2}{[1 + (\partial\eta/\partial x)^2 + (\partial\eta/\partial y)^2]^{3/2}}$ and Γ is the surface tension coefficient.

The heat transfer must be the same on both sides of the interface:

$$(\tilde{Q}_z)_{\text{liq}} = (\tilde{Q})_{\text{gas}} \tag{Eq 107a}$$

or

$$\left(k\frac{\partial T}{\partial z}\right)_{\text{liq}} = \left(k\frac{\partial T}{\partial z}\right)_{\text{gas}} \tag{Eq 107b}$$

Equation 107(b) accounts for only conduction at the surface.

Simplified Free Surface. It is assumed that the upper fluid only exerts pressure on the lower surface and shear, heat transfer and nonlinear slope terms are neglected. The conditions become:

$$p_{\text{liq}} \approx p_{\text{gas}} - \Gamma\left(\frac{\partial^2\eta}{\partial x^2} + \frac{\partial^2\eta}{\partial y^2}\right) \tag{Eq 108}$$

where $w_{\text{liq}} \approx \dfrac{\partial \eta}{\partial t}$; $\left(\dfrac{\partial V}{\partial z}\right)_{\text{liq}} \approx 0$; $\left(\dfrac{\partial T}{\partial z}\right)_{\text{liq}} \approx 0$.

For open-channel flow, surface tension is also neglected and:

$$p_{liq} \approx p_{atm} \qquad \text{(Eq 109)}$$

Inviscid Flow. Only the normal velocities must match at any solid surface:

$$(V_n)_{fluid} = (V_n)_{wall} \qquad \text{(Eq 110)}$$

DIMENSIONAL ANALYSIS

Dimensional analysis enables the formulation of functional relationships in a set of nondimensional groups composed of physical variables, with the groups numbering less than the variables. For dimensional analysis, physical variables must be known or assumed. An equation expressing a relationship between flow quantities must be dimensionally homogeneous. Physical quantities used in fluid flow problems can be expressed in terms of the fundamental units of mass (M), length (L), and time (T). Temperature is not required in basic fluid problems.

The dimensions of various physical quantities used in fluid mechanics are presented in Table 1. This table is based on the M, L, T primary system.

THE PI THEOREM

This theorem is critical to all applications of dimensional analysis and can be stated as follows: if a dimensional quantity u, an unknown, is expressed in terms of n other dimensional quantities $x_1, \ldots, x_n$ by:

$$u = f(x_1, \ldots, x_n) \qquad \text{(Eq 111)}$$

and if the first m variables $x_1, \ldots, x_m$ have independent dimensions, then Eq 111 can be written as:

$$\Pi = f(1, 1, \ldots, \Pi_1, \ldots, \Pi_{n-m}) \qquad \text{(Eq 112)}$$

The terms $\Pi, \Pi_1, \Pi_2, \ldots, \Pi_{n-m}$ are forms of $u, x_{m+1}, \ldots, x_n$, respectively, made dimensionless by forming combinations with $x_1, \ldots, x_m$.

Any dimensional relationship that expresses one physical variable, the unknown, in terms of n other physical variables, of which m have independent dimensions, can be arranged as a relationship between the unknown in dimensionless form and $n - m$ dimensionless combinations of the remaining variables. The pi theorem is valid only if the relationship in Eq 111 is true regardless of what system of units is being used.

POWER PRODUCT METHOD

This method is a practical application of the pi theorem, and it is best described using an example taken from John & Haberman and used by permission. To determine the frictional force exerted by a flowing fluid on a smooth pipe, assume that the significant physical quantities are the fluid density ρ, the average fluid velocity V, the interior surface area of pipe S, the dynamic viscosity μ, the internal diameter of pipe D, and the frictional force F exerted on the pipe by the fluid. This relationship takes the form:

$$F = F(\rho, V, S, \mu, D) \tag{Eq 113}$$

This type of expression can generally be expanded into a power series in the form:

$$F = c_1 \rho^{\alpha_1} V^{\alpha_2} S^{\alpha_3} \mu^{\alpha_4} D^{\alpha_5} + c_2 \rho^{\beta_1} V^{\beta_2} S^{\beta_3} \mu^{\beta_4} D^{\beta_5} + \ldots \tag{Eq 114}$$

where the α and β terms represent numerical exponents that depend on the nature of the function F and the c's represent dimensionless numerical coefficients. The terms on the right-hand side of Eq 114 are added so every term must have the same dimensions.

Substituting the physical dimensions from Table 1 into Eq 114 produces:

$$\frac{ML}{T^2} = \left(\frac{M}{L^3}\right)^{\alpha_1} \left(\frac{L}{T}\right)^{\alpha_2} (L^2)^{\alpha_3} \left(\frac{M}{LT}\right)^{\alpha_4} L^{\alpha_5} +$$

$$\left(\frac{M}{L^3}\right)^{\beta_1} \left(\frac{L}{T}\right)^{\beta_2} (L^2)^{\beta_3} \left(\frac{M}{LT}\right)^{\beta_4} L^{\beta_5} + \ldots$$

For each term, like exponents for the primary dimensions M, L, and T are collected to obtain three algebraic equations with five unknowns. For the first term we obtain:

$$
\begin{aligned}
\text{for } M: \quad & 1 = \alpha_1 + \alpha_4 \\
\text{for } L: \quad & 1 = -3\alpha_1 + \alpha_2 + 2\alpha_3 - \alpha_4 + \alpha_5 \\
\text{for } T: \quad & -2 = -\alpha_2 - \alpha_4
\end{aligned}
$$

For the second term we obtain:

$$
\begin{aligned}
\text{for } M: \quad & 1 = \beta_1 + \beta_4 \\
\text{for } L: \quad & 1 = -3\beta_1 + \beta_2 + 2\beta_3 - \beta_4 + \beta_5 \\
\text{for } T: \quad & -2 = -\beta_2 - \beta_4
\end{aligned}
$$

and so on. Solving these equations in terms of two of the unknowns, say, α_4, α_5 and β_4, β_5, we obtain:

$$
\begin{aligned}
\alpha_1 &= 1 - \alpha_4 & \beta_1 &= 1 - \beta_4 \\
\alpha_2 &= 2 - \alpha_4 & \text{and} \quad \beta_2 &= 2 - \beta_4 \\
\alpha_3 &= 1 - \frac{\alpha_4}{2} - \frac{\alpha_5}{2} & \beta_3 &= 1 - \frac{\beta_4}{2} - \frac{\beta_5}{2}
\end{aligned}
$$

Substituting these values into Eq 114 yields:

$$F = \rho V^2 S \left[c_1 \left(\frac{\mu}{\rho D V}\right)^{\alpha_4} \left(\frac{D^2}{S}\right)^{(\alpha_4 + \alpha_5)/2} + \right.$$

$$\left. c_2 \left(\frac{\mu}{\rho D V}\right)^{\beta_4} \left(\frac{D^2}{S}\right)^{(\beta_4 + \beta_5)/2} + \ldots \right] \tag{Eq 115a}$$

Table 1   Dimensions of various physical quantities

Quantity	Symbol	Dimensions (M, L, T)
Length	l	L
Time	t	T
Mass	m	M
Force	F	ML/T^2
Velocity (linear)	V	L/T
Acceleration (linear)	a	L/T^2
Area	A	L^2
Volume	V	L^3
Pressure	p	M/LT^2
Density	ρ	M/L^3
Acceleration due to gravity	g	L/T^2
Dynamic viscosity	μ	M/LT
Kinematic viscosity	ν	L^2/T
Surface tension	σ	M/T^2
Angle (radians)	θ	No dimensions
Velocity (angular)	ω	$1/T$
Acceleration (angular)	α	$1/T^2$
Torque or moment	T_0	ML^2/T^2
Work, energy	W	ML^2/T^2
Momentum (linear)	mV	ML/T
Volume flow rate	Q	L^3/T
Mass flow rate	$\dot{m}$	M/T
Power	P	ML^2/T^3
Moment of inertia	I	ML^2
Momentum (angular)	$I\omega$	ML^2/T

From John and Haberman (Ref 1) with permission

The right-hand series is a function of $\mu/\rho DV$ and D^2/S, and F can be written symbolically as:

$$F = \rho V^2 Sf\left(\frac{\mu}{\rho DV}, \frac{D^2}{S}\right) \qquad \text{(Eq 115b)}$$

Only one term need be considered in Eq 115a to obtain the functional relationship between the physical quantities. In addition, the functional re-

Table 2   Dimensionless groups in fluid mechanics

Parameter	Definition	Qualitative ratio of effects	Importance
Reynolds number ... $Re = \dfrac{\rho V L}{\mu}$		$\dfrac{\text{Inertia}}{\text{Viscosity}}$	General Flow
Mach number ...... $M = \dfrac{V}{a}$		$\dfrac{\text{Flow speed}}{\text{Sound speed}}$	Compressible flow
Froude number..... $Fr = \dfrac{V^2}{gL}$		$\dfrac{\text{Inertia}}{\text{Gravity}}$	Free-surface flow
Weber number ..... $We = \dfrac{\rho V^2 L}{\Gamma}$		$\dfrac{\text{Inertia}}{\text{Surface tension}}$	Free-surface flow
Cavitation number (Euler number)... $Ca = \dfrac{p - p_v}{\rho V^2}$		$\dfrac{\text{Pressure}}{\text{Inertia}}$	Cavitation
Prandtl number .... $Pr = \dfrac{\mu c_p}{k}$		$\dfrac{\text{Dissipation}}{\text{Conduction}}$	Heat convection
Eckert number ..... $Ec = \dfrac{V^2}{c_p T_0}$		$\dfrac{\text{Kinetic energy}}{\text{Enthalpy}}$	Dissipation
Specific heat ratio .. $\kappa = \dfrac{c_p}{c_v}$		$\dfrac{\text{Enthalpy}}{\text{Internal energy}}$	Compressible flow
Strouhal number ... $St = \dfrac{\omega L}{V}$		$\dfrac{\text{Oscillation}}{\text{Mean speed}}$	Oscillating flow
Roughness ratio .... $\dfrac{\varepsilon}{L}$		$\dfrac{\text{Wall roughness}}{\text{Body length}}$	Turbulent, rough walls
Grashof number .... $Gr = \dfrac{\beta \Delta T g L^3 \rho^2}{\mu^2}$		$\dfrac{\text{Buoyancy}}{\text{Viscosity}}$	Natural convection
(β = coeff. of volumetric expansion)			
Temperature ratio.. $\dfrac{T_w}{T_0}$		$\dfrac{\text{Wall temperature}}{\text{Stream temperature}}$	Heat transfer

From White (Ref 2) with permission

lationship between F, ρ, V, S, μ, and D is equivalent to a relationship between the three nondimensional products, expressed as:

$$\frac{F}{\frac{1}{2}\rho V^2 S} = f\left(\frac{\rho VD}{\mu}, \frac{D^2}{S}\right) \tag{Eq 116}$$

where the product $F/\rho V^2 S$ is multiplied by 2. Therefore, in an experimental investigation of the relationship between the force F and the other physical parameters, only the relation between the following nondimensional parameters needs to be determined:

$$\frac{F}{\frac{1}{2}\rho V^2 S} \quad \text{(called the force coefficient)}$$

$$\frac{\rho VD}{\mu} \quad \text{(called the Reynolds number)}$$

$$\frac{D^2}{S} \quad \text{(a ratio of cross-sectional area and surface area)}$$

Table 2 gives important dimensionless groups used in fluid mechanics.

NONDIMENSIONALIZATION OF THE BASIC EQUATIONS

A very powerful technique for finding dimensionless parameters involves the basic equations of flow. A brief example concerns the incompressible flow equations with constant viscosity. Rewriting the continuity and momentum equations previously presented:

$$\mathbf{\nabla} \cdot \mathbf{V} = 0 \qquad \text{(Eq 69)}$$

$$\rho \frac{d\mathbf{V}}{dt} = \rho\mathbf{g} - \mathbf{\nabla}p + \mu\nabla^2\mathbf{V} \qquad \text{(Eq 85)}$$

Equations 69 and 85 contain the three basic dimensions *MLT*. Variables p, $\mathbf{V}$, x, y, z, and t can be made nondimensional using the density and two reference constants which might be characteristic of the particular fluid flow:

$$\text{Reference velocity} = U \qquad \text{reference length} = L$$

The inlet or freestream velocity could be used for U and L could be the diameter of a body immersed in the stream. Relevant dimensionless variables can be defined as:

$$\mathbf{V}' = \frac{\mathbf{V}}{U}$$

$$x' = \frac{x}{L} \qquad y' = \frac{y}{L} \qquad z' = \frac{z}{L}$$

$$t' = \frac{tU}{L} \qquad p' = \frac{p + \rho gz}{\rho U^2}$$

All these are fairly obvious except for p', where the gravity effect is included.

Since ρ, U, and L are all constants, the derivatives in Eq 69 and 85 can be handled in dimensionless form with dimensional coefficients. The resulting dimensionless equations of motion are as follows:

Continuity:

$$\mathbf{\nabla}' \cdot \mathbf{V}' = 0 \qquad \text{(Eq 117)}$$

Momentum:

$$\frac{d\mathbf{V}'}{dt'} = -\mathbf{\nabla}'p' + \frac{\mu}{\rho UL}\nabla'^2(\mathbf{V}') \qquad \text{(Eq 118)}$$

The Reynolds number is introduced by the process, $\text{Re} = \dfrac{\rho UL}{\mu}$.

FLOW IN PIPES AND DUCTS

When a fluid flows through a pipe, fluid at the wall has zero velocity; layers of fluid at greater distances from the pipe wall have higher velocities, with the maximum velocity occurring at the pipe centerline. Velocity distribution depends on the type of flow and the type of flow is important in determining the magnitude of the frictional forces acting on the fluid. There are two basic types of flow. With laminar flow, the fluid flows in smooth layers. The shear stress in the fluid is caused by the sliding of one layer of fluid over another. As the velocity of the flow is increased, the flow becomes turbulent. Turbulent flow is characterized by an irregular, random motion of fluid particles in time and space. Velocity fluctuations occur both in the flow direction and normal to the flow direction. Particle motion in a direction normal to the flow acts as an equivalent shear stress in that momentum is exchanged between fluid layers. This turbulent shear stress may be many times greater than laminar stress. The interchange of momentum between faster- and slower-moving particles leads to a more uniform velocity profile. Transition from laminar to turbulent flow in a duct generally occurs at a Reynolds number of approximately 2200.

FLOW IN A CIRCULAR DUCT

GENERAL ANALYSIS

The steady-flow energy equation for an inclined pipe is:

$$\frac{p_1}{\rho} + \tfrac{1}{2}\lambda_1 V_1^2 + gz_1 = \frac{p_2}{\rho} + \tfrac{1}{2}\lambda_2 V_2^2 + gz_2 + gh_L \qquad \text{(Eq 119)}$$

where the average velocities are used and there are no shaft-work or heat-transfer effects. If the flow is taken to be incompressible and fully developed, the head loss is given by:

$$h_L = \left(z_1 + \frac{p_1}{\rho g}\right) - \left(z_2 + \frac{p_2}{\rho g}\right) = \Delta\left(z + \frac{p}{\rho g}\right) = \Delta z + \frac{\Delta p}{\rho g} \qquad \text{(Eq 120)}$$

since $\lambda_1 = \lambda_2$ and $V_1 = V_2$.

From the momentum equation, h_L is related to the shear stress by:

$$\Delta z + \frac{\Delta p}{\rho g} = h_L = \frac{2\tau_w}{\rho g}\frac{L}{R} \qquad \text{(Eq 121)}$$

in which R and L are the pipe radius and length, respectively. From dimensional analysis:

$$f = \frac{8\tau_w}{\rho V^2} \qquad \text{(Eq 122)}$$

where f is called the Darcy friction factor. The head loss now becomes:

$$h_L = f\frac{L}{d}\frac{V^2}{2g} \qquad \text{(Eq 123)}$$

which is the Darcy-Weisbach equation. This equation is valid for flows through a pipe of any cross section (using a suitable effective diameter in place of d) and for laminar and turbulent flow. The friction factor is obtained from the analysis of specific types of flows.

EQUATIONS OF MOTION

The continuity equation in cylindrical coordinates is given by:

$$\frac{1}{r}\frac{\partial}{\partial r}(rv_r) + \frac{1}{r}\frac{\partial}{\partial \theta}(v_\theta) + \frac{\partial u}{\partial z} = 0 \qquad \text{(Eq 124)}$$

The velocity component u represents the component along the axis of the duct. For fully developed flow, $u = u(r)$ only, and:

$$\frac{1}{r}\frac{\partial}{\partial r}(rv_r) = 0 \qquad \text{(Eq 125)}$$

The momentum differential equation in cylindrical coordinates reduces to:

$$\frac{1}{r}\frac{\partial}{\partial r}(r\tau) = \frac{d}{dx}(p + \rho gz) \qquad \text{(Eq 126)}$$

since $v_r = 0$ everywhere, the term τ can be laminar or turbulent shear. The shear stress distribution across the pipe becomes:

$$\tau = \tfrac{1}{2}r\frac{d}{dx}(p + \rho gz) = C_1 r \qquad \text{(Eq 127)}$$

where C_1 is a constant. At $r = R$, τ equals the wall shear stress:

$$\tau_w = \tfrac{1}{2}R\left(\frac{\Delta p + \rho g\,\Delta z}{L}\right) \qquad \text{(Eq 128)}$$

a result also apparent from Eq 121.

LAMINAR FLOW

For laminar flow, $\tau = \mu\,du/dr$ and:

$$\mu\frac{du}{dr} = \frac{r}{2}\left[\frac{d}{dx}(p + \gamma z)\right] \qquad \text{(Eq 129)}$$

For laminar fully developed pipe flow, the velocity profile is found to be:

$$u = \frac{1}{4\mu}\left[-\frac{d}{dx}(p + \rho gz)\right](R^2 - r^2) \qquad \text{(Eq 130)}$$

This distribution is called Hagen-Poiseuille flow. The maximum velocity is:

$$u_{max} = \frac{R^2}{4\mu}\left[-\frac{d}{dx}(p + \rho gz)\right] \qquad \text{(Eq 131)}$$

The volume flux and the average velocity in laminar flow are given by Eq 132 and 133, respectively:

$$Q = \tfrac{1}{2}u_{max}\pi R^2 = \frac{\pi R^4}{8\mu}\left[-\frac{d}{dx}(p + \rho gz)\right] \qquad \text{(Eq 132)}$$

$$V = \frac{Q}{A} = \frac{1}{2} u_{max} \qquad \text{(Eq 133)}$$

For a horizontal tube ($\Delta z = 0$), the pressure drop in a length L is:

$$\Delta p = \frac{8 \mu L Q}{\pi R^4} \qquad \text{(Eq 134)}$$

The wall shear stress is given as:

$$\tau_w = \left[\mu \frac{du}{dr} \right]_{r=R} = \frac{2 \mu u_{max}}{R} = \frac{1}{2} R \left[\frac{d}{dx} (p + \rho g z) \right] \qquad \text{(Eq 135)}$$

Using Eq 137 with Eq 122 gives the following friction factor for laminar flow:

$$f = \frac{64}{\text{Re}_d} \qquad \text{(Eq 136)}$$

where Re_d is the Reynolds number using pipe diameter as the scale length. The laminar head loss now is expressed as:

$$h_L = \frac{128 \mu L Q}{\pi \rho g d^4} \qquad \text{(Eq 137)}$$

TURBULENT FLOW

Concepts of Turbulence. The dominant characteristic of turbulent flow is the mixing action caused by eddies of varying size. Turbulence produces velocity fluctuations in the fluid, Fig. 17 showing the irregular distribution of the velocity component in the direction of flow. However, averaging the velocity over a sufficient amount of time at various points across the section produces a smooth profile as shown. If the mean velocity at a given point is taken over a relatively long period of time, it becomes virtually constant and the flow can be termed steady.

Reynolds' Averaging Concept. Osborne Reynolds (1895) rewrote the basic equations of motion using mean or time-averaged turbulent variables. The time mean value of a turbulent function such as the velocity component $u(x, y, z, t)$ is defined by:

$$\bar{u} = \frac{1}{T} \int_0^T u \, dt \qquad \text{(Eq 138)}$$

where T is an averaging period. The fluctuation u' is defined as the deviation of u from its average value (Fig. 18):

$$u' = u - \bar{u} \qquad \text{(Eq 139)}$$

This fluctuation has a zero mean value, $\bar{u}' = 0$. The mean square of a fluctuation, however, is not zero and is a measure of the intensity of the turbulence:

$$\overline{u'^2} = \frac{1}{T} \int_0^T u^2 \, dt \neq 0 \qquad \text{(Eq 140)}$$

The mean fluctuation products such as $\overline{u'v'}$ and $\overline{u'p'}$ are generally not zero in a turbulent flow either. Splitting the pressure and the other two velocity components into mean and fluctuating variables gives:

$$v = \bar{v} + v' \qquad w = \bar{w} + w' \qquad p = \bar{p} + p' \tag{Eq 141}$$

When these terms are substituted into the continuity and momentum equations and the time average for each equation is found, the following form of the continuity relation is the result:

$$\frac{\partial \bar{u}}{\partial x} + \frac{\partial \bar{v}}{\partial y} + \frac{\partial \bar{w}}{\partial z} = 0 \tag{Eq 142}$$

The momentum equation in the x-direction becomes:

$$\rho \frac{d\bar{u}}{dt} = -\frac{\partial \bar{p}}{\partial x} + \rho g_x + \frac{\partial}{\partial x}\left(\mu \frac{\partial \bar{u}}{\partial x} - \rho \overline{u'^2}\right) + \frac{\partial}{\partial y}\left(\mu \frac{\partial \bar{u}}{\partial y} - \rho \overline{u'v'}\right) +$$

$$\frac{\partial}{\partial z}\left(\mu \frac{\partial \bar{u}}{\partial z} - \rho \overline{u'w'}\right) \tag{Eq 143}$$

The three terms $-\rho \overline{u'^2}$, $-\rho \overline{u'v'}$, and $-\rho \overline{u'w'}$ are called turbulent stresses (Reynold's stresses), but they are actually convective acceleration terms. A simpler x-momentum equation may be used since $-\rho \overline{u'v'}$ is dominant:

$$\rho \frac{d\bar{u}}{dt} \approx -\frac{\partial \bar{p}}{\partial x} + \rho g_x + \frac{\partial \tau}{\partial y} \tag{Eq 144a}$$

where

$$\tau = \mu \frac{\partial \bar{u}}{\partial y} - \rho \overline{u'v'} = \tau_{\text{lam}} + \tau_{\text{turb}} \tag{Eq 144b}$$

Velocity Profile Near Wall. There are several ways to describe the profile of the velocity near the wall in turbulent flow, but no single equation

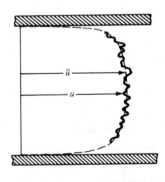

Figure 17   Turbulent flow

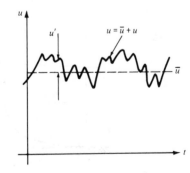

Figure 18   Definition of mean and fluctuating turbulent velocity

has been found that adequately traces the entire profile. Generally, turbulent flow near a boundary is divided into three regions (see Fig. 19):

- The wall layer where viscous shear dominates, sometimes referred to as the viscous sublayer
- The outer layer where turbulent shear dominates
- The overlap layer where both types of shear are important. This region includes what is sometimes called the buffer layer

For the wall layer:

$$\bar{u}^+ = \frac{\bar{u}_w}{\bar{u}^*} = F\left(\frac{y\bar{u}^*}{\nu}\right) \qquad \bar{u}^* = \left(\frac{\tau_w}{\rho}\right)^{1/2} \tag{Eq 145}$$

where τ_w is wall shear, the scale factor $\bar{u}^*$ is the friction velocity, $\bar{u}_w$ refers to the velocity near the wall, and the bars over the symbols indicate that they are related to the mean velocity profile. Equation 145 is called the law of the wall, although some consider the law of the wall to include the overlap region also. The wall law actually follows the linear relationship:

$$\bar{u}^+ = \frac{\bar{u}}{\bar{u}^*} = \frac{y\bar{u}^*}{\nu} = y^+ \tag{Eq 146}$$

Experiments have shown that the viscous layer exists in the region from the wall to about $y^+ = 5$. This is an effective bound for Eq 146.

In the outer layer, $\bar{u}$ is essentially independent of molecular viscosity, but its deviation from the stream velocity U depends on the thickness of the layer, δ, and the other properties:

$$(U - \bar{u})_{\substack{\text{outer} \\ \text{layer}}} = g(\delta, \tau_w, \rho, y) \tag{Eq 147}$$

The following functional relationship holds for the outer layer:

$$\frac{U - \bar{u}}{\bar{u}^*} = G\left(\frac{y}{\delta}\right) \tag{Eq 148}$$

This is called the velocity-defect law.

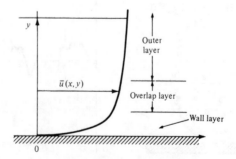

Figure 19 Typical velocity in turbulent flow near a wall

The overlap-layer velocity must vary logarithmically with y if the outer and inner layer are to overlap smoothly:

$$\frac{\bar{u}}{\bar{u}^*} = A \ln \frac{y\bar{u}^*}{\nu} + B \qquad \text{overlap layer} \tag{Eq 149}$$

Constants A and B have the approximate values of 5.75 and 5.56 respectively. This logarithmic law holds for values of y^+ between about 30 and 500. It will intersect with Eq 146 at $y^+ = 11.84$. The range between $y^+ = 5$ and 30 is referred to as the buffer layer, a region in which experimental data is not matched extremely well by either Eq 146 or 149. An equation having the same form as Eq 149 is obtainable from the Prandtl mixing length theory which proposes a model for the turbulent shear stress component of Eq 144b.

Circular Pipe Equations. If the logarithmic profile can be assumed to correlate the local mean velocity, $\bar{u}(r)$, all the way across the pipe of radius R then:

$$\frac{\bar{u}(r)}{\bar{u}^*} \approx A \ln \frac{(R - r)\bar{u}^*}{\nu} + B \tag{Eq 150}$$

With $A = 5.75$ and $B = 5.56$, the average velocity in the pipe is:

$$\frac{V}{\bar{u}^*} \approx 2.44 \ln \frac{R\bar{u}^*}{\nu} + 1.34 \tag{Eq 151}$$

$V/\bar{u}^*$ is directly related to the Darcy friction factor by:

$$\frac{V}{\bar{u}^*} = \left(\frac{\rho V^2}{\tau_w}\right)^{1/2} = \left(\frac{8}{f}\right)^{1/2} \tag{Eq 152}$$

The following relationship may be found from Eq 151 and Eq 152:

$$\frac{1}{f^{1/2}} \approx 1.99 \log (\mathrm{Re}_d f^{1/2}) - 1.02 \tag{Eq 153}$$

where $\mathrm{Re}_d = Vd/\nu$ and $d = 2R$. An equation developed by Prandtl leads to a better fit of the friction factor data:

$$\frac{1}{f^{1/2}} = 2.0 \log (\mathrm{Re}_d f^{1/2}) - 0.8 \tag{Eq 154}$$

Two alternate approximations from which f can be calculated are:

$$f \approx \begin{cases} 0.316\, \mathrm{Re}_d^{-1/4} & 4000 < \mathrm{Re}_d < 10^5 \quad \text{Blasius (1911)} \\ 1.02\,(\log \mathrm{Re}_d)^{-2.5} & \text{White (1974)} \end{cases} \tag{Eq 155}$$

Using the Blasius correlation from Eq 155, the head loss for a horizontal pipe is:

$$h_L = \frac{\Delta p}{\rho g} = f \frac{L}{d} \frac{V^2}{2g} \approx 0.316 \left(\frac{\mu}{\rho Vd}\right)^{1/4} \frac{L}{d} \frac{V^2}{2g} \tag{Eq 156}$$

for low turbulent Reynolds numbers.

The maximum velocity for turbulent flow in a pipe is given by:

$$\frac{\bar{u}_{\max}}{\bar{u}^*} \approx A \ln \frac{R\bar{u}^*}{\nu} + B \tag{Eq 157}$$

The mean velocity is related to this maximum by:

$$\frac{V}{\bar{u}_{\max}} \approx (1 + 1.33\sqrt{f})^{-1} \tag{Eq 158}$$

Defining the dimensionless sublayer thickness as $y^+ = 5$, the thickness of the sublayer, y_s, related to the diameter of a tube is:

$$\frac{y_s}{d} = \frac{5\nu/\bar{u}^*}{d} = \frac{14.1}{\mathrm{Re}_d f^{1/2}} \tag{Eq 159}$$

Unlike laminar flow, turbulent flow is strongly affected by wall roughness. If ϵ represents the roughness height, we can define three regimes for rough walls:

- $\epsilon\bar{u}^*/\nu < 5$: hydraulically smooth walls in which roughness has no effect on friction
- $5 < \epsilon\bar{u}^*/\nu < 70$: transitional region in which roughness has a moderate effect on Reynolds-number
- $\epsilon\bar{u}^*/\nu > 70$: fully rough flow where friction is independent of Reynolds number (sublayer is completely broken up)

For fully rough flow, the logarithmic law modified for roughness becomes:

$$\bar{u}^+ = A \ln \frac{y}{\epsilon} + 8.5 \tag{Eq 160}$$

The average velocity and friction factor for fully rough flow are then seen to be:

Table 3 Average roughness of commercial pipes

Material (new)	ϵ (ft)
Riveted steel	0.003–0.03
Concrete	0.001–0.01
Wood stave	0.0006–0.003
Cast iron	0.00085
Galvanized iron	0.0005
Asphalted cast iron	0.0004
Commercial steel or wrought iron	0.00015
Drawn tubing	0.000005
Glass	Smooth

Adapted from White (Ref 2)

$$\frac{V}{u^*} = 2.44 \ln \frac{d}{\varepsilon} + 3.2 \qquad \text{(Eq 161a)}$$

and

$$\frac{1}{f^{1/2}} = -2.0 \log \frac{\varepsilon/d}{3.7} \qquad \text{(Eq 161b)}$$

The accepted design formula developed by C.F. Colebrook is:

$$\frac{1}{f^{1/2}} = -2.0 \log \left(\frac{\varepsilon/d}{3.7} + \frac{2.51}{\text{Re}_d f^{1/2}} \right) \qquad \text{(Eq 162)}$$

The friction factor chart compiled by L.F. Moody that appears in most fluid mechanics texts was computed from this equation. Common values for ε are given in Table 3.

NON-CIRCULAR DUCTS

If the friction factor is defined in terms of average shear:

$$f = \frac{8\tau_w}{\rho V^2} \qquad \text{(Eq 163)}$$

for a non-circular duct where $V = Q/A$. From Eq 163, a head-loss expression can be obtained:

$$h_L = f \frac{L}{4R_h} \frac{V^2}{2g} \qquad \text{(Eq 164)}$$

where R_h is the hydraulic radius. The hydraulic diameter is usually defined as:

$$D_h = \frac{4A}{P} = \frac{4 \times \text{area}}{\text{wetted perimeter}} = 4R_h \qquad \text{(Eq 165)}$$

Using this definition of D_h, Eq 164 is seen to be equivalent to Eq 123 for the circular pipe. Dimensional analysis indicates that the friction factor f based upon hydraulic diameter correlates with Reynolds number and roughness ratio based upon hydraulic diameter. The accuracy in calculating the f used in Eq 164 by substituting the hydraulic diameter into circular pipe equations is given by:

Laminar flow: $\quad f \approx \dfrac{64}{\text{Re}_{D_h}} \qquad \pm 40\% \qquad$ (Refer to Eq 136)

Turbulent flow: $\quad f \approx f_{circ}\left(\text{Re}_{D_h}, \dfrac{\varepsilon}{D_h} \right) \qquad \pm 15\%$

The f_{circ} in the last expression refers to friction factors computed using Eq 162.

FLOW BETWEEN PARALLEL PLATES

Flow between parallel plates (Fig. 20) a distance h apart is the limiting case of flow through a wide rectangular channel. The momentum equation in cartesian coordinates for fully developed flow is:

$$0 = -\frac{dp}{dx} + \rho g_x + \frac{d\tau}{dy} \qquad \text{(Eq 166)}$$

subject to $u = 0$ at $y = +h/2$ and $-h/2$. The velocity profile for laminar parallel-plate flow $\left(\text{using } \tau = \mu \dfrac{du}{dy} \right)$ is found to be:

$$u = \frac{1}{8\mu} \left[-\frac{d}{dx}(p + \rho gz) \right] (h^2 - 4y^2) \qquad \text{(Eq 167)}$$

The term z in this equation represents the direction parallel to the gravitational acceleration $\mathbf{g}$. From this profile, and assuming a very large width b, the following expressions for the volume flow rate, average velocity and wall shear stress can be found:

$$Q = \frac{bh^3}{12\mu} \left[-\frac{d}{dx}(p + \rho gz) \right] \qquad \text{(Eq 168)}$$

$$V = \frac{Q}{bh} = \frac{h^2}{12\mu} \left[-\frac{d}{dx}(p + \rho gz) \right] \qquad \text{(Eq 169)}$$

and

$$\tau_w = \frac{h}{2} \left[\left(-\frac{d}{dx}(p + \rho gz) \right) \right] \qquad \text{(Eq 170)}$$

The friction factor can then be defined as:

$$f = \frac{8\tau_w}{\rho V^2} = \frac{48\mu}{\rho Vh} = \frac{48}{\text{Re}_h} \qquad \text{(Eq 171)}$$

where the Reynolds number is based on h. If the Reynolds number in Eq 171

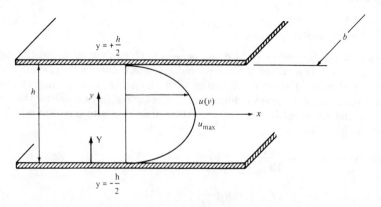

Figure 20   Fully developed flow between parallel plates

is instead defined according to the hydraulic diameter $(D_h = 2h)$ then the friction factor becomes:

$$f = \frac{96}{\text{Re}_{D_h}}$$

(Eq 172)

For turbulent flow between parallel plates, again, using the logarithmic law:

$$\frac{\bar{u}(y)}{\bar{u}^*} \approx A \ln \frac{Y\bar{u}^*}{\nu} + B \qquad 0 < Y < \frac{h}{2}$$

(Eq 173)

where Y represents the coordinate measured from the lower plate. The mean velocity is:

$$V = \bar{u}^* \left(A \ln \frac{h\bar{u}^*}{2\nu} + B - A \right)$$

(Eq 174)

from which the friction factor equation becomes:

$$\frac{1}{f^{1/2}} \approx 2.0 \log (\text{Re}_{D_h} f^{1/2}) - 1.19$$

(Eq 175)

If the Reynolds number is multiplied by 0.64, this expression may be rewritten to the same form as Eq 154:

$$\frac{1}{f^{1/2}} = 2.0 \log (0.64 \, \text{Re}_{D_h} f^{1/2}) - 0.8$$

(Eq 176)

The turbulent friction can therefore be predicted most accurately when an effective diameter equal to 0.64 times the hydraulic diameter is used.

CONCENTRIC CIRCULAR ANNULUS

For the annular region formed by two concentric cylinders (Fig. 21), the velocity profile is given by:

$$u(r) = \frac{1}{4\mu} \left[-\frac{d}{dx}(p + \rho gz) \right] \left[a^2 - r^2 + (a^2 - b^2) \frac{\ln(a/r)}{\ln(b/a)} \right]$$

(Eq 177)

and the volumetric flow rate becomes:

$$Q = \frac{\pi}{8\mu} \left[-\frac{d}{dx}(p + \rho gz) \right] \left[a^4 - b^4 - \frac{(a^2 - b^2)^2}{\ln(a/b)} \right]$$

(Eq 178)

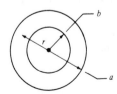

Figure 21   Cross
section of concentric
circular annulus

The maximum velocity can be shown to occur at the radius:

$$r = \left[\frac{a^2 - b^2}{2 \ln(a/b)} \right]^{1/2}$$

(Eq 179)

The friction factor is defined with respect to the head loss, because wall shear stress is different on the inner and outer walls. Therefore:

$$f = h_L \frac{D_h}{L} \frac{2g}{V^2}$$

(Eq 180)

where:

$$V = \frac{Q}{\pi(a^2 - b^2)}$$

(Eq 180)

and

$$D_h = 2(a - b)$$

(Eq 181)

The friction factor for laminar flow in a concentric can also be stated in a form similar to Eq 136:

$$f = \frac{64\zeta}{Re_{D_h}} \qquad \zeta = \frac{(a - b)^2(a^2 - b^2)}{a^4 - b^4 - (a^2 - b^2)^2/[\ln(a/b)]}$$

(Eq 182)

For turbulent flow, the friction factor can be found by using an effective diameter $(d = 2(a - b)/\zeta)$ in Eq 162 in place of the pipe diameter.

ADDITIONAL CROSS SECTIONS

If laminar flow results are known, such as those in Table 4, a turbulent flow friction factor may be found by computing an effective diameter, $D_{eff} = [64/(f \cdot Re)]D_h$, and using it in the appropriate friction factor equation (Eq 154 or 162). If no laminar results are available, then the D_h for the particular geometry of the duct should be used in Eq 154, 162, or in a Moody chart plotted from Eq 162.

LOSSES IN PIPE SYSTEMS OTHER THAN FRICTION

Losses for the following are added to h_L due to friction:

- Pipe entrance or exit
- Expansions or contractions
- Fittings (bends, elbows, tees)
- Valves

The head loss caused by these factors, $h_L = \Delta p/\rho g$, may be defined in terms of a loss coefficient:

Loss coefficient $K = \dfrac{h_L}{V^2/2g}$

(Eq 183)

Table 4   Laminar friction constants $f \cdot$ Re for rectangular and triangular ducts

Rectangular		Isosceles triangle	
b/a	$f \cdot \mathrm{Re}_{D_h}$	θ, deg	$f \cdot \mathrm{Re}_{D_h}$
0.0	96.00	0	48.0
0.05	89.91	10	51.6
0.1	84.68	20	52.9
0.125	82.34	30	53.3
0.167	78.81	40	52.9
0.25	72.93	50	52.0
0.4	65.47	60	51.1
0.5	62.19	70	49.5
0.75	57.89	80	48.3
1.0	56.91	90	48.0

Adapted from White (Ref 2) with permission

This coefficient is often related to an equivalent length:

$$h_L = f \frac{L_{\mathrm{eq}}}{d} \frac{V^2}{2g} = K \frac{V^2}{2g} \qquad \text{(Eq 184a)}$$

where

$$L_{\mathrm{eq}} = \frac{Kd}{f} \qquad \text{(Eq 184b)}$$

The total head loss (friction plus other losses) is given by:

$$(h_L)_{tot} = \frac{V^2}{2g} \left(\frac{fL}{d} + \sum K \right) \qquad \text{(Eq 185)}$$

Losses must be summed separately if the pipe size changes since V^2 will also change. Values for loss coefficients are tabulated in a number of references in fluid mechanics.

PIPING SYSTEMS

Parallel Pipes. Considering the two parallel pipes of Fig. 22, the head loss must be the same in each ($h_{L_1} = h_{L_2}$) because the pressure difference across each pipe is the same. Therefore:

$$f_1 \frac{L_1}{D_1} \frac{{V_1}^2}{2g} = f_2 \frac{L_2}{D_2} \frac{{V_2}^2}{2g}$$

and:

$$\left(\frac{V_1}{V_2}\right)^2 = \frac{f_2}{f_1} \frac{L_2}{L_1} \frac{D_1}{D_2}$$

(Eq 186)

Some trial-and-error analysis may be required if f_1 and f_2 are in the range where they are functions of the Reynolds number.

Networks. Analysis of a piping network having more branches than the parallel system of Fig. 22 is complex algebraically, but follows some basic rules:

- The net flow into any junction must be zero
- The net head loss around any closed loop must be zero
- All head losses must satisfy appropriate pipe loss correlations (such as Eq 162)

These rules are applied to each junction and independent loop in the network, and a set of simultaneous algebraic equations is obtained for the flow rates in each pipe leg and the head loss in each loop. Because the equations are not linear, the solution must be obtained by iterative techniques.

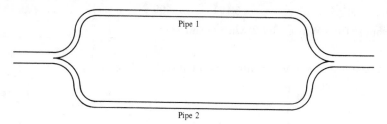

Figure 22   Parallel pipe network

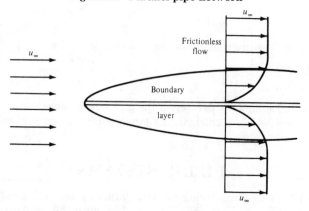

Figure 23   Boundary layer on flat plate

BOUNDARY LAYER FLOW

High Reynolds number flow, which describes most flow situations for common low-viscosity fluids such as air and water, implies that inertial forces in the fluid are predominant over viscous forces. The effect of viscosity is small over most of the flow field. The layer of fluid at the wall, however, has zero velocity relative to the surface, and the resulting large velocity gradients occurring near a surface indicate that viscous effects cannot be neglected in this region. Away from the wall, the velocity gradients are small, and the viscous forces are negligible in comparison with the inertial forces.

The effects of viscosity can therefore be confined to a thin layer in the vicinity of the surface, called the boundary layer. Outside the boundary layer, the flow can be treated as nonviscous (see Fig. 23). Although the boundary layer is thin, it gives rise to viscous drag caused by the shear stresses, and dominates the transfer of heat from the surface.

LAMINAR AND TURBULENT BOUNDARY LAYERS

Near the leading edge of the flat plate shown in Fig. 24 the boundary layer is laminar. Farther along the plate, transition occurs to a turbulent boundary layer where mixing results in a more uniform velocity profile. The previously mentioned viscous or laminar sublayer also develops somewhere downstream of the transition region. Shear stress in the laminar region of the boundary layer is given by the familiar:

$$\tau = \mu \, \frac{du}{dy} \qquad \text{(Eq 187)}$$

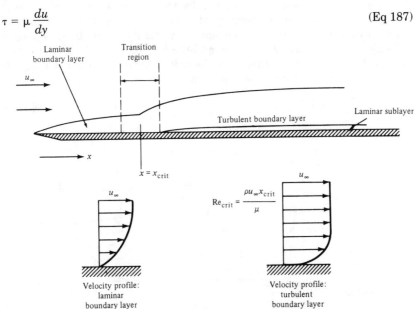

Figure 24   Development of laminar and turbulent boundary layers on a flat plate. From John and Haberman (Ref 1) with permission

In the turbulent portion of the boundary layer, a turbulent kinematic viscosity, or eddy viscosity, ε, is defined so the turbulent shear stress becomes:

$$\tau_t = \rho \varepsilon \frac{du}{dy} \tag{Eq 188}$$

EQUATIONS OF MOTION—LAMINAR BOUNDARY LAYER

The boundary layer flow is assumed to be steady, two-dimensional, incompressible, and with no variation of μ. Gravitational forces are neglected. The radius of curvature of the surface is assumed large, and the pressure does not vary in the y-direction (see Fig. 25). The boundary layer thickness, δ, is normally defined as the distance from the surface where the velocity, u, is 99% of the free stream velocity, u_∞. The continuity equation for this system is:

$$\frac{\partial u}{\partial x} + \frac{\partial v}{\partial y} = 0 \tag{Eq 189}$$

and the momentum equation reduces to the form:

$$-\frac{\partial p}{\partial x} + \mu \frac{\partial^2 u}{\partial y^2} = \rho \left(u \frac{\partial u}{\partial x} + v \frac{\partial u}{\partial y} \right) \tag{Eq 190}$$

where the boundary conditions are:

$$u = v = 0 \qquad \text{at } y = 0$$
$$u = u_\infty \qquad \text{at } y = \delta$$

The free stream velocity, u_∞, is given by the potential flow solution about the body. The pressure gradient is also available from the potential flow solution by applying Bernoulli's equation. For a flat plate, the free stream velocity is constant along the plate and the Bernoulli equation shows there is no pressure variation outside the boundary layer. Thus, for a flat plate boundary layer, the momentum equation is:

$$u \frac{\partial u}{\partial x} + v \frac{\partial u}{\partial y} = \nu \frac{\partial^2 u}{\partial y^2} \tag{Eq 191}$$

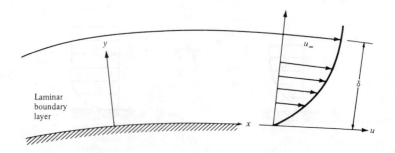

Figure 25

LAMINAR FLOW SOLUTIONS

Blasius Solution (Flat Plate Aligned with Flow). Blasius (1908) arrived at a solution to the flat plate equations by assuming that the shape of a nondimensional velocity distribution did not vary from section to section along the plate (similarity assumption). The velocity ratio (u/u_∞) was considered to be a function of y/δ which did not change with x. The solution, obtained using infinite series or numerical means, is shown in Fig. 26. The dimensionless velocity is plotted against a dimensionless distance from the wall.

From the Blasius curve in Fig. 26, the boundary layer thickness (where $u = .99u_\infty$) is computed to be:

$$\delta = \frac{5.0x}{\sqrt{Re_x}} \tag{Eq 192}$$

where

$$Re_x = \frac{\rho u_\infty x}{\mu}$$

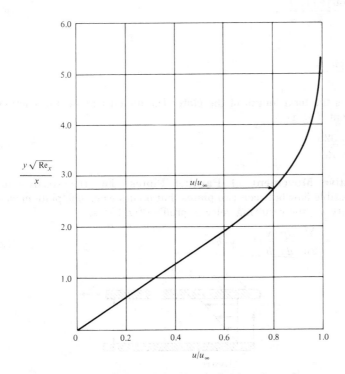

Figure 26 Velocity distribution in laminar boundary layer—Blasius profile

and x is the distance from the leading edge of the plate. Other methods have been used to define a boundary layer thickness, one being the displacement thickness, δ^*, which represents the displacement of the external flow due to the boundary layer. The displacement thickness is defined as:

$$\delta^* = \int_0^\infty \left(1 - \frac{u}{u_\infty}\right) dy \qquad\text{(Eq 193)}$$

Using the Blasius solution, this becomes:

$$\delta^* = \frac{1.73x}{\sqrt{\mathrm{Re}_x}} \qquad\text{(Eq 194)}$$

The wall shear stress on the flat plate is obtained by:

$$\tau_w = 0.332\mu \frac{u_\infty}{x} \sqrt{\mathrm{Re}_x} \qquad\text{(Eq 195)}$$

The local skin friction coefficient, C_{fx}, then becomes:

$$C_{fx} = \frac{\tau_w}{\frac{1}{2}\rho u_\infty^2} = \frac{0.664}{\sqrt{\mathrm{Re}_x}} \qquad\text{(Eq 196)}$$

and total drag on the plate is found to be:

$$D = \frac{0.664 b \rho u_\infty^2 L}{\sqrt{\mathrm{Re}_L}} \qquad\text{(Eq 197)}$$

where

$$\mathrm{Re}_L = \frac{\rho u_\infty L}{\mu}$$

and L is the total length of the plate. The dimensionless skin friction drag coefficient, C_{D_f}, is:

$$C_{Df} = \frac{1.328}{\sqrt{\mathrm{Re}_L}} \qquad\text{(Eq 198)}$$

Relative Movement of Parallel Plates. For the steady-state, incompressible flow between two plates that occurs when one plate moves with a velocity u_0, the resulting velocity profile (Fig. 27) is:

$$u = \frac{u_0}{h} y - \frac{h^2}{2\mu} \frac{dp}{dy} \frac{y}{h} (1 - y/h) \qquad\text{(Eq 199)}$$

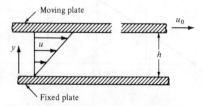

Figure 27   Flow between fixed plate and moving plate

For no pressure gradient, this becomes:

$$u = \frac{u_0}{h} y \qquad \text{(Eq 200)}$$

which is defined as Couette flow.

TURBULENT BOUNDARY LAYER

The three regions described for turbulent flow near a wall shown in Fig. 19 apply to an external boundary layer as well as to flow in a duct. The equations for the velocity profiles in those regions also apply (Eq 146, 148, 149). The discussion here will therefore deal with an approximate method for analyzing the boundary layer.

Momentum Integral Method. The Karman momentum integral method requires writing the continuity and momentum equations for a control volume extending from the wall surface to the outer edge of the boundary layer (Fig. 28). Analyzing this control volume gives the momentum integral equation for two-dimensional, incompressible steady flow:

$$\rho \frac{d}{dx} \left(\int_0^\delta u^2 \, dy \right) - \rho u_\infty \frac{d}{dx} \left(\int_0^\delta u \, dy \right) = -\delta \frac{dp}{dx} - \tau_w \qquad \text{(Eq 201)}$$

This is valid for both laminar and turbulent boundary layer flows, but does not yield any information about the details of the flow at a particular point. A functional relationship of u and y must be assumed so wall shear stress can be computed. A rough assumption can provide relatively good results. The pressure gradient is dealt with knowing that

$$\frac{dp}{dx} = - \frac{u_\infty}{\rho} \frac{du_\infty}{dx},$$

a relationship obtainable from the Bernoulli equation.

Assuming a linear profile on a flat plate as shown in Fig. 29 and using the integral equation gives the following results. For the assumed profile, shear stress at the wall is:

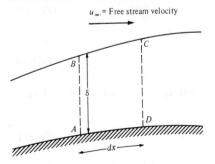

Figure 28   Control volume for integral analysis

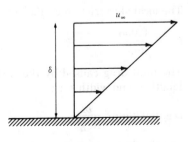

Figure 29   Linear profile on flat plate

$$\tau_w = \mu \frac{u_\infty}{\delta}$$

(Eq 202)

The boundary layer thickness becomes:

$$\delta = \frac{3.46x}{\sqrt{\text{Re}_x}}$$

(Eq 203)

and the displacement thickness is:

$$\delta^* = \frac{1.73x}{\sqrt{\text{Re}_x}}$$

(Eq 204)

The skin friction coefficient is given by:

$$C_{fx} = \frac{0.578}{\sqrt{\text{Re}_x}}$$

(Eq 205)

In Eq 205, the result can be seen to be reasonably close to that for the Blasius solution.

A profile based on the power law equation:

$$\frac{u}{u_\infty} = \left(\frac{y}{\delta}\right)^{1/7}$$

(Eq 206)

gives a very good correlation with experimental data over a wide range of turbulent Reynolds numbers on a flat plate. This profile is not valid in the immediate vicinity of the wall, and experimental data must be used to obtain an expression for τ_w. For the Reynolds number range $5 \times 10^5 < \text{Re}_x < 10^7$, the following formula correlates well with data:

$$\frac{\tau_w}{\rho u_\infty^2} = 0.0225 \left(\frac{\nu}{u_\infty \delta}\right)^{1/4}$$

(Eq 207)

The boundary layer thickness becomes:

$$\delta = 0.37x \left(\frac{u_\infty x}{\nu}\right)^{-1/5}$$

(Eq 208)

with the displacement thickness being:

$$\delta^* = 0.046x \,(\text{Re}_x)^{-1/5}$$

(Eq 209)

The local skin friction coefficient is computed by:

$$C_{fx} = \frac{0.058}{\text{Re}_x^{1/5}}$$

(Eq 210)

The total drag caused by the turbulent boundary layer over a flat plate of length L and width b is:

$$D = 0.036\rho u_\infty^2 \frac{bL}{\text{Re}_L^{1/5}}$$

(Eq 211)

and the dimensionless skin friction drag coefficient becomes:

$$C_{D_f} = \frac{0.072}{\text{Re}^{1/5}}$$

(Eq 212)

Experiments have shown that a constant of 0.074 fits the data better. This expression is valid over the Reynolds number range $5 \times 10^5 < \mathrm{Re}_L < 10^7$.

For a flat plate with a laminar boundary layer starting at the leading edge and a turbulent layer that begins some distance beyond the leading edge, the drag can be computed as follows:

$$D = \text{Turbulent drag (from } x = 0 \text{ to } x = L)$$
$$- \text{Turbulent drag (from } x = 0 \text{ to } x = x_{\text{crit}})$$
$$+ \text{Laminar drag (from } x = 0 \text{ to } x = x_{\text{crit}})$$

where x_{crit} is the location of the transition from laminar to turbulent. The total drag coefficient, C_D, is:

$$C_D = C_{D_t} - \frac{1700}{\mathrm{Re}_L} \qquad \text{(Eq 213)}$$

where C_{D_t} is the turbulent drag coefficient. This equation is valid up to $\mathrm{Re}_L = 1 \times 10^7$. An expression for C_{D_f} which seems to fit experimental data over a wider range of Reynolds numbers is:

$$C_{D_f} = \frac{0.455}{(\log \mathrm{Re}_L)^{2.58}} - \frac{1700}{\mathrm{Re}_L} \qquad \text{(Eq 214)}$$

This equation is valid for turbulent Reynolds numbers up to 10^9.

The analysis of flat plate boundary layers seems rather specialized, but many thin, non-flat shapes can be considered in the same way since the basic differential equation (Eq 190) and integral equation (Eq 201) do not change. The variation of free stream velocity along the body must be known to arrive at a solution as this allows determination of the pressure gradient. The presence of an adverse pressure gradient which accompanies decelerating flow can lead to separation of the boundary layer. This compounds the problems in analyzing the flow. More detail on boundary layer solutions is given in the references of Schlichting and Streeter.

INVISCID OR IDEAL FLOW

Since viscous forces are confined to the boundary layer, to the separated region near the rear of the body, and to the wake region (Fig. 30), most of the flow field can be treated as inviscid. The pressure distribution found for ideal (potential) flow can usually be used for the pressure distribution in the boundary layer, although it must be realized that separation of the boundary layer and formation of a wake will affect the ideal solution.

The continuity equation that is applicable for steady, incompressible inviscid flow is a two-dimensional version of Eq 68. The x-momentum equation for this situation becomes:

$$-\frac{1}{\rho} \frac{\partial p}{\partial x} = u \frac{\partial u}{\partial x} + v \frac{\partial u}{\partial y} \qquad \text{(Eq 215)}$$

and the y-momentum equation is given by:

$$-\frac{1}{\rho}\frac{\partial p}{\partial y} - g = u\frac{\partial v}{\partial x} + v\frac{\partial v}{\partial y} \qquad \text{(Eq 216)}$$

These equations are used to solve for u, v, and p, subject to the boundary condition that the velocity normal to a surface is zero. The x- and y-momentum equations are called Euler's equations.

The stream function may be introduced to aid in solution of the equations. It is defined by the relations:

$$u = \frac{\partial \psi}{\partial y} \qquad v = -\frac{\partial \psi}{\partial x} \qquad \text{(Eq 217)}$$

These satisfy the continuity equation identically and thus reduce the total number of equations to be solved. The local velocity vector is in the direction of the tangent of the streamline, as shown in Fig. 31 and therefore:

$$\frac{dy}{dx} = \frac{v}{u} \qquad \text{(Eq 218)}$$

From this equation and the definition of ψ, we obtain:

$$\frac{\partial \psi}{\partial y}\,dy + \frac{\partial \psi}{\partial x}\,dx = 0$$

The total differential $(d\psi)$ of the stream function is given by:

$$d\psi = \frac{\partial \psi}{\partial x}\,dx + \frac{\partial \psi}{\partial y}\,dy = -v\,dx + u\,dy$$

and it follows that $d\psi = 0$ along a streamline (the stream function remains constant along a streamline). Integrating this velocity expression to get ψ produces the result:

$$\psi_2 - \psi_1 = \int_1^2 (-v\,dx + u\,dy) \qquad \text{(Eq 219)}$$

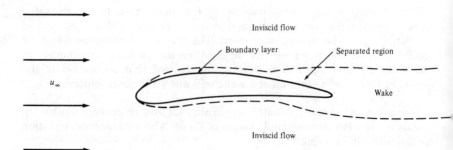

Figure 30   Regions of flow for body immersed in fluid

The difference in ψ between two points in a flow field is therefore the volumetric flow rate between the points.

Another function used in solving ideal flow problems is the velocity potential $\phi(x, y)$, which is defined as:

$$u = \frac{\partial\phi}{\partial x} \qquad v = \frac{\partial\phi}{\partial y} \qquad\qquad\text{(Eq 220)}$$

A flow which is irrotational is termed a potential flow and the velocity is defined by a potential function, ϕ:

$$\mathbf{V} = \nabla\phi \qquad\qquad\text{(Eq 221)}$$

The differential equation for potential flow may be found using Eq 220 with the continuity equation giving:

$$\nabla^2\phi = 0 \qquad\qquad\text{(Eq 222)}$$

or Laplace's equation. For any equipotential line:

$$d\phi = \frac{\partial\phi}{\partial x}\,dx + \frac{\partial\phi}{\partial y}\,dy = 0 = u\,dx - v\,dy$$

From this we can get (for constant ϕ):

$$\left.\frac{dy}{dx}\right|_{\phi=\text{const}} = -\frac{\partial\phi/\partial x}{\partial\phi/\partial y} = -\frac{u}{v}$$

Considering the streamline concept, the following statement is valid:

$$\left.\frac{dy}{dx}\right|_{\psi+\text{const}} = -\frac{\partial\psi/\partial x}{\partial\psi/\partial y} = \frac{v}{u}$$

and

$$\left(\left.\frac{dy}{dx}\right|_{\psi=\text{const}}\right)\left(\left.\frac{dy}{dx}\right|_{\phi=\text{const}}\right) = -1$$

This indicates that the streamlines and equipotential lines are perpendicular. If the flow is irrotational, that is, if a velocity potential can exist, then the following must be true:

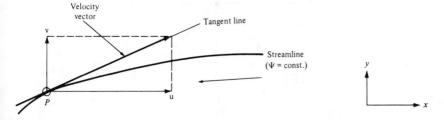

Figure 31   Velocity vector and streamline relationship

$$\frac{\partial u}{\partial y} - \frac{\partial v}{\partial x} = 0 \qquad \text{(Eq 223)}$$

Thus, the vorticity is zero for irrotational flow, and fluid elements do not rotate.

RESULTS OF INVISCID FLOW ANALYSIS

The result of integrating the Euler equations between points in an irrotational flow field is:

$$\frac{1}{2} V^2 + \frac{p}{\rho} + gy = C \qquad \text{(Eq 224)}$$

where $V^2 = u^2 + v^2$ is the total velocity with components u and v, and C is constant throughout the region of irrotational flow. This is the Bernoulli equation, which is now seen to apply between points in an irrotational field.

The expanded form of Laplace's equation for cartesian coordinates is:

$$\frac{\partial^2 \phi}{\partial x^2} + \frac{\partial^2 \phi}{\partial y^2} = 0 \qquad \text{(Eq 225)}$$

In polar coordinates it becomes:

$$\frac{\partial^2 \phi}{\partial r^2} + \frac{1}{r} \frac{\partial \phi}{\partial r} + \frac{1}{r^2} \frac{\partial^2 \phi}{\partial \theta^2} = 0 \qquad \text{(Eq 226)}$$

These equations can be solved subject to velocity boundary conditions and the resulting potential is then used to establish velocity components. Some solutions for simple flow patterns are now presented.

Source Flow. For flow out of a point source (Fig. 32), the velocity potential is given by:

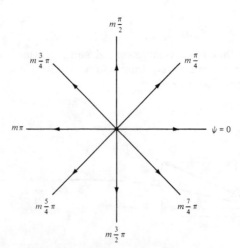

Figure 32 Streamlines for source flow

$$\phi = m \ln r \qquad \text{(Eq 227)}$$

The stream function is zero everywhere and the velocity components are:

$$v_r = \frac{\partial \phi}{\partial r} = \frac{m}{r} \qquad \text{(Eq 228)}$$

$$v_\theta = 0$$

The term m (the source strength) is related to Q (the volume flow rate) by:

$$m = \frac{Q}{2\pi} \qquad \text{(Eq 229)}$$

When the value of m is negative, we have flow into the origin, or sink flow.

Free Vortex Flow. Flow in a free vortex (Fig. 33) results in a potential having the form:

$$\phi = -C\theta \qquad \text{(Eq 230)}$$

where C is a constant. The stream function and velocity components are given by:

$$\psi = C \ln r \qquad \text{(Eq 231)}$$

$$v_r = \frac{\partial \phi}{\partial r} = 0 \qquad v\theta = \frac{1}{r}\frac{\partial \phi}{\partial \theta} = -\frac{C}{r} \qquad \text{(Eq 232)}$$

Uniform Flow. For the flow shown in Fig. 34, the stream function becomes:

$$\psi = u_\infty y \qquad \text{(Eq 233)}$$

In this case, the velocity potential and the velocity components become:

$$\phi = u_\infty x \qquad \text{(Eq 234)}$$

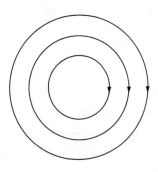

Figure 33 Streamlines for free vortex flow

$$u = \frac{\partial \phi}{\partial x} = u_\infty \qquad v = \frac{\partial \phi}{\partial y} = 0 \tag{Eq 235}$$

SUPERPOSITION OF POTENTIAL FLOWS

Since Laplace's equation is a linear differential equation, complicated flows can be found by combining simple potential flows. For two flows having velocity potentials ϕ_1 and ϕ_2, each potential would satisfy Laplace's equation:

$$\frac{\partial^2 \phi_1}{\partial x^2} + \frac{\partial^2 \phi_1}{\partial y^2} = 0 \qquad \frac{\partial^2 \phi_2}{\partial x^2} + \frac{\partial^2 \phi_2}{\partial y^2} = 0$$

By superposition, the sum of these, $\phi = \phi_1 + \phi_2$, is also a solution:

$$\frac{\partial^2 (\phi_1 + \phi_2)}{\partial x^2} + \frac{\partial^2 (\phi_1 + \phi_2)}{\partial y^2} = 0 \tag{Eq 236}$$

Half-Body. Flow about a half-body is shown in Fig. 35. The expressions for the velocity potential and stream function are found by combining the results for source and uniform stream flows, and are given by:

$$\phi = u_\infty r \cos \theta + m \ln r \tag{Eq 237}$$

$$\psi = u_\infty r \sin \theta + m \theta \tag{Eq 238}$$

The velocity components of the resulting flow field are found to be:

$$v_r = \frac{1}{r} \frac{\partial \psi}{\partial \theta} = \frac{1}{r} (u_\infty r \cos \theta + m)$$

and $\tag{Eq 239}$

$$v_\theta = - \frac{\partial \psi}{\partial r} = -u_\infty \sin \theta$$

Rankine Body. Flow about a Rankine body is found using a source and sink combination in a uniform flow (Fig. 36). The resulting velocity potential, stream function, and velocity components are:

$$\phi = u_\infty x + m \left[\ln \sqrt{(x + a)^2 + y^2} - \ln \sqrt{(x - a)^2 - y^2} \right] \tag{Eq 240}$$

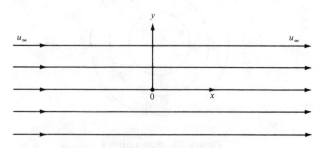

Figure 34   Streamlines in uniform flow

$$\psi = u_x y - m \tan^{-1} \frac{2ay}{x^2 + y^2 - a^2} \qquad \text{(Eq 241)}$$

$$u = u_\infty + m \left[\frac{x + a}{(x + a)^2 + y^2} - \frac{x - a}{(x - a)^2 + y^2} \right] \qquad \text{(Eq 242)}$$

$$v = m \left[\frac{y}{(x + a)^2 + y^2} - \frac{y}{(x - a)^2 + y^2} \right]$$

Cylinder. Flow around a circular cylinder (Fig. 37) is a special case of the Rankine body in which the source and sink are superimposed. This is also called doublet flow. The velocity potential and stream function for this situation become:

$$\phi = u_\infty \cos \theta \left[r + \frac{R^2}{r} \right] \qquad \text{(Eq 243)}$$

$$\psi = u_\infty \sin \theta \left[r - \frac{R^2}{r} \right] \qquad \text{(Eq 244)}$$

while the velocity components are:

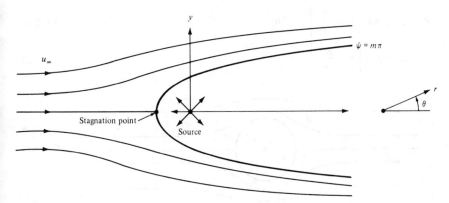

Figure 35 Flow about a two-dimensional half-body

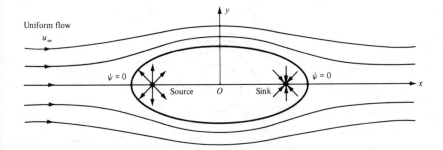

Figure 36 Flow about a Rankine body

$$v_r = u_\infty \cos \theta \left[1 - \frac{R^2}{r^2} \right]$$

$$v_\theta = -u_\infty \sin \theta \left[1 + \frac{R^2}{r^2} \right]$$

(Eq 245)

The pressure at any point in the flow field is given by:

$$p = p_\infty + \frac{\rho}{2} (u_\infty^{\,2} - v_r^{\,2} - v_\theta^{\,2})$$

(Eq 246)

this relationship being derived from the Bernoulli equation. The pressure coefficient may now be defined as:

$$C_p = \frac{(p - p_\infty)}{\frac{1}{2} \rho u_\infty^{\,2}} = 1 - 4 \sin^2 \theta$$

(Eq 247)

Circular Cylinder with Circulation. This situation is modeled by superimposing free vortex flow upon uniform flow past a cylinder. The streamline pattern is shown in Fig. 38. The velocity potential and stream function relationships can be shown to be:

$$\phi = u_\infty \cos \theta \left[r + \frac{R^2}{r} \right] - C \theta$$

(Eq 248)

$$\psi = u_\infty \sin \theta \left[r - \frac{R^2}{r} \right] + C \ln r$$

(Eq 249)

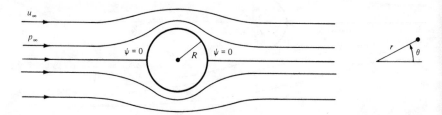

Figure 37   Streamlines around a circular cylinder

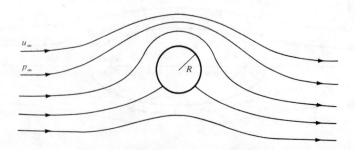

Figure 38   Streamlines around a circular cylinder with circulation

where C is a constant. These results give rise to the following velocity components:

$$v_r = u_\infty \cos\theta \left[1 - \frac{R^2}{r^2} \right]$$

$$v_\theta = -u_\infty \sin\theta \left[1 + \frac{R^2}{r^2} \right] - \frac{C}{r} \qquad \text{(Eq 250)}$$

Using Bernoullis equation and Eq 250, the pressure distribution over the cylinder is found to be:

$$p = p_\infty + \frac{1}{2}\rho u_\infty^2 \left[1 - \left(2\sin\theta + \frac{C}{Ru_\infty} \right)^2 \right] \qquad \text{(Eq 251)}$$

When pressure in the flow field of a cylinder without circulation (Eq 246) is integrated over the surface of the cylinder, it is found that there is no net vertical or horizontal pressure on the cylinder. If Eq 251 is integrated over the surface of the cylinder, however, the net vertical force, L, is:

$$L = 2\pi\rho u_\infty C \qquad \text{(Eq 252)}$$

The symbol L is called the lift and the quantity $2\pi C$ is designated by the symbol Γ, which is called the circulation. Circulation is also defined as:

$$\Gamma = \int_S v_\theta \, dl \qquad \text{(Eq 253)}$$

where v_θ is the velocity tangent to the surface and the integration is performed over the surface of the object. The circulation concept is used to determine theoretical lift on air foils.

DRAG AND LIFT ON BODIES IN A FLUID

Drag. Total drag on a body is the sum of two types of drag: skin friction drag and pressure drag. The drag coefficient is defined as:

$$C_D = \frac{F_D}{\frac{1}{2}\rho u_\infty^2 A} \qquad \text{(Eq 254)}$$

where u_∞ is the free stream velocity, A is the projected frontal area of the body normal to the flow direction, and F_D is the drag force.

The drag coefficient, C_D, for smooth and rough long circular cylinders in uniform flow is shown in Fig. 39. The constant form of the curve in the range $1000 < \text{Re}_D < 10^5$ is due to separation of the laminar boundary layer from the cylinder. The reduction in C_D at a Reynolds number of approximately 4×10^5 is due to the boundary layer on the surface of the cylinder becoming turbulent prior to separation. The higher velocity turbulent fluid near the wall can resist an adverse pressure gradient longer and the large pressure drag caused by early separation is avoided. The sharp decrease in C_D is called the drag crisis. This occurs at lower Re_D for rough surfaces. Some values for C_D on other bodies are given in Table 5.

Table 5 Approximate C_D values for representative bodies

Type of body	Length ratio	Re	C_D
Rectangular plate	$l/b = 1$	$>10^4$	1.18
	$l/b = 5$	$>10^4$	1.20
	$l/b = 10$	$>10^4$	1.30
	$l/b = 20$	$>10^4$	1.50
	$l/b = \infty$	$>10^4$	1.98
Square rod	∞	$>10^4$	2.00
Square rod	∞	$>10^4$	1.50
Hemispherical shell		$>10^4$	0.39
Hemispherical shell		$>10^4$	1.40
Cone—60° vertex		$>10^4$	0.49

From Roberson and Crowe (Ref 8) with permission

Lift. The fluid moving over the top surface of the body in Fig. 40 must accelerate more rapidly as the angle of attack, α, is increased. The fluid traveling over the lower surface undergoes a more gradual acceleration, and the resultant difference in pressure between upper and lower surfaces yields a positive lift force on the body. The lift coefficient is defined as:

$$C_L = \frac{L}{\frac{1}{2}\rho u_\infty^2 A} \qquad \text{(Eq 255)}$$

where L is the lift force, and A is the planform area of the body. For small angles of attack, the lift coefficient varies linearly with angle of attack. Airfoils are designed so that lift can occur at zero angle of attack. An additional type of drag is associated with lift and is caused by vortices at the tip of a wing that result from pressure differences above and below the wing. This drag is called the induced drag. The coefficient of induced drag C_{D_i} is given by:

$$C_{D_i} = \frac{C_L{}^2}{\pi(b^2/A)}$$ (Eq 256)

where the ratio b^2/A is called the aspect of ratio of the wing, and A is the planform area. The term b is the finite width of the wing. The total drag coefficient of a rectangular wing is computed by:

$$C_{D_{\text{total}}} = C_D + C_{D_i}$$ (Eq 257)

ONE-DIMENSIONAL COMPRESSIBLE FLOW

Compressible flows are those in which appreciable density changes occur as the result of the flow. An expression for the velocity of propagation of an infinitesimal disturbance that can occur in a compressible fluid is the sonic velocity. The velocity of sound in a material, a, is defined from the continuity and momentum equations to be:

$$\frac{dp}{d\rho} = a^2$$ (Eq 258)

Considering that flow across a sound wave is adiabatic and reversible (isentropic), Eq 258 can be written as:

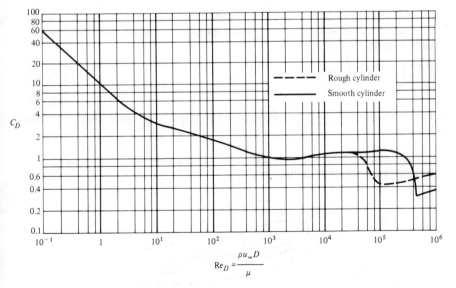

Figure 39 Drag coefficient of circular cylinders of diameter D. From Schlichting (Ref 6) with permission

$$a = \sqrt{\left(\frac{\partial p}{\partial \rho}\right)_s} \qquad \text{(Eq 259)}$$

For a perfect gas, the sound velocity can be written as:

$$a = \sqrt{\kappa R T} \qquad \text{(Eq 260)}$$

where $\kappa = \dfrac{c_p}{c_v}$, the ratio of the constant pressure and constant volume specific heats.

The Mach number, M, is the ratio of flow velocity to sound velocity:

$$M = \frac{V}{a} \qquad \text{(Eq 261)}$$

There are basically two regimes defined for compressible flow. For $M < 1$, subsonic flow exists, and for $M > 1$, supersonic flow.

TOTAL OR STAGNATION PROPERTIES

Certain flow properties are useful when dealing with compressible flow. Stagnation or total temperature, T_t, is defined as the temperature reached when a flow is brought adiabatically to rest at a point in a steady flow process. This is defined as:

$$T_t = T\left(1 + \frac{\kappa - 1}{2} M^2\right) \qquad \text{(Eq 262)}$$

For adiabatic flow, the stagnation temperature is constant along a streamline.

Stagnation or total pressure of a flowing stream, p_t, is the pressure attained at a point by bringing the flow isentropically to rest in a steady flow process. It is defined as:

$$\frac{p_t}{p} = \left(1 + \frac{\kappa - 1}{2} M^2\right)^{\kappa/(\kappa - 1)} \qquad \text{(Eq 263)}$$

For isentropic flow, the stagnation pressure remains constant along a streamline.

Total density is the density attained when a steady flow is brought isentropically to rest. It is defined by:

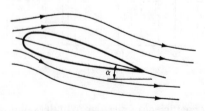

Figure 40

$$\frac{\rho_t}{\rho} = \left(1 + \frac{\kappa - 1}{2} M^2\right)^{1/(\kappa - 1)}$$ (Eq 264)

If the flow is isentropic, then ρ_t is a constant along streamlines.

The kinetic pressure is a property sometimes encountered when computing drag. For an ideal gas it is defined as:

$$q = \frac{1}{2} \frac{pV^2}{RT}$$ (Eq 265)

It is related to Mach number by the relationship:

$$q = \frac{\kappa}{2} pM^2$$ (Eq 266)

where p must always be an absolute pressure.

NORMAL SHOCK WAVES

A shock is a very sudden change of fluid properties occurring in a supersonic flow. A normal shock wave is a wave normal to the flow direction and is shown in Fig. 41. Flow across a shock is not isentropic, so $s_2 > s_1$. The continuity equation for steady flow with constant area dictates that $\rho_1 V_1 = \rho_2 V_2$. The momentum equation for this situation becomes:

$$p_1 + \rho_1 V_1^2 = p_2 + \rho_2 V_2^2$$ (Eq 267)

For a perfect gas with constant specific heats, $a^2 = \kappa RT$, and the momentum equation takes the form:

$$p_1(1 + \kappa M_1^2) = p_2(1 + \kappa M_2^2)$$ (Eq 268)

For adiabatic flow, this becomes:

$$T_1\left(1 + \frac{\kappa - 1}{2} M_1^2\right) = T_2\left(1 + \frac{\kappa - 1}{2} M_2^2\right)$$ (Eq 269)

Eq 269 takes into account that the stagnation temperature remains constant across the shock.

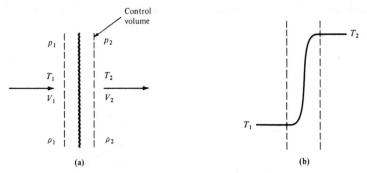

Figure 41   Shock wave effects. (a) Normal shock wave. (b) Temperature variation across a shock

The expression relating the Mach numbers is found to be:

$$M_2{}^2 = \frac{M_1{}^2 + \dfrac{2}{\kappa - 1}}{\dfrac{2\kappa}{\kappa - 1}M_1{}^2 - 1} \tag{Eq 270}$$

For $M_1 > 1$, M_2 must be <1, and a compression shock exists ($p_2 > p_1$). The second law of thermodynamics allows only for the existance of compression shocks.

ISENTROPIC FLOW THROUGH A DUCT OF VARYING AREA

For this case, the flow through the duct is considered to be isentropic as well as steady and one-dimensional. The continuity equation can be written as:

$$\frac{d\rho}{\rho} + \frac{dA}{A} + \frac{dV}{V} = 0 \tag{Eq 271}$$

and the momentum equation becomes:

$$dp + \rho V\, dV = 0 \tag{Eq 272}$$

Eq 271 and 272 can be combined to get:

$$dp(1 - M^2) = \rho V^2 \frac{dA}{A} \tag{Eq 273a}$$

This equation can be altered to obtain the form:

$$\frac{1}{V}\frac{dV}{dx} = \frac{1}{A(M^2 - 1)}\frac{dA}{dx} \tag{Eq 273b}$$

Eq 273(a) and 273(b) indicate that in subsonic flow ($M < 1$) an increase in area results in a decrease in velocity and a corresponding increase in pressure. The opposite occurs when the area is decreased. When the flow is supersonic ($M > 1$), however, an increasing area brings an increase in velocity and a decrease in pressure. This means that subsonic flow cannot be accelerated beyond the sonic velocity in a converging nozzle and that acceleration to supersonic velocities can only happen in the Laval nozzle (converging-diverging) pictured in Fig. 42.

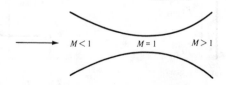

$M < 1$ $\qquad$ $M = 1$ $\qquad$ $M > 1$

Figure 42   Laval nozzle

Relationships in the Converging-Diverging Nozzle. The relationship between area and Mach number in a converging-diverging nozzle is found to be:

$$\frac{A}{A_*} = \frac{1}{M}\left\{\frac{1 + [(\kappa - 1)/2]M^2}{(\kappa + 1)/2}\right\}^{(\kappa + 1)/2(\kappa - 1)} \tag{Eq 274}$$

Equation 274 is valid for all Mach numbers, and the area ratio, A/A_*, is the ratio of the area at the station where the Mach number is M to the area at the throat (where $M = 1$). The mass flow rate in the nozzle may be given in terms of total pressure or density as noted in these equations:

$$\dot{m} = \rho_t \sqrt{\kappa R T_t} \, A_*\left(\frac{2}{\kappa + 1}\right)^{(\kappa + 1)/2(\kappa - 1)} \tag{Eq 275}$$

and

$$\dot{m} = \frac{p_t A_*}{\sqrt{R T_t}} \, \kappa^{1/2}\left(\frac{2}{\kappa + 1}\right)^{(\kappa + 1)/2(\kappa - 1)} \tag{Eq 276}$$

The density ratio in the converging-diverging nozzle is given by:

$$\frac{\rho_*}{\rho} = \left\{\frac{1 + [(\kappa - 1)/2]M^2}{(\kappa + 1)/2}\right\}^{1/(\kappa - 1)} \tag{Eq 277}$$

This is a parallel relationship to Eq 274 and ρ_* refers to the density at the throat ($M = 1$). A temperature ratio is also available:

$$\frac{T_*}{T} = \frac{1 + [(\kappa - 1)/2]M^2}{(\kappa + 1)/2} \tag{Eq 278}$$

where T_* is taken at the throat.

For a nozzle at the outflow of a reservoir (Fig. 43), there exists a pressure, p_{crit}, such that if p_b falls below p_{crit}, the mass flow rate ceases to change and the

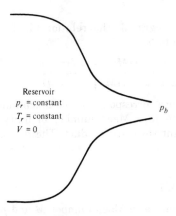

Reservoir
p_r = constant
T_r = constant
$V = 0$

p_b

Figure 43

pressure distribution in the nozzle remains as it was when $p_b = p_{crit}$. The flow is then said to be choked. The critical pressure ratio is defined by:

$$\left(\frac{p_b}{p_r}\right)_{crit} = \left(\frac{2}{\kappa + 1}\right)^{\kappa/(\kappa - 1)}$$

(Eq 279)

COMPRESSIBLE PIPE FLOW

Adiabatic Flow. When the duct area is constant, the continuity equation for uniform adiabatic flow becomes:

$$\frac{dV}{V} + \frac{d\rho}{\rho} = 0$$

and the energy equation can be written as:

$$\frac{\kappa R \, dT}{\kappa - 1} + V \, dV = 0$$

(Eq 280)

The momentum equation is:

$$\rho V \, dV + dp + \frac{f\rho V^2 \, dx}{2D} = 0$$

(Eq 281)

where D is the pipe diameter and f is the Darcy-Weisbach friction factor.

The above equations (Eq 280, 281 and continuity) lead to a differential equation relating the change in Mach number with respect to distance:

$$\frac{(1 - M^2) \, dM}{M^3 \{1 + [(\kappa - 1)/2]M^2\}} = \frac{\kappa f \, dx}{2D}$$

(Eq 282)

Eq 282 indicates that if the flow is subsonic, Mach number increases with distance, and if the flow is supersonic, the Mach number decreases along the pipe. Wall friction, therefore, causes the Mach number to approach unity.

When Eq 282 is integrated, the relationship between M and distance along the pipe is seen to be:

$$\frac{1 - M^2}{\kappa M^2} + \frac{\kappa + 1}{2\kappa} \ln\left[\frac{(\kappa + 1)M^2}{2 + (\kappa - 1)M^2}\right] = \frac{f(x_* - x_M)}{D}$$

(Eq 283)

where x_M is the distance corresponding to a Mach number of M and x_* is the distance corresponding to a Mach number of unity. The friction factor is assumed to be constant through the duct. The pressure ratio in the pipe is given by:

$$\frac{p_M}{p_*} = \frac{1}{M}\left[\frac{\kappa + 1}{2 + (\kappa - 1)M^2}\right]^{1/2}$$

(Eq 284)

where p_M is the pressure at a Mach number M and p_* refers to the location where $M = 1$.

Isothermal Flow. For isothermal flow in a constant area duct, the speed of sound is constant and the momentum equation is given by:

$$\kappa M^2 \frac{dV}{V} + \frac{dp}{p} + \frac{\kappa f M^2 dx}{2D} = 0 \tag{Eq 285}$$

Applying the continuity equation to Eq 285 gives:

$$\frac{dM}{dx} = \frac{f}{2D} \frac{\kappa M^3}{1 - \kappa M^2} \tag{Eq 286}$$

If the Mach number is less than $1/\sqrt{\kappa}$, then it increases with distance; the opposite trend occurs for Mach numbers exceeding $1/\sqrt{\kappa}$. The Mach number must always approach $1/\sqrt{\kappa}$. The Mach number is now related to distance by:

$$\frac{f(x_T - x_M)}{D} = \ln(\kappa M^2) + \frac{(1 - \kappa M^2)}{\kappa M^2} \tag{Eq 287}$$

where x_M is the distance along the pipe where Mach number M occurs, and x_T is the maximum length at which $M = 1/\sqrt{\kappa}$. The pressure ratio in the duct becomes:

$$\frac{p_M}{p_T} = \frac{1}{\sqrt{\kappa}M} \tag{Eq 288}$$

where p_M is the pressure at Mach number M, and p_T occurs at the point where $M = 1/\sqrt{\kappa}$.

REFERENCES

1. John, J. E. A. and Haberman, W. L., *Introduction to Fluid Mechanics*, 2nd ed., Prentice-Hall, Englewood Cliffs, NJ, 1980
2. White, F. M., *Fluid Mechanics*, McGraw-Hill, New York, 1979
3. Streeter, V. L. and Wylie, E. B., *Fluid Mechanics*, 6th ed., McGraw-Hill, New York, 1975
4. Shames, I. R., *Mechanics of Fluids*, 2nd ed., McGraw-Hill, New York, 1982
5. Fox, R. W. and McDonald, A. T., *Introduction to Fluid Mechanics*, John Wiley & Sons, New York, 1973
6. Schlichting, H., *Boundary Layer Theory*, 7th ed., McGraw-Hill, New York, 1979
7. White, F. M., *Viscous Fluid Flow*, McGraw-Hill, New York, 1974
8. Roberson, J. A. and Crowe, C. T., *Engineering Fluid Mechanics*, 2nd ed., Houghton Mifflin, Boston, 1980
9. Streeter, V. L., Ed., *Handbook of Fluid Dynamics*, 1st ed., McGraw-Hill, New York, 1961

Index